5th EDITION

Introductory Algebra:
An Applied Approach

Richard N. Aufmann
Palomar College, California

Vernon C. Barker
Palomar College, California

Joanne S. Lockwood
Plymouth State College, New Hampshire

HOUGHTON MIFFLIN COMPANY
Boston   New York

Senior Sponsoring Editor: Maureen O'Connor
Senior Associate Editor: Dawn Nuttall
Editorial Assistant: John Brister
Project Editor: Tamela Ambush
Editorial Assistant: Ryan Jones
Senior Production/Design Coordinator: Carol Merrigan
Senior Manufacturing Coordinator: Marie Barnes
Marketing Manager: Ros Kane

Photo Credits

Chapter 1: Peter Beck/The Stock Market; Chapter 2: Peter Cade/TSI; Chapter 3: Elena Rooraid/PhotoEdit; Chapter 4: Tony Freeman/PhotoEdit; Chapter 5: Carol Lundeen; Chapter 6: Joseph Nettis/Stock, Boston, Inc.; Chapter 7: Jeff Zaruba/The Stock Market; Chapter 8: Roger Tully/TSI; Chapter 9: Spencer Grant/PhotoEdit; Chapter 10: Richard Hutchings/PhotoEdit; Chapter 11: Michael Newman/PhotoEdit.

Cover Designer: Harold Burch Designs, NYC

Cover Image: Steven Edson, © Photonica

Printed in the U.S.A.

Library of Congress Catalog Card Number: 98-71981

ISBN Numbers
   Text: 0-395-90706-3
   Instructor's Annotated Edition: 0-395-92321-2

56789-WC-02 01

Contents

3   Solving Equations   85

4   Polynomials   161

5 **Factoring**   203

6 **Rational Expressions**   253

7 Linear Equations in Two Variables 313

8   Systems of Linear Equations   365

9   Inequalities   407

Preface

The fifth edition of *Introductory Algebra: An Applied Approach* provides mathematically sound and comprehensive coverage of the topics considered essential in an introductory algebra course. The text has been designed not only to meet the needs of the traditional college student but also to serve the needs of returning students whose mathematical proficiency may have declined during years away from formal education.

In this new edition of *Introductory Algebra: An Applied Approach,* we have continued to integrate some of the approaches suggested by AMATYC. Each chapter begins with a mathematical vignette in which there may be a historical note, an application, or a curiosity related to mathematics. At the end of each section there are "Applying the Concepts" exercises, which include writing, synthesis, critical thinking, and challenge problems. Each chapter ends with a "Focus on Problem Solving," which introduces students to problem-solving strategies. This is followed by "Projects and Group Activities," which can be used for cooperative learning activities.

INSTRUCTIONAL FEATURES

Interactive Approach

Introductory Algebra: An Applied Approach uses an interactive style that provides a student with an opportunity to try a skill as it is presented. Each section is divided into objectives, and every objective contains one or more sets of matched-pair examples. The first example in each set is worked out; the second example, called "You Try It," is for the student to work. By solving this problem, the student practices concepts as they are presented in the text. There are complete worked-out solutions to these examples in an appendix at the end of the book. By comparing their solution to the solution in the appendix, students are able to obtain immediate feedback on and reinforcement of the concept.

Emphasis on Problem-Solving Strategies

Introductory Algebra: An Applied Approach features a carefully developed approach to problem solving that emphasizes developing strategies to solve problems. Students are encouraged to develop their own strategies, to draw diagrams, and to write strategies as part of their solution to a problem. In each case, model strategies are presented as guides for students to follow as they attempt the "You Try It" problem. Having students provide strategies is a natural way to incorporate writing into the math curriculum.

Emphasis on Applications

The traditional approach to teaching algebra covers only the straightforward manipulation of numbers and variables and thereby fails to teach students the practical value of algebra. By contrast, *Introductory Algebra: An Applied Approach* contains an extensive collection of contemporary application problems. Wherever appropriate, the last objective of a section presents applications that require the student to use the skills covered in that section to solve practical problems. This carefully integrated applied approach generates student awareness of the value of algebra as a real-life tool.

Completely Integrated Learning System Organized by Objectives

Each chapter begins with a list of the learning objectives included within that chapter. Each of the objectives is then restated in the chapter to remind the student of the current topic of discussion. The same objectives that organize the text are also used as the structure for exercises, testing programs, and the Computer

Tutor. For each objective in the text, there is a corresponding computer tutorial and a corresponding set of test questions.

AN INTERACTIVE APPROACH

Instructors have long realized the need for a text that requires students to use a skill as it is being taught. *Introductory Algebra: An Applied Approach* uses an interactive technique that meets this need. Every objective, including the one shown below, contains at least one pair of examples. One of the examples is worked. The second example in the pair (You Try It) is not worked so that students may "interact" with the text by solving it. To provide immediate feedback, a complete worked-out solution to this example is provided in the Solutions Section at the end of the book. The benefit of this interactive style is that students can immediately determine whether a new skill has been learned before attempting a homework assignment or moving on to the next skill.

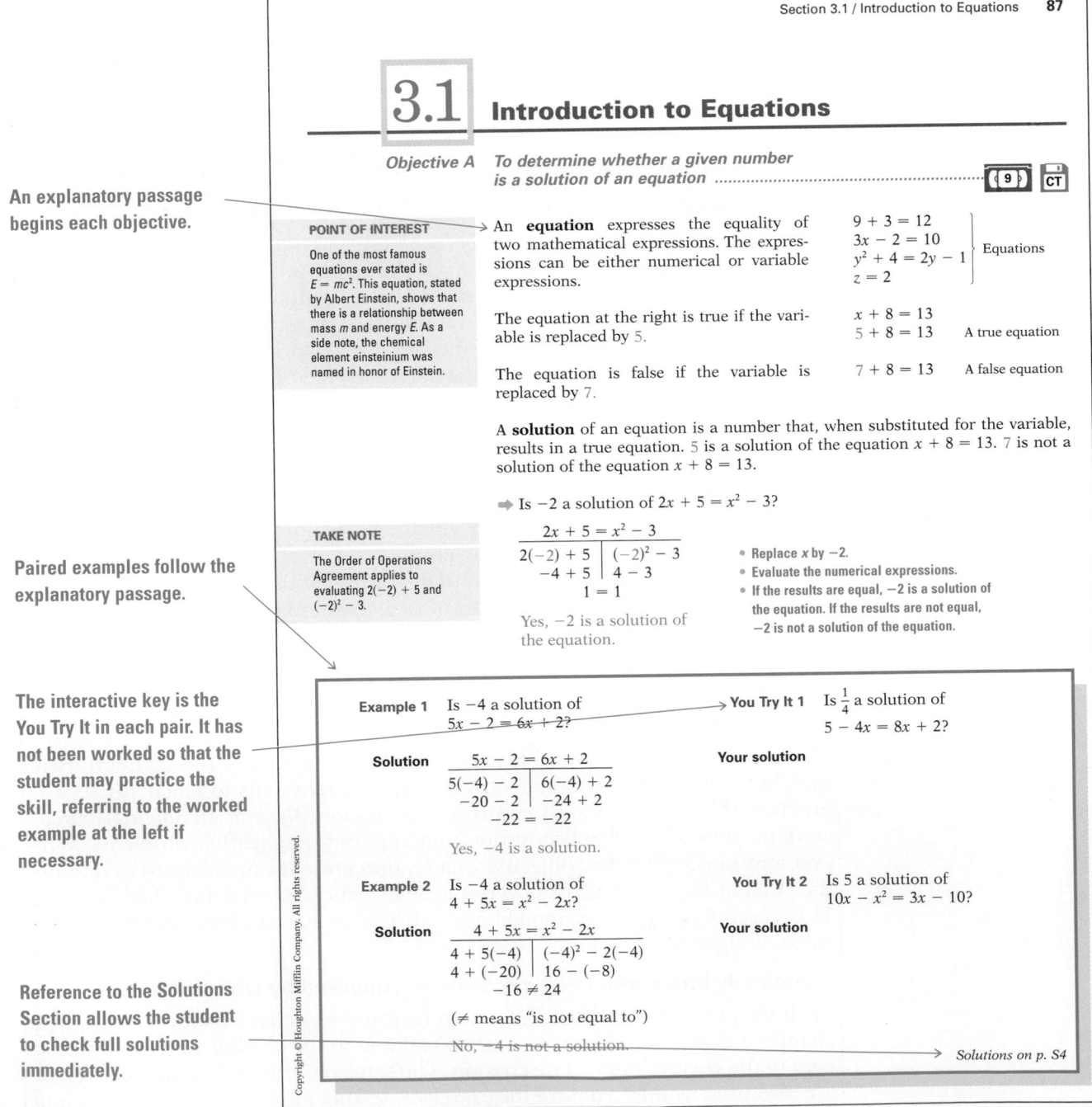

Section 3.1 / Introduction to Equations   **87**

3.1 Introduction to Equations

Objective A   **To determine whether a given number is a solution of an equation** .... 9 CT

An explanatory passage begins each objective.

POINT OF INTEREST

One of the most famous equations ever stated is $E = mc^2$. This equation, stated by Albert Einstein, shows that there is a relationship between mass m and energy E. As a side note, the chemical element einsteinium was named in honor of Einstein.

An **equation** expresses the equality of two mathematical expressions. The expressions can be either numerical or variable expressions.

$$9 + 3 = 12$$
$$3x - 2 = 10$$
$$y^2 + 4 = 2y - 1$$
$$z = 2$$
Equations

The equation at the right is true if the variable is replaced by 5.

$$x + 8 = 13$$
$$5 + 8 = 13 \quad \text{A true equation}$$

The equation is false if the variable is replaced by 7.

$$7 + 8 = 13 \quad \text{A false equation}$$

A **solution** of an equation is a number that, when substituted for the variable, results in a true equation. 5 is a solution of the equation $x + 8 = 13$. 7 is not a solution of the equation $x + 8 = 13$.

➡ Is -2 a solution of $2x + 5 = x^2 - 3$?

TAKE NOTE

The Order of Operations Agreement applies to evaluating $2(-2) + 5$ and $(-2)^2 - 3$.

Paired examples follow the explanatory passage.

$$2x + 5 = x^2 - 3$$

$2(-2) + 5$	$(-2)^2 - 3$
$-4 + 5$	$4 - 3$
$1 =$	1

• Replace x by -2.
• Evaluate the numerical expressions.
• If the results are equal, -2 is a solution of the equation. If the results are not equal, -2 is not a solution of the equation.

Yes, -2 is a solution of the equation.

The interactive key is the You Try It in each pair. It has not been worked so that the student may practice the skill, referring to the worked example at the left if necessary.

Example 1   Is -4 a solution of $5x - 2 = 6x + 2$?

Solution
$$5x - 2 = 6x + 2$$
$$5(-4) - 2 \mid 6(-4) + 2$$
$$-20 - 2 \mid -24 + 2$$
$$-22 = -22$$

Yes, -4 is a solution.

You Try It 1   Is $\frac{1}{4}$ a solution of $5 - 4x = 8x + 2$?

Your solution

Example 2   Is -4 a solution of $4 + 5x = x^2 - 2x$?

Solution
$$4 + 5x = x^2 - 2x$$
$$4 + 5(-4) \mid (-4)^2 - 2(-4)$$
$$4 + (-20) \mid 16 - (-8)$$
$$-16 \neq 24$$

($\neq$ means "is not equal to")

No, -4 is not a solution.

You Try It 2   Is 5 a solution of $10x - x^2 = 3x - 10$?

Your solution

Reference to the Solutions Section allows the student to check full solutions immediately.

Solutions on p. S4

AN EMPHASIS ON APPLICATIONS

The traditional teaching approach neglects the difficulties that students have in making the transition from arithmetic to algebra. One of the most troublesome and uncomfortable transitions for the student is from concrete arithmetic to symbolic algebra. *Introductory Algebra: An Applied Approach* recognizes the formidable task the student faces by introducing variables in a very natural way—through applications of mathematics. A secondary benefit of this approach is that the student becomes aware of the value of algebra as a real-life tool.

The solution of an application problem in *Introductory Algebra: An Applied Approach* is always accompanied by two parts: **Strategy** and **Solution**. The strategy is a written description of the steps that are necessary to solve the problem; the solution is the implementation of the strategy. This format provides students with a structure for problem solving. It also encourages students to write strategies for solving problems, which, in turn, fosters organizing problem-solving strategies in a logical way.

A strategy, which the student may use in solving an application problem, is stated.

The strategy is used in the solution of the worked example.

Students are encouraged to write a strategy for the application problems they solve.

---

142   Chapter 3 / Solving Equations

Example 2
A chemist wishes to make 2 L of an 8% acid solution by mixing a 10% acid solution and a 5% acid solution. How many liters of each solution should the chemist use?

Strategy

x L of 10% acid + $(2 - x)$ L of 5% acid = 2 L of 8% acid

Liters of 10% solution: x
Liters of 5% solution: $2 - x$

	Amount	Percent	Quantity
10% solution	x	0.10	$0.10x$
5% solution	$2 - x$	0.05	$0.05(2 - x)$
8% solution	2	0.08	$0.08(2)$

The sum of the quantities before mixing is equal to the quantity after mixing.

You Try It 2
A pharmacist dilutes 5 L of a 12% solution with a 6% solution. How many liters of the 6% solution are added to make an 8% solution?

Your strategy

Solution
$$0.10x + 0.05(2 - x) = 0.08(2)$$
$$0.10x + 0.10 - 0.05x = 0.16$$
$$0.05x + 0.10 = 0.16$$
$$0.05x = 0.06$$
$$x = 1.2$$

$$2 - x = 2 - 1.2 = 0.8$$

The chemist needs 1.2 L of the 10% solution and 0.8 L of the 5% solution.

Your solution

Solution on p. S8

OBJECTIVE-SPECIFIC APPROACH

Many mathematics texts are not organized in a manner that facilitates management of learning. Typically, students are left to wander through a maze of apparently unrelated lessons, exercise sets, and tests. *Introductory Algebra: An Applied Approach* solves this problem by organizing all lessons, exercise sets, computer tutorials, and tests around a carefully constructed hierachy of objectives. The advantage of this objective-by-objective organization is that it enables the student who is uncertain at any step in the learning process to refer easily to the original presentation and review that material.

The Objective-Specific Approach also gives the instructor greater control over the management of student progress. The Computerized Test Generator and the printed Test Bank are organized by the same objectives as the text. These references are provided with the answers to the test items, thereby allowing the instructor to quickly determine those objectives for which a student may need additional instruction.

The Computer Tutor is also organized around the objectives of the text. As a result, supplemental instruction is available for any objectives that are troublesome for a student.

An objective statement names the topic of each lesson.

3.1 Introduction to Equations

Objective A *To determine whether a given number is a solution of an equation* .... [CT]

The exercise sets correspond to the objectives in the text.

3.1 Exercises

Objective A

1. Is 4 a solution of $2x = 8$?

2. Is 3 a solution of $y + 4 = 7$?

3. Is -1 a solution of $2b - 1 = 3$?

4. Is -2 a solution of $3a - 4 = 10$?

5. Is 1 a solution of $4 - 2m = 3$?

6. Is 2 a solution of $7 - 3n = 2$?

The answers to the odd-numbered exercises are provided in the Answer Section.

SECTION 3.1

1. Yes **3.** No **5.** No **7.** Yes **9.** Yes **11.** Yes **13.** No **15.** Yes **17.** Yes **19.** Yes **21.** No

23. 6 **25.** 16 **27.** 7 **29.** -2 **31.** 1 **33.** 0 **35.** 3 **37.** -10 **39.** -3 **41.** -14 **43.** 2

The answers to the Chapter Review Exercises, the Chapter Test, and the Cumulative Review Exercises show the objective to study if the student incorrectly answers the exercise.

CHAPTER REVIEW

1. 21 [3.1B] **2.** 10 [3.3B] **3.** 7 [3.2A] **4.** No [3.1A] **5.** 20 [3.1C] **6.** -2 [3.3B] **7.** 30 is 250% of 12. [3.1D] **8.** 4 [3.3A] **9.** -1 [3.3B] **10.** 4 [3.3A] **11.** The cost is $671.25. [3.2B]

CHAPTER TEST

1. -5 [3.3A] **2.** -5 [3.1B] **3.** -3 [3.2A] **4.** 2 [3.3B] **5.** No [3.1A] **6.** 5 [3.2A] **7.** 0.5% of 8 is 0.04. [3.1D] **8.** $-\frac{1}{3}$ [3.3B] **9.** 2 [3.3A] **10.** -12 [3.1C] **11.** 10 lb of the $.70 rye flour and 5 lb of the

CUMULATIVE REVIEW

1. 6 [1.2B] **2.** -48 [1.3A] **3.** $-\frac{19}{48}$ [1.4C] **4.** -2 [1.4D] **5.** 54 [1.5A] **6.** 24 [1.5B]

7. 6 [2.1A] **8.** $-17x$ [2.2A] **9.** $-5a - 2b$ [2.2A] **10.** $2x$ [2.2B] **11.** $36y$ [2.2B]

ADDITIONAL LEARNING AIDS

Chapter Opener

The Chapter Opener relates a historical, contemporary, or interesting note about mathematics or its application.

Focus on Problem Solving

At the end of each chapter there is a Focus on Problem Solving, the purpose of which is to introduce the student to various successful problem-solving strategies. Each Focus consists of a problem and an appropriate strategy to solve the problem. Strategies such as guessing, trying to solve a simpler but similar problem, drawing a diagram, and looking for patterns are some of the techniques that are demonstrated.

Projects and Group Activities

The Projects and Group Activities feature can be used as extra credit or cooperative learning activities. The projects cover various aspects of mathematics including use of calculators, extended applications, and additional problem-solving strategies.

Chapter Summaries

At the end of each chapter there is a Chapter Summary that includes Key Words and Essential Rules that were covered in the chapter. These chapter summaries provide a single point of reference as the student prepares for a test.

Study Skills

The To the Student preface provides suggestions for using this text and approaches to creating good study habits. Students are referred to this preface at appropriate places in the text.

Computer Tutor

This state-of-the-art Tutor is a networkable, interactive, algorithmically driven software package. Features include full-color graphics, a glossary, extensive hints, animated solution steps, and a comprehensive class management system. Written by the authors, the Tutor and the text are in the same voice.

Glossary

A Glossary at the end of the book includes definitions of terms used in the text.

Margin Notes

There are three types of margin notes in the student text. *Point of Interest* notes feature interesting sidelights of the topic being discussed. The *Take Note* feature warns students that a procedure may be particularly involved or reminds students that there are certain checks of their work that should be performed. *Calculator Notes* provide suggestions for using a calculator in certain situations. In addition, there are *Instructor Notes* that are printed only in the Instructor's Annotated Edition. These notes provide suggestions for presenting the material or related material that can be used in class.

Index of Applications

The Index of Applications illustrates the power and scope of mathematics and its application. This may help some students see the benefits of mathematics as a tool that is used in everyday experiences.

EXERCISES

End-of-Section Exercises

Introductory Algebra: An Applied Approach contains more than 6000 exercises. At the end of each section there are exercise sets that are keyed to the corresponding learning objectives. The exercises are carefully developed to ensure that students can apply the concepts in the section to a variety of problem situations. Data Analysis exercises are identified by ◔. Calculator exercises are identified by ▦ .

Applying the Concepts Exercises

The End-of-Section Exercises are followed by Applying the Concepts Exercises. These sections contain a variety of exercise types, including:

- challenge problems
- problems that require the student to determine if a statement is always true, sometimes true, or never true
- problems that ask students to determine incorrect procedures

Writing Exercises

Within the "Applying the Concepts Exercises," there are Writing Exercises denoted by ✏ . These exercises ask students to write about a topic in the section or to research and report on a related topic.

Chapter Review Exercises

Review Exercises are found at the end of each chapter. These exercises are selected to help the student integrate all of the topics presented in the chapter. The answers to all Review Exercises are given in the answer section at the end of the book. Along with the answer, there is a reference to the objective that pertains to each exercise.

Chapter Test Exercises

The Chapter Test Exercises are designed to simulate a possible test of the material in the chapter. The answers to all Chapter Test Exercises are given in the answer section at the end of the book. Along with the answer, there is a reference to the objective that pertains to each exercise.

Cumulative Review Exercises

Cumulative Review Exercises, which appear at the end of each chapter (beginning with Chapter 2), help students maintain skills learned in previous chapters. The answers to all Cumulative Review Exercises are given in the answer section. Along with the answer, there is a reference to the objective that pertains to each exercise.

NEW TO THIS EDITION

The major change for this edition has been the integration of the application problems from Chapter 4 of the previous edition throughout the text. Chapter 3, Solving Equations, now contains a significant number of application problems that allow students to apply their equation-solving skills as they learn them. This helps connect the mathematics they are learning with its real-world applications.

Similar triangles and applications of similar triangles have been added to Chapter 6, Rational Expressions.

Problems on investment have been moved to Chapter 8, Systems of Equations.

We have added some problems that have too much data, thereby requiring the student to select the information needed to solve the problem.

For some exercises, not enough information is given to reach a single answer. Thus, there is more than one answer that satisfies the conditions of the problem.

The skill development exercises were thoroughly reviewed to ensure that there was adequate representation of various problem types. As a result of this review, we have changed or replaced some drill exercises to include problem types that were missing.

Approximately one-third of all the application problems were changed to reflect current data and trends. New application problems were added to demonstrate to students the variety of problems that require mathematical analysis.

Career notes were added to the chapter opener pages to illustrate to students the diverse ways in which mathematics is used in the workplace.

We have more than doubled the number of projects and group activities. Some of these projects have suggested Internet sites so that the student may continue to explore a topic.

In response to suggestions by users, the Chapter Review Exercises are no longer categorized by section. Thus there are no organizational clues to students as to the type of skill needed to solve an exercise. The answers to all Chapter Review Exercises are in the answer section. Along with the answer, there is a reference to the objective that pertains to each exercise.

SUPPLEMENTS FOR THE INSTRUCTOR

Instructor's Annotated Edition

The Instructor's Annotated Edition is an exact replica of the student text except that answers to all exercises are given in the text. Also, there are Instructor Notes in the margin that offer suggestions for presenting the material in that objective.

Instructor's Resource Manual with Chapter Tests

The Instructor's Resource Manual contains the printed Chapter Tests, which are the first of three sources of testing material. Eight printed tests—four free-response and four multiple-choice—are provided for each chapter. In addition, there are Cumulative Tests after Chapters 3, 6, 9, 11, and a Final Exam. The Instructor's Resource Manual also includes suggestions for course sequencing and outlines for the answers to the Writing Exercises.

Computerized Test Generator

The Computerized Test Generator is the second source of testing material. The database contains more than 2000 test items. The Test Generator is designed to provide an unlimited number of tests for each chapter, cumulative chapter tests, and a final exam. It is available for Windows and the Macintosh. Both versions also provide **on-line testing** and **gradebook** functions.

Printed Test Bank

The printed Test Bank, the third component of the testing material, is a printout of all items in the Computerized Test Generator. Instructors who do not have access to a computer can use the Test Bank to select items to include on a test being prepared by hand.

Solutions Manual

The Solutions Manual contains worked-out solutions for all end-of-section exercises, Chapter Review Exercises, Chapter Test Exercises, Cumulative Review Exercises, and the Final Exam.

SUPPLEMENTS FOR THE STUDENT

Student Solutions Manual

The Student Solutions Manual contains the complete solutions to all odd-numbered exercises in the text.

Computer Tutor

The content of this interactive, state-of-the-art tutorial software was written by the authors and is in the same voice as the text. The Tutor supports every topic in the text. Problems are algorithmically generated; solution steps are animated; lessons and problems are presented in a colorful, lively manner, and an integrated classroom management system tracks and reports student performance. Features include:

- assessment
- free-response problems
- ability to repeat same problem type

- ability to print problems
- syllabus customization
- ability to bookmark

The Computer Tutor can be used in several ways: (1) to cover material the student missed because of absence; (2) to reinforce instruction on a concept that the student has not yet mastered; (3) to review material in preparation for exams.

The networkable Tutor is available on CD-ROM or floppy disk for Windows. There is also a version available for the Macintosh. The Tutor is free to any school upon adoption of this text; however, students can purchase a copy of the Tutor on floppy disk for home use.

Within each section of the book, a computer icon **CT** appears next to each objective. The icon serves as a reminder that there is a Computer Tutor lesson corresponding to that objective.

Videotapes

Within each section of the text, a videotape icon appears next to an objective for which there is a corresponding video. The icon contains the reference number of the appropriate video. Each video topic is motivated through an application, and the necessary mathematics to solve that problem are then presented.

ACKNOWLEDGMENTS

We sincerely wish to thank the following reviewers, who reviewed the manuscript in various stages of development, for their valuable contributions:

Thomas Blackburn, *Northeastern Illinois University;* **Kim Brown,** *Tarrant County Junior College, NE;* **Floyd Fisher,** *Hillyer College, University of Hartford, CT;* **Ann L. Flamm,** *Reading Area Community College, PA;* **Mary Ellen Gallegos,** *San Francisco Community College, CA;* **Laura Hoye,** *Trident Technical College, SC;* **Michael A. Jones; Randy Leifson,** *Pierce College, WA;* **David Longshore,** *Victor Valley College, CA;* **Dr. Glenn Neiner,** *Red Rocks Community College, CO;* **Thomas M. O'Keefe,** *Bucks County Community College, PA;* **Leah C. Pierce,** *Chaffey College, CA;* **Bernard J. Piña,** *DABCC—New Mexico State University;* **Deana J. Richmond; Betty Jo Slozak,** *Wayne Community College, NC;* **Trudy Streilein,** *Harford Community College, MD.*

Special thanks to Dan Clegg of Palomar College for some of the new application problems.

To the Student

Take an active role in the learning process.

Many students feel that they will never understand math, while others appear to do very well with little effort. Oftentimes what makes the difference is that successful students take an active role in the learning process.

Do the homework.

Attend class regularly.

Participate in class.

Learning mathematics requires your *active* participation. Although doing homework is one way you can actively participate, it is not the only way. First, you must attend class regularly and become an active participant. Second, you must become actively involved with the textbook.

Introductory Algebra: An Applied Approach was written and designed with you in mind as a participant. Here are some suggestions on how to use the features of this textbook.

Use the features of the text.

There are 11 chapters in this text. Each chapter is divided into sections, and each section is subdivided into learning objectives. Each learning objective is labeled with a letter from A to D.

Read the objective statement.

Read the objective material.

Study the in-text examples.

First, read each objective statement carefully so you will understand the learning goal that is being presented. Next, read the objective material carefully, being sure to note each bold word. These words indicate important concepts that you should familiarize yourself with. Study carefully each in-text example (denoted by an orange arrow), noting the techniques and strategies used to solve the example.

Use the boxed examples.

1. Study the example on the left.

2. Solve the You Try It example.

3. Check your work against the solution in the back of the book.

You will then come to the key learning feature of this text, the *boxed examples.* These examples have been designed to assist you in a very specific way. Notice that in each example box, the example on the left is completely worked out and the "You Try It" example on the right is not. *You* are expected to work the right-hand example (in the space provided) in order to immediately test your understanding of the material you have just studied.

You should study the worked-out example carefully by working through each step presented. This allows you to focus on each step and reinforces the technique for solving that type of problem. You can then use the worked-out example as a model for solving similar problems.

Next, try to solve the "You Try It" example using the problem-solving techniques that you have just studied. When you have completed your solution, check your work by turning to the page in the Appendix where the complete solution can be found. The page number on which the solution appears is printed at the bottom of the example box in the right-hand corner. By checking your solution, you will know immediately whether or not you fully understand the skill you just studied.

Do the exercises.

Check your answers to the odd-numbered exercises.

When you have completed studying an objective, do the exercises in the exercise set that corresponds to that objective. The exercises are labeled with the same letter as the objective. Math is a subject that needs to be learned in small sections and practiced continually in order to be mastered. Doing all of the exercises in each exercise set will help you to master the problem-solving techniques necessary for success. As you work through the exercises for an objective, check your answers to the odd-numbered exercises with those in the back of the book.

Read the Chapter Summary.

Do the Chapter Review exercises.

After completing a chapter, read the Chapter Summary. This summary highlights the important topics covered in the chapter. Following the Chapter Summary are a Chapter Review, a Chapter Test, and a Cumulative Review (beginning with Chapter 2). Doing the review exercises is an important way of testing your understanding of the chapter. The answer to each review exercise is given at the back of the book. Each answer to the Chapter Test and Cumulative Review is followed

Check your answers.

Restudy objectives
you missed.

Do the Chapter Test.

Check your answers.

Restudy objectives
you missed.

by a reference that tells which objective that exercise was taken from. For example, (4.2B) means Section 4.2, Objective B. After checking your answers, restudy any objective that you missed. It may be very helpful to retry some of the exercises for that objective to reinforce your problem-solving techniques.

The Chapter Test should be used to prepare for an exam. We suggest that you try the Chapter Test a few days before your actual exam. Take the test in a quiet place and try to complete the test in the same amount of time you will be allowed for your exam. When taking the Chapter Test, practice the strategies of successful test takers: 1) scan the entire test to get a feel for the questions; 2) read the directions carefully; 3) work the problems that are easiest for you first; and, perhaps most importantly, 4) try to stay calm.

When you have completed the Chapter Test, check your answers. If you missed a question, review the material in that objective and rework some of the exercises from that objective. This will strengthen your ability to perform the skills in that objective.

The Cumulative Review allows you to refresh the skills you have learned in previous chapters. This is very important in mathematics. By consistently reviewing previous material, you will retain the skills already learned as you build new ones.

Remember, to be successful: attend class regularly; read the textbook carefully; actively participate in class; work with your textbook using the "You Try It" examples for immediate feedback and reinforcement of each skill; do all of the homework assignments; review constantly; and work carefully.

Index of Applications

1

Real Numbers

County agricultural agents work with farmers to help them produce better crops. Many agents are specialists in soils. They teach farmers about the physical and chemical characteristics of the soil, helping them to make the most productive use of their land. Agricultural agents must have a good understanding of percents in order to analyze the composition of nutrients in farmland. Their goal is to assist farmers in improving the quality and quantity of crop yields and in controlling diseases and pests.

Objectives

Section 1.1
To use inequality symbols with integers
To use opposites and absolute value

Section 1.2
To add integers
To subtract integers
To solve application problems

Section 1.3
To multiply integers
To divide integers
To solve application problems

Section 1.4
To write a rational number in simplest form and as a decimal
To convert between percents, fractions, and decimals
To add or subtract rational numbers
To multiply or divide rational numbers
To solve application problems

Section 1.5
To evaluate exponential expressions
To use the Order of Operations Agreement to simplify expressions

Early Egyptian Fractions

One of the earliest written documents of mathematics is the Rhind Papyrus. This tablet was found in Egypt in 1858, but it is estimated that the writings date back to 1650 B.C.

The Rhind Papyrus contains over 80 problems. A study of these problems has enabled mathematicians and scientists to understand some of the ways the early Egyptians used mathematics.

Evidence gained from the Papyrus shows that the Egyptian method of calculating with fractions was much different from the methods used today. All fractions were represented in terms of what are called "unit fractions." A unit fraction is a fraction in which the numerator is 1. This fraction was symbolized (using modern numbers) with a bar over the number. For example,

$$\overline{3} = \frac{1}{3} \qquad\qquad \overline{15} = \frac{1}{15}$$

The early Egyptians also tended to deal with powers of 2 (2, 4, 8, 16, …). As a result, representing fractions with 2 in the numerator in terms of unit fractions was an important matter. The Rhind Papyrus has a table giving the equivalent unit fractions for all fractions with odd denominators from 5 to 101 and 2 as the numerator. Some of these are listed below.

$$\frac{2}{5} = \overline{3}\ \overline{15} \qquad \left(\frac{2}{5} = \frac{1}{3} + \frac{1}{15}\right)$$

$$\frac{2}{7} = \overline{4}\ \overline{28}$$

$$\frac{2}{11} = \overline{6}\ \overline{66}$$

1.1 Introduction to Integers

Objective A   **To use inequality symbols with integers** ....

TAKE NOTE

We suggest you read "To the Student" on page xix. It provides an explanation of the organization of the chapters and lessons of this text.

It seems to be a human characteristic to group similar items. For instance, a biologist places similar animals in groups called *species*. Nutritionists classify foods according to *food groups*; for example, pasta, crackers, and rice are among the foods in the bread group.

Mathematicians place objects with similar properties in groups called *sets*. A **set** is a collection of objects. The objects in a set are called the **elements** of the set.

The **roster method** of writing sets encloses a list of the elements in braces. The set of sections within an orchestra is written {brass, percussion, string, woodwind}.

The numbers that we use to count objects, such as the number of students in a classroom or the number of horses on a ranch, are the *natural numbers*.

$$\textbf{Natural numbers} = \{1, 2, 3, 4, 5, 6, 7, 8, 9, 10, \ldots\}$$

The three dots mean that the list of natural numbers continues on and on and that there is no largest natural number.

POINT OF INTEREST

The Alexandrian astronomer Ptolemy began using *omicron*, *o*, the first letter of the Greek word that means "nothing," as the symbol for zero in 150 A.D. It was not until the 13th century, however, that Fibonacci introduced 0 to the Western world as a placeholder so that we could distinguish, for example, 45 from 405.

The natural numbers alone do not provide all the numbers that are useful in applications. For instance, a meteorologist also needs the number zero and numbers below zero.

$$\textbf{Integers} = \{\ldots, -5, -4, -3, -2, -1, 0, 1, 2, 3, 4, 5, \ldots\}$$

Each integer can be shown on a number line. The integers to the left of zero on the number line are called **negative integers.** The integers to the right of zero are called **positive integers,** or natural numbers. Zero is neither a positive nor a negative integer.

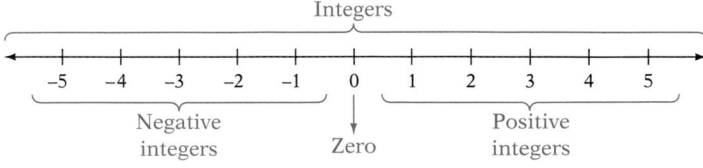

The **graph** of an integer is shown by placing a heavy dot on the number line directly above the number. The graphs of -3 and 4 are shown on the number line below.

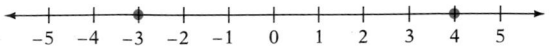

Consider the sentences below.

> The quarterback threw the football and the receiver caught *it*.
> A student purchased a computer and used *it* to write history papers.

In the first sentence, *it* is used to mean the football; in the second sentence, *it* means the computer. In language, the word *it* can stand for many different objects. Similarly, in mathematics, a letter of the alphabet can be used to stand for a number. Such a letter is called a **variable.** Variables are used in the following definition of inequality symbols.

Inequality Symbols

If a and b are two numbers and a is to the left of b on the number line, then a **is less than** b. This is written $a < b$.

If a and b are two numbers and a is to the right of b on the number line, then a **is greater than** b. This is written $a > b$.

Negative 4 is less than negative 1.

$-4 < -1$

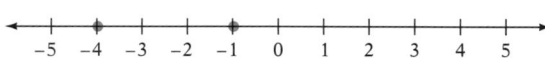

5 is greater than 0.

$5 > 0$

There are also inequality symbols for **is less than or equal to** ($\leq$) or **is greater than or equal to** ($\geq$).

$7 \leq 15$ 7 is less than or equal to 15.
This is true because $7 < 15$.

$6 \leq 6$ 6 is less than or equal to 6.
This is true because $6 = 6$.

The symbol $\in$ means "is an element of." $2 \in B$ is read "2 is an element of set B."

Given $C = \{3, 5, 9\}$, then $3 \in C$, $5 \in C$, and $9 \in C$. $7 \notin C$ is read "7 is not an element of set C."

Example 1
Use the roster method to write the set of negative integers greater than or equal to -4.

Solution
$A = \{-4, -3, -2, -1\}$ • A set is designated
by a capital letter.

You Try It 1
Use the roster method to write the set of positive integers less than 7.

Your solution 6, 5, 4, 3, 2, 1

Solution on p. S1

Example 2
Given $A = \{-6, -2, 0\}$, which elements of set A are less than or equal to -2?

Solution
Find the order relation between each element of set A and -2.

$-6 < -2$
$-2 = -2$
$0 > -2$

The elements -6 and -2 are less than or equal to -2.

You Try It 2
Given $B = \{-5, -1, 5\}$, which elements of set B are greater than -1?

Your solution $-5 < -1, -1 = -1, 5 > -1$

Solution on p. S1

Objective B   ***To use opposites and absolute value*** ....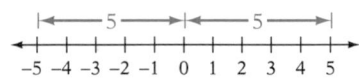

Two numbers that are the same distance from zero on the number line but are on opposite sides of zero are **opposite numbers,** or **opposites.** The opposite of a number is also called its **additive inverse.**

The opposite of 5 is -5.

The opposite of -5 is 5.

The negative sign can be read "the opposite of."

$$-(2) = -2 \qquad \text{The opposite of 2 is } -2.$$
$$-(-2) = 2 \qquad \text{The opposite of } -2 \text{ is } 2.$$

The **absolute value** of a number is its distance from zero on the number line. Therefore, the absolute value of a number is a positive number or zero. The symbol for absolute value is two vertical bars, $|\ |$.

The distance from 0 to 3 is 3. Therefore, the absolute value of 3 is 3.

$$|3| = 3$$

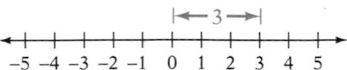

The distance from 0 to -3 is 3. Therefore, the absolute value of -3 is 3.

$$|-3| = 3$$

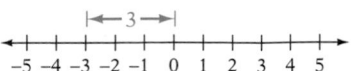

POINT OF INTEREST

The definition of *absolute value* given in the box is written in what is called rhetorical style. That is, it is written without the use of variables. This is how *all* mathematics was written prior to the Renaissance. During that period from the 14th to the 16th century, the idea of expressing a variable symbolically was developed. In terms of that symbolism, the definition of absolute value is

$$|x| = \begin{cases} x, & x > 0 \\ 0, & x = 0 \\ -x, & x < 0 \end{cases}$$

Absolute Value

The absolute value of a positive number is the number itself. For example, $|9| = 9$.

The absolute value of zero is zero. $|0| = 0$

The absolute value of a negative number is the opposite of the negative number. For example, $|-7| = 7$.

➡ Evaluate: $-|-12|$

$-|-12| = -12$ • The absolute value sign does not affect the negative sign in front of the absolute value sign.

Example 3
Evaluate $|-4|$ and $-|-10|$.

Solution
$|-4| = 4$
$-|-10| = -10$

You Try It 3
Evaluate $|-5|$ and $-|-23|$.

Your solution
$5, -23$

Example 4
Given $A = \{-12, 0, 4\}$, find the additive inverse of each element of set A.

Solution
$-(-12) = 12$
$-0 = 0$ • Zero is neither positive nor negative.
$-(4) = -4$

You Try It 4
Given $B = \{-11, 0, 8\}$, find the additive inverse of each element of set B.

Your solution
$11, 0, -8$

Example 5
Given $C = \{-17, 0, 14\}$, find the absolute value of each element of set C.

Solution
$|-17| = 17$
$|0| = 0$
$|14| = 14$

-17, 0, 14

You Try It 5
Given $D = \{-37, 0, 29\}$, find the absolute value of each element of set D.

Your solution
$37, 0, -29$

Solutions on p. S1

1.1 Exercises

· ·

Objective A

Place the correct symbol, $<$ or $>$, between the two numbers.

1. 8 -6 **2.** -14 16   **3.** -12 1   **4.** 35   28   **5.** 42   19

6. -42 27   **7.** 0 -31 **8.** -17 0   **9.** 53 -46 **10.** -27 -38

Answer True or False.

11. $-13 > 0$ **12.** $-20 > 3$ **13.** $12 > -31$ **14.** $9 > 7$ **15.** $-5 > -2$

16. $-44 > -21$ **17.** $-4 > -120$ **18.** $0 > -8$ **19.** $-1 \geq -1$ **20.** $-10 \leq -10$

For Exercises 21–26, use the roster method to write the set.

21. the natural numbers less than 9   **22.** the natural numbers less than or equal to 6

23. the positive integers less than or equal to 8   **24.** the positive integers less than 4

25. the negative integers greater than -7 **26.** the negative integers greater than or equal to -5

27. Given $A = \{-7, 0, 2, 5\}$, which elements of set A are greater than 2?   **28.** Given $B = \{-8, 0, 7, 15\}$, which elements of set B are greater than 7?

29. Given $D = \{-23, -18, -8, 0\}$, which elements of set D are less than -8?   **30.** Given $C = \{-33, -24, -10, 0\}$, which elements of set C are less than -10?

31. Given $E = \{-35, -13, 21, 37\}$, which elements of set E are greater than -10?   **32.** Given $F = \{-27, -14, 14, 27\}$, which elements of set F are greater than -15?

33. Given $B = \{-52, -46, 0, 39, 58\}$, which elements of set B are less than or equal to 0?   **34.** Given $A = \{-12, -9, 0, 12, 34\}$, which elements of set A are greater than or equal to 0?

35. Given $C = \{-23, -17, 0, 4, 29\}$, which elements of set C are greater than or equal to -17?   **36.** Given $D = \{-31, -12, 0, 11, 45\}$, which elements of set D are less than or equal to -12?

37. Given that set A is the positive integers less than 10, which elements of set A are greater than or equal to 5?

38. Given that set B is the positive integers less than or equal to 12, which elements of set B are greater than 6?

39. Given that set D is the negative integers greater than or equal to -10, which elements of set D are less than -4?

40. Given that set C is the negative integers greater than -8, which elements of set C are less than or equal to -3?

Objective B

Find the additive inverse.

41. 4   **42.** 8   **43.** -9 **44.** -28 **45.** -36

Evaluate.

46. $-(-14)$ **47.** $-(-40)$ **48.** $-(77)$ **49.** $-(39)$ **50.** $-(-13)$

51. $|-74|$ **52.** $|-96|$ **53.** $-|-82|$ **54.** $-|-53|$ **55.** $-|81|$

Place the correct symbol, $<$ or $>$, between the values of the two numbers.

56. $|-83|$ $|58|$ **57.** $|22|$ $|-19|$ **58.** $|43|$ $|-52|$ **59.** $|-71|$ $|-92|$

60. $|-68|$ $|-42|$ **61.** $|12|$ $|-31|$ **62.** $|-45|$ $|-61|$ **63.** $|-28|$ $|43|$

64. Given $A = \{-8, -5, -2, 1, 3\}$ find
  a. the opposite of each element of set A
  b. the absolute value of each element of set A

65. Given $B = \{-11, -7, -3, 1, 5\}$, find
  a. the opposite of each element of set B
  b. the absolute value of each element of set B

APPLYING THE CONCEPTS

66. If x represents a negative integer, then $-x$ represents a _____ integer.

67. If x is an integer, is the inequality $|x| < -3$ always true, sometimes true, or never true?

68. In your own words, explain the meaning of the absolute value of a number and the additive inverse of a number.

1.2 Addition and Subtraction of Integers

Objective A   *To add integers* ....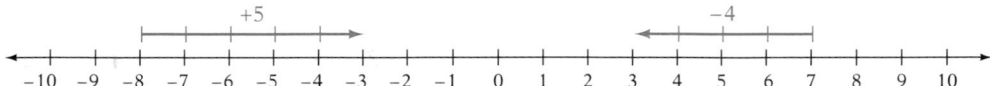

A number can be represented anywhere along the number line by an arrow. A positive number is represented by an arrow pointing to the right, and a negative number is represented by an arrow pointing to the left. The size of the number is represented by the length of the arrow.

Addition is the process of finding the total of two numbers. The numbers being added are called **addends.** The total is called the **sum.** Addition of integers can be shown on the number line. To add integers, start at zero and draw an arrow representing the first number. At the tip of the first arrow, draw a second arrow representing the second number. The sum is below the tip of the second arrow.

$4 + 2 = 6$

$-4 + (-2) = -6$

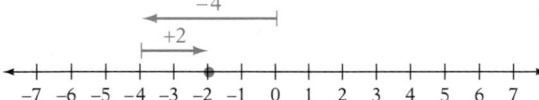

$-4 + 2 = -2$

$4 + (-2) = 2$

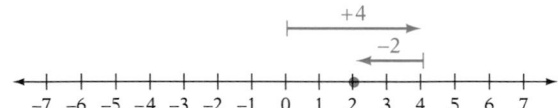

The pattern for addition shown on the number lines above is summarized in the following rules for adding integers.

Addition of Integers

To add two numbers with the same sign, add the absolute values of the numbers. Then attach the sign of the addends.

To add two numbers with different signs, find the absolute value of each number. Subtract the smaller of the two numbers from the larger. Then attach the sign of the number with the larger absolute value.

➡ Add: $-12 + (-26)$

$-12 + (-26) = -38$ • The signs are the same. Add the absolute values of the numbers $(12 + 26)$. Attach the sign of the addends.

➡ Add: $-19 + 8$

$|-19| = 19$ • The signs are different. Find the absolute value of each number.
$|8| = 8$

$19 - 8 = 11$ • Subtract the smaller number from the larger.

$-19 + 8 = -11$ • Attach the sign of the number with the larger absolute value. Because $|-19| > |8|$, use the sign of -19.

➡ Add: $-23 + 47 + (-18) + (-5)$

$-23 + 47 + (-18) + (-5)$

$= 24 + (-18) + (-5)$

$= 6 + (-5)$

$= 1$

• To add more than two numbers, add the first two numbers. Then add the sum to the third number. Continue until all the numbers are added.

Example 1
Add: $-52 + (-39)$

Solution
$-52 + (-39) = -91$

You Try It 1
Add: $100 + (-43)$

Your solution

Example 2
Add: $37 + (-52) + (-21) + (-7)$

Solution
$37 + (-52) + (-21) + (-7)$
$= -15 + (-21) + (-7)$
$= -36 + (-7)$
$= -43$

You Try It 2
Add: $-51 + 42 + 17 + (-102)$

Your solution

Solutions on p. S1

Objective B   *To subtract integers* ....

Look at the two expressions below and note that each expression equals the same number.

$$8 - 3 = 5 \quad \text{8 minus 3 is 5.}$$
$$8 + (-3) = 5 \quad \text{8 plus the opposite of 3 is 5.}$$

This example suggests that to subtract two numbers, we add the opposite of the second number to the first number.

First number	−	second number	=	First number	+	the opposite of the second number		

$$40 \quad - \quad 60 \quad = \quad 40 \quad + \quad (-60) \quad = -20$$

$$-40 \quad - \quad 60 \quad = \quad -40 \quad + \quad (-60) \quad = -100$$

$$-40 \quad - \quad (-60) \quad = \quad -40 \quad + \quad 60 \quad = 20$$

$$40 \quad - \quad (-60) \quad = \quad 40 \quad + \quad 60 \quad = 100$$

➡ Subtract: $-21 - (-40)$

Change this sign to plus.

$$-21 - (-40) = -21 + 40 = 19$$

Change -40 to the opposite of -40.

• Rewrite each subtraction as addition of the opposite. Then add.

➡ Subtract: $15 - 51$

Change this sign to plus.

$$15 - 51 = 15 + (-51) = -36$$

Change 51 to the opposite of 51.

• Rewrite each subtraction as addition of the opposite. Then add.

➡ Subtract: $-12 - (-21) - 15$

$$-12 - (-21) - 15 = -12 + 21 + (-15)$$
$$= 9 + (-15)$$
$$= -6$$

• Rewrite each subtraction as addition of the opposite. Then add.

Example 3　Subtract: $-11 - 15$

Solution　$-11 - 15 = -11 + (-15)$
$\qquad\qquad\quad = -26$

You Try It 3　Subtract: $19 - (-32)$

Your solution

Example 4　Subtract:
$\qquad\qquad -14 - 18 - (-21) - 4$

Solution　$-14 - 18 - (-21) - 4$
$\qquad = -14 + (-18) + 21 + (-4)$
$\qquad = -32 + 21 + (-4)$
$\qquad = -11 + (-4)$
$\qquad = -15$

You Try It 4　Subtract:
$\qquad\qquad -9 - (-12) - 17 - 4$

Your solution

Solutions on p. S1

Objective C **To solve application problems** ....

Positive and negative numbers are used to express the profitability of a company. A profit is recorded as a positive number; a loss is recorded as a negative number.

The bar graph below shows the net earnings or loss for Chrysler Corporation for the years 1992 to 1996. Calculate the total net earnings for Chrysler Corporation for the years 1992 to 1994.

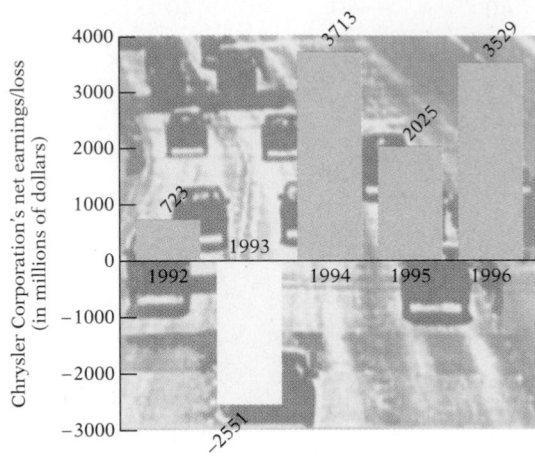

Source: Chrysler Corporation's 1996 Report to Shareholders

Strategy
To determine the total net earnings, add the profits and losses for the years 1992, 1993, and 1994.

Solution
$$723 + (-2551) + 3713 = -1828 + 3713$$
$$= 1885$$

The total net earnings for 1992 to 1994 were $1885 million.

Example 5
The average temperature on Mercury's sunlit side is 950°F. The average temperature on Mercury's dark side is −346°F. Find the difference between these two average temperatures.

Strategy
To find the difference, subtract the average temperature on the dark side (−346) from the average temperature on the sunlit side (950).

Solution
$$950 - (-346) = 950 + 346$$
$$= 1296$$
The difference between these average temperatures is 1296°F.

You Try It 5
Mar's average daytime temperature is −17°F. Mar's average nighttime temperature is −130°F. Find the difference between these two average temperatures.

Your strategy

Your solution

Solution on p. S1

1.2 Exercises

· ·

TAKE NOTE

"To the Student" on page xix discusses the exercise sets in this textbook.

Objective A

Add.

1. $-3 + (-8)$ **2.** $-6 + (-9)$ **3.** $-8 + 3$ **4.** $-9 + 2$

5. $-3 + (-80)$ **6.** $-12 + (-1)$ **7.** $-23 + (-23)$ **8.** $-12 + (-12)$

9. $16 + (-16)$ **10.** $-17 + 17$ **11.** $48 + (-53)$ **12.** $19 + (-41)$

13. $-17 + (-3) + 29$ **14.** $13 + 62 + (-38)$ **15.** $-3 + (-8) + 12$ **16.** $-27 + (-42) + (-18)$

17. $13 + (-22) + 4 + (-5)$ **18.** $-14 + (-3) + 7 + (-21)$

19. $-22 + 20 + 2 + (-18)$ **20.** $-6 + (-8) + 14 + (-4)$

21. $-16 + (-17) + (-18) + 10$ **22.** $-25 + (-31) + 24 + 19$

23. $26 + (-15) + (-11) + (-12)$ **24.** $-32 + 40 + (-8) + (-19)$

25. $-17 + (-18) + 45 + (-10)$ **26.** $23 + (-15) + 9 + (-15)$

27. $46 + (-17) + (-13) + (-50)$ **28.** $-37 + (-17) + (-12) + (-15)$

29. $-14 + (-15) + (-11) + 40$ **30.** $28 + (-19) + (-8) + (-1)$

31. $-23 + (-22) + (-21) + 5$ **32.** $-31 + 9 + (-16) + (-15)$

33. $72 + (-22) + (-14) + (-9)$ **34.** $-22 + (-17) + 58 + 29$

Objective B

Subtract.

35. $16 - 8$ **36.** $12 - 3$ **37.** $7 - 14$ **38.** $6 - 9$

39. $-7 - 2$ **40.** $-9 - 4$ **41.** $7 - (-2)$ **42.** $3 - (-4)$

43. $-6 - (-3)$ **44.** $-4 - (-2)$ **45.** $6 - (-12)$ **46.** $-12 - 16$

47. $-4 - 3 - 2$ **48.** $4 - 5 - 12$ **49.** $12 - (-7) - 8$

50. $-12 - (-3) - (-15)$ **51.** $-19 - (-19) - 18$ **52.** $-8 - (-8) - 14$

53. $-17 - (-8) - (-9)$ **54.** $7 - 8 - (-1)$ **55.** $-30 - (-65) - 29 - 4$

56. $42 - (-82) - 65 - 7$ **57.** $-16 - 47 - 63 - 12$ **58.** $42 - (-30) - 65 - (-11)$

59. $-47 - (-67) - 13 - 15$ **60.** $-18 - 49 - (-84) - 27$ **61.** $-19 - 17 - (-36) - 12$

62. $48 - 19 - 29 - 51$ **63.** $21 - (-14) - 43 - 12$ **64.** $17 - (-17) - 14 - 21$

Objective C   *Application Problems*

65. The temperature at which mercury boils is 360°C. Mercury freezes at −39°C. Find the difference between the temperature at which mercury boils and the temperature at which it freezes.

66. The temperature at which radon boils is −62°C. Radon freezes at −71°C. Find the difference between the temperature at which radon boils and the temperature at which it freezes.

The elevation, or height, of places on the earth is measured in relation to sea level, or the average level of the ocean's surface. The table below shows height above sea level as a positive number and depth below sea level as a negative number. Use the table for Exercises 67 to 70.

Continent	Highest Elevation (in meters)		Lowest Elevation (in meters)	
Africa	Mt. Kilimanjaro	5895	Qattara Depression	−133
Asia	Mt. Everest	8848	Dead Sea	−400
Europe	Mt. Elbrus	5634	Caspian Sea	−28
America	Mt. Aconcagua	6960	Death Valley	−86

67. Find the difference in elevation between Mt. Aconcagua and Death Valley.

68. What is the difference in elevation between Mt. Kilimanjaro and the Qattara Depression?

69. For which continent shown is the difference between the highest and lowest elevations greatest?

70. For which continent shown is the difference between the highest and lowest elevations smallest?

The table at the right shows the boiling point and the melting point in degrees Celsius of three chemical elements. Use this table for Exercises 71 and 72.

Chemical Element	Boiling Point	Melting Point
Carbon	4827	−355
Radon	−62	−71
Xenon	−107	−112

71. Find the difference between the boiling point and the melting point of carbon.

72. Find the difference between the boiling point and the melting point of xenon.

The graph at the right shows the net income or loss for US Airways for the years 1991 to 1996. Use this graph for Exercises 73 to 75.

73. Determine the total net loss for US Airways for the years 1994 to 1996.

74. Calculate the total net loss for US Airways for the years 1991 to 1996.

75. Find the difference between the net losses in 1994 and in 1992.

Sources: Transportation Department, US Airways

A meteorologist may report a wind-chill temperature. This is the equivalent temperature, including the effects of wind and temperature, that a person would feel in calm air conditions. The table below gives the wind-chill temperature for various wind speeds and temperature. For instance, when the temperature is 5°F and the wind is blowing at 15 mph, the wind-chill temperature is −25°F. Use this table for Exercises 76 and 77.

Wind-Chill Factors																	
Wind Speed (mph)	Thermometer Reading (degrees Fahrenheit)																
	35	**30**	**25**	**20**	**15**	**10**	**5**	**0**	**−5**	**−10**	**−15**	**−20**	**−25**	**−30**	**−35**	**−40**	**−45**
5	33	27	21	19	12	7	0	−5	−10	−15	−21	−26	−31	−36	−42	−47	−52
10	22	16	10	3	−3	−9	−15	−22	−27	−34	−40	−46	−52	−58	−64	−71	−77
15	16	9	2	−5	−11	−18	−25	−31	−38	−45	−51	−58	−65	−72	−78	−85	−92
20	12	4	−3	−10	−17	−24	−31	−39	−46	−53	−60	−67	−74	−81	−88	−95	−103
25	8	1	−7	−15	−22	−29	−36	−44	−51	−59	−66	−74	−81	−88	−96	−103	−110
30	6	−2	−10	−18	−25	−33	−41	−49	−56	−64	−71	−79	−86	−93	−101	−109	−116
35	4	−4	−12	−20	−27	−35	−43	−52	−58	−67	−74	−82	−89	−97	−105	−113	−120
40	3	−5	−13	−21	−29	−37	−45	−53	−60	−69	−76	−84	−92	−100	−107	−115	−123
45	2	−6	−14	−22	−30	−38	−46	−54	−62	−70	−78	−85	−93	−102	−109	−117	−125

76. When the thermometer reading is −5°F, what is the difference between the wind-chill factor when the wind is blowing 10 mph and when the wind is blowing 30 mph?

77. When the thermometer reading is −20°F, what is the difference between the wind-chill factor when the wind is blowing 15 mph and when the wind is blowing 25 mph?

APPLYING THE CONCEPTS

78. If a and b are integers, is the expression $|a + b| = |a| + |b|$ always true, sometimes true, or never true?

79. Is the difference between two integers always smaller than either one of the numbers in the difference? If not, give an example for which the difference between two integers is greater than either integer.

1.3 Multiplication and Division of Integers

Objective A   *To multiply integers* ....

Several different symbols are used to indicate multiplication. The numbers being multiplied are called **factors;** for instance, 3 and 2 are factors in each of the examples at the right. The result is called the **product.** Note that when parentheses are used and there is no arithmetic symbol, the operation is multiplication.

$$3 \times 2 = 6$$
$$3 \cdot 2 = 6$$
$$(3)(2) = 6$$
$$3(2) = 6$$
$$(3)2 = 6$$

Multiplication is repeated addition of the same number. The product 3×5 is shown on the number line below.

5 is added 3 times.
$$3 \times 5 = 5 + 5 + 5 = 15$$

Now consider the product of a positive and a negative number.

-5 is added 3 times.
$$3(-5) = (-5) + (-5) + (-5) = -15$$

This suggests that the product of a positive number and a negative number is negative. Here are a few more examples.

$$4(-7) = -28 \qquad\qquad -6 \cdot 7 = -42 \qquad\qquad (-8)7 = -56$$

To find the product of two negative numbers, look at the pattern at the right. As -5 multiplies a sequence of decreasing integers, the products increase by 5.

The pattern can be continued by requiring that the product of two negative numbers be positive.

These numbers decrease by 1.   These numbers increase by 5.

$$-5 \times 3 = -15$$
$$-5 \times 2 = -10$$
$$-5 \times 1 = -5$$
$$-5 \times 0 = 0$$
$$-5 \times (-1) = 5$$
$$-5 \times (-2) = 10$$
$$-5 \times (-3) = 15$$

Multiplication of Integers

To multiply two numbers with the same sign, multiply the absolute values of the numbers. The product is positive.

To multiply two numbers with different signs, multiply the absolute values of the number. The product is negative.

➡️ Multiply: $-2(5)(-7)(-4)$

$$-2(5)(-7)(-4) = -10(-7)(-4)$$
$$= 70(-4) = -280$$

• To multiply more than two numbers, multiply the first two. Then multiply the product by the third number. Continue until all the numbers are multiplied.

Consider the products shown at the right. Note that when there is an even number of negative factors, the product is positive. When there is an odd number of negative factors, the product is negative.

$$(-3)(-5) = 15$$
$$(-2)(-5)(-6) = -60$$
$$(-4)(-3)(-5)(-7) = 420$$
$$(-3)(-3)(-5)(-4)(-5) = -900$$
$$(-6)(-3)(-4)(-2)(-10)(-5) = 7200$$

This idea can be summarized by the following useful rule: **The product of an even number of negative factors is positive; the product of an odd number of negative factors is negative.**

Example 1 Multiply: $(-3)4(-5)$

Solution $(-3)4(-5) = (-12)(-5) = 60$

You Try It 1 Multiply: $8(-9)10$

Your solution

Example 2 Multiply: $12(-4)(-3)(-5)$

Solution $12(-4)(-3)(-5) = (-48)(-3)(-5)$
$$= 144(-5) = -720$$

You Try It 2 Multiply: $(-2)3(-8)7$

Your solution

Solutions on p. S1

Objective B   **To divide integers** ....

For every division problem there is a related multiplication problem.

$$\frac{8}{2} = 4 \qquad \text{because} \qquad 4 \cdot 2 = 8.$$

division   related multiplication

This fact and the rules for multiplying integers can be used to illustrate the rules for dividing integers.

Note in the following examples that the quotient of two numbers with the same sign is positive.

$$\frac{12}{3} = 4 \text{ because } 4 \cdot 3 = 12. \qquad \frac{-12}{-3} = 4 \text{ because } 4(-3) = -12.$$

The next two examples illustrate that the quotient of two numbers with different signs is negative.

$$\frac{12}{-3} = -4 \text{ because } (-4)(-3) = 12. \qquad \frac{-12}{3} = -4 \text{ because } (-4)3 = -12.$$

> **Division of Integers**
>
> **To divide two numbers with the same sign,** divide the absolute values of the numbers. The quotient is positive.
>
> **To divide two numbers with different signs,** divide the absolute values of the numbers. The quotient is negative.

➡ Simplify: $-\dfrac{-56}{7}$

$$-\dfrac{-56}{7} = -\left(\dfrac{-56}{7}\right) = -(-8) = 8$$

The properties of division are stated below. In these statements, the symbol $\neq$ is read "is not equal to."

> **Properties of Zero and One in Division**
>
> If $a \neq 0$, $\dfrac{0}{a} = 0$.   Zero divided by any number other than zero is zero.
>
> If $a \neq 0$, $\dfrac{a}{a} = 1$.   Any number other than zero divided by itself is one.
>
> $\dfrac{a}{1} = a$.   A number divided by one is the number.
>
> $\dfrac{a}{0}$ is undefined.   Division by zero is not defined.

The fact that $\dfrac{-12}{3} = -4$, $\dfrac{12}{-3} = -4$, and $-\dfrac{12}{3} = -4$ suggests the following rule.

If a and b are integers, and $b \neq 0$, then $\dfrac{-a}{b} = \dfrac{a}{-b} = -\dfrac{a}{b}$.

Example 3   Divide: $(-120) \div (-8)$

Solution $(-120) \div (-8) = 15$

You Try It 3   Divide: $(-135) \div (-9)$

Your solution

Example 4   Divide: $\dfrac{95}{-5}$

Solution $\dfrac{95}{-5} = -19$

You Try It 4   Divide: $\dfrac{-72}{4}$

Your solution

Example 5   Simplify: $-\dfrac{-81}{3}$

Solution $-\dfrac{-81}{3} = -(-27) = 27$

You Try It 5   Simplify: $-\dfrac{36}{-12}$

Your solution

Solutions on p. S1

Objective C   To solve application problems

In many courses, your course grade depends on the *average* of all your test scores. You compute the average by calculating the sum of all your test scores and then dividing that result by the number of tests. Statisticians call this average an **arithmetic mean.** Besides its application to finding the average of your test scores, the arithmetic mean is used in many other situations.

Stock market analysts calculate the **moving average** of a stock. This is the arithmetic mean of the changes in the value of a stock for a given number of days. To illustrate the procedure, we will calculate the 5-day moving average of a stock. In actual practice, a stock market analyst may use 15 days, 30 days, or some other number.

The table below shows the amount of increase or decrease, in cents, in the closing price of a stock for a 10-day period.

Day 1	Day 2	Day 3	Day 4	Day 5	Day 6	Day 7	Day 8	Day 9	Day 10
+50	−175	+225	0	−275	−75	−50	+50	−475	−50

To calculate the 5-day moving average of this stock, determine the average of the stock for days 1 through 5, days 2 through 6, days 3 through 7, and so on.

Days 1–5	Days 2–6	Days 3–7	Days 4–8	Days 5–9	Days 6–10
+50	−175	+225	0	−275	−75
−175	+225	0	−275	−75	−50
+225	0	−275	−75	−50	+50
0	−275	−75	−50	+50	−475
−275	−75	−50	+50	−475	−50
Sum = −175	Sum = −300	Sum = −175	Sum = −350	Sum = −825	Sum = −600
$Av = \frac{-175}{5} = -35$	$Av = \frac{-300}{5} = -60$	$Av = \frac{-175}{5} = -35$	$Av = \frac{-350}{5} = -70$	$Av = \frac{-825}{5} = -165$	$Av = \frac{-600}{5} = -120$

The 5-day moving average is the list of means: -35, -60, -35, -70, -165, and -120. If the list tends to increase, the price of the stock is showing an upward trend; if it decreases, the price of the stock is showing a downward trend. These trends help an analyst recommend stocks.

Example 6

The daily high temperatures (in degrees Celsius) for six days in Anchorage, Alaska, were $-14°$, $3°$, $0°$, $-8°$, $2°$, and $-1°$. Find the average daily high temperature.

Strategy

To find the average daily high temperature:

- Add the six temperature readings.
- Divide the sum by 6.

Solution

$-14 + 3 + 0 + (-8) + 2 + (-1) = -18$

$-18 \div 6 = -3$

The average daily high temperature was $-3°C$.

You Try It 6

The daily low temperatures (in degrees Celsius) during one week were recorded as $-6°$, $-7°$, $0°$, $-5°$, $-8°$, $-1°$, and $-1°$. Find the average daily low temperature.

Your strategy

Your solution

Solution on p. S1

1.3 Exercises

· ·

Objective A

Multiply.

1. $(14)3$ **2.** $17(6)$ **3.** $-7 \cdot 4$ **4.** $-8 \cdot 7$ **5.** $(-12)(-5)$ **6.** $(-13)(-9)$

7. $-11(23)$ **8.** $-8(21)$ **9.** $(-17)14$ **10.** $(-15)12$ **11.** $6(-19)$ **12.** $17(-13)$

13. $7(5)(-3)$ **14.** $(-3)(-2)8$ **15.** $9(-7)(-4)$ **16.** $(-2)(6)(-4)$

17. $16(-3)5$ **18.** $20(-4)3$ **19.** $-4(-3)8$ **20.** $-5(-9)6$

21. $-3(-8)(-9)$ **22.** $-7(-6)(-5)$ **23.** $(-9)7(5)$ **24.** $(-8)7(10)$

25. $7(-2)(5)(-6)$ **26.** $(-3)7(-2)8$ **27.** $-9(-4)(-8)(-10)$ **28.** $-11(-3)(-5)(-2)$

29. $7(9)(-11)4$ **30.** $-12(-4)7(-2)$ **31.** $(-14)9(-11)0$ **32.** $(-13)(15)(-19)0$

Objective B

Divide.

33. $12 \div (-6)$ **34.** $18 \div (-3)$ **35.** $(-72) \div (-9)$ **36.** $(-64) \div (-8)$ **37.** $-42 \div 6$

38. $(-56) \div 8$ **39.** $(-144) \div 12$ **40.** $(-93) \div (-3)$ **41.** $48 \div (-8)$ **42.** $57 \div (-3)$

43. $\dfrac{-49}{7}$ **44.** $\dfrac{-45}{5}$ **45.** $\dfrac{-44}{-4}$ **46.** $\dfrac{-36}{-9}$ **47.** $\dfrac{98}{-7}$

48. $\dfrac{85}{-5}$ **49.** $-\dfrac{-120}{8}$ **50.** $-\dfrac{-72}{4}$ **51.** $-\dfrac{-80}{-5}$ **52.** $-\dfrac{-114}{-6}$

53. $0 \div (-9)$ **54.** $0 \div (-14)$ **55.** $\dfrac{-261}{9}$ **56.** $\dfrac{-128}{4}$ **57.** $9 \div 0$

58. $(-21) \div 0$ **59.** $\dfrac{132}{-12}$ **60.** $\dfrac{250}{-25}$ **61.** $\dfrac{0}{0}$ **62.** $\dfrac{-58}{0}$

Objective C   *Application Problems*

63. The high temperatures for a six-day period in Barrow, Alaska, were −23°F, −29°F, −21°F, −28°F, −28°F, and −27°F. Calculate the average daily high temperature.

64. The low temperatures for a ten-day period in a midwestern city were −4°F, −9°F, −5°F, −2°F, 4°F, −1°F, −1°F, −2°F, −2°F, and 2°F. Calculate the average daily low temperature for this city.

65. The value of a share of McDonald's stock on April 4, 1997, was $48.50. The table below shows the amount of increase or decrease, to the nearest 25 cents, from the April 4 closing price of the stock for a 10-day period. Calculate the five-day moving average for this stock.

Day 1	Day 2	Day 3	Day 4	Day 5	Day 6	Day 7	Day 8	Day 9	Day 10
−25	50	100	−25	−50	−125	75	50	125	−50

66. The value of a share of Disney stock on April 4, 1997, was $72.625. The table below shows the amount of increase or decrease, to the nearest 25 cents, from the April 4 closing price of the stock for a 10-day period. Calculate the five-day moving average for this stock.

Day 1	Day 2	Day 3	Day 4	Day 5	Day 6	Day 7	Day 8	Day 9	Day 10
100	0	25	25	25	−175	−125	275	175	25

67. To discourage random guessing on a multiple-choice exam, a professor assigns 5 points for a correct answer, −2 points for an incorrect answer, and 0 points for leaving the question blank. What is the score for a student who had 20 correct answers, 13 incorrect answers, and left 7 questions blank?

68. To discourage random guessing on a multiple-choice exam, a professor assigns 7 points for a correct answer, −3 points for an incorrect answer, and −1 point for leaving the question blank. What is the score for a student who had 17 correct answers, 8 incorrect answers, and left 2 questions blank?

APPLYING THE CONCEPTS

69. If $x \in \{-6, -2, 7\}$, for which value of x does the expression $-3x$ have the greatest value?

70. Explain why $0 \div 0$ is not defined.

71. If $-4x$ equals a positive integer, is x a positive or a negative integer? Explain your answer.

1.4 Operations with Rational Numbers

Objective A   *To write a rational number in simplest form and as a decimal* ....

A *rational number* is the quotient of two integers. A rational number written in this way is commonly called a fraction. Here are some examples of rational numbers.

$$\frac{3}{4}, \quad \frac{-4}{9}, \quad \frac{15}{-4}, \quad \frac{8}{1}, \quad -\frac{5}{6}$$

> **Rational Numbers**
>
> A **rational number** is a number that can be written in the form $\frac{a}{b}$, where a and b are integers and $b \neq 0$.

Because an integer can be written as the quotient of the integer and 1, every integer is a rational number. For instance,

$$\frac{6}{1} = 6 \qquad \frac{-8}{1} = -8$$

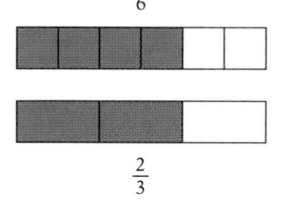

A fraction is in **simplest form** when there are no common factors in the numerator and the denominator. The fractions $\frac{4}{6}$ and $\frac{2}{3}$ are equivalent fractions because they represent the same part of a whole. However, the fraction $\frac{2}{3}$ is in simplest form because there are no common factors (other than 1) in the numerator and denominator.

To write a fraction in simplest form, eliminate the common factors from the numerator and denominator by using the fact that $1 \cdot \frac{a}{b} = \frac{a}{b}$.

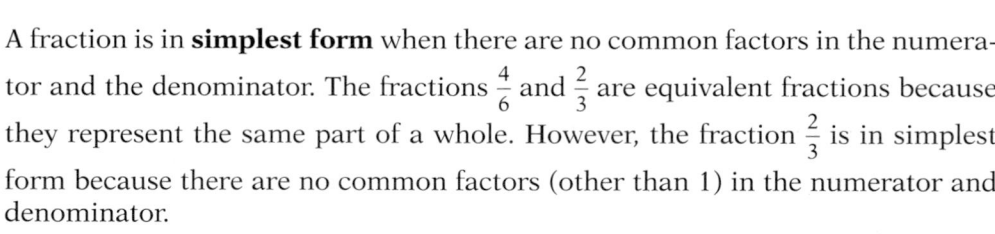

The process of eliminating common factors is usually written as shown at the right.

$$\frac{4}{6} = \frac{\overset{1}{\cancel{2}} \cdot 2}{\underset{1}{\cancel{2}} \cdot 3} = \frac{2}{3}$$

If you have difficulty determining the common factors, write the numerator and denominator in terms of prime factors. (Recall that a prime number is a number divisible only by itself and 1. The first ten prime numbers are 2, 3, 5, 7, 11, 13, 17, 19, 23, and 29.)

➡ Write $\frac{18}{30}$ in simplest form.

$$\frac{18}{30} = \frac{\overset{1}{\cancel{2}} \cdot \overset{1}{\cancel{3}} \cdot 3}{\underset{1}{\cancel{2}} \cdot \underset{1}{\cancel{3}} \cdot 5} = \frac{3}{5}$$

A number written in **decimal notation** is also a rational number.

three tenths $0.3 = \dfrac{3}{10}$ forty-three thousandths $0.043 = \dfrac{43}{1000}$

A rational number written as a fraction can be written in decimal notation by dividing the numerator of the fraction by the denominator. Think of the fraction bar as meaning "divided by."

➡ Write $\dfrac{5}{8}$ as a decimal.

$$
\begin{array}{r}
0.625 \\
8\overline{)5.000} \\
-4\,8 \\ \hline
20 \\
-16 \\ \hline
40 \\
-40 \\ \hline
0
\end{array}
$$

• Divide the numerator, 5, by the denominator, 8.

• Dividing the numerator by the denominator resulted in a remainder of 0. The decimal 0.625 is called a terminating decimal.

$$\dfrac{5}{8} = 0.625$$

➡ Write $\dfrac{4}{11}$ in decimal notation.

$$
\begin{array}{r}
0.3636 \\
11\overline{)4.0000} \\
-3\,3 \\ \hline
70 \\
-66 \\ \hline
40 \\
-33 \\ \hline
70 \\
-66 \\ \hline
4
\end{array}
$$

• Divide the numerator, 4, by the denominator, 11.

• No matter how long we continue to divide, the remainder is never zero. The decimal $0.\overline{36}$ is a repeating decimal. The bar over the 36 indicates that these digits repeat.

$$\dfrac{4}{11} = 0.\overline{36}$$

Every rational number can be written as a terminating or a repeating decimal. Some numbers—for example, $\sqrt{7}$ and π—have decimal representations that never terminate or repeat. These numbers are called **irrational numbers.**

$$\sqrt{7} \approx 2.6457513\ldots \quad \pi \approx 3.1415926\ldots$$

The rational numbers and the irrational numbers taken together are called the **real numbers.**

Example 1   Write $\frac{3}{20}$ as a decimal.

Solution $\frac{3}{20} = 3 \div 20 = 0.15$

You Try It 1   Write $\frac{4}{9}$ as a decimal. Place a bar over the repeating digits of the decimal.

Your solution

Solution on p. S1

Objective B   *To convert between percents, fractions, and decimals* ....

"A population growth rate of 3%," "a manufacturer's discount of 25%," and "an 8% increase in pay" are typical examples of the many ways in which percent is used in applied problems. **Percent** means "parts of 100." Thus 27% means 27 parts of 100.

In applied problems involving a percent, it may be necessary to rewrite a percent as a fraction or decimal, or to rewrite a fraction or decimal as a percent.

To write a percent as a fraction, remove the percent sign and multiply by $\frac{1}{100}$.

$$27\% = 27\left(\frac{1}{100}\right) = \frac{27}{100}$$

To write a percent as a decimal, remove the percent sign and multiply by 0.01.

$$33\% \quad = \quad 33(0.01) \quad = \quad 0.33$$

> Move the decimal point two places to the left. Then remove the percent sign.

A fraction or decimal can be written as a percent by multiplying by 100%. For example, $\frac{5}{8}$ is changed to a percent as follows.

$$\frac{5}{8} = \frac{5}{8}(100\%) = \frac{500}{8}\% = 62.5\%, \quad \text{or} \quad 62\frac{1}{2}\%$$

To write a decimal as a percent, multiply by 100%.

$$0.82 \quad = \quad 0.82(100\%) \quad = \quad 82\%$$

> Move the decimal point two places to the right. Then write the percent sign.

Example 2
Write 130% as a fraction and as a decimal.

Solution

$130\% = 130\left(\frac{1}{100}\right) = \frac{130}{100} = \frac{13}{10}$

$130\% = 130(0.01) = 1.30$

You Try It 2
Write 125% as a fraction and as a decimal.

Your solution

Solution on p. S1

Example 3

Write $33\frac{1}{3}\%$ as a fraction.

Solution

$$33\frac{1}{3}\% = 33\frac{1}{3}\left(\frac{1}{100}\right) = \frac{100}{3}\left(\frac{1}{100}\right) = \frac{1}{3}$$

You Try It 3

Write $16\frac{2}{3}\%$ as a fraction.

Your solution

Example 4

Write $\frac{5}{6}$ as a percent.

Solution

$$\frac{5}{6} = \frac{5}{6}(100\%) = \frac{500}{6}\% = 83\frac{1}{3}\%$$

You Try It 4

Write $\frac{9}{16}$ as a percent.

Your solution

Example 5

Write 0.027 as a percent.

Solution

$$0.027 = 0.027(100\%) = 2.7\%$$

You Try It 5

Write 0.043 as a percent.

Your solution

Solutions on p. S1

Objective C **To add or subtract rational numbers** ....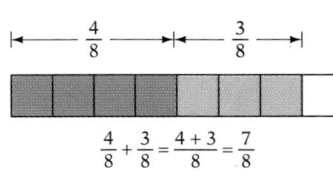

Four of the 8 squares have dark shading. This is $\frac{4}{8}$ of the entire rectangle. Three of the 8 squares have light shading. This is $\frac{3}{8}$ of the entire rectangle. So 7 of the 8 squares, or $\frac{7}{8}$, of the entire rectangle is shaded.

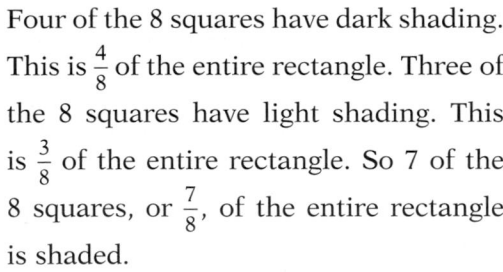

$$\frac{4}{8} + \frac{3}{8} = \frac{4+3}{8} = \frac{7}{8}$$

Addition of Fractions

To add two fractions with the same denominator, add the numerators and place the sum over the common denominator.

$$\frac{a}{c} + \frac{b}{c} = \frac{a+b}{c}$$

To add fractions with different denominators, first rewrite the fractions as equivalent fractions with a common denominator. Then add the fractions. The common denominator is the **least common multiple** (LCM) of the denominators. This is the smallest number that is a multiple of each of the denominators. It can be found by first writing each denominator as a product of prime factors. The LCM must contain the factors of each denominator.

$$6 = 2 \cdot 3$$
$$10 = 2 \cdot 5 \qquad \overbrace{\text{Factors of 10}} \\ \text{LCM} = 2 \cdot 3 \cdot 5 = 30 \\ \underbrace{}_{\text{Factors of 6}}$$

➡ Add: $-\dfrac{5}{6} + \dfrac{3}{10}$

The LCM of 6 and 10 is 30. Rewrite each fraction as an equivalent fraction with a denominator of 30. Then add the fractions.

$$-\frac{5}{6} + \frac{3}{10} = -\frac{25}{30} + \frac{9}{30} = \frac{-25 + 9}{30} = \frac{-16}{30} = -\frac{8}{15}$$

To subtract fractions with the same denominator, subtract the numerators and place the difference over the common denominator.

➡ Subtract: $-\dfrac{4}{9} - \left(-\dfrac{7}{12}\right)$

The LCM of 9 and 12 is 36. Rewrite each fraction as an equivalent fraction with a denominator of 36. Then subtract the fractions.

$$-\frac{4}{9} - \left(-\frac{7}{12}\right) = -\frac{16}{36} - \left(-\frac{21}{36}\right) = \frac{-16 - (-21)}{36} = \frac{-16 + 21}{36} = \frac{5}{36}$$

To add or subtract decimals, write the numbers so that the decimal points are in a vertical line. Then proceed as in the addition or subtraction of integers. Write the decimal point in the answer directly below the decimal points in the problem.

➡ Add: $-114.039 + 84.76$

$$\begin{array}{r} 114.039 \\ -\ \ 84.76 \\ \hline 29.279 \end{array}$$

- The signs are different. Find the difference between the absolute values of the numbers. $|{-114.039}| = 114.039;\ |84.76| = 84.76$

$$-114.039 + 84.76 = -29.279$$

- Attach the sign of the number with the larger absolute value. Because $|{-114.039}| > |84.76|$, use the sign of -114.039.

Example 6

Subtract: $\dfrac{5}{16} - \dfrac{7}{40}$

Solution

The LCM of 16 and 40 is 80.

$$\frac{5}{16} - \frac{7}{40} = \frac{25}{80} - \frac{14}{80} = \frac{25 - 14}{80} = \frac{11}{80}$$

Example 7

Simplify: $-\dfrac{3}{4} + \dfrac{1}{6} - \dfrac{5}{8}$

Solution

The LCM of 4, 6, and 8 is 24.

$$-\frac{3}{4} + \frac{1}{6} - \frac{5}{8} = -\frac{18}{24} + \frac{4}{24} - \frac{15}{24}$$

$$= \frac{-18 + 4 - 15}{24} = \frac{-29}{24} = -\frac{29}{24}$$

You Try It 6

Subtract: $\dfrac{5}{9} - \dfrac{11}{12}$

Your solution

You Try It 7

Simplify: $-\dfrac{7}{8} - \dfrac{5}{6} + \dfrac{3}{4}$

Your solution

Solutions on p. S2

Example 8   Subtract: $42.987 - 98.61$ **You Try It 8**   Subtract: $16.127 - 67.91$

Solution $42.987 - 98.61$ **Your solution**

$$= 42.987 + (-98.61)$$
$$= -55.623$$

Solution on p. S2

Objective D   *To multiply or divide rational numbers* ....

The product of two fractions is the product of the numerators divided by the product of the denominators.

➡ Multiply: $\dfrac{3}{8} \times \dfrac{12}{17}$

$$\dfrac{3}{8} \times \dfrac{12}{17} = \dfrac{3 \cdot 12}{8 \cdot 17}$$
　• Multiply the numerators.
　 Multiply the denominators.

$$= \dfrac{3 \cdot \overset{1}{\cancel{2}} \cdot \overset{1}{\cancel{2}} \cdot 3}{2 \cdot \underset{1}{\cancel{2}} \cdot \underset{1}{\cancel{2}} \cdot 17} = \dfrac{9}{34}$$
　• Divide by the common factors.

The **reciprocal** of a fraction is the fraction with the numerator and denominator interchanged. For instance, the reciprocal of $\dfrac{2}{3}$ is $\dfrac{3}{2}$, and the reciprocal of $-\dfrac{5}{2}$ is $-\dfrac{2}{5}$. To divide fractions, multiply by the reciprocal of the divisor.

➡ Divide: $\dfrac{3}{10} \div \left(-\dfrac{18}{25}\right)$

$$\dfrac{3}{10} \div \left(-\dfrac{18}{25}\right) = -\left(\dfrac{3}{10} \div \dfrac{18}{25}\right) = -\left(\dfrac{3}{10} \cdot \dfrac{25}{18}\right) = -\left(\dfrac{3 \cdot 25}{10 \cdot 18}\right)$$
　• The signs are different. The quotient is negative.

$$= -\left(\dfrac{\overset{1}{\cancel{3}} \cdot \overset{1}{\cancel{5}} \cdot 5}{2 \cdot \underset{1}{\cancel{5}} \cdot 2 \cdot \underset{1}{\cancel{3}} \cdot 3}\right) = -\dfrac{5}{12}$$

To multiply decimals, multiply as with integers. Write the decimal point in the product so that the number of decimal places in the product equals the sum of the number of decimal places in the factors.

➡ Multiply: -6.89×0.00035

$$
\begin{array}{r}
6.89 \\
\times\ 0.00035 \\
\hline
3445 \\
2067 \\
\hline
0.0024115
\end{array}
$$
2 decimal places
5 decimal places
　• Multiply the absolute values.

7 decimal places

$-6.89 \times 0.00035 = -0.0024115$
　• The signs are different. The product is negative.

To divide decimals, move the decimal point in the divisor to the right so that it becomes a whole number. Move the decimal point in the dividend the same number of places to the right. Place the decimal point in the quotient directly over the decimal point in the dividend. Then divide as with whole numbers.

TAKE NOTE

The symbol $\approx$ is used to indicate that the quotient is an approximate value that has been rounded off.

➡ Divide: $1.32 \div 0.27$. Round to the nearest tenth.

$$
0.27{\overline{\smash{\big)}\,1.32{.}00}}^{\displaystyle 4.88 \approx 4.9}
$$

$$
\begin{array}{r}
-108 \\ \hline
240 \\
-216 \\ \hline
240 \\
-216 \\ \hline
24
\end{array}
$$

• Move the decimal point 2 places to the right in the divisor and then in the dividend. Place the decimal point in the quotient directly over the decimal point in the dividend.

Example 9

Multiply: $\dfrac{2}{3}\left(-\dfrac{9}{10}\right)$

Solution

The product is negative.

$$\frac{2}{3}\left(-\frac{9}{10}\right) = -\left(\frac{2}{3} \cdot \frac{9}{10}\right) = -\frac{2 \cdot 9}{3 \cdot 10}$$

$$= -\frac{\overset{1}{\cancel{2}} \cdot \overset{1}{\cancel{3}} \cdot 3}{\underset{1}{\cancel{3}} \cdot \underset{1}{\cancel{2}} \cdot 5} = -\frac{3}{5}$$

You Try It 9

Multiply: $-\dfrac{7}{12}\left(\dfrac{9}{14}\right)$

Your solution

Example 10

Divide: $-\dfrac{5}{8} \div \left(-\dfrac{5}{40}\right)$

Solution

The quotient is positive.

$$-\frac{5}{8} \div \left(-\frac{5}{40}\right) = \frac{5}{8} \div \frac{5}{40} = \frac{5}{8} \cdot \frac{40}{5} = \frac{5 \cdot 40}{8 \cdot 5}$$

$$= \frac{\overset{1}{\cancel{5}} \cdot \overset{1}{\cancel{2}} \cdot \overset{1}{\cancel{2}} \cdot \overset{1}{\cancel{2}} \cdot 5}{\underset{1}{\cancel{2}} \cdot \underset{1}{\cancel{2}} \cdot \underset{1}{\cancel{2}} \cdot \underset{1}{\cancel{5}}} = \frac{5}{1} = 5$$

You Try It 10

Divide: $-\dfrac{3}{8} \div \left(-\dfrac{5}{12}\right)$

Your solution

Example 11

Multiply: -4.29×8.2

Solution

Multiply the absolute values.
The product is negative.

$$-4.29 \times 8.2 = -35.178$$

You Try It 11

Multiply: -5.44×3.8

Your solution

Example 12

Divide: $-0.0792 \div (-0.42)$
Round to the nearest hundredth.

Solution

Divide the absolute values.
The quotient is positive.

$$-0.0792 \div (-0.42) \approx 0.19$$

You Try It 12

Divide: $-0.394 \div 1.7$
Round to the nearest hundredth.

Your solution

Solutions on p. S2

Objective E   **To solve application problems** ....

One of the applications of percent is to express a portion of a total as a percent. For instance, a recent survey of 450 mall shoppers found that 270 preferred the mall closest to their home even though it did not have the same store variety as a mall farther from home. The percent of shoppers who preferred the mall closest to home can be found by converting a fraction to a percent.

$$\frac{\text{Portion preferring mall closest to home}}{\text{Total number surveyed}} = \frac{270}{450}$$

$$= 0.60 = 60\%$$

According to the Congressional Budget Office, the U.S. federal budget deficit in 1996 was $107.3 billion. The number 107.3 billion means

$$107.3 \times \underbrace{1,000,000,000}_{\text{1 billion}} = 107,300,000,000$$

Numbers such as 107.3 billion are used in many instances because they are easy to read and offer an approximation to the actual number. Such numbers are used in Example 13 and You Try It 13.

Example 13

The actual and projected spending for software, equipment, and services for intranets is shown in the bar graph below. Find the difference between expenditures in 2000 and in 1998.

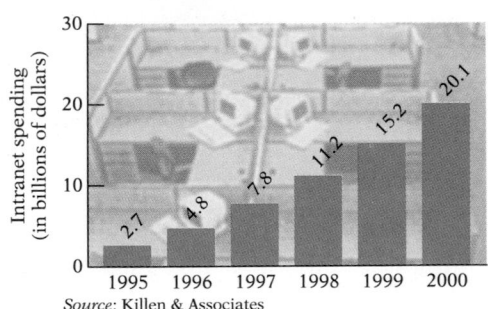

Source: Killen & Associates

Strategy

To find the difference, subtract the expenditures in 1998 ($11.2 billion) from those in 2000 ($20.1 billion).

Solution

20.1 − 11.2 = 8.9

The difference is $8.9 billion.

You Try It 13

The circle graph below shows the breakdown of the population of the United States by generation. What percent of the population of the United States is in the baby-boomer generation? Round to the nearest percent.

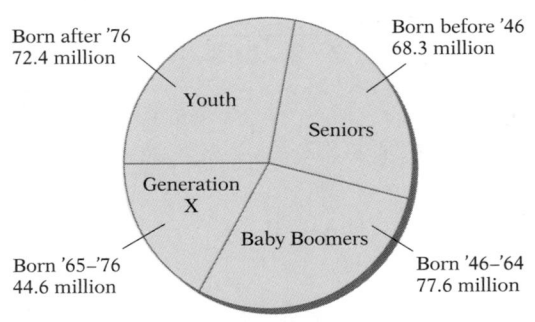

Born after '76
72.4 million

Born before '46
68.3 million

Youth

Seniors

Generation X

Baby Boomers

Born '65–'76
44.6 million

Born '46–'64
77.6 million

Source: Data from U.S. Census Bureau

Your strategy

Your solution

Solution on p. S2

1.4 Exercises

· ·

Objective A

Write each fraction in simplest form.

1. $\dfrac{7}{21}$ **2.** $\dfrac{10}{15}$ **3.** $\dfrac{8}{22}$ **4.** $\dfrac{8}{60}$ **5.** $\dfrac{50}{75}$

6. $\dfrac{20}{44}$ **7.** $\dfrac{12}{8}$ **8.** $\dfrac{36}{9}$ **9.** $\dfrac{0}{36}$ **10.** $\dfrac{12}{18}$

11. $\dfrac{60}{100}$ **12.** $\dfrac{14}{45}$ **13.** $\dfrac{44}{60}$ **14.** $\dfrac{19}{51}$ **15.** $\dfrac{23}{46}$

Write as a decimal. Place a bar over the repeating digits of a repeating decimal.

16. $\dfrac{4}{5}$ **17.** $\dfrac{1}{6}$ **18.** $\dfrac{5}{6}$ **19.** $\dfrac{1}{8}$ **20.** $\dfrac{7}{8}$

21. $\dfrac{2}{9}$ **22.** $\dfrac{8}{9}$ **23.** $\dfrac{5}{11}$ **24.** $\dfrac{7}{12}$ **25.** $\dfrac{11}{12}$

26. $\dfrac{9}{16}$ **27.** $\dfrac{15}{16}$ **28.** $\dfrac{7}{18}$ **29.** $\dfrac{17}{18}$ **30.** $\dfrac{1}{20}$

Objective B

Write as a fraction and a decimal.

31. 75%   **32.** 40%   **33.** 64%   **34.** 88%   **35.** 125%

36. 160%   **37.** 19%   **38.** 87%   **39.** 5%   **40.** 8%

Write as a fraction.

41. $11\frac{1}{9}\%$ **42.** $4\frac{2}{7}\%$ **43.** $12\frac{1}{2}\%$ **44.** $37\frac{1}{2}\%$ **45.** $66\frac{2}{3}\%$

46. $\frac{1}{4}\%$ **47.** $\frac{1}{2}\%$ **48.** $6\frac{1}{4}\%$ **49.** $83\frac{1}{3}\%$ **50.** $5\frac{3}{4}\%$

Write as a decimal.

51. 7.3%   **52.** 9.1%   **53.** 15.8%   **54.** 16.7%   **55.** 0.3%

56. 0.9%   **57.** 9.9%   **58.** 9.15%   **59.** 121.2%   **60.** 18.23%

Write as a percent.

61. 0.15   **62.** 0.37   **63.** 0.05   **64.** 0.02   **65.** 0.175

66. 0.125   **67.** 1.15   **68.** 1.36   **69.** 0.008   **70.** 0.004

71. $\frac{27}{50}$ **72.** $\frac{83}{100}$ **73.** $\frac{1}{3}$ **74.** $\frac{3}{8}$ **75.** $\frac{5}{11}$

76. $\frac{4}{9}$ **77.** $\frac{7}{8}$ **78.** $\frac{9}{20}$ **79.** $1\frac{2}{3}$ **80.** $2\frac{1}{2}$

Objective C

Simplify.

81. $\frac{2}{3} + \frac{5}{12}$ **82.** $\frac{1}{2} + \frac{3}{8}$ **83.** $\frac{5}{8} - \frac{5}{6}$ **84.** $\frac{1}{9} - \frac{5}{27}$

85. $-\dfrac{5}{12} - \dfrac{3}{8}$

86. $-\dfrac{5}{6} - \dfrac{5}{9}$

87. $-\dfrac{6}{13} + \dfrac{17}{26}$

88. $-\dfrac{7}{12} + \dfrac{5}{8}$

89. $\dfrac{5}{8} - \left(-\dfrac{3}{4}\right)$

90. $\dfrac{3}{5} - \dfrac{11}{12}$

91. $\dfrac{11}{12} - \dfrac{5}{6}$

92. $-\dfrac{2}{3} - \left(-\dfrac{11}{18}\right)$

93. $-\dfrac{5}{8} - \left(-\dfrac{11}{12}\right)$

94. $\dfrac{1}{3} + \dfrac{5}{6} - \dfrac{2}{9}$

95. $\dfrac{1}{2} - \dfrac{2}{3} + \dfrac{1}{6}$

96. $-\dfrac{3}{8} - \dfrac{5}{12} - \dfrac{3}{16}$

97. $-\dfrac{5}{16} + \dfrac{3}{4} - \dfrac{7}{8}$

98. $\dfrac{1}{2} - \dfrac{3}{8} - \left(-\dfrac{1}{4}\right)$

99. $\dfrac{3}{4} - \left(-\dfrac{7}{12}\right) - \dfrac{7}{8}$

100. $\dfrac{1}{3} - \dfrac{1}{4} - \dfrac{1}{5}$

101. $\dfrac{2}{3} - \dfrac{1}{2} + \dfrac{5}{6}$

102. $\dfrac{5}{16} + \dfrac{1}{8} - \dfrac{1}{2}$

103. $\dfrac{5}{8} - \left(-\dfrac{5}{12}\right) + \dfrac{1}{3}$

104. $\dfrac{1}{8} - \dfrac{11}{12} + \dfrac{1}{2}$

105. $7.56 + 0.462$

106. $1.09 + 6.2$

107. $-32.1 - 6.7$

108. $5.13 - 8.179$

109. $-13.092 + 6.9$

110. $2.54 - 3.6$

111. $5.43 + 7.925$

112. $-16.92 - 6.925$

113. $-3.87 + 8.546$

114. $6.9027 - 17.692$

115. $2.09 - 6.72 - 5.4$

116. $-18.39 + 4.9 - 23.7$

117. $19 - (-3.72) - 82.75$

118. $-3.07 - (-2.97) - 17.4$

119. $16.4 - (-3.09) - 7.93$ **120.** $-3.09 - 4.6 - (-27.3)$ **121.** $2.66 - (-4.66) - 8.2$

122. $-0.34 - (-4.35) - 3.2$ **123.** $7.5 - 12.8 - (-0.57)$ **124.** $2.8 - (-3.44) + 2.3$

Objective D

Simplify.

125. $\dfrac{1}{2} \times \left(-\dfrac{3}{4}\right)$ **126.** $-\dfrac{2}{9} \times \left(-\dfrac{3}{14}\right)$ **127.** $\left(-\dfrac{3}{8}\right)\left(-\dfrac{4}{15}\right)$

128. $\left(-\dfrac{3}{4}\right)\left(-\dfrac{8}{27}\right)$ **129.** $-\dfrac{1}{2}\left(\dfrac{8}{9}\right)$ **130.** $\dfrac{5}{12}\left(-\dfrac{8}{15}\right)$

131. $\dfrac{5}{8}\left(-\dfrac{7}{12}\right)\dfrac{16}{25}$ **132.** $\left(\dfrac{5}{12}\right)\left(-\dfrac{8}{15}\right)\left(-\dfrac{1}{3}\right)$ **133.** $\dfrac{1}{2}\left(-\dfrac{3}{4}\right)\left(-\dfrac{5}{8}\right)$

134. $\dfrac{3}{8} \div \dfrac{1}{4}$ **135.** $\dfrac{5}{6} \div \left(-\dfrac{3}{4}\right)$ **136.** $-\dfrac{5}{12} \div \dfrac{15}{32}$

137. $-\dfrac{7}{8} \div \dfrac{4}{21}$ **138.** $\dfrac{7}{10} \div \dfrac{2}{5}$ **139.** $-\dfrac{15}{64} \div \left(-\dfrac{3}{40}\right)$

140. $\dfrac{1}{8} \div \left(-\dfrac{5}{12}\right)$ **141.** $-\dfrac{4}{9} \div \left(-\dfrac{2}{3}\right)$ **142.** $-\dfrac{6}{11} \div \dfrac{4}{9}$

143. $1.2(3.47)$ **144.** $(-0.8)6.2$ **145.** $(-1.89)(-2.3)$

146. $(6.9)(-4.2)$ **147.** $1.06(-3.8)$ **148.** $-2.7(-3.5)$

149. $1.2(-0.5)(3.7)$ **150.** $-2.4(6.1)(0.9)$ **151.** $2.3(-0.6)(0.8)$

152. $-1.2(-0.55)(1.9)$ **153.** $0.44(-2.3)(-0.5)$ **154.** $-3.4(-22.1)(-0.5)$

155. $1.8(0.33)(-0.4)$ **156.** $4.5(-0.22)(-0.8)$ **157.** $-24.7 \div 0.09$

Simplify. Round to the nearest hundredth.

158. $-1.27 \div (-1.7)$ **159.** $9.07 \div (-3.5)$ **160.** $0.0976 \div 0.042$

161. $-6.904 \div 1.35$ **162.** $-7.894 \div (-2.06)$ **163.** $-354.2086 \div 0.1719$

Objective E   *Application Problems*

164. When a U.S. company does business with another country, it is necessary to convert U.S. currency into the currency of the other country. These *exchange rates* are determined by various factors. The exchange rates for some currencies during one day in July 1997 are shown in the table at the right.

    a. If you sold goods worth 1.2 million U.S. dollars to France, how many French francs would you receive?

    b. How many U.S. dollars, to the nearest cent, are equivalent to 1 Libyan dinar?

Foreign Currency per U.S. Dollar	
Canadian dollar	1.3936
French franc	5.7827
Libyan dinar	0.3555

165. The circle graph at the right shows the sources of donations to social causes. What percent of the total is contributed by corporations? Round to the nearest percent.

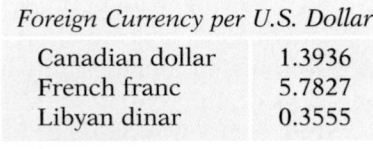

Giving, by Source (in billions of dollars)

Corporations $7.4
Bequests $9.8
Foundations $10.4
Individuals $116.2

Source: *Giving USA*, 1996, AAFRC Trust for Philanthropy

166. The table below shows the first-quarter profits and losses for 1997 for three companies in the toy industry. Profits are shown as positive numbers; losses are shown as negative numbers. One-quarter of a year is three months.

    a. If earnings were to continue throughout the year at the same level, what would the annual earnings or losses be for Mattel, Inc.?

    b. For the quarter shown, what was the average monthly profit or loss for Acclaim Entertainment?

Toy Company	First Quarter 1997 Profits
Acclaim Entertainment	−16.842 million
Hasbro, Inc.	25.694 million
Mattel, Inc.	−204.624 million

Source: *The Wall Street Journal*, May 5, 1997

167. Movies made in the United States that are not blockbusters in this country may make considerable money abroad. At the right is a table showing five films and their box-office grosses, in millions of dollars, at home and in foreign countries.

Box-Office Grosses (in millions of dollars)

Film	U. S.	Foreign
Judge Dredd	34.7	44.1
Spy Hard	26.6	30.6
Waterworld	88.2	78.2
The Juror	22.7	17.6
Highlander III	13.8	9.1

Source: *Time Magazine*, July 7, 1997

    a. What percent of *Waterworld*'s total gross was from foreign countries? Round to the nearest percent.

    b. What percent of *Judge Dredd*'s total gross here and abroad was its U.S. box-office gross? Round to the nearest percent.

    c. Which of the films listed grossed more than half their box-office income in foreign countries?

168. According to the Federal Highway Administration, the average car is driven approximately 10,300 mi per year and uses approximately 495 gal of gas. Assuming that the average cost of gasoline is $1.097 per gallon, which includes $.443 for all taxes, and that there are 1.53 million cars on the road, determine how much total tax is paid for gasoline in one year. (You may not need all the data given in this problem.)

APPLYING THE CONCEPTS

169. A magic square is one in which the numbers in every row, column, and diagonal sum to the same number. Complete the magic square at the right.

$\frac{2}{3}$		
	$\frac{1}{6}$	$\frac{5}{6}$
		$-\frac{1}{3}$

170. If a and b are rational numbers and $a < b$, is it always possible to find a rational number c such that $a < c < b$? If not, explain why. If so, show how to find one.

171. For each part below, find a rational number r that satisfies the condition.

    a. $r^2 < r$ **b.** $r^2 = r$ **c.** $r^2 > r$

172. In a survey of consumers, approximately 43% said they would be willing to pay between $1000 and $2000 more for a new car if the car had an EPA rating of 80 mpg. If your car now gets 28 mpg and you drive approximately 10,000 mi per year, in how many months would your savings on gasoline pay for the increased cost of such a car? Assume the average cost for gasoline is $1.06 per gallon.

173. Find three different natural numbers a, b, and c such that $\frac{1}{a} + \frac{1}{b} + \frac{1}{c}$ is a natural number.

Exponents and the Order of Operations Agreement

Objective A   *To evaluate exponential expressions* ....

Repeated multiplication of the same factor can be written using an exponent.

$$2 \cdot 2 \cdot 2 \cdot 2 \cdot 2 = 2^5 \leftarrow \text{exponent}$$
$$\uparrow \text{---base}$$

$$a \cdot a \cdot a \cdot a = a^4 \leftarrow \text{exponent}$$
$$\uparrow \text{---base}$$

The **exponent** indicates how many times the factor, called the **base,** occurs in the multiplication. The multiplication $2 \cdot 2 \cdot 2 \cdot 2 \cdot 2$ is in **factored form.** The exponential expression 2^5 is in **exponential form.**

2^1 is read "2 to the first power" or just "2." Usually the exponent 1 is not written.

2^2 is read "2 to the second power" or "2 squared."

2^3 is read "2 to the third power" or "2 cubed."

2^4 is read "2 to the fourth power."

a^4 is read "*a* to the fourth power."

There is a geometric interpretation of the first three natural-number powers.

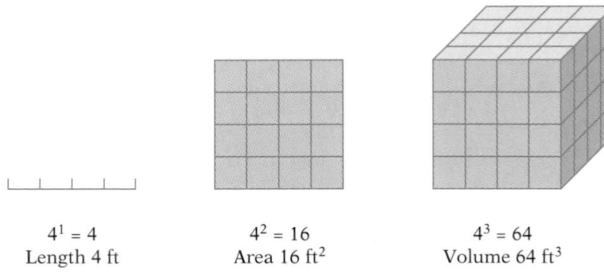

$4^1 = 4$ $4^2 = 16$ $4^3 = 64$
Length 4 ft   Area 16 ft^2 Volume 64 ft^3

To evaluate an exponential expression, write each factor as many times as indicated by the exponent. Then multiply.

➡ Evaluate $(-2)^4$.

$(-2)^4 = (-2)(-2)(-2)(-2)$ • **Write −2 as a factor 4 times.**

$\quad\quad = 16$ • **Multiply.**

➡ Evaluate -2^4.

$-2^4 = -(2 \cdot 2 \cdot 2 \cdot 2)$ • **Write 2 as a factor 4 times.**

$\quad\quad = -16$ • **Multiply.**

Example 1   Evaluate -5^3.

Solution $-5^3 = -(5 \cdot 5 \cdot 5) = -125$

You Try It 1   Evaluate -6^3.

Your solution

Example 2   Evaluate $(-4)^4$.

Solution $(-4)^4 = (-4)(-4)(-4)(-4)$
$= 256$

You Try It 2   Evaluate $(-3)^4$.

Your solution

Example 3   Evaluate $(-3)^2 \cdot 2^3$.

Solution $(-3)^2 \cdot 2^3 = (-3)(-3) \cdot (2)(2)(2)$
$= 9 \cdot 8 = 72$

You Try It 3   Evaluate $(3^3)(-2)^3$.

Your solution

Example 4   Evaluate $\left(-\dfrac{2}{3}\right)^3$.

Solution $\left(-\dfrac{2}{3}\right)^3 = \left(-\dfrac{2}{3}\right)\left(-\dfrac{2}{3}\right)\left(-\dfrac{2}{3}\right)$
$= -\dfrac{2 \cdot 2 \cdot 2}{3 \cdot 3 \cdot 3} = -\dfrac{8}{27}$

You Try It 4   Evaluate $\left(-\dfrac{2}{5}\right)^2$.

Your solution

Example 5   Evaluate $-4(0.7)^2$.

Solution $-4(0.7)^2 = -4(0.7)(0.7)$
$= -2.8(0.7) = -1.96$

You Try It 5   Evaluate $-3(0.3)^3$.

Your solution

Solutions on p. S2

Objective B   **To use the Order of Operations Agreement to simplify expressions** ....

Let's evaluate $2 + 3 \cdot 5$.

There are two arithmetic operations, addition and multiplication, in this expression. The operations could be performed in different orders.

Multiply first. $2 + \underline{3 \cdot 5}$ Add first. $\underline{2 + 3} \cdot 5$

Then add. $\underline{2 + 15}$ Then multiply. $\underline{5 \cdot 5}$
$\underbrace{}_{17}$ $\underbrace{}_{25}$

In order to prevent more than one answer for a numerical expression, an Order of Operations Agreement has been established.

The Order of Operations Agreement

Step 1   Perform operations inside grouping symbols. Grouping symbols include parentheses ( ), brackets [ ], braces { }, and the fraction bar.

Step 2   Simplify exponential expressions.

Step 3   Do multiplication and division as they occur from left to right.

Step 4   Do addition and subtraction as they occur from left to right.

➡ Evaluate $12 - 24(8 - 5) \div 2^2$.

$12 - 24(8 - 5) \div 2^2 = 12 - 24(3) \div 2^2$	• Perform operations inside grouping symbols.
$= 12 - 24(3) \div 4$	• Simplify exponential expressions.
$= 12 - 72 \div 4$	• Do multiplication and division as they occur from left to right.
$= 12 - 18$	
$= -6$	• Do addition and subtraction as they occur from left to right.

One or more of the above steps may not be needed to evaluate an expression. In that case, proceed to the next step in the Order of Operations Agreement.

➡ Evaluate $\dfrac{4 + 8}{2 + 1} - (3 - 1) + 2$.

$\dfrac{4 + 8}{2 + 1} - (3 - 1) + 2 = \dfrac{12}{3} - 2 + 2$	• Perform operations above and below the fraction bar and inside parentheses.
$= 4 - 2 + 2$	• Do multiplication and division as they occur from left to right.
$= 2 + 2$	• Do addition and subtraction as they occur from left to right.
$= 4$	

When an expression has grouping symbols inside grouping symbols, perform the operations inside the inner grouping symbols first.

➡ Evaluate $6 \div [4 - (6 - 8)] + 2^2$.

$6 \div [4 - (6 - 8)] + 2^2 = 6 \div [4 - (-2)] + 2^2$	• Perform operations inside grouping symbols.
$= 6 \div 6 + 2^2$	
$= 6 \div 6 + 4$	• Simplify exponential expressions.
$= 1 + 4$	• Do multiplication and division as they occur from left to right.
$= 5$	• Do addition and subtraction as they occur from left to right.

Example 6

Evaluate $(1.75 - 1.3)^2 \div 0.025 + 6.1$.

Solution

$(1.75 - 1.3)^2 \div 0.025 + 6.1$
$= (0.45)^2 \div 0.025 + 6.1$
$= 0.2025 \div 0.025 + 6.1$
$= 8.1 + 6.1$
$= 14.2$

You Try It 6

Evaluate $(6.97 - 4.72)^2 \cdot 4.5 \div 0.05$.

Your solution

Solution on p. S2

Example 7

Evaluate $4 - 3[4 - 2(6 - 3)] \div 2$.

Solution

$4 - 3[4 - 2(6 - 3)] \div 2$
$= 4 - 3[4 - 2 \cdot 3] \div 2$
$= 4 - 3[4 - 6] \div 2$
$= 4 - 3[-2] \div 2$
$= 4 + 6 \div 2$
$= 4 + 3$
$= 7$

You Try It 7

Evaluate $18 - 5[8 - 2(2 - 5)] \div 10$.

Your solution

Example 8

Evaluate $27 \div (5 - 2)^2 + (-3)^2 \cdot 4$.

Solution

$27 \div (5 - 2)^2 + (-3)^2 \cdot 4$
$= 27 \div 3^2 + (-3)^2 \cdot 4$
$= 27 \div 9 + 9 \cdot 4$
$= 3 + 9 \cdot 4$
$= 3 + 36$
$= 39$

You Try It 8

Evaluate $36 \div (8 - 5)^2 - (-3)^2 \cdot 2$.

Your solution

Example 9

Evaluate $\dfrac{5}{8} - \left(\dfrac{2}{5} - \dfrac{1}{2}\right) \div \left(\dfrac{2}{3}\right)^2$.

Solution

$\dfrac{5}{8} - \left(\dfrac{2}{5} - \dfrac{1}{2}\right) \div \left(\dfrac{2}{3}\right)^2$

$= \dfrac{5}{8} - \left(-\dfrac{1}{10}\right) \div \left(\dfrac{2}{3}\right)^2$

$= \dfrac{5}{8} + \dfrac{1}{10} \div \dfrac{4}{9}$

$= \dfrac{5}{8} + \dfrac{1}{10} \cdot \dfrac{9}{4}$

$= \dfrac{5}{8} + \dfrac{9}{40}$

$= \dfrac{25}{40} + \dfrac{9}{40}$

$= \dfrac{34}{40} = \dfrac{17}{20}$

You Try It 9

Evaluate $\dfrac{5}{8} \div \left(\dfrac{1}{3} - \dfrac{3}{4}\right) + \dfrac{7}{12}$.

Your solution

Solutions on pp. S2–S3

1.5 Exercises

· ·

Objective A

Evaluate.

1. 6^2
    2. 7^4
    3. -7^2
    4. -4^3
    5. $(-3)^2$

6. $(-2)^3$
    7. $(-3)^4$
    8. $(-5)^3$
    9. $\left(\dfrac{1}{2}\right)^2$
    10. $\left(-\dfrac{3}{4}\right)^3$

11. $(0.3)^2$
    12. $(1.5)^3$
    13. $\left(\dfrac{2}{3}\right)^2 \cdot 3^3$
    14. $\left(-\dfrac{1}{2}\right)^3 \cdot 8$
    15. $(0.3)^3 \cdot 2^3$

16. $(0.5)^2 \cdot 3^3$
    17. $(-3) \cdot 2^2$
    18. $(-5) \cdot 3^4$
    19. $(-2) \cdot (-2)^3$

20. $(-2) \cdot (-2)^2$
    21. $2^3 \cdot 3^3 \cdot (-4)$
    22. $(-3)^3 \cdot 5^2 \cdot 10$
    23. $(-7) \cdot 4^2 \cdot 3^2$

24. $(-2) \cdot 2^3 \cdot (-3)^2$
    25. $\left(\dfrac{2}{3}\right)^2 \cdot \dfrac{1}{4} \cdot 3^3$
    26. $\left(\dfrac{3}{4}\right)^2 \cdot (-4) \cdot 2^3$
    27. $8^2 \cdot (-3)^5 \cdot 5$

Objective B

Evaluate by using the Order of Operations Agreement.

28. $4 - 8 \div 2$
    29. $2^2 \cdot 3 - 3$
    30. $2(3 - 4) - (-3)^2$

31. $16 - 32 \div 2^3$
    32. $24 - 18 \div 3 + 2$
    33. $8 - (-3)^2 - (-2)$

34. $8 - 2(3)^2$
    35. $16 - 16 \cdot 2 \div 4$
    36. $12 + 16 \div 4 \cdot 2$

37. $16 - 2 \cdot 4^2$
    38. $27 - 18 \div (-3^2)$
    39. $4 + 12 \div 3 \cdot 2$

40. $16 + 15 \div (-5) - 2$

41. $14 - 2^2 - (4 - 7)$

42. $3 - 2[8 - (3 - 2)]$

43. $-2^2 + 4[16 \div (3 - 5)]$

44. $6 + \dfrac{16 - 4}{2^2 + 2} - 2$

45. $24 \div \dfrac{3^2}{8 - 5} - (-5)$

46. $96 \div 2[12 + (6 - 2)] - 3^2$

47. $4[16 - (7 - 1)] \div 10$

48. $18 \div 2 - 4^2 - (-3)^2$

49. $18 \div (9 - 2^3) + (-3)$

50. $16 - 3(8 - 3)^2 \div 5$

51. $4(-8) \div [2(7 - 3)^2]$

52. $\dfrac{(-19) + (-2)}{6^2 - 30} \div (2 - 4)$

53. $16 - 4 \cdot \dfrac{3^3 - 7}{2^3 + 2} - (-2)^2$

54. $(0.2)^2 \cdot (-0.5) + 1.72$

55. $0.3(1.7 - 4.8) + (1.2)^2$

56. $(1.8)^2 - 2.52 \div 1.8$

57. $(1.65 - 1.05)^2 \div 0.4 + 0.8$

58. $\dfrac{3}{8} \div \left(\dfrac{5}{6} + \dfrac{2}{3}\right)$

59. $\left(\dfrac{5}{12} - \dfrac{9}{16}\right)\dfrac{3}{7}$

60. $\left(\dfrac{3}{4}\right)^2 - \left(\dfrac{1}{2}\right)^3 \div \dfrac{3}{5}$

APPLYING THE CONCEPTS

61. The following was offered as the simplification of $6 + 2(4 - 9)$.

$$6 + 2(4 - 9) = 6 + 2(-5)$$
$$= 8(-5)$$
$$= -40$$

If this is a correct simplification, write yes for the answer. If it is incorrect, write no and explain the incorrect step.

62. The following was offered as the simplification of $2 \cdot 3^3$.

$$2 \cdot 3^3 = 6^3 = 216$$

If this is a correct simplification, write yes for the answer. If it is incorrect, write no and explain the incorrect step.

Focus on Problem Solving

Inductive Reasoning

Suppose you take 9 credit hours each semester. The total number of credit hours you have taken at the end of each semester can be described in a list of numbers.

$$9, 18, 27, 36, 45, 54, 63,\ldots$$

The list of numbers that indicates the total credit hours is an ordered list of numbers, called a **sequence**. Each number in a sequence is called a **term** of the sequence. The list is ordered because the position of a number in the list indicates the semester in which that number of credit hours has been taken. For example, the 7th term of the sequence is 63, and a total of 63 credit hours have been taken after the 7th semester.

Assuming the pattern is continued, find the next three numbers in the pattern

$$-6, -10, -14, -18,\ldots$$

This list of numbers is a sequence. The first step in solving this problem is to observe the pattern in the list of numbers. In this case, each number in the list is 4 less than the previous number. The next three numbers are $-22, -26, -30$.

This process of discovering the pattern in a list of numbers is inductive reasoning. **Inductive reasoning** involves making generalizations from specific examples; in other words, we reach a conclusion by making observations about particular facts or cases.

Try the following exercises. Each exercise requires inductive reasoning.

Name the next two terms in the sequence.

1. 1, 3, 5, 7, 1, 3, 5, 7, 1,…

2. 1, 4, 2, 5, 3, 6, 4,…

3. 1, 2, 4, 7, 11, 16,…

4. A, B, C, G, H, I, M,…

Draw the next shape in the sequence.

5.

6. |• ||• ||•• |||•• |||•••

Solve.

7. Convert $\frac{1}{11}, \frac{2}{11}, \frac{3}{11}, \frac{4}{11}$, and $\frac{5}{11}$ to decimals. Then use the pattern you observe to convert $\frac{6}{11}, \frac{7}{11}$, and $\frac{9}{11}$ to decimals.

8. Convert $\frac{1}{33}$, $\frac{2}{33}$, $\frac{4}{33}$, $\frac{5}{33}$, and $\frac{7}{33}$ to decimals. Then use the pattern you observe to convert $\frac{8}{33}$, $\frac{13}{33}$, and $\frac{19}{33}$ to decimals.

Projects and Group Activities

The $\boxed{+/-}$ Key on a Calculator

Using your calculator to simplify numerical expressions sometimes requires use of the $\boxed{+/-}$ key or, on some calculators, the negative key, which is frequently shown as $\boxed{(-)}$. These keys change the sign of the number currently in the display. To enter -4:

- For those calculators with $\boxed{+/-}$, press 4 and then $\boxed{+/-}$.
- For those calculators with $\boxed{(-)}$, press $\boxed{(-)}$ and then 4.

Here are the keystrokes for evaluating the expression $3(-4) - (-5)$.

Calculators with $\boxed{+/-}$ key: 3 $\boxed{\times}$ 4 $\boxed{+/-}$ $-$ 5 $\boxed{+/-}$ $\boxed{=}$

Calculators with $\boxed{(-)}$ key: 3 $\boxed{\times}$$\boxed{(-)}$ 4 $\boxed{-}$$\boxed{(-)}$ 5 $\boxed{=}$

This example illustrates that calculators make a distinction between negative and minus. To perform the operation $3 - (-3)$, you cannot enter 3 $\boxed{-}$$\boxed{-}$ 3. This would result in 0, which is not the correct answer. You must enter

3 $\boxed{-}$ 3 $\boxed{+/-}$ $\boxed{=}$ or   3 $\boxed{-}$$\boxed{(-)}$ 3 $\boxed{=}$

Use a calculator to evaluate each of the following exercises.

1. $-16 \div 2$ **2.** $3(-8)$ **3.** $47 - (-9)$

4. $-50 - (-14)$ **5.** $4 - (-3)^2$ **6.** $-8 + (-6)^2 - 7$

Moving Averages

Stock	Div	PE	Sales 100s	High	Low	Close	Chg.
			A				
AAR	.48	23	2495	$13\frac{1}{4}$	$11\frac{7}{8}$	$12\frac{1}{4}$	$-\frac{7}{8}$
ACMin	.96		814	$11\frac{1}{8}$	11	11	$-\frac{1}{8}$
ACM Op	.80a		324	$9\frac{3}{4}$	$9\frac{3}{8}$	$9\frac{5}{8}$	$+\frac{1}{4}$
ACM Sc	.96a		1104	$11\frac{3}{8}$	$11\frac{1}{4}$	$11\frac{3}{8}$	
ACMSp	.80a		497	$9\frac{1}{2}$	$9\frac{1}{2}$	$9\frac{1}{2}$	
ACM MI	1.08a		678	$10\frac{3}{4}$	$10\frac{5}{8}$	$10\frac{3}{4}$	$+\frac{1}{8}$
ACMMM	.78		156	$9\frac{1}{4}$	$9\frac{1}{8}$	$9\frac{1}{8}$	
ADT wt			742	$15\frac{1}{8}$	$13\frac{3}{8}$	$11\frac{1}{2}$	
ADT			4357	$9\frac{1}{2}$	9	$9\frac{1}{8}$	
AFLAC	.44	16	1355	$35\frac{1}{2}$	$34\frac{3}{4}$	$34\frac{7}{8}$	$-\frac{1}{2}$
AL Lab	.18	168	911	$23\frac{1}{2}$	$22\frac{1}{4}$	$23\frac{1}{2}$	$+13\frac{3}{8}$

Objective 1.3C on page 20 describes how to find the moving average of a stock. Use this method to calculate the five-day moving average for at least three different stocks. Discuss and compare the results for the different stocks.

For this project, you will need to use stock tables, which are printed in the business section of major newspapers. Your college library should have copies of these publications. In a stock table, the column headed "Chg." provides the change in the price of a share of the stock; that is, it gives the difference between the closing price for the day shown and the closing price for the previous day. The symbol + indicates the change was an increase in price; the symbol − indicates the change was a decrease in price.

www.fedstats.gov Information regarding the history of the federal budget can be found on the World Wide Web. Go to the web site www.fedstats.gov. Click on "Fast Facts" and then on "Frequently Requested Tables." In the list of tables printed to the screen, find the table entitled "Federal Budget - Summary." Click on it. When the federal budget table appears on the screen, look for the column that lists each year's surplus or deficit. You will see that a negative sign (−) is used to show a deficit. Note that it states near the top of the screen that the figures in the table are in millions of dollars.

1. During which years shown in the table was there a surplus?
2. During which year was the deficit the greatest?
3. Find the difference between the surplus or deficit this year and the surplus or deficit five years ago.
4. What is the difference between the surplus or deficit this year and the surplus or deficit a decade ago?
5. Determine what two numbers in the table are being subtracted in each row in order to arrive at the number in the surplus or deficit column.
6. Describe the trend of the federal deficit over the last ten years.

Chapter Summary

Key Words   A *set* is a collection of objects. The objects in a set are called the *elements* of the set.

The *roster method* of writing sets encloses a list of the elements in braces.

The set of *natural numbers* is {1, 2, 3, 4, 5, 6, 7,…}.

The set of *integers* is {…, −4, −3, −2, −1, 0, 1, 2, 3, 4,…}.

A number *a is less than* another number *b*, written $a < b$, if *a* is to the left of *b* on the number line.

A number *a is greater than* another number *b*, written $a > b$, if *a* is to the right of *b* on the number line.

The symbol ≤ means *is less than or equal to*. The symbol ≥ means *is greater than or equal to*.

Two numbers that are the same distance from zero on the number line but on opposite sides of zero are *opposite numbers*, or *opposites*. The opposite of a number is also called its *additive inverse*.

The *absolute value* of a number is its distance from zero on the number line.

A *rational number* is a number of the form $\frac{a}{b}$, where *a* and *b* are integers and *b* is not equal to zero. A rational number written in this form is commonly called a fraction.

A fraction is in *simplest form* when there are no common factors in the numerator and the denominator.

The *reciprocal* of a fraction is the fraction with the numerator and denominator interchanged.

An *irrational number* is a number that has a decimal representation that never terminates or repeats.

The rational numbers and the irrational numbers taken together are called the *real numbers.*

Percent means "parts of 100." Thus 63% means 63 parts of 100 parts.

An expression of the form a^n is in *exponential form*, where a is the *base* and n is the *exponent*.

Essential Rules   ***To add two numbers with the same sign,*** add the absolute values of the numbers. Then attach the sign of the addends.

To add two numbers with different signs, find the absolute value of each number. Subtract the smaller of the two numbers from the larger. Then attach the sign of the number with the larger absolute value.

To subtract two integers, add the opposite of the second integer to the first integer.

To multiply two numbers with the same sign, multiply the absolute values of the factors. The product is positive.

To multiply two numbers with different signs, multiply the absolute values of the factors. The product is negative.

To divide two numbers with the same sign, divide the absolute values of the numbers. The quotient is positive.

To divide two numbers with different signs, divide the absolute values of the numbers. The quotient is negative.

Properties of Zero and One in Division   If $a \neq 0$, $0 \div a = 0$.
If $a \neq 0$, $a \div a = 1$.
$a \div 1 = a$.
$a \div 0$ is undefined.

To convert a percent to a decimal, remove the percent sign and multiply by 0.01.

To convert a percent to a fraction, remove the percent sign and multiply by $\frac{1}{100}$.

To convert a fraction to a percent, multiply by 100%.

To convert a decimal to a percent, multiply by 100%.

The Order of Operations Agreement

Step 1   Perform all operations inside grouping symbols. Grouping symbols include parentheses, brackets, braces, and the fraction bar.

Step 2   Simplify any numerical expressions containing exponents.

Step 3   Do multiplication and division as they occur from left to right.

Step 4   Do addition and subtraction as they occur from left to right.

Chapter Review

1. Add: $-13 + 7$

2. Write $\frac{7}{25}$ as a decimal.

3. Evaluate -5^2.

4. Evaluate $5 - 2^2 + 9$.

5. Place the correct symbol, $<$ or $>$, between the two numbers.
$-4 \quad 2$

6. Write 6.2% as a decimal.

7. Multiply: $(-6)(7)$

8. Simplify: $\frac{1}{3} - \frac{1}{6} + \frac{5}{12}$

9. Evaluate $15 \cdot (6 - 4)^2$.

10. Given $A = \{-4, 0, 11\}$, which elements of set A are less than -1?

11. Subtract: $5.17 - 6.238$

12. Write $\frac{5}{8}$ as a percent.

13. Write $\frac{2}{15}$ as a decimal. Place a bar over the repeating digits of the decimal.

14. Subtract: $9 - 13$

15. Find the additive inverse of -4.

16. Divide: $-32 \div (-4)$

17. Divide: $-100 \div 5$

18. Write $79\frac{1}{2}\%$ as a fraction.

19. Evaluate $-3^2 + 4[18 + (12 - 20)]$.

20. Add: $-3 + (-12) + 6 + (-4)$

21. Write $\frac{19}{35}$ as a percent. Write the remainder in fractional form.

22. Evaluate $\left(\frac{2}{3}\right)^4$.

23. Multiply: $4.32(-1.07)$

24. Evaluate $-|-5|$.

25. Subtract: $16 - (-3) - 18$

26. Divide: $-\frac{18}{35} \div \frac{27}{28}$

27. Given $C = \{-7, 0, 9\}$ find the absolute value of each element of set C.

28. Multiply: $-9(-9)$

29. Place the correct symbol between the two numbers.
$-|6| \quad |-10|$

30. Evaluate $\frac{5^2 + 11}{2^2 + 5} \div (2^3 - 2^2)$.

31. To discourage random guessing on a multiple-choice exam, a professor assigns 6 points for a correct answer, -4 points for an incorrect answer, and -2 points for leaving a question blank. What is the score for a student who had 21 correct answers, 5 incorrect answers, and left 4 questions blank?

32. The graph at the right shows the average number of messages received each day per employee. What percent of all the messages is E-mail? Round to the nearest tenth of a percent.

33. The temperature at which mercury boils is 357°C. The temperature at which mercury freezes is -39°C. Find the difference between the boiling point and the freezing point of mercury.

Source: Institute for the Future/Gallup Organization

Chapter Test

1. Divide: $-561 \div (-33)$

2. Write $\frac{5}{6}$ as a percent. Write the remainder in fractional form.

3. Evaluate $\frac{3}{4} \cdot (4)^2$.

4. Multiply: $6.02(-0.89)$

5. Subtract: $16 - 30$

6. Write $37\frac{1}{2}\%$ as a fraction.

7. Add: $-\frac{2}{5} + \frac{7}{15}$

8. Evaluate $\frac{-10 + 2}{2 + (-4)} \div 2 + 6$.

9. Multiply: $-5(-6)(3)$

10. Find the opposite of -4.

11. Evaluate $(-3^3) \cdot 2^2$.

12. Given $B = \{-5, -3, 0, 4\}$, which elements of set B are greater than 2?

13. Place the correct symbol, $<$ or $>$, between the two numbers.
    $-2 \quad -40$

14. Evaluate $-|-4|$.

15. Write 45% as a fraction and as a decimal.

16. Add: $-22 + 14 + (-8)$

17. Multiply: $-4 \cdot 12$

18. Evaluate $16 \div 2[8 - 3(4 - 2)] + 1$.

19. Subtract: $16 - (-30) - 42$

20. Divide: $\dfrac{5}{12} \div \left(-\dfrac{5}{6}\right)$

21. Write 1.025 as a percent.

22. Evaluate $3^2 - 4 + 20 \div 5$.

23. Write $\dfrac{7}{9}$ as a decimal. Place a bar over the repeating digit of the decimal.

24. The table below shows the first-quarter profits and losses for 1997 for five companies in the paper industry. Profits are shown as positive numbers; losses are shown as negative numbers. One-quarter of a year is three months.

  a. If earnings were to continue throughout the year at the same level, what would be the annual earnings or losses for Bowater, Inc.?

  b. For the quarter shown, what was the average monthly profit or loss for Boise Cascade?

Paper Company	First Quarter 1997 Profits
Boise Cascade	–15,210,000
Bowater, Inc.	–3,140,000
Champion International	–37,083,000
Consolidated Paper	28,056,000
International Paper Company	34,000,000

Source: *The Wall Street Journal*, May 5, 1997

25. At the end of the trading day on July 30, the price of one share of Nike stock was $\$62\frac{3}{4}$. The change in the price of a share on July 31 was $-\frac{1}{8}$. What was the price of one share of Nike stock at the end of the trading day on July 31?

CHAPTER

2

Variable Expressions

Objectives

Section 2.1

To evaluate a variable expression

Section 2.2

To simplify a variable expression using the Properties of Addition

To simplify a variable expression using the Properties of Multiplication

To simplify a variable expression using the Distributive Property

To simplify general variable expressions

Section 2.3

To translate a verbal expression into a variable expression, given the variable

To translate a verbal expression into a variable expression and then simplify

To translate application problems

Nutritionists are hired by schools, hospitals, and other institutions to plan appealing meals that supply the nutrition needed to maintain good health. To plan a balanced diet, they need to know the recommended daily requirements of vitamins and minerals and the vitamin and mineral content of different foods. As meal planning requires dealing with so many "variables," a knowledge of variable expressions is very helpful in this career.

History of Variables

Prior to the 16th century, unknown quantities were represented by words. In Latin, the language in which most scholarly works were written, the word *res*, meaning "thing," was used. In Germany the word *zahl*, meaning "number," was used. In Italy the word *cosa*, also meaning "thing," was used.

Then in 1637, René Descartes, a French mathematician, began using the letters x, y, and z to represent variables. It is interesting to note, on examining Descartes's work, that toward the end of the book the letters y and z were no longer used and x became the choice for a variable.

One explanation of why the letters y and z appeared less frequently has to do with the nature of printing presses during Descartes's time. A printer had a large tray that contained all the letters of the alphabet. There were many copies of each letter, especially those letters that are used frequently. For example, there were more e's than q's. Because the letters y and z do not occur frequently in French, a printer would have few of these letters on hand. Consequently, when Descartes started using these letters as variables, it quickly depleted the printer's supply and x's had to be used instead.

Today, x is used by most nations as the standard letter for a single unknown. In fact, x-rays were so named because the scientists who discovered them did not know what they were and thus labeled them the "unknown rays" or x-rays.

2.1 Evaluating Variable Expressions

Objective A   *To evaluate a variable expression* ....

Often we discuss a quantity without knowing its exact value—for example, the price of gold next month, the cost of a new automobile next year, or the tuition cost for next semester. Recall that a letter of the alphabet is used to stand for a quantity that is unknown or that can change, or *vary*. The letter is called a **variable.** An expression that contains one or more variables is called a **variable expression.**

A variable expression is shown at the right. The expression can be rewritten by writing subtraction as the addition of the opposite.

$$3x^2 - 5y + 2xy - x - 7$$

$$3x^2 + (-5y) + 2xy + (-x) + (-7)$$

Note that the expression has 5 addends. The **terms** of a variable expression are the addends of the expression. The expression has 5 terms.

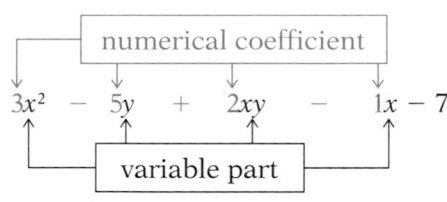

The terms $3x^2$, $-5y$, $2xy$, and $-x$ are **variable terms.**

The term -7 is a **constant term,** or simply a **constant.**

Each variable term is composed of a **numerical coefficient** and a **variable part** (the variable or variables and their exponents).

When the numerical coefficient is 1 or -1, the 1 is usually not written ($x = 1x$ and $-x = -1x$).

numerical coefficient

$$3x^2 - 5y + 2xy - 1x - 7$$

variable part

Variable expressions occur naturally in science. In a physics lab, a student may discover that a weight of 1 pound will stretch a spring $\frac{1}{2}$ inch. Two pounds will stretch the spring 1 inch. By experimenting, the student can discover that the distance the spring will stretch is found by multiplying the weight by $\frac{1}{2}$. By letting W represent the weight attached to the spring, the student can represent the distance the spring stretches by the variable expression $\frac{1}{2}W$.

With a weight of W pounds, the spring will stretch $\frac{1}{2} \cdot W = \frac{1}{2}W$ inches.

With a weight of 10 pounds, the spring will stretch $\frac{1}{2} \cdot 10 = 5$ inches. The number 10 is called the **value** of the variable W.

With a weight of 3 pounds, the spring will stretch $\frac{1}{2} \cdot 3 = 1\frac{1}{2}$ inches.

Replacing each variable by its value and then simplifying the resulting numerical expression is called **evaluating the variable expression.**

CALCULATOR NOTE

See the appendix "Guidelines for Using Graphing Calculators" for instructions on using a graphing calculator to evaluate variable expressions.

➡ Evaluate $ab - b^2$ when $a = 2$ and $b = -3$.

Replace each variable in the expression by its value. Then use the Order of Operations Agreement to simplify the resulting numerical expression.

$ab - b^2$

$$2(-3) - (-3)^2 = -6 - 9$$
$$= -15$$

When $a = 2$ and $b = -3$, the value of $ab - b^2$ is -15.

Example 1   Name the variable terms of the expression $2a^2 - 5a + 7$.

Solution $2a^2$ and $-5a$

You Try It 1   Name the constant term of the expression $6n^2 + 3n - 4$.

Your solution

Example 2   Evaluate $x^2 - 3xy$ when $x = 3$ and $y = -4$.

Solution $x^2 - 3xy$
$$3^2 - 3(3)(-4) = 9 - 3(3)(-4)$$
$$= 9 - 9(-4)$$
$$= 9 - (-36)$$
$$= 9 + 36 = 45$$

You Try It 2   Evaluate $2xy + y^2$ when $x = -4$ and $y = 2$.

Your solution

Example 3   Evaluate $\dfrac{a^2 - b^2}{a - b}$ when $a = 3$ and $b = -4$.

Solution $\dfrac{a^2 - b^2}{a - b}$
$$\frac{3^2 - (-4)^2}{3 - (-4)} = \frac{9 - 16}{3 - (-4)}$$
$$= \frac{-7}{7} = -1$$

You Try It 3   Evaluate $\dfrac{a^2 + b^2}{a + b}$ when $a = 5$ and $b = -3$.

Your solution

Example 4   Evaluate $x^2 - 3(x - y) - z^2$ when $x = 2$, $y = -1$, and $z = 3$.

Solution $x^2 - 3(x - y) - z^2$
$$2^2 - 3[2 - (-1)] - 3^2$$
$$= 2^2 - 3(3) - 3^2$$
$$= 4 - 3(3) - 9$$
$$= 4 - 9 - 9$$
$$= -5 - 9$$
$$= -14$$

You Try It 4   Evaluate $x^3 - 2(x + y) + z^2$ when $x = 2$, $y = -4$, and $z = -3$.

Your solution

Solutions on p. S3

2.1 Exercises

· ·

Objective A

Name the terms of the variable expression. Then underline the constant term.

1. $2x^2 + 5x - 8$

2. $-3n^2 - 4n + 7$

3. $6 - a^4$

Name the variable terms of the expression. Then underline the variable part of each term.

4. $9b^2 - 4ab + a^2$

5. $7x^2y + 6xy^2 + 10$

6. $5 - 8n - 3n^2$

Name the coefficients of the variable terms.

7. $x^2 - 9x + 2$

8. $12a^2 - 8ab - b^2$

9. $n^3 - 4n^2 - n + 9$

Evaluate the variable expression when $a = 2$, $b = 3$, and $c = -4$.

10. $3a + 2b$

11. $a - 2c$

12. $-a^2$

13. $2c^2$

14. $-3a + 4b$

15. $3b - 3c$

16. $b^2 - 3$

17. $-3c + 4$

18. $16 \div (2c)$

19. $6b \div (-a)$

20. $bc \div (2a)$

21. $b^2 - 4ac$

22. $a^2 - b^2$

23. $b^2 - c^2$

24. $(a + b)^2$

25. $a^2 + b^2$

26. $2a - (c + a)^2$

27. $(b - a)^2 + 4c$

28. $b^2 - \dfrac{ac}{8}$

29. $\dfrac{5ab}{6} - 3cb$

30. $(b - 2a)^2 + bc$

Evaluate the variable expression when $a = -2$, $b = 4$, $c = -1$, and $d = 3$.

31. $\dfrac{b + c}{d}$

32. $\dfrac{d - b}{c}$

33. $\dfrac{2d + b}{-a}$

34. $\dfrac{b + 2d}{b}$

35. $\dfrac{b - d}{c - a}$

36. $\dfrac{2c - d}{-ad}$

37. $(b + d)^2 - 4a$

38. $(d - a)^2 - 3c$

39. $(d - a)^2 \div 5$

40. $3(b - a) - bc$

41. $\dfrac{b - 2a}{bc^2 - d}$

42. $\dfrac{b^2 - a}{ad + 3c}$

43. $\dfrac{1}{3}d^2 - \dfrac{3}{8}b^2$

44. $\dfrac{5}{8}a^4 - c^2$

45. $\dfrac{-4bc}{2a - b}$

46. $-\dfrac{3}{4}b + \dfrac{1}{2}(ac + bd)$

47. $-\dfrac{2}{3}d - \dfrac{1}{5}(bd - ac)$

48. $(b - a)^2 - (d - c)^2$

49. $(b + c)^2 + (a + d)^2$

50. $4ac + (2a)^2$

51. $3dc - (4c)^2$

APPLYING THE CONCEPTS

52. Explain in your own words the meaning of "evaluate an algebraic expression."

Evaluate the following expressions for $x = 2$, $y = 3$, and $z = -2$.

53. $3^x - x^3$

54. z^x

55. $x^x - y^y$

56. $y^{(x^2)}$

57. For each of the following, determine the first natural number x, greater than 1, for which the second expression is larger than the first.

    a. $x^3, 3^x$ **b.** $x^4, 4^x$ **c.** $x^5, 5^x$ **d.** $x^6, 6^x$

58. On the basis of your answer to Exercise 57, make a conjecture that appears to be true about the expressions x^n and n^x, where $n = 3, 4, 5, 6, 7, \ldots$ and x is a natural number greater than 1.

2.2   Simplifying Variable Expressions

Objective A   **To simplify a variable expression using the Properties of Addition** ....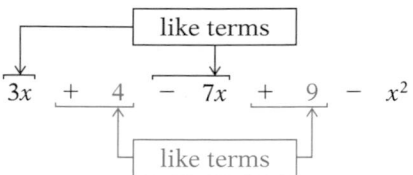

Like terms of a variable expression are terms with the same variable part. (Because $x^2 = x \cdot x$, x^2 and x are not like terms.)

Constant terms are like terms. 4 and 9 are like terms.

$$\underbrace{3x}_{} + \overbrace{4 - 7x + 9}^{} - x^2$$
like terms / like terms

To simplify a variable expression, use the Distributive Property to combine like terms by adding the numerical coefficients. The variable part remains unchanged.

> **Distributive Property**
>
> If a, b, and c are real numbers, then $a(b + c) = ab + ac$.

The Distributive Property can also be written $ba + ca = (b + c)a$. This form is used to simplify a variable expression.

To simplify $2x + 3x$, use the Distributive Property to add the numerical coefficients of the like variable terms. This is called **combining like terms.**

$$\begin{aligned} 2x + 3x &= (2 + 3)x \\ &= 5x \end{aligned}$$

➡ Simplify: $5y - 11y$

$$\begin{aligned} 5y - 11y &= (5 - 11)y \qquad \bullet \textbf{ Use the Distributive Property.} \\ &= -6y \end{aligned}$$

➡ Simplify: $5 + 7p$

The terms 5 and $7p$ are not like terms.

The expression $5 + 7p$ is in simplest form.

TAKE NOTE

Simplifying an expression means combining like terms. A constant term (5) and a variable term (7p) are not like terms and therefore cannot be combined.

> **The Associative Property of Addition**
>
> If a, b, and c are real numbers, then $(a + b) + c = a + (b + c)$.

When three or more terms are added, the terms can be grouped (with parentheses, for example) in any order. The sum is the same. For example,

$$\begin{aligned} (3x + 5x) + 9x &= 3x + (5x + 9x) \\ 8x + 9x &= 3x + 14x \\ 17x &= 17x \end{aligned}$$

> **The Commutative Property of Addition**
>
> If a and b are real numbers, then $a + b = b + a$.

When two like terms are added, the terms can be added in either order. The sum is the same. For example,

$$2x + (-4x) = -4x + 2x$$
$$-2x = -2x$$

> **The Addition Property of Zero**
>
> If a is a real number, then $a + 0 = 0 + a = a$.

The sum of a term and zero is the term. For example,

$$5x + 0 = 0 + 5x = 5x$$

> **The Inverse Property of Addition**
>
> If a is a real number, then $a + (-a) = (-a) + a = 0$.

The sum of a term and its opposite is zero. The opposite of a number is called its **additive inverse.**

$$7x + (-7x) = -7x + 7x = 0$$

→ Simplify: $8x + 4y - 8x + y$

$8x + 4y - 8x + y$
$= (8x - 8x) + (4y + y)$

$= 0 + 5y = 5y$

- Use the Commutative and Associative Properties of Addition to rearrange and group like terms.
- Combine like terms.

→ Simplify: $4x^2 + 5x - 6x^2 - 2x + 1$

$4x^2 + 5x - 6x^2 - 2x + 1$
$= (4x^2 - 6x^2) + (5x - 2x) + 1$

$= -2x^2 + 3x + 1$

- Use the Commutative and Associative Properties of Addition to rearrange and group like terms.
- Combine like terms.

Example 1   Simplify: $3x + 4y - 10x + 7y$

Solution $3x + 4y - 10x + 7y = -7x + 11y$

You Try It 1   Simplify: $3a - 2b - 5a + 6b$

Your solution

Example 2   Simplify: $x^2 - 7 + 4x^2 - 16$

Solution $x^2 - 7 + 4x^2 - 16 = 5x^2 - 23$

You Try It 2   Simplify: $-3y^2 + 7 + 8y^2 - 14$

Your solution

Solutions on p. S3

Objective B   *To simplify a variable expression using the Properties of Multiplication* ....

In simplifying variable expressions, the following Properties of Multiplication are used.

> **The Associative Property of Multiplication**
>
> If a, b, and c are real numbers, then $(a \cdot b) \cdot c = a \cdot (b \cdot c)$.

When three or more factors are multiplied, the factors can be grouped in any order. The product is the same. For example,

$$2(3x) = (2 \cdot 3)x = 6x$$

> **The Commutative Property of Multiplication**
>
> If a and b are real numbers, then $a \cdot b = b \cdot a$.

Two factors can be multiplied in either order. The product is the same. For example,

$$(2x) \cdot 3 = 3 \cdot (2x) = 6x$$

> **The Multiplication Property of One**
>
> If a is a real number, then $a \cdot 1 = 1 \cdot a = a$.

The product of a term and one is the term. For example,

$$(8x)(1) = (1)(8x) = 8x$$

> **The Inverse Property of Multiplication**
>
> If a is a real number, and a is not equal to zero, then
>
> $$a \cdot \frac{1}{a} = \frac{1}{a} \cdot a = 1$$

$\frac{1}{a}$ is called the **reciprocal** of a. $\frac{1}{a}$ is also called the **multiplicative inverse** of a. The product of a number and its reciprocal is one. For example,

$$7 \cdot \frac{1}{7} = \frac{1}{7} \cdot 7 = 1$$

The multiplication properties just discussed are used to simplify variable expressions.

➡ Simplify: $2(-x)$

$$\begin{aligned} 2(-x) &= 2(-1 \cdot x) \\ &= [2(-1)]x \\ &= -2x \end{aligned}$$

• Use the Associative Property of Multiplication to group factors.

➡ Simplify: $\dfrac{3}{2}\left(\dfrac{2x}{3}\right)$

$$\dfrac{3}{2}\left(\dfrac{2x}{3}\right) = \dfrac{3}{2}\left(\dfrac{2}{3}x\right)$$

• Note that $\dfrac{2x}{3} = \dfrac{2}{3}x$.

$$= \left(\dfrac{3}{2} \cdot \dfrac{2}{3}\right)x$$

• Use the Associative Property of Multiplication to group factors.

$$= 1 \cdot x$$

$$= x$$

➡ Simplify: $(16x)2$

$$(16x)2 = 2(16x)$$
$$= (2 \cdot 16)x$$
$$= 32x$$

• Use the Commutative and Associative Properties of Multiplication to rearrange and group factors.

Example 3 Simplify: $-2(3x^2)$

Solution $-2(3x^2) = -6x^2$

You Try It 3 Simplify: $-5(4y^2)$

Your solution

Example 4 Simplify: $-5(-10x)$

Solution $-5(-10x) = 50x$

You Try It 4 Simplify: $-7(-2a)$

Your solution

Example 5 Simplify: $(6x)(-4)$

Solution $(6x)(-4) = -24x$

You Try It 5 Simplify: $(-5x)(-2)$

Your solution

Solutions on p. S3

Objective C   ***To simplify a variable expression using the Distributive Property*** ....

Recall that the Distributive Property states that if a, b, and c are real numbers, then

$$a(b + c) = ab + ac$$

The Distributive Property is used to remove parentheses from a variable expression.

➡ Simplify: $3(2x + 7)$

$$3(2x + 7) = 3(2x) + 3(7)$$

$$= 6x + 21$$

• Use the Distributive Property. Multiply each term inside the parentheses by 3.

➡ Simplify: $-5(4x + 6)$

$$-5(4x + 6) = -5(4x) + (-5) \cdot 6$$ • **Use the Distributive Property.**
$$= -20x - 30$$

➡ Simplify: $-(2x - 4)$

$$-(2x - 4) = -1(2x - 4)$$ • **Use the Distributive Property.**
$$-1(2x) - (-1)(4)$$
$$= -2x + 4$$

Note: When a negative sign immediately precedes the parentheses, the sign of each term inside the parentheses is changed.

➡ Simplify: $-\dfrac{1}{2}(8x - 12y)$

$$-\frac{1}{2}(8x - 12y) = -\frac{1}{2}(8x) - \left(-\frac{1}{2}\right)(12y)$$ • **Use the Distributive Property.**

$$= -4x + 6y$$

An extension of the Distributive Property is used when an expression contains more than two terms.

➡ Simplify: $3(4x - 2y - z)$

$$3(4x - 2y - z) = 3(4x) - 3(2y) - 3(z)$$ • **Use the Distributive Property.**
$$= 12x - 6y - 3z$$

Example 6
Simplify: $7(4 + 2x)$

Solution
$7(4 + 2x) = 28 + 14x$

You Try It 6
Simplify: $5(3 + 7b)$

Your solution

Example 7
Simplify: $(2x - 6)2$

Solution
$(2x - 6)2 = 4x - 12$

You Try It 7
Simplify: $(3a - 1)5$

Your solution

Example 8
Simplify: $-3(-5a + 7b)$

Solution
$-3(-5a + 7b) = 15a - 21b$

You Try It 8
Simplify: $-8(-2a + 7b)$

Your solution

Solutions on p. S3

Example 9	Simplify: $3(x^2 - x - 5)$	**You Try It 9**	Simplify: $3(12x^2 - x + 8)$
Solution	$3(x^2 - x - 5) = 3x^2 - 3x - 15$	**Your solution**	
Example 10	Simplify: $-2(x^2 + 5x - 4)$	**You Try It 10**	Simplify: $3(-a^2 - 6a + 7)$
Solution	$-2(x^2 + 5x - 4)$ $= -2x^2 - 10x + 8$	**Your solution**	

Solutions on p. S3

Objective D *To simplify general variable expressions* ....

When simplifying variable expressions, use the Distributive Property to remove parentheses and brackets used as grouping symbols.

➡ Simplify: $4(x - y) - 2(-3x + 6y)$

$$4(x - y) - 2(-3x + 6y)$$

$$= 4x - 4y + 6x - 12y$$ • Use the Distributive Property.

$$= 10x - 16y$$ • Combine like terms.

Example 11	Simplify: $2x - 3(2x - 7y)$	**You Try It 11**	Simplify: $3y - 2(y - 7x)$
Solution	$2x - 3(2x - 7y) = 2x - 6x + 21y$ $= -4x + 21y$	**Your solution**	
Example 12	Simplify: $7(x - 2y) - (-x - 2y)$	**You Try It 12**	Simplify: $-2(x - 2y) - (-x + 3y)$
Solution	$7(x - 2y) - (-x - 2y)$ $= 7x - 14y + x + 2y$ $= 8x - 12y$	**Your solution**	
Example 13	Simplify: $2x - 3[2x - 3(x + 7)]$	**You Try It 13**	Simplify: $3y - 2[x - 4(2 - 3y)]$
Solution	$2x - 3[2x - 3(x + 7)]$ $= 2x - 3[2x - 3x - 21]$ $= 2x - 3[-x - 21]$ $= 2x + 3x + 63$ $= 5x + 63$	**Your solution**	

Solutions on p. S3

2.2 Exercises

· ·

Objective A

Simplify.

1. $6x + 8x$ **2.** $12x + 13x$ **3.** $9a - 4a$ **4.** $12a - 3a$

5. $4y + (-10y)$ **6.** $8y + (-6y)$ **7.** $-3b - 7$ **8.** $-12y - 3$

9. $-12a + 17a$ **10.** $-3a + 12a$ **11.** $5ab - 7ab$ **12.** $9ab - 3ab$

13. $-12xy + 17xy$ **14.** $-15xy + 3xy$ **15.** $-3ab + 3ab$ **16.** $-7ab + 7ab$

17. $-\dfrac{1}{2}x - \dfrac{1}{3}x$ **18.** $-\dfrac{2}{5}y + \dfrac{3}{10}y$ **19.** $\dfrac{3}{8}x^2 - \dfrac{5}{12}x^2$ **20.** $\dfrac{2}{3}y^2 - \dfrac{4}{9}y^2$

21. $3x + 5x + 3x$ **22.** $8x + 5x + 7x$ **23.** $5a - 3a + 5a$ **24.** $10a - 17a + 3a$

25. $-5x^2 - 12x^2 + 3x^2$ **26.** $-y^2 - 8y^2 + 7y^2$ **27.** $7x + (-8x) + 3y$

28. $8y + (-10x) + 8x$ **29.** $7x - 3y + 10x$ **30.** $8y + 8x - 8y$

31. $3a + (-7b) - 5a + b$ **32.** $-5b + 7a - 7b + 12a$ **33.** $3x + (-8y) - 10x + 4x$

34. $3y + (-12x) - 7y + 2y$ **35.** $x^2 - 7x + (-5x^2) + 5x$ **36.** $3x^2 + 5x - 10x^2 - 10x$

Objective B

Simplify.

37. $4(3x)$ **38.** $12(5x)$ **39.** $-3(7a)$ **40.** $-2(5a)$ **41.** $-2(-3y)$

42. $-5y(-6y)$ **43.** $(4x)2$ **44.** $(6x)12$ **45.** $(3a)(-2)$ **46.** $(7a)(-4)$

47. $(-3b)(-4)$ **48.** $(-12b)(-9)$ **49.** $-5(3x^2)$ **50.** $-8(7x^2)$ **51.** $\frac{1}{3}(3x^2)$

52. $\frac{1}{6}(6x^2)$ **53.** $\frac{1}{5}(5a)$ **54.** $\frac{1}{8}(8x)$ **55.** $-\frac{1}{2}(-2x)$ **56.** $-\frac{1}{4}(-4a)$

57. $-\frac{1}{7}(-7n)$ **58.** $-\frac{1}{9}(-9b)$ **59.** $(3x)\left(\frac{1}{3}\right)$ **60.** $(12x)\left(\frac{1}{12}\right)$ **61.** $(-6y)\left(-\frac{1}{6}\right)$

62. $(-10n)\left(-\frac{1}{10}\right)$ **63.** $\frac{1}{3}(9x)$ **64.** $\frac{1}{7}(14x)$ **65.** $-\frac{1}{5}(10x)$ **66.** $-\frac{1}{8}(16x)$

67. $-\frac{2}{3}(12a^2)$ **68.** $-\frac{5}{8}(24a^2)$ **69.** $-\frac{1}{2}(-16y)$ **70.** $-\frac{3}{4}(-8y)$ **71.** $(16y)\left(\frac{1}{4}\right)$

72. $(33y)\left(\frac{1}{11}\right)$ **73.** $(-6x)\left(\frac{1}{3}\right)$ **74.** $(-10x)\left(\frac{1}{5}\right)$ **75.** $(-8a)\left(-\frac{3}{4}\right)$ **76.** $(21y)\left(-\frac{3}{7}\right)$

Objective C

Simplify.

77. $-(x + 2)$ **78.** $-(x + 7)$ **79.** $2(4x - 3)$ **80.** $5(2x - 7)$

81. $-2(a + 7)$ **82.** $-5(a + 16)$ **83.** $-3(2y - 8)$ **84.** $-5(3y - 7)$

85. $(5 - 3b)7$ **86.** $(10 - 7b)2$ **87.** $\frac{1}{3}(6 - 15y)$ **88.** $\frac{1}{2}(-8x + 4y)$

89. $3(5x^2 + 2x)$ **90.** $6(3x^2 + 2x)$ **91.** $-2(-y + 9)$ **92.** $-5(-2x + 7)$

93. $(-3x - 6)5$ **94.** $(-2x + 7)7$ **95.** $2(-3x^2 - 14)$ **96.** $5(-6x^2 - 3)$

97. $-3(2y^2 - 7)$ **98.** $-8(3y^2 - 12)$ **99.** $3(x^2 - y^2)$ **100.** $5(x^2 + y^2)$

101. $-\frac{2}{3}(6x - 18y)$ **102.** $-\frac{1}{2}(x - 4y)$ **103.** $-(6a^2 - 7b^2)$

104. $3(x^2 + 2x - 6)$ **105.** $4(x^2 - 3x + 5)$ **106.** $-2(y^2 - 2y + 4)$

107. $\frac{1}{2}(2x - 6y + 8)$ **108.** $-\frac{1}{3}(6x - 9y + 1)$ **109.** $4(-3a^2 - 5a + 7)$

110. $-5(-2x^2 - 3x + 7)$ **111.** $-3(-4x^2 + 3x - 4)$ **112.** $3(2x^2 + xy - 3y^2)$

113. $5(2x^2 - 4xy - y^2)$ **114.** $-(3a^2 + 5a - 4)$ **115.** $-(8b^2 - 6b + 9)$

Objective D

Simplify.

116. $4x - 2(3x + 8)$ **117.** $6a - (5a + 7)$ **118.** $9 - 3(4y + 6)$

119. $10 - (11x - 3)$ **120.** $5n - (7 - 2n)$ **121.** $8 - (12 + 4y)$

122. $3(x + 2) - 5(x - 7)$ **123.** $2(x - 4) - 4(x + 2)$ **124.** $12(y - 2) + 3(7 - 3y)$

125. $6(2y - 7) - (3 - 2y)$ **126.** $3(a - b) - (a + b)$ **127.** $2(a + 2b) - (a - 3b)$

128. $4[x - 2(x - 3)]$ **129.** $2[x + 2(x + 7)]$ **130.** $-2[3x + 2(4 - x)]$

131. $-5[2x + 3(5 - x)]$ **132.** $-3[2x - (x + 7)]$ **133.** $-2[3x - (5x - 2)]$

134. $2x - 3[x - (4 - x)]$ **135.** $-7x + 3[x - (3 - 2x)]$ **136.** $-5x - 2[2x - 4(x + 7)] - 6$

APPLYING THE CONCEPTS

137. Determine whether the statement is true or false. If the statement is false, give an example that illustrates that it is false.
    a. Division is a commutative operation.
    b. Division is an associative operation.
    c. Subtraction is an associative operation.
    d. Subtraction is a commutative operation.

138. Is the statement "any number divided by itself is 1" a true statement? If not, for what number or numbers is the statement not true?

139. Does every number have a multiplicative inverse? If not, which real number or numbers do not have a multiplicative inverse?

140. In your own words, explain the distributive property.

141. Give examples of two operations that occur in everyday experience that are not commutative (for example, putting on socks and then shoes).

142. Define an operation $\otimes$ as $a \otimes b = (a \cdot b) - (a + b)$. For example, $7 \otimes 5 = (7 \cdot 5) - (7 + 5) = 35 - 12 = 23$.
    a. Is $\otimes$ a commutative operation? Support your answer.

    b. Is $\otimes$ an associative operation? Support your answer.

2.3 Translating Verbal Expressions into Variable Expressions

Objective A   *To translate a verbal expression into a variable expression, given the variable* ....

One of the major skills required in applied mathematics is to translate a verbal expression into a variable expression. This requires recognizing the verbal phrases that translate into mathematical operations. A partial list of the verbal phrases used to indicate the different mathematical operations follows.

Addition	added to	6 added to y	$y + 6$
	more than	8 more than x	$x + 8$
	the sum of	the sum of x and z	$x + z$
	increased by	t increased by 9	$t + 9$
	the total of	the total of 5 and y	$5 + y$
Subtraction	minus	x minus 2	$x - 2$
	less than	7 less than t	$t - 7$
	decreased by	m decreased by 3	$m - 3$
	the difference between	the difference between y and 4	$y - 4$
Multiplication	times	10 times t	$10t$
	of	one half of x	$\frac{1}{2}x$
	the product of	the product of y and z	yz
	multiplied by	y multiplied by 11	$11y$
Division	divided by	x divided by 12	$\frac{x}{12}$
	the quotient of	the quotient of y and z	$\frac{y}{z}$
	the ratio of	the ratio of t to 9	$\frac{t}{9}$
Power	the square of	the square of x	x^2
	the cube of	the cube of a	a^3

➡ Translate "14 less than the cube of x" into a variable expression.

14 *less than* the *cube* of x

$x^3 - 14$

Translating a phrase that contains the word *sum, difference, product,* or *quotient* can sometimes cause a problem. In the examples at the right, note where the operation symbol is placed.

the *sum* of x and y $x + y$

the *difference* between x and y $x - y$

the *product* of x and y $x \cdot y$

the *quotient* of x and y $\dfrac{x}{y}$

➡ Translate "the difference between the square of x and the sum of y and z" into a variable expression.

the difference between the square of x and the sum of y and z

$x^2 - (y + z)$

Example 1
Translate "the total of 3 times n and n" into a variable expression.

Solution
the total of 3 times n and n
$3n + n$

You Try It 1
Translate "the difference between twice n and one-third of n" into a variable expression.

Your solution

Example 2
Translate "m decreased by the sum of n and 12" into a variable expression.

Solution
m decreased by the sum of n and 12
$m - (n + 12)$

You Try It 2
Translate "the quotient of 7 less than b and 15" into a variable expression.

Your solution

Solutions on p. S3

Objective B   *To translate a verbal expression into a variable expression and then simplify* ....

In most applications that involve translating phrases into variable expressions, the variable to be used is not given. To translate these phrases, a variable must be assigned to an unknown quantity before the variable expression can be written.

➡ Translate "a number multiplied by the total of six and the cube of the number" into a variable expression.

the unknown number: n

• Assign a variable to one of the unknown quantities.

the cube of the number: n^3
the total of six and the cube of the number: $6 + n^3$

• Use the assigned variable to write an expression for any other unknown quantity.

$n(6 + n^3)$

• Use the assigned variable to write the variable expression.

Example 3

Translate "a number added to the product of four and the square of the number" into a variable expression.

Solution

the unknown number: n
the square of the number: n^2
the product of four and the square of the number: $4n^2$
$n + 4n^2$

You Try It 3

Translate "negative four multiplied by the total of ten and the cube of a number" into a variable expression.

Your solution

Example 4

Translate "four times the sum of half of a number and fourteen" into a variable expression. Then simplify.

Solution

the unknown number: n

half of the number: $\frac{1}{2}n$

the sum of half of the number and

fourteen: $\frac{1}{2}n + 14$

$4\left(\frac{1}{2}n + 14\right)$
$2n + 56$

You Try It 4

Translate "five times the difference between a number and sixty" into a variable expression. Then simplify.

Your solution

Solutions on p. S4

Objective C   To translate application problems ·················

Many of the applications of mathematics require that you identify the unknown quantity, assign a variable to that quantity, and then attempt to express other unknown quantities in terms of the variable.

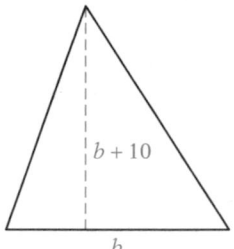

➡ The height of a triangle is 10 ft longer than the base of the triangle. Express the height of the triangle in terms of the base of the triangle.

the base of the triangle: b

- Assign a variable to the base of the triangle.

the height is 10 more than the base: $b + 10$

- Express the height of the triangle in terms of b.

Example 5

The length of a swimming pool is 4 ft less than two times the width. Express the length of the pool in terms of the width.

Solution

the width of the pool: w
the length is 4 ft less than two times the width: $2w - 4$

You Try It 5

The speed of a new jet plane is twice the speed of an older model. Express the speed of the new model in terms of the speed of the older model.

Your solution

Example 6

A banker divided $5000 between two accounts, one paying 10% annual interest and the second paying 8% annual interest. Express the amount invested in the 10% account in terms of the amount invested in the 8% account.

Solution

the amount invested at 8%: x
the amount invested at 10%: $5000 - x$

You Try It 6

A guitar string 6 ft long was cut into two pieces. Express the length of the shorter piece in terms of the length of the longer piece.

Your solution

Solutions on p. S4

2.3 Exercises

Objective A

Translate into a variable expression.

1. the sum of 8 and y

2. a less than 16

3. t increased by 10

4. p decreased by 7

5. z added to 14

6. q multiplied by 13

7. 20 less than the square of x

8. 6 times the difference between m and 7

9. the sum of three-fourths of n and 12

10. b decreased by the product of 2 and b

11. 8 increased by the quotient of n and 4

12. the product of -8 and y

13. the product of 3 and the total of y and 7

14. 8 divided by the difference between x and 6

15. the product of t and the sum of t and 16

16. the quotient of 6 less than n and twice n

17. 15 more than one-half of the square of x

18. 19 less than the product of n and -2

19. the total of 5 times the cube of n and the square of n

20. the ratio of 9 more than m to m

21. r decreased by the quotient of r and 3

22. four-fifths of the sum of w and 10

23. the difference between the square of x and the total of x and 17

24. s increased by the quotient of 4 and s

25. the product of 9 and the total of z and 4

26. n increased by the difference between 10 times n and 9

Objective B

Translate into a variable expression. Then simplify.

27. twelve minus a number

28. a number divided by eighteen

29. two-thirds of a number

30. twenty more than a number

31. the quotient of twice a number and nine

32. ten times the difference between a number and fifty

33. eight less than the product of eleven and a number

34. the sum of five-eighths of a number and six

35. nine less than the total of a number and two

36. the difference between a number and three more than the number

37. the quotient of seven and the total of five and a number

38. four times the sum of a number and nineteen

39. five increased by one-half of the sum of a number and three

40. the quotient of fifteen and the sum of a number and twelve

41. a number added to the difference between twice the number and four

42. the product of two-thirds and the sum of a number and seven

43. the product of five less than a number and seven

44. the difference between forty and the quotient of a number and twenty

45. the quotient of five more than twice a number and the number

46. the sum of the square of a number and twice the number

47. a number decreased by the difference between three times the number and eight

48. the sum of eight more than a number and one-third of the number

49. a number added to the product of three and the number

50. a number increased by the total of the number and nine

51. five more than the sum of a number and six

52. a number decreased by the difference between eight and the number

53. a number minus the sum of the number and ten

54. the difference between one-third of a number and five-eighths of the number

55. the sum of one-sixth of a number and four-ninths of the number

56. two more than the total of a number and five

57. the sum of a number divided by three and the number

58. twice the sum of six times a number and seven

Objective C   *Application Problems*

59. In November 1996, the average sale price of a home in Vail, Colorado, was $143,600 more than the average sale price of a home in Carmel, California. Express the average sale price of a home in Vail in terms of the average sale price of a home in Carmel.

60. According to *USA Today*, in Norway, annual spending per person for books is $40 more than it is in the United States. Express the annual spending per person for books in Norway in terms of the annual spending per person for books in the United States.

61. A rope 12 ft long was cut into two pieces of different length. Use one variable to express the lengths of the two pieces.

62. Twenty gallons of crude oil were poured into two containers of different sizes. Use one variable to express the amount of oil poured into each container.

63. Two cars start at the same place and travel at different rates in opposite directions. Two hours later the cars are 200 mi apart. Express the distance traveled by the slower car in terms of the distance traveled by the faster car.

64. According to the *Wall Street Journal*, in a recent year, retail sales in Boston were one-half the retail sales in Los Angeles. Express the retail sales in Boston in terms of the retail sales in Los Angeles.

65. According to the IRS, it should take about one-fourth the time to prepare Schedule A than to prepare Form 1040. Express the time it should take to prepare Schedule A in terms of the time it should take to prepare Form 1040.

66. The diameter of a basketball is approximately 4 times the diameter of a baseball. Express the diameter of a basketball in terms of the diameter of a baseball.

67. The world population in the year 2050 is expected to be twice the world population in 1990. Express the world population in 2050 in terms of the world population in 1990.

APPLYING THE CONCEPTS

68. A wire whose length is given as x inches is bent into a square. Express the length of a side of the square in terms of x.

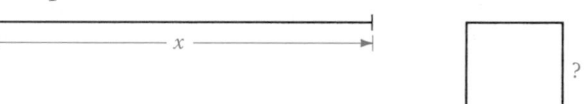

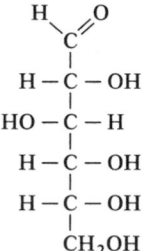

69. The chemical formula for glucose (sugar) is $C_6H_{12}O_6$. This formula means that there are 12 hydrogen atoms for every 6 carbon atoms and 6 oxygen atoms in each molecule of glucose (see the figure to the right). If x represents the number of atoms of oxygen in a pound of sugar, express the number of hydrogen atoms in the pound of sugar.

70. Translate the expressions $5x + 8$ and $5(x + 8)$ into phrases.

71. In your own words, explain how variables are used.

72. Explain the similarities and the differences between the expressions "the difference between x and 5" and "5 less than x."

Focus on Problem Solving

From Concrete to Abstract

In your study of algebra, you will find that the problems are less concrete than those you studied in arithmetic. Problems that are concrete provide information pertaining to a specific instance. Algebra is more abstract. Abstract problems are theoretical; they are stated without reference to a specific instance. Let's look at an example of an abstract problem.

How many minutes are in h hours?

A strategy that can be used to solve this problem is to solve the same problem after substituting a number for the variable.

How many minutes are in 5 hours?

You know that there are 60 minutes in 1 hour. To find the number of minutes in 5 hours, multiply 5 by 60.

$60 \cdot 5 = 300$ There are 300 minutes in 5 hours.

Use the same procedure to find the number of minutes in h hours: multiply h by 60.

$60 \cdot h = 60h$ There are $60h$ minutes in h hours.

This problem might be taken a step further:

If you walk one mile in x minutes, how far can you walk in h hours?

Consider the same problem using numbers in place of the variables.

If you walk one mile in 20 minutes, how far can you walk in 3 hours?

To solve this problem, you need to calculate the number of minutes in 3 hours (multiply 3 by 60), and divide the result by the number of minutes it takes to walk one mile (20 minutes).

$\dfrac{60 \cdot 3}{20} = \dfrac{180}{20} = 9$ If you walk one mile in 20 minutes, you can walk 9 miles in 3 hours.

Use the same procedure to solve the related abstract problem. Calculate the number of minutes in h hours (multiply h by 60), and divide the result by the number of minutes it takes to walk one mile (x minutes).

$\dfrac{60 \cdot h}{x} = \dfrac{60h}{x}$ If you walk one mile in x minutes, you can walk $\dfrac{60h}{x}$ miles in h hours.

At the heart of the study of algebra is the use of variables. It is the variables in the problems above that make them abstract. But it is variables that allow us to generalize situations and state rules about mathematics.

Try each of the following problems.

1. How many hours are in d days?

2. You earn d dollars an hour. What are your wages for working h hours?

3. If p is the price of one share of stock, how many shares can you purchase with d dollars?

4. A company pays a television station d dollars to air a commercial lasting s seconds. What is the cost per second?

5. After every v video tape rentals, you are entitled to one free rental. You have rented t tapes, where $t < v$. How many more do you need to rent before you are entitled to a free rental?

6. Your car gets g miles per gallon. How many gallons of gasoline does your car consume traveling t miles?

7. If you drink j ounces of juice each day, how many days will q quarts of the juice last?

8. A TV station has m minutes of commercials each hour. How many ads lasting s seconds each can be sold for each hour of programming?

9. A factory worker can assemble p products in m minutes. How many products can the factory worker assemble in h hours?

10. If one candy bar costs n nickels, how many candy bars can be purchased with q quarters?

Projects and Group Activities

Prime and Composite Numbers

A **prime number** is a natural number greater than 1 whose only natural-number factors are itself and 1. The number 11 is a prime number because the only natural-number factors of 11 are 11 and 1.

Eratosthenes, a Greek philosopher and astronomer who lived from 270 to 190 B.C., devised a method of identifying prime numbers. It is called the **Sieve of Eratosthenes.** The procedure is illustrated below.

1	2	3	4	5	6	7	8	9	10
11	12	13	14	15	16	17	18	19	20
21	22	23	24	25	26	27	28	29	30
31	32	33	34	35	36	37	38	39	40
41	42	43	44	45	46	47	48	49	50
51	52	53	54	55	56	57	58	59	60
61	62	63	64	65	66	67	68	69	70
71	72	73	74	75	76	77	78	79	80
81	82	83	84	85	86	87	88	89	90
91	92	93	94	95	96	97	98	99	100

List all the natural numbers from 1 to 100. Cross out the number 1, because it is not a prime number. The number 2 is prime; circle it. Cross out all the other multiples of 2 (4, 6, 8,...), because they are not prime. The number 3 is prime; circle it. Cross out all the other multiples of 3 (6, 9, 12,...) that are not already crossed out. The number 4, the next consecutive number in the list, has already been crossed out. The number 5 is prime; circle it. Cross out all the other multiples of 5 that are not already crossed out. Continue in this manner until all the prime numbers less than 100 are circled.

A **composite number** is a natural number greater than 1 that has a natural-number factor other than itself and 1. The number 21 is a composite number because it has factors of 3 and 7. All the numbers crossed out in the preceding table, except the number 1, are composite numbers.

1. Use the Sieve of Eratosthenes to find the prime numbers between 100 and 200.

2. How many prime numbers are even numbers?

3. Find the "twin primes" between 1 and 200. Twin primes are two prime numbers whose difference is 2. For instance, 3 and 5 are twin primes; 5 and 7 are also twin primes.

4. **a.** List two prime numbers that are consecutive natural numbers.
   b. Can there be any other pairs of prime numbers that are consecutive natural numbers?

5. Some primes are the sum of a square and 1. For example, $5 = 2^2 + 1$. Find another prime p such that $p = n^2 + 1$, where n is a natural number.

6. Find a prime number p such that $p = n^2 - 1$, where n is a natural number.

7. **a.** 4! (which is read "4 factorial") is equal to $4 \cdot 3 \cdot 2 \cdot 1$. Show that 4! + 2, 4! + 3, and 4! + 4 are all composite numbers.
   b. 5! (which is read "5 factorial") is equal to $5 \cdot 4 \cdot 3 \cdot 2 \cdot 1$. Will 5! + 2, 5! + 3, 5! + 4, and 5! + 5 generate four consecutive composite numbers?
   c. Use the notation 6! to represent a list of five consecutive composite numbers.

Investigation into Operations with Even and Odd Integers

Complete each statement with the word *even* or *odd*.

1. If k is an odd integer, then $k + 1$ is an _____ integer.

2. If k is an odd integer, then $k - 2$ is an _____ integer.

3. If n is an integer, then $2n$ is an _____ integer.

4. If m and n are even integers, then $m - n$ is an _____ integer.

5. If m and n are even integers, then mn is an _____ integer.

6. If m and n are odd integers, then $m + n$ is an _____ integer.

7. If m and n are odd integers, then $m - n$ is an _____ integer.

8. If m and n are odd integers, then mn is an _____ integer.

9. If m is an even integer and n is an odd integer, then $m - n$ is an _____ integer.

10. If m is an even integer and n is an odd integer, then $m + n$ is an _____ integer.

Chapter Summary

Key Words

A *variable* is a letter that is used to stand for a quantity that is unknown.

A *variable expression* is an expression that contains one or more variables.

The *terms* of a variable expression are the addends of the expression. A *variable term* is composed of a *numerical coefficient* and a *variable part*. A *constant term* has no variable part.

Replacing the variables in a variable expression with numbers and then simplifying the numerical expression is called *evaluating the variable expression.*

Like terms of a variable expression are terms that have the same variable part. Adding or subtracting the like terms of a variable expression is called *combining like terms.*

The *additive inverse* of a number is the opposite of the number.

The *multiplicative inverse* of a number is the reciprocal of the number.

Essential Rules

The Associative Property of Addition
If a, b, and c are real numbers, then $(a + b) + c = a + (b + c)$.

The Commutative Property of Addition
If a and b are real numbers, then $a + b = b + a$.

The Addition Property of Zero
If a is a real number, then $a + 0 = 0 + a = a$.

The Inverse Property of Addition
If a is a real number, then $a + (-a) = (-a) + a = 0$.

The Associative Property of Multiplication
If a, b, and c are real numbers, then $(ab)c = a(bc)$.

The Commutative Property of Multiplication
If a and b are real numbers, then $ab = ba$.

The Multiplication Property of One
If a is a real number, then $1 \cdot a = a \cdot 1 = a$.

The Inverse Property of Multiplication
If a is a nonzero real number, then $a\left(\dfrac{1}{a}\right) = \left(\dfrac{1}{a}\right)a = 1$.

The Distributive Property
If a, b, and c are real numbers, then $a(b + c) = ab + ac$.

Chapter Review

1. Simplify: $3(x^2 - 8x - 7)$

2. Simplify: $7x + 4x$

3. Simplify: $6a - 4b + 2a$

4. Simplify: $(-50n)\left(\dfrac{1}{10}\right)$

5. Evaluate $(5c - 4a)^2 - b$ when $a = -1$, $b = 2$, and $c = 1$.

6. Simplify: $5(2x - 7)$

7. Simplify: $2(6y^2 + 4y - 5)$

8. Simplify: $\dfrac{1}{4}(-24a)$

9. Simplify: $-6(7x^2)$

10. Simplify: $-9(7 + 4x)$

11. Simplify: $12y - 17y$

12. Evaluate $2bc \div (a + 7)$ when $a = 3$, $b = -5$, and $c = 4$.

13. Simplify: $6(8y - 3) - 8(3y - 6)$

14. Simplify: $5c + (-2d) - 3d - (-4c)$

15. Simplify: $5(4x)$

16. Simplify: $-4(2x - 9) + 5(3x + 2)$

17. Evaluate $(b - a)^2 + c$ when $a = -2$, $b = 3$, and $c = 4$.

18. Simplify: $-9r + 2s - 6s + 12s$

19. Simplify: $4x - 3x^2 + 2x - x^2$

20. Simplify: $5[2 - 3(6x - 1)]$

21. Simplify: $(7a^2 - 2a + 3)4$

22. Simplify: $18 - (4x - 2)$

23. Evaluate $a^2 - b^2$ when $a = 3$ and $b = 4$.

24. Simplify: $-3(-12y)$

25. Translate "two-thirds of the total of x and 10" into a variable expression.

26. A candy bar contains eight more calories than twice the number of calories in an apple. Express the number of calories in a candy bar in terms of the number of calories in an apple.

27. Translate "three times a number plus the product of five and one less than the number" into a variable expression. Then simplify.

28. Translate "the product of 4 and x" into a variable expression.

29. A club treasurer has some five-dollar bills and some ten-dollar bills. The treasurer has a total of 35 bills. Express the number of five-dollar bills in terms of the number of ten-dollar bills.

30. Translate "the difference between twice a number and one-half of the number" into a variable expression. Then simplify.

31. A baseball card collection contains five times as many National League players' cards as American League players' cards. Express the number of National League players' cards in the collection in terms of the number of American League players' cards.

32. Translate "6 less than x" into a variable expression.

33. Translate "a number plus twice the number" into a variable expression. Then simplify.

Chapter Test

1. Simplify: $3x - 5x + 7x$

2. Simplify: $-3(2x^2 - 7y^2)$

3. Simplify: $2x - 3(x - 2)$

4. Simplify: $2x + 3[4 - (3x - 7)]$

5. Simplify: $3x - 7y - 12x$

6. Evaluate $b^2 - 3ab$ when $a = 3$ and $b = -2$.

7. Simplify: $\frac{1}{5}(10x)$

8. Simplify: $5(2x + 4) - 3(x - 6)$

9. Simplify: $-5(2x^2 - 3x + 6)$

10. Simplify: $3x + (-12y) - 5x - (-7y)$

11. Evaluate $\frac{-2ab}{2b - a}$ when $a = -4$ and $b = 6$.

12. Simplify: $(12x)\left(\frac{1}{4}\right)$

13. Simplify: $-7y^2 + 6y^2 - (-2y^2)$

14. Simplify: $-2(2x - 4)$

15. Simplify: $\frac{2}{3}(-15a)$

16. Simplify: $-2[x - 2(x - y)] + 5y$

17. Simplify: $(-3)(-12y)$

18. Simplify: $5(3 - 7b)$

19. Translate "the difference between the squares of a and b" into a variable expression.

20. Translate "ten times the difference between a number and 3" into a variable expression. Then simplify.

21. Translate "the sum of a number and twice the square of the number" into a variable expression.

22. The speed of a pitcher's fastball is twice the speed of the catcher's return throw. Express the speed of the fastball in terms of the speed of the return throw.

23. Translate "three less than the quotient of six and a number" into a variable expression.

24. Translate "b decreased by the product of b and seven" into a variable expression.

25. A wire is cut into two lengths. The length of the longer piece is 3 in. less than four times the length of the shorter piece. Express the length of the longer piece in terms of the length of the shorter piece.

Cumulative Review

1. Add: $-4 + 7 + (-10)$

2. Subtract: $-16 - (-25) - 4$

3. Multiply: $(-2)(3)(-4)$

4. Divide: $(-60) \div 12$

5. Write $1\frac{1}{4}$ as a decimal.

6. Simplify: $\frac{7}{12} - \frac{11}{16} - \left(-\frac{1}{3}\right)$

7. Simplify: $\frac{5}{12} \div \left(2\frac{1}{2}\right)$

8. Simplify: $\left(-\frac{9}{16}\right) \cdot \left(\frac{8}{27}\right) \cdot \left(-\frac{3}{2}\right)$

9. Write $\frac{3}{4}$ as a percent.

10. Simplify: $-2^5 \div (3 - 5)^2 - (-3)$

11. Simplify: $\left(-\frac{3}{4}\right)^2 - \left(\frac{3}{8} - \frac{11}{12}\right)$

12. Evaluate $a^2 - 3b$ when $a = 2$ and $b = -4$.

13. Simplify: $-2x^2 - (-3x^2) + 4x^2$

14. Simplify: $5a - 10b - 12a$

15. Simplify: $\frac{1}{2}(12a)$

16. Simplify: $\left(-\frac{5}{6}\right)(-36b)$

17. Simplify: $3(8 - 2x)$

18. Simplify: $-2(-3y + 9)$

19. Write $37\frac{1}{2}\%$ as a fraction.

20. Write 1.05% as a decimal.

21. Simplify: $-4(2x^2 - 3y^2)$

22. Simplify: $-3(3y^2 - 3y - 7)$

23. Simplify: $-3x - 2(2x - 7)$

24. Simplify: $4(3x - 2) - 7(x + 5)$

25. Simplify: $2x + 3[x - 2(4 - 2x)]$

26. Simplify: $3[2x - 3(x - 2y)] + 3y$

27. Translate "the sum of one-half of b and b" into a variable expression.

28. Translate "10 divided by the difference between y and 2" into a variable expression.

29. Translate "the difference between eight and the quotient of a number and twelve" into a variable expression.

30. Translate "the sum of a number and two more than the number" into a variable expression. Then simplify.

31. Translate and simplify "twelve more than the product of three plus a number and five."

32. A "triple-speed" CD-ROM drive spins three times faster than a normal CD-ROM drive. Express the speed of the "triple-speed" CD-ROM drive in terms of that of the normal CD-ROM drive.

3

Solving Equations

It is the job of construction electricians to install heating, lighting, air conditioning, controls, communications, and other types of electrical equipment. Electricians follow specifications such as blueprints to connect equipment to power sources and circuit breakers. In their work, they must apply various algebraic and scientific formulas. One equation in Ohm's Law is $IR = V$, where I is current, R is resistance, and V is voltage. For example, if $I = 10$ amps and $R = 12$ ohms, then $V = 120$ volts.

Objectives

Section 3.1
To determine whether a given number is a solution of an equation

To solve an equation of the form $x + a = b$

To solve an equation of the form $ax = b$

To solve application problems using the basic percent equation

Section 3.2
To solve an equation of the form $ax + b = c$

To solve application problems using formulas

Section 3.3
To solve an equation of the form $ax + b = cx + d$

To solve an equation containing parentheses

To solve application problems using formulas

Section 3.4
To solve integer problems

To translate a sentence into an equation and solve

Section 3.5
To solve perimeter problems

To solve problems involving angles formed by intersecting lines

To solve problems involving the angles of a triangle

Section 3.6
To solve value mixture problems

To solve percent mixture problems

To solve uniform motion problems

Mersenne Primes

A prime number that can be written in the form $2^n - 1$, where n is also prime, is called a **Mersenne prime.** The table at the right shows some Mersenne primes.

$$3 = 2^2 - 1$$
$$7 = 2^3 - 1$$
$$31 = 2^5 - 1$$
$$127 = 2^7 - 1$$

Not every prime number is a Mersenne prime. For example, 5 is a prime number but not a Mersenne prime. Also, not all numbers in the form $2^n - 1$, where n is prime, yield a prime number. For example, $2^{11} - 1 = 2047$, which is not a prime number.

The search for Mersenne primes has been quite extensive, especially since the advent of the computer. One reason for the extensive research into large prime numbers (not only Mersenne primes) involves cryptology.

Cryptology is the study of making or breaking secret codes. One method of making a code that is difficult to break is called public-key cryptology. For this method to work, it is necessary to use very large prime numbers. To keep anyone from breaking the code, each prime should have at least 200 digits.

Today, the largest known Mersenne prime is $2^{6972593} - 1$. This number has 2,098,960 digits in its representation.

Another Mersenne prime got special recognition in a postage-meter stamp. It is the number $2^{11213} - 1$. This number has 3276 digits in its representation.

3.1   Introduction to Equations

Objective A   *To determine whether a given number is a solution of an equation* ....

An **equation** expresses the equality of two mathematical expressions. The expressions can be either numerical or variable expressions.

$$\left.\begin{array}{l} 9 + 3 = 12 \\ 3x - 2 = 10 \\ y^2 + 4 = 2y - 1 \\ z = 2 \end{array}\right\} \text{Equations}$$

The equation at the right is true if the variable is replaced by 5.

$x + 8 = 13$
$5 + 8 = 13$ A true equation

The equation is false if the variable is replaced by 7.

$7 + 8 = 13$ A false equation

A **solution** of an equation is a number that, when substituted for the variable, results in a true equation. 5 is a solution of the equation $x + 8 = 13$. 7 is not a solution of the equation $x + 8 = 13$.

➡ Is -2 a solution of $2x + 5 = x^2 - 3$?

$$\begin{array}{c|c} \multicolumn{2}{c}{2x + 5 = x^2 - 3} \\ \hline 2(-2) + 5 & (-2)^2 - 3 \\ -4 + 5 & 4 - 3 \\ 1 & = 1 \end{array}$$

Yes, -2 is a solution of the equation.

- Replace x by -2.
- Evaluate the numerical expressions.
- If the results are equal, -2 is a solution of the equation. If the results are not equal, -2 is not a solution of the equation.

Example 1   Is -4 a solution of
$5x - 2 = 6x + 2$?

Solution

$$\begin{array}{c|c} \multicolumn{2}{c}{5x - 2 = 6x + 2} \\ \hline 5(-4) - 2 & 6(-4) + 2 \\ -20 - 2 & -24 + 2 \\ -22 & = -22 \end{array}$$

Yes, -4 is a solution.

You Try It 1   Is $\frac{1}{4}$ a solution of
$5 - 4x = 8x + 2$?

Your solution

Example 2   Is -4 a solution of
$4 + 5x = x^2 - 2x$?

Solution

$$\begin{array}{c|c} \multicolumn{2}{c}{4 + 5x = x^2 - 2x} \\ \hline 4 + 5(-4) & (-4)^2 - 2(-4) \\ 4 + (-20) & 16 - (-8) \\ -16 & \neq 24 \end{array}$$

($\neq$ means "is not equal to")

No, -4 is not a solution.

You Try It 2   Is 5 a solution of
$10x - x^2 = 3x - 10$?

Your solution

Solutions on p. S4

Objective B   ***To solve an equation of the form*** *x + a = b* ....

To **solve an equation** means to find a solution of the equation. The simplest equation to solve is an equation of the form *variable = constant*, because the constant is the solution.

The solution of the equation $x = 5$ is 5 because $5 = 5$ is a true equation.

The solution of the equation at the right is 7 because $7 + 2 = 9$ is a true equation.

$$x + 2 = 9 \qquad\qquad 7 + 2 = 9$$

Note that if 4 is added to each side of the equation $x + 2 = 9$, the solution is still 7.

$$x + 2 = 9$$
$$x + 2 + 4 = 9 + 4$$
$$x + 6 = 13 \qquad\qquad 7 + 6 = 13$$

If -5 is added to each side of the equation $x + 2 = 9$, the solution is still 7.

$$x + 2 = 9$$
$$x + 2 + (-5) = 9 + (-5)$$
$$x - 3 = 4 \qquad\qquad 7 - 3 = 4$$

Equations that have the same solution are **equivalent equations.** The equations $x + 2 = 9$, $x + 6 = 13$, and $x - 3 = 4$ are equivalent equations; each equation has 7 as its solution. These examples suggest that adding the same number to each side of an equation produces equivalent equations. This is called the *Addition Property of Equations.*

Addition Property of Equations

The same number can be added to each side of an equation without changing its solution. In symbols, the equation $a = b$ has the same solution as the equation $a + c = b + c$.

In solving an equation, the goal is to rewrite the given equation in the form *variable = constant*. The Addition Property of Equations is used to remove a *term* from one side of the equation by adding the opposite of that term to each side of the equation.

➡ Solve: $x - 4 = 2$

$$x - 4 = 2$$ • The goal is to rewrite the equation as *variable = constant*.

$$x - 4 + 4 = 2 + 4$$ • Add 4 to each side of the equation.

$$x + 0 = 6$$ • Simplify.

$$x = 6$$ • The equation is in the form *variable = constant*.

Check: $x - 4 = 2$
$$\dfrac{6 - 4 \;\vert\; 2}{}$$
$$2 = 2 \qquad \text{A true equation}$$

The solution is 6.

Because subtraction is defined in terms of addition, the Addition Property of Equations also makes it possible to subtract the same number from each side of an equation without changing the solution of the equation.

➡ Solve: $y + \dfrac{3}{4} = \dfrac{1}{2}$

$$y + \frac{3}{4} = \frac{1}{2}$$

• The goal is to rewrite the equation in the form *variable = constant*.

$$y + \frac{3}{4} - \frac{3}{4} = \frac{1}{2} - \frac{3}{4}$$

• Subtract $\dfrac{3}{4}$ from each side of the equation.

$$y + 0 = \frac{2}{4} - \frac{3}{4}$$

• Simplify.

$$y = -\frac{1}{4}$$

• The equation is in the form *variable = constant*.

The solution is $-\dfrac{1}{4}$. You should check this solution.

Example 3   Solve: $x + \dfrac{3}{4} = \dfrac{1}{3}$

You Try It 3   Solve: $\dfrac{5}{6} = y - \dfrac{3}{8}$

Solution

$$x + \frac{3}{4} = \frac{1}{3}$$

$$x + \frac{3}{4} - \frac{3}{4} = \frac{1}{3} - \frac{3}{4}$$

$$x + 0 = \frac{4}{12} - \frac{9}{12}$$

$$x = -\frac{5}{12}$$

The solution is $-\dfrac{5}{12}$.

Your solution

Solution on p. S4

Objective C   ***To solve an equation of the form ax = b*** ....  CT

The solution of the equation at the right is 3 because $2 \cdot 3 = 6$ is a true equation.

$$2x = 6 \qquad\qquad 2 \cdot 3 = 6$$

Note that if each side of $2x = 6$ is multiplied by 5, the solution is still 3.

$$2x = 6$$
$$5(2x) = 5 \cdot 6$$
$$10x = 30 \qquad\qquad 10 \cdot 3 = 30$$

If each side of $2x = 6$ is multiplied by -4, the solution is still 3.

$$2x = 6$$
$$(-4)(2x) = (-4) \cdot 6$$
$$-8x = -24 \qquad\qquad -8 \cdot 3 = -24$$

The equations $2x = 6$, $10x = 30$, and $-8x = -24$ are equivalent equations; each equation has 3 as its solution. These examples suggest that multiplying each side of an equation by the same number produces equivalent equations.

> **Multiplication Property of Equations**
>
> Each side of an equation can be multiplied by the same *nonzero* number without changing the solution of the equation. In symbols, if $c \neq 0$, then the equation $a = b$ has the same solutions as the equation $ac = bc$.

The Multiplication Property of Equations is used to remove a coefficient by multiplying each side of the equation by the reciprocal of the coefficient.

➡ Solve: $\frac{3}{4}z = 9$

$$\frac{3}{4}z = 9$$ • The goal is to rewrite the equation in the form *variable = constant*.

$$\frac{4}{3} \cdot \frac{3}{4}z = \frac{4}{3} \cdot 9$$ • Multiply each side of the equation by $\frac{4}{3}$.

$$1 \cdot z = 12$$ • Simplify.

$$z = 12$$ • The equation is in the form *variable = constant*.

The solution is 12. You should check this solution.

Because division is defined in terms of multiplication, each side of an equation can be divided by the same nonzero number without changing the solution of the equation.

➡ Solve: $6x = 14$

$$6x = 14$$ • The goal is to rewrite the equation in the form *variable = constant*.

$$\frac{6x}{6} = \frac{14}{6}$$ • Divide each side of the equation by 6.

$$x = \frac{7}{3}$$ • Simplify. The equation is in the form *variable = constant*.

The solution is $\frac{7}{3}$.

When using the Multiplication Property of Equations, multiply each side of the equation by the reciprocal of the coefficient when the coefficient is a fraction. Divide each side of the equation by the coefficient when the coefficient is an integer or decimal.

Example 4   Solve: $\dfrac{3x}{4} = -9$ **You Try It 4**   Solve: $-\dfrac{2x}{5} = 6$

Solution $\dfrac{3x}{4} = -9$ **Your solution**

$$\frac{4}{3} \cdot \frac{3}{4}x = \frac{4}{3}(-9)$$ • $\left[\dfrac{3x}{4} = \dfrac{3}{4}x\right]$

$$x = -12$$

The solution is -12.

Example 5   Solve: $5x - 9x = 12$ **You Try It 5**   Solve: $4x - 8x = 16$

Solution $5x - 9x = 12$ **Your solution**
$$-4x = 12$$ • Combine like terms.
$$\frac{-4x}{-4} = \frac{12}{-4}$$
$$x = -3$$

The solution is -3.

Solutions on p. S4

Objective D   *To solve application problems using the basic percent equation* .... 〔10〕 [CT]

An equation that is used frequently in mathematics applications is the basic percent equation.

> **Basic Percent Equation**
>
> Percent · Base = Amount
>
> P · B = A

In many application problems involving percent, the base follows the word "of."

➡ 20% of what number is 30?

$P \cdot B = A$	• Use the basic percent equation.
$0.20B = 30$	• $P = 20\% = 0.20$, $A = 30$, and B is unknown.
$\dfrac{0.20B}{0.20} = \dfrac{30}{0.20}$	• Solve for B.
$B = 150$	

The number is 150.

➡ 70 is what percent of 80?

$P \cdot B = A$	• Use the basic percent equation.
$P(80) = 70$	• $B = 80$, $A = 70$, and P is unknown.
$\dfrac{P(80)}{80} = \dfrac{70}{80}$	• Solve for P.
$P = 0.875$	• The question asked for a percent.
$P = 87.5\%$	Convert the decimal to a percent.

70 is 87.5% of 80.

➡ According to the Travel Industry Association of America, a typical traveler's total vacation bill is $1442. Of that amount, $735 is paid in cash. To the nearest percent, what percent of a typical traveler's vacation bill is paid in cash?

Strategy   To determine the percent, use the basic percent equation.
$B = 1442$, $A = 735$, and P is unknown.

Solution
$$P \cdot B = A$$
$$P(1442) = 735$$
$$\frac{P(1442)}{1442} = \frac{735}{1442}$$
$$P \approx 0.51 = 51\%$$

A typical traveler pays 51% of the vacation bill in cash.

In most cases, you should write the percent as a decimal before solving the basic percent equation. However, some percents are more easily written as a fraction. For example,

$$33\frac{1}{3}\% = \frac{1}{3} \qquad\qquad 66\frac{2}{3}\% = \frac{2}{3} \qquad\qquad 16\frac{2}{3}\% = \frac{1}{6} \qquad\qquad 83\frac{1}{3}\% = \frac{5}{6}$$

Example 6

12 is $33\frac{1}{3}\%$ of what number?

Solution

$$P \cdot B = A$$

$$\frac{1}{3}B = 12 \qquad \bullet\; 33\frac{1}{3}\% = \frac{1}{3}$$

$$3 \cdot \frac{1}{3}B = 3 \cdot 12$$

$$B = 36$$

12 is $33\frac{1}{3}\%$ of 36.

You Try It 6

18 is $16\frac{2}{3}\%$ of what number?

Your solution

Example 7

In a recent year, 238 U.S. airports collected $1.1 billion in passenger taxes. Of this amount, $88 million was spent on noise reduction. What percent of the passenger taxes collected was spent on noise reduction?

Strategy

To find the percent, solve the basic percent equation using B = 1.1 billion = 1100 million and A = 88 million. The percent is unknown.

Solution

$$P \cdot B = A$$

$$P(1100) = 88$$

$$\frac{P(1100)}{1100} = \frac{88}{1100}$$

$$P = 0.08$$

8% of the passenger taxes collected was spent on noise reduction.

You Try It 7

The federal government ran a deficit of $23.1 billion in March of 1997. The deficit in March of 1996 was $47.1 billion. What percent of the March 1996 deficit was the March 1997 deficit? Round to the nearest tenth of a percent.

Your strategy

Your solution

Solutions on p. S4

3.1 Exercises

. . . .

Objective A

1. Is 4 a solution of
$2x = 8$?

2. Is 3 a solution of
$y + 4 = 7$?

3. Is -1 a solution of
$2b - 1 = 3$?

4. Is -2 a solution of
$3a - 4 = 10$?

5. Is 1 a solution of
$4 - 2m = 3$?

6. Is 2 a solution of
$7 - 3n = 2$?

7. Is 5 a solution of
$2x + 5 = 3x$?

8. Is 4 a solution of
$3y - 4 = 2y$?

9. Is 0 a solution of
$4a + 5 = 3a + 5$?

10. Is 3 a solution of
$z^2 + 1 = 4 + 3z$?

11. Is 2 a solution of
$2x^2 - 1 = 4x - 1$?

12. Is -1 a solution of
$y^2 - 1 = 4y + 3$?

13. Is -2 a solution of
$m^2 - 4 = m + 3$?

14. Is 5 a solution of
$x^2 + 2x + 1 = (x + 1)^2$?

15. Is -6 a solution of
$(n - 2)^2 = n^2 - 4n + 4$?

16. Is 4 a solution of
$x(x + 1) = x^2 + 5$?

17. Is 3 a solution of
$2a(a - 1) = 3a + 3$?

18. Is $-\dfrac{1}{4}$ a solution of
$8t + 1 = -1$?

19. Is $\dfrac{1}{2}$ a solution of
$4y + 1 = 3$?

20. Is $\dfrac{2}{5}$ a solution of
$5m + 1 = 10m - 3$?

21. Is $\dfrac{3}{4}$ a solution of
$8x - 1 = 12x + 3$?

Objective B

Solve and check.

22. $x + 5 = 7$

23. $y + 3 = 9$

24. $b - 4 = 11$

25. $z - 6 = 10$

26. $2 + a = 8$

27. $5 + x = 12$

28. $m + 9 = 3$

29. $t + 12 = 10$

30. $n - 5 = -2$

31. $x - 6 = -5$

32. $b + 7 = 7$

33. $y - 5 = -5$

34. $a - 3 = -5$ **35.** $x - 6 = -3$ **36.** $z + 9 = 2$ **37.** $n + 11 = 1$

38. $10 + m = 3$ **39.** $8 + x = 5$ **40.** $9 + x = -3$ **41.** $10 + y = -4$

42. $b - 5 = -3$ **43.** $t - 6 = -4$ **44.** $4 + x = 10$ **45.** $9 + a = 20$

46. $2 = x + 7$ **47.** $-8 = n + 1$ **48.** $4 = m - 11$ **49.** $-6 = y - 5$

50. $12 = 3 + w$ **51.** $-9 = 5 + x$ **52.** $4 = -10 + b$ **53.** $-7 = -2 + x$

54. $13 = -6 + a$ **55.** $m + \dfrac{2}{3} = -\dfrac{1}{3}$ **56.** $c + \dfrac{3}{4} = -\dfrac{1}{4}$ **57.** $x - \dfrac{1}{2} = \dfrac{1}{2}$

58. $x - \dfrac{2}{5} = \dfrac{3}{5}$ **59.** $\dfrac{5}{8} + y = \dfrac{1}{8}$ **60.** $\dfrac{4}{9} + a = -\dfrac{2}{9}$

61. $m + \dfrac{1}{2} = -\dfrac{1}{4}$ **62.** $b + \dfrac{1}{6} = -\dfrac{1}{3}$ **63.** $x + \dfrac{2}{3} = \dfrac{3}{4}$

64. $n + \dfrac{2}{5} = \dfrac{2}{3}$ **65.** $-\dfrac{5}{6} = x - \dfrac{1}{4}$ **66.** $-\dfrac{1}{4} = c - \dfrac{2}{3}$

67. $d + 1.3619 = 2.0148$ **68.** $w + 2.932 = 4.801$ **69.** $-0.813 + x = -1.096$

70. $-1.926 + t = -1.042$ **71.** $6.149 = -3.108 + z$ **72.** $5.237 = -2.014 + x$

Objective C

Solve and check.

73. $5x = -15$

74. $4y = -28$

75. $3b = 0$

76. $2a = 0$

77. $-3x = 6$

78. $-5m = 20$

79. $-3x = -27$

80. $-\dfrac{1}{6}n = -30$

81. $20 = \dfrac{1}{4}c$

82. $18 = 2t$

83. $-32 = 8w$

84. $-56 = 7x$

85. $0 = -5x$

86. $0 = -8a$

87. $-32 = -4y$

88. $-54 = 6c$

89. $49 = -7t$

90. $\dfrac{x}{3} = 2$

91. $\dfrac{x}{4} = 3$

92. $-\dfrac{y}{2} = 5$

93. $-\dfrac{b}{3} = 6$

94. $\dfrac{3}{4}y = 9$

95. $\dfrac{2}{5}x = 6$

96. $-\dfrac{2}{3}d = 8$

97. $-\dfrac{3}{5}m = 12$

98. $\dfrac{2n}{3} = 0$

99. $\dfrac{5x}{6} = 0$

100. $\dfrac{-3z}{8} = 9$

101. $\dfrac{-4x}{5} = -12$

102. $-6 = -\dfrac{2}{3}y$

103. $-15 = -\dfrac{1}{5}x$

104. $\dfrac{2}{5}a = 3$

105. $\dfrac{3x}{4} = 2$

106. $\dfrac{3}{4}c = \dfrac{3}{5}$

107. $\dfrac{2}{9} = \dfrac{2}{3}y$

108. $-\dfrac{6}{7} = -\dfrac{3}{4}b$

109. $\dfrac{1}{5}x = -\dfrac{1}{10}$

110. $-\dfrac{2}{3}y = -\dfrac{8}{9}$

111. $-1 = \dfrac{2n}{3}$

112. $-\dfrac{3}{4} = \dfrac{a}{8}$

113. $-\dfrac{2}{5}m = -\dfrac{6}{7}$ **114.** $5x + 2x = 14$ **115.** $3n + 2n = 20$ **116.** $7d - 4d = 9$

117. $10y - 3y = 21$ **118.** $2x - 5x = 9$ **119.** $\dfrac{x}{1.46} = 3.25$ **120.** $\dfrac{z}{2.95} = -7.88$

121. $3.47a = 7.1482$ **122.** $2.31m = 2.4255$ **123.** $-3.7x = 7.881$ **124.** $\dfrac{n}{2.65} = 9.08$

Objective D

125. What is 35% of 80?   **126.** What percent of 8 is 0.5?   **127.** Find 1.2% of 60.

128. 8 is what percent of 5?   **129.** 125% of what is 80?   **130.** What percent of 20 is 30?

131. 12 is what percent of 50?   **132.** What percent of 125 is 50?   **133.** Find 18% of 40.

134. What is 25% of 60?   **135.** 12% of what is 48?   **136.** 45% of what is 9?

137. What is $33\dfrac{1}{3}\%$ of 27?   **138.** Find $16\dfrac{2}{3}\%$ of 30.   **139.** What percent of 12 is 3?

140. 10 is what percent of 15?   **141.** 60% of what is 3?   **142.** 75% of what is 6?

143. 12 is what percent of 6?   **144.** 20 is what percent of 16?   **145.** $5\dfrac{1}{4}\%$ of what is 21?

146. $37\frac{1}{2}\%$ of what is 15?

147. Find 15.4% of 50.

148. What is 18.5% of 46?

149. 1 is 0.5% of what?

150. 3 is 1.5% of what?

151. $\frac{3}{4}\%$ of what is 3?

152. $\frac{1}{2}\%$ of what is 3?

153. Find 125% of 16.

154. What is 250% of 12?

155. 16.43 is what percent of 20.45? Round to the nearest hundredth of a percent.

156. Find 18.37% of 625.43. Round to the nearest hundredth.

157. A university consists of three colleges: business, engineering, and fine arts. There are 2900 students in the business college, 1500 students in the engineering college, and 1000 students in the fine arts college. What percent of the total number of students in the university are in the fine arts college? Round to the nearest percent.

158. Approximately 21% of air is oxygen. Using this estimate, determine how many liters of oxygen there are in a room containing 21,600 L of air.

Corporate Sponsorships
(in millions of dollars)

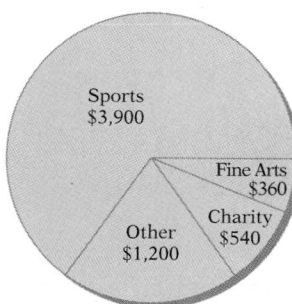

Source: IEG Sponsorship Report

159. The circle graph at the right represents corporate spending in 1997 of $6 billion to sponsor events. What percent of the amount spent by companies was spent on sports?

160. In 1950, 12% of mothers with children under age 6 worked outside the home. By 1995, that percent had increased to 64%. How many more mothers with children under age 6 worked outside the home in 1995 than in 1950?

161. The Energy Information Administration reports that if every U.S. household switched 4 h of lighting per day from incandescent bulbs to compact fluorescent bulbs, we would save 31.7 billion kilowatt-hours (kWh) a year, or 33% of the total electricity used for home lighting. What is the total electricity used for home lighting in this country? Round to the nearest tenth of a billion.

162. To override a presidential veto, at least $66\frac{2}{3}\%$ of the Senate must vote to override the veto. There are 100 senators in the Senate. What is the minimum number of votes needed to override a veto?

163. According to *Time* (March 1997), in 1996 Coca-Cola Company declared its intention to repurchase 206 million shares of the company, or 8.3% of the company's outstanding common stock. How many shares of Coca-Cola Company common stock were outstanding at the time of this announcement? Round to the nearest million.

164. A Holstein cow in Wisconsin recently set a milk production record. She averaged 174 lb of milk per day for 365 days. What percent of the average daily milk production in 1996 was the production by this Wisconsin Holstein? See the graph at the right. Round to the nearest percent.

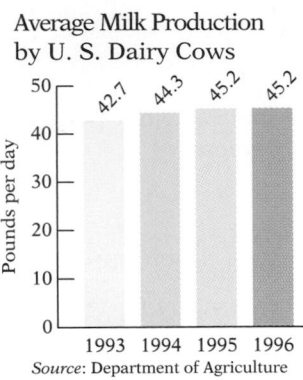

Average Milk Production by U. S. Dairy Cows

Source: Department of Agriculture

165. According to *Working Woman* (July–August 1997), in 1996, total consumer spending in the United States was $4.69 trillion. Of that amount, 1.58% was spent on new cars. In 1986, total consumer spending in the United States was $3.72 trillion, of which 3.09% was spent on new cars.
   a. During which year was more money spent on new cars?
   b. How much more? Round to the nearest billion.

APPLYING THE CONCEPTS

166. Solve the equation $ax = b$ for x. Is the solution you have written valid for all real numbers a and b?

167. **a.** Make up an equation of the form $x + a = b$ that has 2 as a solution.
   b. Make up an equation of the form $ax = b$ that has -1 as a solution.

168. Solve.   **a.** $\dfrac{3}{\dfrac{1}{x}} = 5$ **b.** $\dfrac{2}{\dfrac{1}{y}} = -2$ **c.** $\dfrac{3x + 2x}{3} = 2$

169. Write out the steps for solving the equation $\frac{1}{2}x = -3$. Identify each Property of Real Numbers or Property of Equations as you use it.

170. In your own words, state the Addition Property and the Multiplication Property of Equations.

171. If a quantity increases by 100%, how many times its original value is the new value?

3.2 General Equations—Part I

Objective A   **To solve an equation of the form $ax + b = c$** ....

In solving an equation of the form $ax + b = c$, the goal is to rewrite the equation in the form *variable = constant*. This requires the application of both the Addition and the Multiplication Properties of Equations.

➡ Solve: $\frac{3}{4}x - 2 = -11$

The goal is to write the equation in the form *variable = constant*.

$$\frac{3}{4}x - 2 = -11$$

$$\frac{3}{4}x - 2 + 2 = -11 + 2$$ • Add 2 to each side of the equation.

$$\frac{3}{4}x = -9$$ • Simplify.

$$\frac{4}{3} \cdot \frac{3}{4}x = \frac{4}{3}(-9)$$ • Multiply each side of the equation by $\frac{4}{3}$.

$$x = -12$$ • The equation is of the form *variable = constant*.

The solution is -12.

TAKE NOTE

Check: $\frac{3}{4}x - 2 = -11$

$$\frac{3}{4}(-12) - 2 \;\big|\; -11$$
$$-9 - 2 \;\big|\; -11$$
$$-11 = -11$$

A true equation

Example 1   Solve: $3x - 7 = -5$

Solution
$$3x - 7 = -5$$
$$3x - 7 + 7 = -5 + 7$$
$$3x = 2$$
$$\frac{3x}{3} = \frac{2}{3}$$
$$x = \frac{2}{3}$$

The solution is $\frac{2}{3}$.

Example 2   Solve: $5 = 9 - 2x$

Solution
$$5 = 9 - 2x$$
$$5 - 9 = 9 - 9 - 2x$$
$$-4 = -2x$$
$$\frac{-4}{-2} = \frac{-2x}{-2}$$
$$2 = x$$

The solution is 2.

You Try It 1   Solve: $5x + 7 = 10$

Your solution

You Try It 2   Solve: $2 = 11 + 3x$

Your solution

Solutions on pp. S4–S5

Example 3

Solve: $2x + 4 - 5x = 10$

Solution

$$2x + 4 - 5x = 10$$
$$-3x + 4 = 10 \qquad \bullet \text{ Combine like terms.}$$
$$-3x + 4 - 4 = 10 - 4$$
$$-3x = 6$$
$$\frac{-3x}{-3} = \frac{6}{-3}$$
$$x = -2$$

The solution is -2.

You Try It 3

Solve: $x - 5 + 4x = 25$

Your solution

Solution on p. S5

Objective B   *To solve application problems using formulas* ....

In this objective we will be solving application problems using formulas. Two of the formulas we will use are related to markup and discount.

Markup

Cost

Selling Price

Cost is the price a business pays for a product. **Selling price** is the price for which a business sells a product to a customer. The difference between selling price and cost is called **markup.** Markup is added to the cost to cover the expenses of operating a business. The diagram at the left illustrates these terms. The total length is the selling price. One part of the diagram is the cost, and the other part is the markup.

When the markup is expressed as a percent of the retailer's cost, it is called the **markup rate.**

The basic markup equations used by a business are

Selling price = cost + markup   Markup = markup rate · cost
$$S \quad = C + M \qquad\qquad M = r \cdot C$$

Substituting $r \cdot C$ for M in the first equation results in $S = C + (r \cdot C)$, or $S = C + rC$.

➡ The manager of a clothing store buys a jacket for \$80 and sells the jacket for \$116. Find the markup rate.

$$S = C + rC \qquad\qquad \bullet \text{ Use the equation } S = C + rC.$$

$$116 = 80 + 80r \qquad\quad \bullet \text{ Given: } C = \$80 \text{ and } S = \$116$$

$$36 = 80r \qquad\qquad\quad \bullet \text{ Subtract 80 from each side of the equation.}$$

$$\frac{36}{80} = \frac{80r}{80} \qquad\qquad \bullet \text{ Divide both sides of the equation by 80.}$$

$$0.45 = r$$

The markup rate is 45%.

Discount
or
Markdown

Sale
Price

Regular
Price

A retailer may reduce the regular price of a product because the goods are damaged, odd sizes, or discontinued items. The **discount,** or **markdown,** is the amount by which a retailer reduces the regular price of a product. The percent discount is called the **discount rate** and is usually expressed as a percent of the original selling price (the regular price).

The basic discount equations used by a business are

$$\frac{\text{Sale}}{\text{price}} = \frac{\text{regular}}{\text{price}} - \text{discount} \qquad\qquad \text{Discount} = \frac{\text{discount}}{\text{rate}} \cdot \frac{\text{regular}}{\text{price}}$$

$$S = R - D \qquad\qquad\qquad\qquad D = r \cdot R$$

Substituting $r \cdot R$ for D in the first equation results in $S = R - (r \cdot R)$, or $S = R - rR$.

➡ A portable computer that regularly sells for $1850 is on sale for $1480. Find the discount rate.

$$S = R - rR$$ • Use the equation $S = R - rR$.

$$1480 = 1850 - 1850r$$ • Given: $S = \$1480$ and $R = 1850$

$$-370 = -1850r$$ • Subtract 1850 from each side of the equation.

$$\frac{-370}{-1850} = \frac{-1850r}{-1850}$$ • Divide each side of the equation by -1850.

$$0.2 = r$$

The discount rate on the portable computer is 20%.

Example 4
A markup rate of 40% was used on a refrigerator that has a selling price of $749. Find the cost of the refrigerator. Use the formula $S = C + rC$.

Strategy
Given: $S = \$749$
$\qquad\quad r = 40\% = 0.40$
Unknown: C

Solution
$$S = C + rC$$
$$749 = C + 0.40C$$ • $C + 0.40C = 1C + 0.40C$
$$749 = 1.40C$$ • Combine like terms.
$$\frac{749}{1.40} = \frac{1.40C}{1.40}$$
$$535 = C$$

The cost of the refrigerator is $535.

You Try It 4
A markup rate of 45% was used on an outboard motor that has a selling price of $986. Find the cost of the outboard motor. Use the formula $S = C + rC$.

Your strategy

Your solution

Solution on p. S5

Example 5

A necklace that is marked down 35% has a sale price of $292.50. Find the regular price of the necklace. Use the formula $S = R - rR$.

Strategy

Given: $S = 292.50$
$\quad\quad\quad r = 35\% = 0.35$

Unknown: R

Solution

$$S = R - rR$$
$$292.50 = R - 0.35R \quad \bullet\ R - 0.35R = 1R - 0.35R$$
$$292.50 = 0.65R \quad\quad \bullet\ \textbf{Combine like terms.}$$
$$\frac{292.50}{0.65} = \frac{0.65R}{0.65}$$
$$450 = R$$

The regular price of the necklace is $450.

Example 6

To determine the total cost of production, an economist uses the equation $T = U \cdot N + F$, where T is the total cost, U is the unit cost, N is the number of units made, and F is the fixed cost. Use this equation to find the number of units made during a month when the total cost was $9000, the unit cost was $25, and the fixed cost was $3000.

Strategy

Given: $T = \$9000$
$\quad\quad\quad U = \$25$
$\quad\quad\quad F = \$3000$

Unknown: N

Solution

$$T = U \cdot N + F$$
$$9000 = 25N + 3000$$
$$6000 = 25N$$
$$\frac{6000}{25} = \frac{25N}{25}$$
$$240 = N$$

There were 240 units made.

You Try It 5

A garage door opener, marked down 25%, is on sale for $159. Find the regular price of the garage door opener. Use the formula $S = R - rR$.

Your strategy

Your solution

You Try It 6

The pressure at a certain depth in the ocean can be approximated by the equation

$P = 15 + \frac{1}{2}D$, where P is the pressure in

pounds per square inch and D is the depth in feet. Use this equation to find the depth when the pressure is 45 pounds per square inch.

Your strategy

Your solution

Solutions on p. S5

3.2 Exercises

· ·

Objective A

Solve and check.

1. $3x + 1 = 10$ **2.** $4y + 3 = 11$ **3.** $2a - 5 = 7$ **4.** $5m - 6 = 9$

5. $5 = 4x + 9$ **6.** $2 = 5b + 12$ **7.** $2x - 5 = -11$ **8.** $3n - 7 = -19$

9. $4 - 3w = -2$ **10.** $5 - 6x = -13$ **11.** $8 - 3t = 2$ **12.** $12 - 5x = 7$

13. $4a - 20 = 0$ **14.** $3y - 9 = 0$ **15.** $6 + 2b = 0$ **16.** $10 + 5m = 0$

17. $-2x + 5 = -7$ **18.** $-5d + 3 = -12$ **19.** $-12x + 30 = -6$ **20.** $-13 = -11y + 9$

21. $2 = 7 - 5a$ **22.** $3 = 11 - 4n$ **23.** $-35 = -6b + 1$ **24.** $-8x + 3 = -29$

25. $-3m - 21 = 0$ **26.** $-5x - 30 = 0$ **27.** $-4y + 15 = 15$ **28.** $-3x + 19 = 19$

29. $9 - 4x = 6$ **30.** $3t - 2 = 0$ **31.** $9x - 4 = 0$ **32.** $7 - 8z = 0$

33. $1 - 3x = 0$ **34.** $9d + 10 = 7$ **35.** $12w + 11 = 5$ **36.** $6y - 5 = -7$

37. $8b - 3 = -9$ **38.** $5 - 6m = 2$ **39.** $7 - 9a = 4$ **40.** $9 = -12c + 5$

41. $10 = -18x + 7$ **42.** $2y + \dfrac{1}{3} = \dfrac{7}{3}$ **43.** $4a + \dfrac{3}{4} = \dfrac{19}{4}$ **44.** $2n - \dfrac{3}{4} = \dfrac{13}{4}$

45. $3x - \dfrac{5}{6} = \dfrac{13}{6}$ **46.** $5y + \dfrac{3}{7} = \dfrac{3}{7}$ **47.** $9x + \dfrac{4}{5} = \dfrac{4}{5}$ **48.** $8 = 7d - 1$

49. $8 = 10x - 5$ **50.** $4 = 7 - 2w$ **51.** $7 = 9 - 5a$ **52.** $8t + 13 = 3$

53. $12x + 19 = 3$ **54.** $-6y + 5 = 13$ **55.** $-4x + 3 = 9$ **56.** $\dfrac{1}{2}a - 3 = 1$

57. $\dfrac{1}{3}m - 1 = 5$ **58.** $\dfrac{2}{5}y + 4 = 6$ **59.** $\dfrac{3}{4}n + 7 = 13$ **60.** $-\dfrac{2}{3}x + 1 = 7$

61. $-\dfrac{3}{8}b + 4 = 10$ **62.** $\dfrac{x}{4} - 6 = 1$ **63.** $\dfrac{y}{5} - 2 = 3$ **64.** $\dfrac{2x}{3} - 1 = 5$

65. $\dfrac{3c}{7} - 1 = 8$ **66.** $4 - \dfrac{3}{4}z = -2$ **67.** $3 - \dfrac{4}{5}w = -9$ **68.** $5 + \dfrac{2}{3}y = 3$

69. $17 + \dfrac{5}{8}x = 7$ **70.** $17 = 7 - \dfrac{5}{6}t$ **71.** $9 = 3 - \dfrac{2x}{7}$ **72.** $3 = \dfrac{3a}{4} + 1$

73. $7 = \dfrac{2x}{5} + 4$ **74.** $5 - \dfrac{4c}{7} = 8$ **75.** $7 - \dfrac{5}{9}y = 9$ **76.** $6a + 3 + 2a = 11$

77. $5y + 9 + 2y = 23$ **78.** $7x - 4 - 2x = 6$ **79.** $11z - 3 - 7z = 9$ **80.** $2x - 6x + 1 = 9$

81. $b - 8b + 1 = -6$ **82.** $3 = 7x + 9 - 4x$ **83.** $-1 = 5m + 7 - m$ **84.** $8 = 4n - 6 + 3n$

85. If $2x - 3 = 7$, evaluate $3x + 4$.

86. If $3x + 5 = -4$, evaluate $2x - 5$.

87. If $4 - 5x = -1$, evaluate $x^2 - 3x + 1$.

88. If $2 - 3x = 11$, evaluate $x^2 + 2x - 3$.

89. If $5x + 3 - 2x = 12$, evaluate $4 - 5x$.

90. If $2x - 4 - 7x = 16$, evaluate $x^2 + 1$.

Objective B   *Application Problems*

Solve. Use the markup equation $S = C + rC$, where S is selling price, C is cost, and r is the markup rate.

91. A watch costing $98 is sold for $156.80. Find the markup rate on the watch.

92. A set of golf clubs costing $360 is sold for $630. Find the markup rate on the set of golf clubs.

93. A markup rate of 40% was used on a basketball with a selling price of $82.60. Find the cost of the basketball.

94. A portable tape player with a selling price of $57 has a markup rate of 50%. Find the cost of the tape player.

95. A freezer costing $360 is sold for $520. Find the markup rate. Round to the nearest tenth of a percent.

96. A sofa costing $320 is sold for $479. Find the markup rate. Round to the nearest tenth of a percent.

97. A digitally recorded compact disk has a selling price of $11.90. The markup rate is 40%. Find the cost of the CD.

98. A markup rate of 25% is used on a computer that has a selling price of $2187.50. Find the cost of the computer.

Solve. Use the discount equation $S = R - rR$, where S is the sale price, R is the regular price, and r is the discount rate.

99. An oak bedroom set with a regular price of $1295 is on sale for $995. Find the discount rate. Round to the nearest tenth of a percent.

100. A stereo system with a regular price of $495 is on sale for $395. Find the markdown rate. Round to the nearest tenth of a percent.

101. A mechanic's tool set is on sale for $180 after a markdown of 40% off the regular price. Find the regular price.

102. A battery with a discount price of $65 is on sale for 22% off the regular price. Find the regular price. Round to the nearest cent.

103. A compact disk player with a regular price of $325 is on sale for $201.50. Find the markdown rate.

104. A luggage set with a regular price of $178 is on sale for $103.24. Find the discount rate.

105. A telescope is on sale for $165 after a markdown of 40% off the regular price. Find the regular price.

106. An exercise bike is on sale for $390, having been marked down 25% of the regular price. Find the regular price.

The distance s, in feet, that an object will fall in t seconds is given by $s = 16t^2 + vt$, where v is the initial velocity of the object in feet per second.

107. Find the initial velocity of an object that falls 80 ft in 2 s.

108. Find the initial velocity of an object that falls 144 ft in 3 s.

A company uses the equation $V = C - 6000t$ to determine the depreciated value V, after t years, of a milling machine that originally cost C dollars. Equations like this are used in accounting for straight-line depreciation.

109. A milling machine originally cost $50,000. In how many years will the depreciated value of the machine be $38,000?

110. A milling machine originally cost $78,000. In how many years will the depreciated value of the machine be $48,000?

Anthropologists approximate the height of a primate by the size of its humerus (the bone from the elbow to the shoulder) using the equation $H = 1.2L + 27.8$, where L is the length of the humerus and H is the height, in inches, of the primate.

111. An anthropologist estimates the height of a primate to be 66 in. What is the approximate length of the humerus of this primate? Round to the nearest tenth of an inch.

112. An anthropologist estimates the height of a primate to be 62 in. What is the approximate length of the humerus of this primate?

Black ice is an ice covering on roads that is especially difficult to see and therefore extremely dangerous for motorists. The distance a car traveling 30 mph will slide after its brakes are applied is related to the outside temperature by the formula $C = \frac{1}{4}D - 45$, where C is the Celsius temperature and D is the distance in feet that the car will slide.

113. Determine the distance a car will slide on black ice when the outside temperature is $-3°C$.

114. Determine the distance a car will slide on black ice when the outside temperature is $-11°C$.

A telephone company estimates that the number N of phone calls per day between two cities of population P_1 and P_2 that are d miles apart is given by the equation $N = \dfrac{2.51P_1P_2}{d^2}$.

115. Estimate the population (P_1) of a city given that the population of a second city (P_2) is 48,000, the number of phone calls per day between the two cities is 1,100,000, and the distance between the cities is 75 mi. Round to the nearest thousand.

116. Estimate the population (P_1) of a city given that the population of a second city (P_2) is 125,000, the number of phone calls per day between the two cities is 2,500,000, and the distance between the cities is 50 mi. Round to the nearest thousand.

The world record time for a 1-mile race can be approximated by the equation $t = 17.08 - 0.0067y$, where t is the time in minutes and y is the year of the race.

117. Approximate the year in which the first "4-minute mile" was run. (The actual year was 1954.) Round to the nearest whole number.

118. In 1985, the world record for a 1-mile race was 3.77 min. For what year does the equation predict this record time? Round to the nearest whole number.

APPLYING THE CONCEPTS

119. A pair of shoes that now sells for $63 has been marked up 40%. Find the markup on the pair of shoes.

120. The sale price of a typewriter is 25% off the regular price. The discount is $70. Find the sale price.

121. The sale price of a television was $180. Find the regular price if the sale price was computed by taking one-third off the regular price followed by an additional 15% discount on the reduced price.

122. A customer buys four tires, three at the regular price and one for 20% off the regular price. The four tires cost $323. What was the regular price of a tire?

123. Solve: $x \div 15 = 25$ remainder 10

124. Does the sentence, "Solve $3x - 4(x - 1)$" make sense? Why or why not?

125. Explain the steps you would take to solve the equation $3x - 4 = 14$. State the Property of Real Numbers or the Property of Equations that is used at each step.

126. The following problem does not contain enough information for us to find only one solution. Supply some additional information so that the problem has exactly one solution. Then write and solve an equation.
The sum of two numbers is 15. Find the numbers.

127. The following problem does not contain enough information. What additional information is needed to answer the question?
How many hours does it take to fly from Los Angeles to New York?

3.3 General Equations—Part II

Objective A   *To solve an equation of the form ax + b = cx + d* ....

In solving an equation of the form $ax + b = cx + d$, the goal is to rewrite the equation in the form *variable = constant*. Begin by rewriting the equation so that there is only one variable term in the equation. Then rewrite the equation so that there is only one constant term.

➡ Solve: $2x + 3 = 5x - 9$

$$2x + 3 = 5x - 9$$

$$2x - 5x + 3 = 5x - 5x - 9$$ • Subtract 5x from each side of the equation.

$$-3x + 3 = -9$$ • Simplify. There is only one variable term.

$$-3x + 3 - 3 = -9 - 3$$ • Subtract 3 from each side of the equation.

$$-3x = -12$$ • Simplify. There is only one constant term.

$$\frac{-3x}{-3} = \frac{-12}{-3}$$ • Divide each side of the equation by −3.

$$x = 4$$ • The equation is in the form *variable = constant*.

The solution is 4. You should verify this by checking this solution.

Example 1   Solve: $4x - 5 = 8x - 7$

Solution

$$4x - 5 = 8x - 7$$

$$4x - 8x - 5 = 8x - 8x - 7$$

$$-4x - 5 = -7$$

$$-4x - 5 + 5 = -7 + 5$$

$$-4x = -2$$

$$\frac{-4x}{-4} = \frac{-2}{-4}$$

$$x = \frac{1}{2}$$

The solution is $\frac{1}{2}$.

You Try It 1   Solve: $5x + 4 = 6 + 10x$

Your solution

Solution on p. S5

Example 2   Solve: $3x + 4 - 5x = 2 - 4x$

Solution

$$3x + 4 - 5x = 2 - 4x$$

$$-2x + 4 = 2 - 4x$$

$$-2x + 4x + 4 = 2 - 4x + 4x$$

$$2x + 4 = 2$$

$$2x + 4 - 4 = 2 - 4$$

$$2x = -2$$

$$\frac{2x}{2} = \frac{-2}{2}$$

$$x = -1$$

The solution is -1.

You Try It 2   Solve: $5x - 10 - 3x = 6 - 4x$

Your solution

Solution on p. S5

Objective B   ***To solve an equation containing parentheses*** ....

When an equation contains parentheses, one of the steps in solving the equation requires the use of the Distributive Property. The Distributive Property is used to remove parentheses from a variable expression.

➡ Solve: $4 + 5(2x - 3) = 3(4x - 1)$

$$4 + 5(2x - 3) = 3(4x - 1)$$

$$4 + 10x - 15 = 12x - 3$$ • **Use the Distributive Property. Then simplify.**

$$10x - 11 = 12x - 3$$

$$10x - 12x - 11 = 12x - 12x - 3$$ • **Subtract 12x from each side of the equation.**

$$-2x - 11 = -3$$ • **Simplify.**

$$-2x - 11 + 11 = -3 + 11$$ • **Add 11 to each side of the equation.**

$$-2x = 8$$ • **Simplify.**

$$\frac{-2x}{-2} = \frac{8}{-2}$$ • **Divide each side of the equation by −2.**

$$x = -4$$ • **The equation is in the form *variable = constant*.**

The solution is -4. You should verify this by checking this solution.

Example 3

Solve: $3x - 4(2 - x) = 3(x - 2) - 4$

Solution

$$3x - 4(2 - x) = 3(x - 2) - 4$$
$$3x - 8 + 4x = 3x - 6 - 4$$
$$7x - 8 = 3x - 10$$
$$7x - 3x - 8 = 3x - 3x - 10$$
$$4x - 8 = -10$$
$$4x - 8 + 8 = -10 + 8$$
$$4x = -2$$
$$\frac{4x}{4} = \frac{-2}{4}$$
$$x = -\frac{1}{2}$$

The solution is $-\frac{1}{2}$.

You Try It 3

Solve: $5x - 4(3 - 2x) = 2(3x - 2) + 6$

Your solution

Example 4

Solve: $3[2 - 4(2x - 1)] = 4x - 10$

Solution

$$3[2 - 4(2x - 1)] = 4x - 10$$
$$3[2 - 8x + 4] = 4x - 10$$
$$3[6 - 8x] = 4x - 10$$
$$18 - 24x = 4x - 10$$
$$18 - 24x - 4x = 4x - 4x - 10$$
$$18 - 28x = -10$$
$$18 - 18 - 28x = -10 - 18$$
$$-28x = -28$$
$$\frac{-28x}{-28} = \frac{-28}{-28}$$
$$x = 1$$

The solution is 1.

You Try It 4

Solve: $-2[3x - 5(2x - 3)] = 3x - 8$

Your solution

Example 5

If $7x = 3x + 12$, evaluate $3x^2 - 7$.

Solution

Solve $7x = 3x + 12$ for x.

$$7x - 3x = 12$$
$$4x = 12$$
$$x = 3$$

Evaluate $3x^2 - 7$ for $x = 3$.

$$3x^2 - 7$$
$$3(3)^2 - 7 = 3(9) - 7$$
$$= 27 - 7$$
$$= 20$$

You Try It 5

If $2x = 5x + 6$, evaluate $-2x + 7$.

Your solution

Solutions on pp. S5–S6

Objective C **To solve application problems using formulas** ....

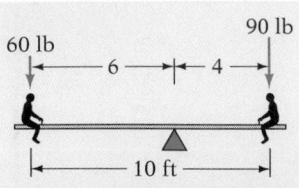

This system balances because

$$F_1x = F_2(d - x)$$
$$60(6) = 90(10 - 6)$$
$$60(6) = 90(4)$$
$$360 = 360$$

A lever system is shown at the right. It consists of a lever, or bar; a fulcrum; and two forces, F_1 and F_2. The distance d represents the length of the lever, x represents the distance from F_1 to the fulcrum, and $d - x$ represents the distance from F_2 to the fulcrum.

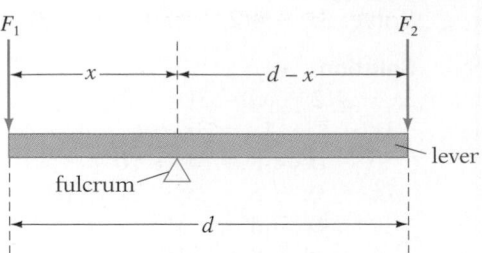

A principle of physics states that when the lever system balances, $F_1 \cdot x = F_2 \cdot (d - x)$.

Example 6

A lever is 15 ft long. A force of 50 lb is applied to one end of the lever, and a force of 100 lb is applied to the other end. Where is the fulcrum located when the system balances?

Strategy

Make a drawing.

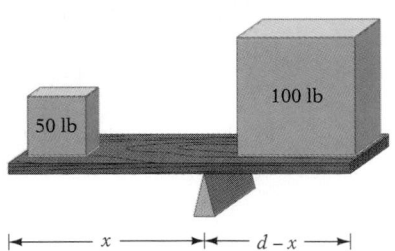

Given: $F_1 = 50$
$\quad\quad\ F_2 = 100$
$\quad\quad\ d = 15$
Unknown: x

Solution

$$F_1 \cdot x = F_2 \cdot (d - x)$$
$$50x = 100(15 - x)$$
$$50x = 1500 - 100x$$
$$50x + 100x = 1500 - 100x + 100x$$
$$150x = 1500$$
$$\frac{150x}{150} = \frac{1500}{150}$$
$$x = 10$$

The fulcrum is 10 ft from the 50-pound force.

You Try It 6

A lever is 25 ft long. A force of 45 lb is applied to one end of the lever, and a force of 80 lb is applied to the other end. Where is the location of the fulcrum when the system balances?

Your strategy

Your solution

Solution on p. S6

3.3 Exercises

· ·

Objective A

Solve and check.

1. $8x + 5 = 4x + 13$ **2.** $6y + 2 = y + 17$ **3.** $5x - 4 = 2x + 5$

4. $13b - 1 = 4b - 19$ **5.** $15x - 2 = 4x - 13$ **6.** $7a - 5 = 2a - 20$

7. $3x + 1 = 11 - 2x$ **8.** $n - 2 = 6 - 3n$ **9.** $2x - 3 = -11 - 2x$

10. $4y - 2 = -16 - 3y$ **11.** $2b + 3 = 5b + 12$ **12.** $m + 4 = 3m + 8$

13. $4y - 8 = y - 8$ **14.** $5a + 7 = 2a + 7$ **15.** $6 - 5x = 8 - 3x$

16. $10 - 4n = 16 - n$ **17.** $5 + 7x = 11 + 9x$ **18.** $3 - 2y = 15 + 4y$

19. $2x - 4 = 6x$ **20.** $2b - 10 = 7b$ **21.** $8m = 3m + 20$

22. $9y = 5y + 16$ **23.** $8b + 5 = 5b + 7$ **24.** $6y - 1 = 2y + 2$

25. $7x - 8 = x - 3$ **26.** $2y - 7 = -1 - 2y$ **27.** $2m - 1 = -6m + 5$

28. If $5x = 3x - 8$, evaluate $4x + 2$.   **29.** If $7x + 3 = 5x - 7$, evaluate $3x - 2$.

30. If $2 - 6a = 5 - 3a$, evaluate $4a^2 - 2a + 1$.   **31.** If $1 - 5c = 4 - 4c$, evaluate $3c^2 - 4c + 2$.

32. If $2y + 3 = 5 - 4y$, evaluate $6y - 7$.   **33.** If $3z + 1 = 1 - 5z$, evaluate $3z^2 - 7z + 8$.

___

Objective B

Solve and check.

34. $5x + 2(x + 1) = 23$

35. $6y + 2(2y + 3) = 16$

36. $9n - 3(2n - 1) = 15$

37. $12x - 2(4x - 6) = 28$

38. $7a - (3a - 4) = 12$

39. $9m - 4(2m - 3) = 11$

40. $5(3 - 2y) + 4y = 3$

41. $4(1 - 3x) + 7x = 9$

42. $5y - 3 = 7 + 4(y - 2)$

43. $5 + 2(3b + 1) = 3b + 5$

44. $6 - 4(3a - 2) = 2(a + 5)$

45. $7 - 3(2a - 5) = 3a + 10$

46. $2a - 5 = 4(3a + 1) - 2$

47. $5 - (9 - 6x) = 2x - 2$

48. $7 - (5 - 8x) = 4x + 3$

49. $3[2 - 4(y - 1)] = 3(2y + 8)$

50. $5[2 - (2x - 4)] = 2(5 - 3x)$

51. $3a + 2[2 + 3(a - 1)] = 2(3a + 4)$

52. $5 + 3[1 + 2(2x - 3)] = 6(x + 5)$

53. $-2[4 - (3b + 2)] = 5 - 2(3b + 6)$

54. $-4[x - 2(2x - 3)] + 1 = 2x - 3$

55. If $4 - 3a = 7 - 2(2a + 5)$, evaluate $a^2 + 7a$.

56. If $9 - 5x = 12 - (6x + 7)$, evaluate $x^2 - 3x - 2$.

57. If $2z - 5 = 3(4z + 5)$, evaluate $\dfrac{z^2}{(z - 2)}$.

58. If $3n - 7 = 5(2n + 7)$, evaluate $\dfrac{n^2}{(2n - 6)}$.

Objective C   *Application Problems*

Solve. Use the lever system equation $F_1x = F_2(d - x)$.

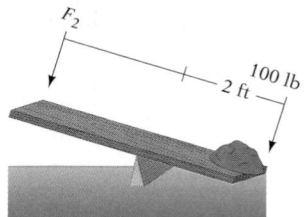

59. A lever 10 ft long is used to move a 100-pound rock. The fulcrum is placed 2 ft from the rock. What force must be applied to the other end of the lever to move the rock?

60. An adult and a child are on a seesaw 14 ft long. The adult weighs 175 lb and the child weighs 70 lb. How many feet from the child must the fulcrum be placed so that the seesaw balances?

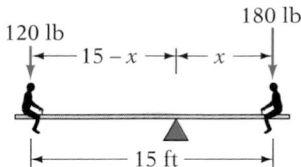

61. Two people are sitting 15 ft apart on a seesaw. One person weighs 180 lb. The second person weighs 120 lb. How far from the 180-pound person should the fulcrum be placed so that the seesaw balances?

62. Two children are sitting on a seesaw that is 12 ft long. One child weighs 60 lb. The other child weighs 90 lb. How far from the 90-pound child should the fulcrum be placed so that the seesaw balances?

63. In preparation for a stunt, two acrobats are standing on a plank 18 ft long. One acrobat weighs 128 lb and the second acrobat weighs 160 lb. How far from the 128-pound acrobat must the fulcrum be placed so that the acrobats are balanced on the plank?

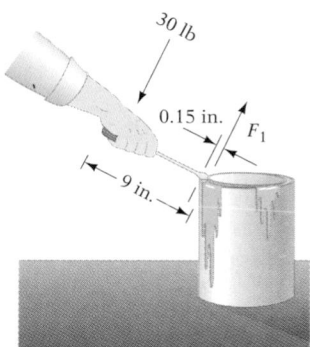

64. A screwdriver 9 in. long is used as a lever to open a can of paint. The tip of the screwdriver is placed under the lip of the can with the fulcrum 0.15 in. from the lip. A force of 30 lb is applied to the other end of the screwdriver. Find the force on the lip of the can.

65. A metal bar 8 ft long is used to move a 150-pound rock. The fulcrum is placed 1.5 ft from the rock. What minimum force must be applied to the other end of the bar to move the rock? Round to the nearest tenth.

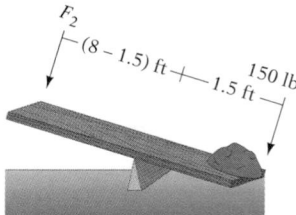

To determine the breakeven point, or the number of units that must be sold so that no profit or loss occurs, an economist uses the formula $Px = Cx + F$, where P is the selling price per unit, x is the number of units that must be sold to break even, C is the cost to make each unit, and F is the fixed cost.

66. A business analyst has determined that the selling price per unit for a laser printer is $1600. The cost to make the laser printer is $950, and the fixed cost is $211,250. Find the breakeven point.

67. A business analyst has determined that the selling price per unit for a gas barbecue is $325. The cost to make one gas barbecue is $175, and the fixed cost is $39,000. Find the breakeven point.

68. A manufacturer of thermostats determines that the cost per unit for a programmable thermostat is $38 and that the fixed cost is $24,400. The selling price for the thermostat is $99. Find the breakeven point.

69. A manufacturing engineer determines that the cost per unit for a desk lamp is $12 and that the fixed cost is $19,240. The selling price for the desk lamp is $49. Find the breakeven point.

70. A manufacturing engineer determines the cost to make one compact disk to be $3.35 and the fixed cost to be $6180. The selling price for each compact disk is $8.50. Find the number of compact disks that must be sold to break even.

71. To manufacture a softball bat requires two steps. The first step is to cut a rough shape. The second step is to sand the bat to its final form. The cost to rough-shape a bat is $.45, and the cost to sand a bat to final form is $1.05. The total fixed cost for the two steps is $16,500. How many softball bats must be sold at a price of $7.00 to break even?

APPLYING THE CONCEPTS

72. Write an equation of the form $ax + b = cx + d$ that has 4 as the solution.

Solve. If the equation has no solution, write "no solution."

73. $3(2x - 1) - (6x - 4) = -9$

74. $7(3x + 6) - 4(3 + 5x) = 13 + x$

75. $\frac{1}{5}(25 - 10a) + 4 = \frac{1}{3}(12a - 15) + 14$

76. $5[m + 2(3 - m)] = 3[2(4 - m) - 5]$

77. The equation $x = x + 1$ has no solution, whereas the solution of the equation $2x + 3 = 3$ is zero. Is there a difference between no solution and a solution of zero? Explain your answer.

78. Archimedes supposedly said, "Give me a long enough lever and I can move the world." Explain what Archimedes meant by that statement.

3.4   Translating Sentences into Equations

Objective A   *To solve integer problems* ....

An equation states that two mathematical expressions are equal. Therefore, to **translate** a sentence into an equation requires recognition of the words or phrases that mean "equals." Some of these phrases are listed below.

$$\left.\begin{array}{l} \text{equals} \\ \text{is} \\ \text{is equal to} \\ \text{amounts to} \\ \text{represents} \end{array}\right\} \text{translate to } =$$

Once the sentence is translated into an equation, the equation can be solved by rewriting the equation in the form *variable = constant*.

➡ Translate "five less than a number is thirteen" into an equation and solve.

The unknown number: n

- Assign a variable to the unknown number.

| Five less than a number | is | thirteen |

- Find two verbal expressions for the same value.

$$n - 5 \quad = \quad 13$$

- Write a mathematical expression for each verbal expression. Write the equals sign.

$$n - 5 + 5 = 13 + 5$$

- Solve the equation.

$$n = 18$$

The number is 18.

TAKE NOTE

You can check the solution to a translation problem.

Check:

5 less than 18 is 13

$$\begin{array}{c|c} 18 - 5 & 13 \\ & 13 = 13 \end{array}$$

Recall that the integers are the numbers $\{\ldots, -4, -3, -2, -1, 0, 1, 2, 3, 4, \ldots\}$. An **even integer** is an integer that is divisible by 2. Examples of even integers are -8, 0, and 22. An **odd integer** is an integer that is not divisible by 2. Examples of odd integers are -17, 1, and 39.

Consecutive integers are integers that follow one another in order. Examples of consecutive integers are shown at the right. (Assume that the variable n represents an integer.)

11, 12, 13
$-8, -7, -6$
$n, n + 1, n + 2$

Examples of **consecutive even integers** are shown at the right. (Assume that the variable n represents an even integer.)

24, 26, 28
$-10, -8, -6$
$n, n + 2, n + 4$

TAKE NOTE

Both consecutive even and consecutive odd integers are represented using $n, n + 2, n + 4, \ldots$.

Examples of **consecutive odd integers** are shown at the right. (Assume that the variable n represents an odd integer.)

19, 21, 23
$-1, 1, 3$
$n, n + 2, n + 4$

➡ The sum of three consecutive odd integers is forty-five. Find the integers.

Strategy

- First odd integer: n
  Second odd integer: $n + 2$
  Third odd integer: $n + 4$
- The sum of the three odd integers is 45.

• Represent three consecutive
  odd integers.

Solution

$$n + (n + 2) + (n + 4) = 45$$ • Write an equation.

$$3n + 6 = 45$$ • Solve the equation.

$$3n = 39$$

$$n = 13$$ • The first odd integer is 13.

$$n + 2 = 13 + 2 = 15$$ • Find the second odd integer.

$$n + 4 = 13 + 4 = 17$$ • Find the third odd integer.

The three consecutive odd integers are 13, 15, and 17.

Example 1

The sum of two numbers is sixteen. The difference between four times the smaller number and two is two more than twice the larger number. Find the two numbers.

Solution

The smaller number: n
The larger number: $16 - n$

The difference between four times the smaller and two	is	two more than twice the larger

$$4n - 2 = 2(16 - n) + 2$$
$$4n - 2 = 32 - 2n + 2$$
$$4n - 2 = 34 - 2n$$
$$4n + 2n - 2 = 34 - 2n + 2n$$
$$6n - 2 = 34$$
$$6n - 2 + 2 = 34 + 2$$
$$6n = 36$$
$$\frac{6n}{6} = \frac{36}{6}$$
$$n = 6 \qquad 16 - n = 16 - 6 = 10$$

The smaller number is 6.
The larger number is 10.

You Try It 1

The sum of two numbers is twelve. The total of three times the smaller number and six amounts to seven less than the product of four and the larger number. Find the two numbers.

Your solution

Solution on p. S6

Example 2

Find three consecutive even integers such that three times the second equals four more than the sum of the first and third.

Strategy

• First even integer: n
Second even integer: $n + 2$
Third even integer: $n + 4$
• Three times the second equals four more than the sum of the first and third.

Solution

$$3(n + 2) = n + (n + 4) + 4$$
$$3n + 6 = 2n + 8$$
$$3n - 2n + 6 = 2n - 2n + 8$$
$$n + 6 = 8$$
$$n = 2$$
$$n + 2 = 2 + 2 = 4$$
$$n + 4 = 2 + 4 = 6$$

The three integers are 2, 4, and 6.

You Try It 2

Find three consecutive integers whose sum is negative six.

Your strategy

Your solution

Solution on p. S6

Objective B   ***To translate a sentence into an equation and solve*** ⋯⋯⋯⋯⋯⋯⋯⋯⋯⋯⋯⋯⋯

Example 3

A wallpaper hanger charges a fee of $25 plus $12 for each roll of wallpaper used in a room. If the total charge for hanging wallpaper is $97, how many rolls of wallpaper were used?

Strategy

To find the number of rolls of wallpaper used, write and solve an equation using n to represent the number of rolls of wallpaper used.

Solution

| $25 plus $12 for each roll of wallpaper | is | $97 |

$$25 + 12n = 97$$
$$12n = 72$$
$$\frac{12n}{12} = \frac{72}{12}$$
$$n = 6$$

6 rolls of wallpaper were used.

You Try It 3

The fee charged by a ticketing agency for a concert is $3.50 plus $17.50 for each ticket purchased. If your total charge for tickets is $161, how many tickets are you purchasing?

Your strategy

Your solution

Solution on p. S6

Example 4

A board 20 ft long is cut into two pieces. Five times the length of the shorter piece is 2 ft more than twice the length of the longer piece. Find the length of each piece.

Strategy

Let x represent the length of the shorter piece. Then $20 - x$ represents the length of the longer piece.

Make a drawing.

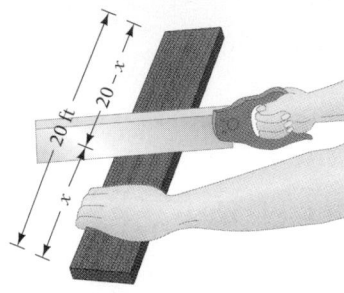

To find the lengths, write and solve an equation using x to represent the length of the shorter piece and $20 - x$ to represent the length of the longer piece.

Solution

Five times the shorter piece	is	2 ft more than twice the longer

$$5x = 2(20 - x) + 2$$
$$5x = 40 - 2x + 2$$
$$5x = 42 - 2x$$
$$5x + 2x = 42 - 2x + 2x$$
$$7x = 42$$
$$\frac{7x}{7} = \frac{42}{7}$$
$$x = 6$$

$20 - x = 20 - 6 = 14$

The shorter piece is 6 ft.
The longer piece is 14 ft.

You Try It 4

A wire 22 in. long is cut into two pieces. The longer piece is 4 in. more than twice the shorter piece. Find the length of each piece.

Your strategy

Your solution

Solution on p. S6

3.4 Exercises

Objective A

In Exercises 1 to 19, translate into an equation and solve.

1. The difference between a number and fifteen is seven. Find the number.

2. The sum of five and a number is three. Find the number.

3. The product of seven and a number is negative twenty-one. Find the number.

4. The quotient of a number and four is two. Find the number.

5. The difference between nine and a number is seven. Find the number.

6. Three-fifths of a number is negative thirty. Find the number.

7. The difference between five and twice a number is one. Find the number.

8. Four more than three times a number is thirteen. Find the number.

9. The sum of twice a number and five is fifteen. Find the number.

10. The difference between nine times a number and six is twelve. Find the number.

11. Six less than four times a number is twenty-two. Find the number.

12. Four times the sum of twice a number and three is twelve. Find the number.

13. Three times the difference between four times a number and seven is fifteen. Find the number.

14. Twelve is six times the difference between a number and three. Find the number.

15. Twice the difference between a number and twenty-five is three times the number. Find the number.

16. The sum of two numbers is twenty. Three times the smaller is equal to two times the larger. Find the two numbers.

17. The sum of two numbers is fifteen. One less than three times the smaller is equal to the larger. Find the two numbers.

18. The sum of two numbers is fourteen. The difference between two times the smaller and the larger is one. Find the two numbers.

19. The sum of two numbers is eighteen. The total of three times the smaller and twice the larger is forty-four. Find the two numbers.

20. The sum of three consecutive odd integers is fifty-one. Find the integers.

21. Find three consecutive even integers whose sum is negative eighteen.

22. Find three consecutive odd integers such that three times the middle integer is one more than the sum of the first and third.

23. Twice the smallest of three consecutive odd integers is seven more than the largest. Find the integers.

24. Find two consecutive even integers such that three times the first equals twice the second.

25. Find two consecutive even integers such that four times the first is three times the second.

26. Seven times the first of two consecutive odd integers is five times the second. Find the integers.

27. Find three consecutive even integers such that three times the middle integer is four more than the sum of the first and third.

Objective B   *Application Problems*

Write an equation and solve.

28. The processor speed of a personal computer is 80 megahertz (mHz). This is one-third of the processor speed of a newer model personal computer. Find the processor speed of the newer personal computer.

29. The storage capacity of a hard-disk drive is 0.5 gigabyte. This is one-fourth of the storage capacity of a second hard-disk drive. Find the storage capacity of the second hard-disk drive.

30. A union charges monthly dues of $4.00 plus $.15 for each hour worked during the month. A union member's dues for March were $29.20. How many hours did the union member work during the month of March?

31. A technical information hotline charges a customer $9.00 plus $.50 per minute to answer questions about software. How many minutes did a customer who received a bill for $14.50 use this service?

32. The total cost to paint the inside of a house was $1346. This cost included $125 for materials and $33 per hour for labor. How many hours of labor were required to paint the inside of the house?

33. The cellular phone service for a business executive is $35 per month plus $.40 per minute of phone use. In a month when the executive's cellular phone bill was $99.80, how many minutes did the executive use the phone?

34. A computer screen consists of tiny dots of light called pixels. In a certain graphics mode, there are 640 horizontal pixels. This is 40 more than 3 times the number of vertical pixels. Find the number of vertical pixels.

35. The cost of electricity in a certain city is $.08 for each of the first 300 kWh (kilowatt-hours) and $.13 for each kilowatt-hour over 300 kWh. Find the number of kilowatt-hours used by a family with a $51.95 electric bill.

36. A 12-foot board is cut into two pieces. Twice the length of the shorter piece is 3 ft less than the longer piece. Find the length of each piece.

37. A 14-yard fishing line is cut into two pieces. Three times the length of the longer piece is four times the length of the shorter piece. Find the length of each piece.

38. Seven thousand dollars is divided into two scholarships. Twice the amount of the smaller scholarship is $1000 less than the larger scholarship. What is the amount of the larger scholarship?

39. An investment of $10,000 is divided into two accounts, one for stocks and one for mutual funds. The value of the stock account is $2000 less than twice the value of the mutual fund account. Find the amount in each account.

APPLYING THE CONCEPTS

40. Make up a word problem that has either the solution of the equation $6x = 124$ or the solution of the equation $8x + 120 = 300$ as the answer to a problem.

41. A formula is an equation that relates variables in a known way. Find two examples of formulas that are used in your college major. Explain what each of the variables represents.

An equation that is never true is called a **contradiction.** For example, $x = x + 1$ is a contradiction; there is no value of x that will make the equation true. An equation that is true for all real numbers is called an **identity.** The equation $x + x = 2x$ is an identity; this equation is true for any real number. A **conditional equation** is one that is true for some real numbers and false for some real numbers. The equation $2x = 4$ is a conditional equation; this equation is true when x is 2 and false for any other real number. Determine whether each equation below is a contradiction, an identity, or a conditional equation. If it is a conditional equation, find the solution.

42. $6x + 2 = 5 + 3(2x - 1)$

43. $3 - 2(4x + 1) = 5 + 8(1 - x)$

44. $3t - 5(t + 1) = 2(2 - t) - 9$

45. $6 + 4(2y + 1) = 5 - 8y$

46. $3v - 2 = 5v - 2(2 + v)$

47. $9z = 15z$

48. It is always important to check the answer to an application problem to be sure the answer makes sense. Consider the following problem. A 4-quart mixture of fruit juices is made from apple juice and cranberry juice. There are 6 more quarts of apple juice than of cranberry juice. Write and solve an equation for the number of quarts of each juice used. Does the answer to this question make sense? Explain.

3.5 Geometry Problems

Objective A   *To solve perimeter problems* ··································

The **perimeter** of a plane geometric figure is a measure of the distance around the figure. Perimeter is used in buying fencing for a lawn or determining how much baseboard is needed for a room.

The perimeter of a triangle is the sum of the lengths of the three sides. Therefore, if a, b, and c represent the lengths of the sides of a triangle, the perimeter, P, of the triangle is given by $P = a + b + c$.

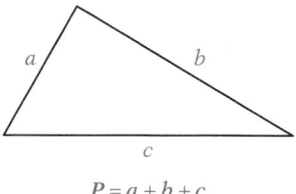

$P = a + b + c$

Two special types of triangles are shown below. An **isosceles triangle** has two sides of equal length. The three sides of an **equilateral triangle** are of equal length.

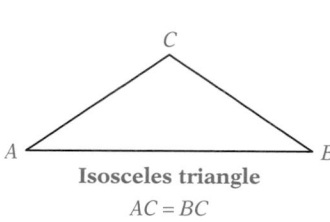

Isosceles triangle
$AC = BC$

Equilateral triangle
$AB = AC = BC$

The perimeter of a rectangle is the sum of the lengths of the four sides. Let L represent the length and W represent the width of a rectangle. Then the perimeter, P, of the rectangle is given by $P = L + W + L + W$. After combining like terms, the formula is $P = 2L + 2W$.

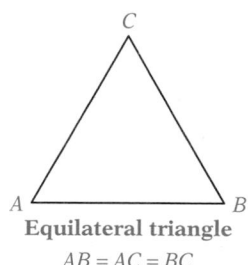

$P = 2L + 2W$

A square is a rectangle in which each side has the same length. Let s represent the length of each side of a square. Then the perimeter, P, of the square is given by $P = s + s + s + s$. After combining like terms, the formula is $P = 4s$.

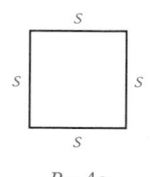

$P = 4s$

Formulas for Perimeters of Geometric Figures

Perimeter of a triangle	$P = a + b + c$
Perimeter of a rectangle	$P = 2L + 2W$
Perimeter of a square	$P = 4s$

➡ The perimeter of a rectangle is 26 ft. The length of the rectangle is 1 ft more than twice the width. Find the width and length of the rectangle.

Strategy

2W + 1

W

- Width: W
  Length: $2W + 1$
- Use the formula for the perimeter of a rectangle.

- Let a variable represent the width.
- Represent the length in terms of that variable.

Solution

$$P = 2L + 2W$$

$$26 = 2(2W + 1) + 2W$$

$$26 = 4W + 2 + 2W$$

$$26 = 6W + 2$$

$$24 = 6W$$

$$4 = W$$

$$L = 2W + 1$$
$$= 2(4) + 1 = 8 + 1 = 9$$

- $P = 26$. Substitute $2W + 1$ for L.
- Use the Distributive Property.
- Combine like terms.
- Subtract 2 from each side of the equation.
- Divide each side of the equation by 6.
- Find the length of the rectangle by substituting 4 for W in $2W + 1$.

The width is 4 ft. The length is 9 ft.

Example 1
The perimeter of an isosceles triangle is 25 ft. The third side of the triangle is 2 ft less than the length of one of the equal sides. Find the measures of each of the three sides of the triangle.

Strategy
- Each equal side: x
  The third side: $x - 2$
- Use the equation for the perimeter of a triangle.

Solution
$$P = a + b + c$$
$$25 = x + x + (x - 2)$$
$$25 = 3x - 2$$
$$27 = 3x$$
$$9 = x$$

$$x - 2 = 9 - 2 = 7$$

Each of the equal sides measures 9 ft.
The third side measures 7 ft.

You Try It 1
A carpenter is designing a square patio with a perimeter of 52 ft. What is the length of each side?

Your strategy

Your solution

Solution on p. S7

Objective B   ***To solve problems involving angles formed by intersecting lines*** ....

A unit used to measure angles is the **degree.** The symbol for degree is °. ∠ is the symbol for angle.

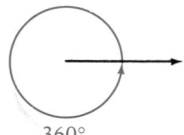

360°

One complete revolution is 360°. It is probable that the Babylonians chose 360° for a circle because they knew that there were 365 days in one year, and 360 is the closest number to 365 that is divisible by many numbers.

A 90° angle is called a **right angle.** The symbol ∟ represents a right angle. Angle *C* (∠*C*) is a right angle.

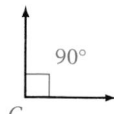

A 180° angle is called a **straight angle.** The angle at the right is a straight angle.

An **acute angle** is an angle whose measure is between 0° and 90°. ∠*A* at the right is an acute angle.

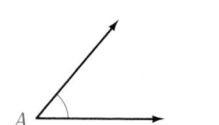

An **obtuse angle** is an angle whose measure is between 90° and 180°. ∠*B* at the right is an obtuse angle.

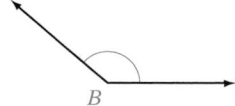

Complementary angles are two angles whose measures have the sum 90°.

∠*D* + ∠*E* = 70° + 20° = 90°

∠*D* and ∠*E* are complementary angles.

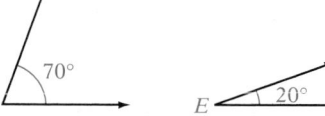

Supplementary angles are two angles whose measures have the sum 180°.

∠*F* + ∠*G* = 130° + 50° = 180°

∠*F* and ∠*G* are supplementary angles.

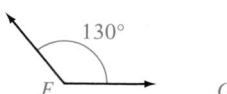 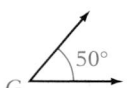

➡ Given the diagram at the left, find *x*.

Strategy

The sum of the measures of the three angles is 360°. To find *x*, write an equation and solve for *x*.

Solution

$$3x + 4x + 5x = 360°$$
$$12x = 360°$$
$$x = 30°$$

The measure of *x* is 30°.

Parallel lines never meet. The distance between them is always the same. The symbol ∥ means "is parallel to." In the figure at the right, $\ell_1 \parallel \ell_2$.

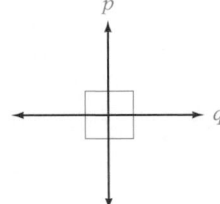

Perpendicular lines are intersecting lines that form right angles. The symbol ⊥ means "is perpendicular to." In the figure at the right, $p \perp q$.

Four angles are formed by the intersection of two lines. If the two lines are perpendicular, each of the four angles is a right angle. If the two lines are not perpendicular, then two of the angles formed are acute angles and two of the angles are obtuse angles. The two acute angles are always opposite each other, and the two obtuse angles are always opposite each other.

In the figure at the right, $\angle w$ and $\angle y$ are acute angles, and $\angle x$ and $\angle z$ are obtuse angles.

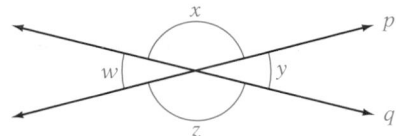

Two angles that are on opposite sides of the intersection of two lines are called **vertical angles.** Vertical angles have the same measure. $\angle w$ and $\angle y$ are vertical angles. $\angle x$ and $\angle z$ are vertical angles.

Vertical angles have the same measure.

$$\angle w = \angle y$$
$$\angle x = \angle z$$

Two angles that share a common side are called **adjacent angles.** For the figure shown above, $\angle x$ and $\angle y$ are adjacent angles, as are $\angle y$ and $\angle z$, $\angle z$ and $\angle w$, and $\angle w$ and $\angle x$. Adjacent angles of intersecting lines are supplementary angles.

Adjacent angles of intersecting lines are supplementary angles.

$$\angle x + \angle y = 180°$$
$$\angle y + \angle z = 180°$$
$$\angle z + \angle w = 180°$$
$$\angle w + \angle x = 180°$$

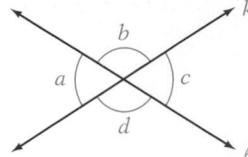

➡ In the diagram at the left, $\angle b = 115°$. Find the measures of angles a, c, and d.

$$\angle a + \angle b = 180°$$
$$\angle a + 115° = 180°$$
$$\angle a = 65°$$

• $\angle a$ is supplementary to $\angle b$ because $\angle a$ and $\angle b$ are adjacent angles of intersecting lines.

$$\angle c = 65°$$

• $\angle c = \angle a$ because $\angle c$ and $\angle a$ are vertical angles.

$$\angle d = 115°$$

• $\angle d = \angle b$ because $\angle d$ and $\angle b$ are vertical angles.

A line that intersects two other lines at different points is called a **transversal.** If the lines cut by a transversal t are parallel lines and the transversal is not perpendicular to the parallel lines, all four acute angles have the same measure and all four obtuse angles have the same measure. In the figure at the right,

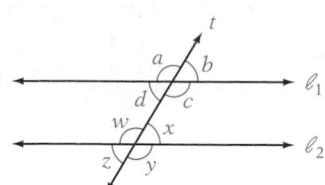

$$\angle b = \angle d = \angle x = \angle z$$
$$\angle a = \angle c = \angle w = \angle y$$

Alternate interior angles are two angles that are on opposite sides of the transversal and between the lines. In the figure above, $\angle c$ and $\angle w$ are alternate interior angles, and $\angle d$ and $\angle x$ are alternate interior angles. Alternate interior angles have the same measure.

Alternate interior angles have the same measure.

$$\angle c = \angle w$$
$$\angle d = \angle x$$

Alternate exterior angles are two angles that are on opposite sides of the transversal and outside the parallel lines. In the figure above, $\angle a$ and $\angle y$ are alternate exterior angles, and $\angle b$ and $\angle z$ are alternate exterior angles. Alternate exterior angles have the same measure.

Alternate exterior angles have the same measure.

$$\angle a = \angle y$$
$$\angle b = \angle z$$

Corresponding angles are two angles that are on the same side of the transversal and are both acute angles or are both obtuse angles. In the figure above, the following pairs of angles are corresponding angles: $\angle a$ and $\angle w$, $\angle d$ and $\angle z$, $\angle b$ and $\angle x$, and $\angle c$ and $\angle y$. Corresponding angles have the same measure.

Corresponding angles have the same measure.

$$\angle a = \angle w$$
$$\angle d = \angle z$$
$$\angle b = \angle x$$
$$\angle c = \angle y$$

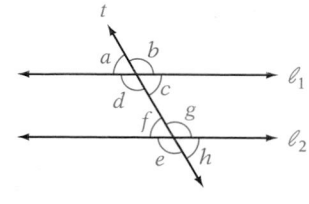

➡ In the diagram at the left, $\ell_1 \parallel \ell_2$ and $\angle f = 58°$. Find the measures of $\angle a$, $\angle c$, and $\angle d$.

$\angle a = \angle f = 58°$ • $\angle a$ and $\angle f$ are corresponding angles.

$\angle c = \angle f = 58°$ • $\angle c$ and $\angle f$ are alternate interior angles.

$\angle d + \angle a = 180°$ • $\angle d$ is supplementary to $\angle a$.
$\angle d + 58° = 180°$
$\angle d = 122°$

Example 2
Find the complement of a 39° angle.

Strategy
To find the complement, let x represent the complement of a 39° angle. Use the fact that complementary angles are two angles whose sum is 90° to write an equation. Solve for x.

Solution
$x + 39° = 90°$
$x = 51°$

The complement of a 39° angle is a 51° angle.

You Try It 2
Find the supplement of a 107° angle.

Your strategy

Your solution

Example 3
Find x.

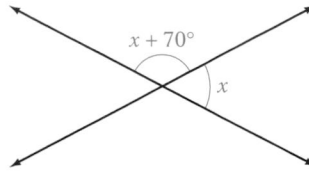

Strategy
The angles labeled are adjacent angles of intersecting lines and are, therefore, supplementary angles. To find x, write an equation and solve for x.

Solution
$x + (x + 70°) = 180°$
$2x + 70° = 180°$
$2x = 110°$
$x = 55°$

You Try It 3
Find x.

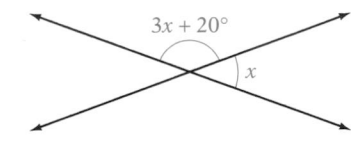

Your strategy

Your solution

Example 4
Given $\ell_1 \parallel \ell_2$, find x.

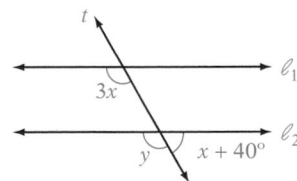

Strategy
$3x = y$ because corresponding angles have the same measure. $y + (x + 40°) = 180°$ because adjacent angles of intersecting lines are supplementary angles. Substitute $3x$ for y and solve for x.

Solution
$3x + (x + 40°) = 180°$
$4x + 40° = 180°$
$4x = 140°$
$x = 35°$

You Try It 4
Given $\ell_1 \parallel \ell_2$, find x.

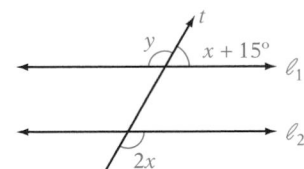

Your strategy

Your solution

Solutions on p. S7

Objective C **To solve problems involving the angles of a triangle** ....

If the lines cut by a transversal are not parallel lines, the three lines will intersect at three points. In the figure at the right, the transversal *t* intersects lines *p* and *q*. The three lines intersect at points *A*, *B*, and *C*. The geometric figure formed by *AB*, *BC*, and *AC* is a **triangle.**

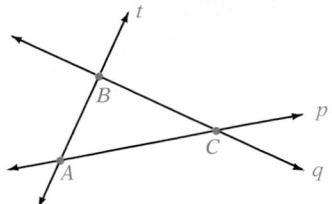

The angles within the region enclosed by the triangle are called **interior angles.** In the figure at the right, angles *a*, *b*, and *c* are interior angles. The sum of the measures of the interior angles is 180°.

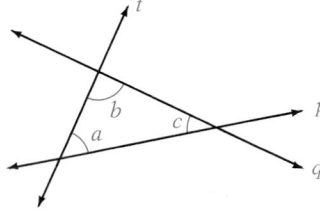

$$\angle a + \angle b + \angle c = 180°$$

> **The Sum of the Measures of the Interior Angles of a Triangle**
>
> The sum of the measures of the interior angles of a triangle is 180°.

An angle adjacent to an interior angle is an **exterior angle.** In the figure at the right, angles *m* and *n* are exterior angles for angle *a*. The sum of the measures of an interior and an exterior angle is 180°.

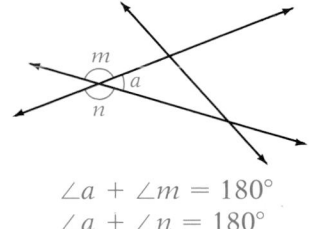

$$\angle a + \angle m = 180°$$
$$\angle a + \angle n = 180°$$

➡ Given that $\angle c = 40°$ and $\angle e = 60°$, find the measure of $\angle d$.

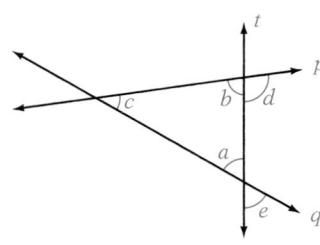

$\angle a = \angle e = 60°$ • $\angle a$ and $\angle e$ are vertical angles.

$\angle c + \angle a + \angle b = 180°$ • The sum of the interior angles is 180°.
$40° + 60° + \angle b = 180°$
$100° + \angle b = 180°$
$\angle b = 80°$

$\angle b + \angle d = 180°$ • $\angle b$ and $\angle d$ are supplementary angles.
$80° + \angle d = 180°$
$\angle d = 100°$

Example 5

Given that $\angle a = 45°$ and $\angle x = 100°$, find the measures of angles b, c, and y.

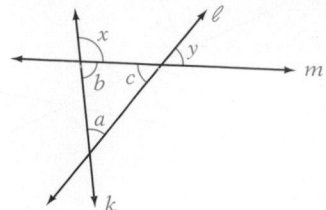

Strategy

- To find the measure of $\angle b$, use the fact that $\angle b$ and $\angle x$ are supplementary angles.
- To find the measure of $\angle c$, use the fact that the sum of the measures of the interior angles of a triangle is 180°.
- To find the measure of $\angle y$, use the fact that $\angle c$ and $\angle y$ are vertical angles.

Solution

$$\angle b + \angle x = 180°$$
$$\angle b + 100° = 180°$$
$$\angle b = 80°$$

$$\angle a + \angle b + \angle c = 180°$$
$$45° + 80° + \angle c = 180°$$
$$125° + \angle c = 180°$$
$$\angle c = 55°$$

$$\angle y = \angle c = 55°$$

Example 6

Two angles of a triangle measure 43° and 86°. Find the measure of the third angle.

Strategy

To find the measure of the third angle, use the fact that the sum of the measures of the interior angles of a triangle is 180°. Write an equation using x to represent the measure of the third angle. Solve the equation for x.

Solution

$$x + 43° + 86° = 180°$$
$$x + 129° = 180°$$
$$x = 51°$$

The measure of the third angle is 51°.

You Try It 5

Given that $\angle y = 55°$, find the measures of angles a, b, and d.

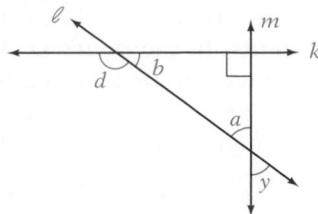

Your strategy

Your solution

You Try It 6

One angle in a triangle is a right angle, and one angle measures 27°. Find the measure of the third angle.

Your strategy

Your solution

Solutions on p. S7

3.5 Exercises

Objective A

1. In an isosceles triangle, the third side is 50% of the length of one of the equal sides. Find the length of each side when the perimeter is 125 ft.

2. In an isosceles triangle, the length of one of the equal sides is 3 times the length of the third side. The perimeter is 21 m. Find the length of each side.

3. The perimeter of a rectangle is 42 m. The length of the rectangle is 3 m less than twice the width. Find the length and width of the rectangle.

4. The width of a rectangle is 25% of the length. The perimeter is 250 cm. Find the length and width of the rectangle.

5. The perimeter of a rectangle is 120 ft. The length of the rectangle is twice the width. Find the length and width of the rectangle.

6. The perimeter of a rectangle is 50 m. The width of the rectangle is 5 m less than the length. Find the length and width of the rectangle.

7. The perimeter of a triangle is 110 cm. One side is twice the second side. The third side is 30 cm more than the second side. Find the length of each side.

8. The perimeter of a triangle is 33 ft. One side of the triangle is 1 ft longer than the second side. The third side is 2 ft longer than the second side. Find the length of each side.

9. The width of the rectangular foundation of a building is 30% of the length. The perimeter of the foundation is 338 ft. Find the length and width of the foundation.

10. The perimeter of a rectangular playground is 440 ft. If the width is 100 ft, what is the length of the playground?

11. A rectangular vegetable garden has a perimeter of 64 ft. The length of the garden is 20 ft. What is the width of the garden?

12. Each of two sides of a triangular banner measures 18 in. If the perimeter of the banner is 46 in., what is the length of the third side of the banner?

13. The perimeter of a square picture frame is 48 in. Find the length of each side of the frame.

14. A square rug has a perimeter of 32 ft. Find the length of each side of the rug.

Objective B

15. Find the complement of a 28° angle.

16. Find the complement of a 46° angle.

17. Find the supplement of a 73° angle.

18. Find the supplement of a 119° angle.

Find the measure of $\angle x$.

19. 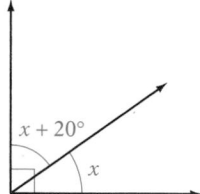   **20.** 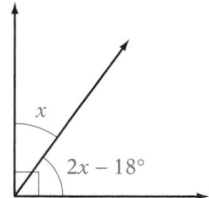   **21.**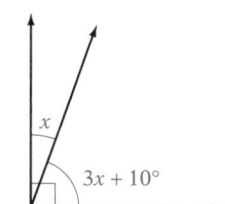

Find the measure of $\angle a$.

22. 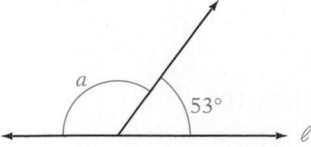   **23.**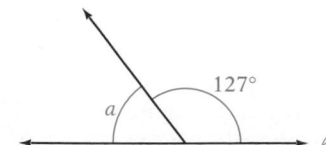

Find the measure of ∠*a*.

24.

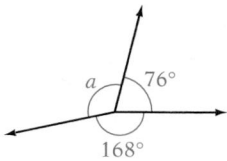

25.

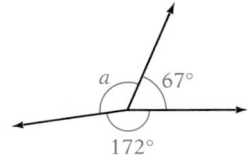

Find *x*.

26.

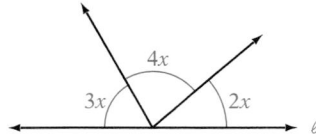

27.

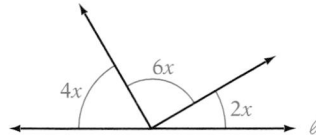

28.

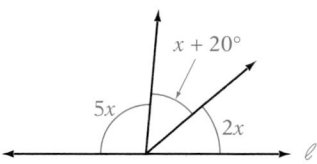

29.

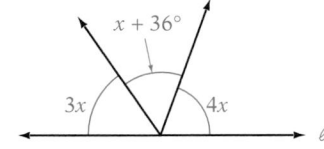

30.

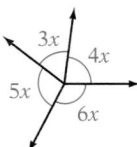

31.

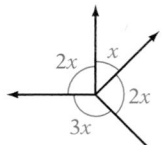

Find the measure of ∠*x*.

32.

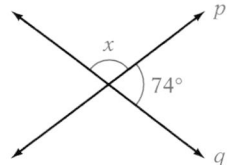

33.

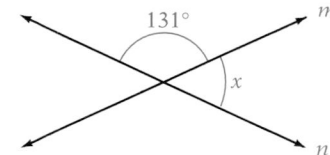

Find *x*.

34.

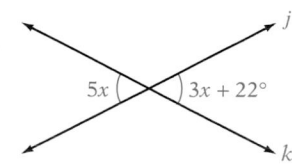

35.

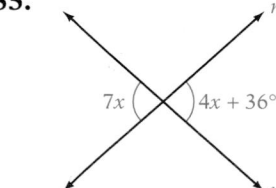

Given that $\ell_1 \parallel \ell_2$, find the measures of angles a and b.

36.

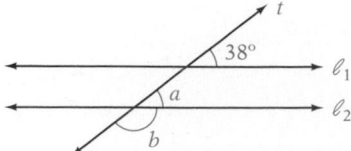

37.

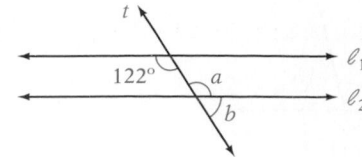

38.

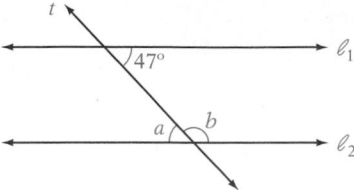

39.

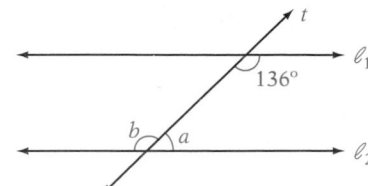

Given that $\ell_1 \parallel \ell_2$, find x.

40.

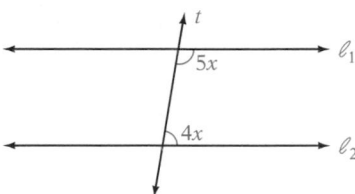

41.

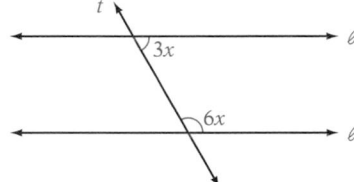

42.

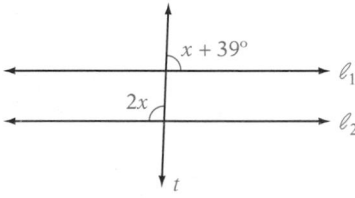

43.

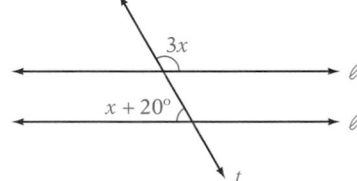

44. Given that $\angle a = 51°$, find the measure of $\angle b$.

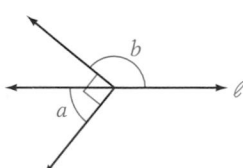

45. Given that $\angle a = 38°$, find the measure of $\angle b$.

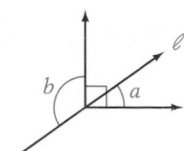

Objective C

46. Given that $\angle a = 95°$ and $\angle b = 70°$, find the measures of angles x and y.

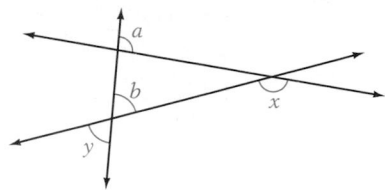

47. Given that $\angle a = 35°$ and $\angle b = 55°$, find the measures of angles x and y.

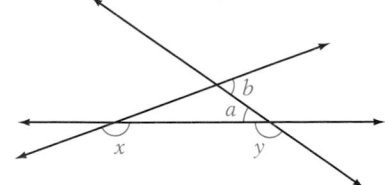

48. Given that $\angle y = 45°$, find the measures of angles a and b.

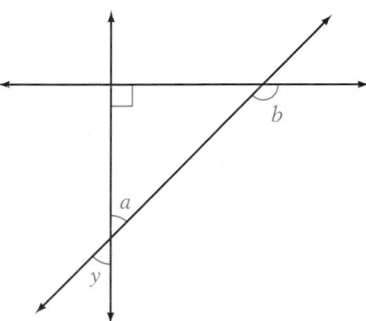

49. Given that $\angle y = 130°$, find the measures of angles a and b.

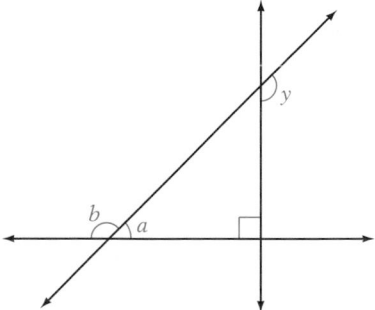

50. Given that $AO \perp OB$, express in terms of x the number of degrees in $\angle BOC$.

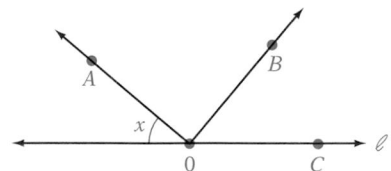

51. Given that $AO \perp OB$, express in terms of x the number of degrees in $\angle AOC$.

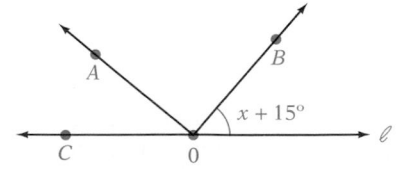

52. One angle in a triangle is a right angle, and one angle measures 30°. What is the measure of the third angle?

53. A triangle has a 45° angle and a right angle. Find the measure of the third angle.

54. Two angles of a triangle measure 42° and 103°. Find the measure of the third angle.

55. Two angles of a triangle measure 62° and 45°. Find the measure of the third angle.

56. A triangle has a 13° angle and a 65° angle. What is the measure of the third angle?

57. A triangle has a 105° angle and a 32° angle. What is the measure of the third angle?

APPLYING THE CONCEPTS

58. A rectangle and an equilateral triangle have the same perimeter. The length of the rectangle is three times the width. Each side of the triangle is 8 cm. Find the length and width of the rectangle.

59. The length of a rectangle is 1 cm more than twice the width. If the length of the rectangle is decreased by 2 cm and the width is decreased by 1 cm, the perimeter is 20 cm. Find the length and width of the original rectangle.

60. For the figure at the right, find the sum of the measures of angles x, y, and z.

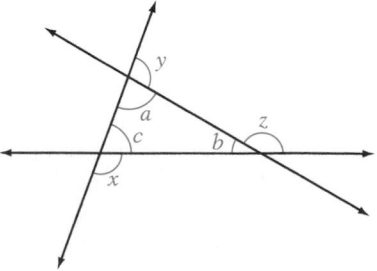

61. For the figure at the right, explain why $\angle a + \angle b = \angle x$. Write a rule that describes the relationship between an exterior angle of a triangle and the opposite interior angles. Use the rule to write an equation involving angles a, c, and z.

62. The length of a rectangle is $14x$. The perimeter is $50x$. Find the width of the rectangle in terms of the variable x.

3.6 Mixture and Uniform Motion Problems

Objective A   *To solve value mixture problems* ....

A value mixture problem involves combining two ingredients that have different prices into a single blend. For example, a coffee merchant may blend two types of coffee into a single blend, or a candy manufacturer may combine two types of candy to sell as a variety pack.

The solution of a value mixture problem is based on the equation $AC = V$, where A is the amount of an ingredient, C is the cost per unit of the ingredient, and V is the value of the ingredient.

TAKE NOTE

The equation $AC = V$ is used to find the value of an ingredient. For example, the value of 4 lb of cashews costing $6 per pound is
$$AC = V$$
$$4 \cdot 6 = V$$
$$\$24 = V$$

➡ A coffee merchant wants to make 6 lb of a blend of coffee costing $5 per pound. The blend is made using a $6-per-pound grade and a $3-per-pound grade of coffee. How many pounds of each of these grades should be used?

> **Strategy for Solving a Value Mixture Problem**
>
> 1. For each ingredient in the mixture, write a numerical or variable expression for the amount of the ingredient used, the unit cost of the ingredient, and the value of the amount used. For the blend, write a numerical or variable expression for the amount, the unit cost of the blend, and the value of the amount. The results can be recorded in a table.

The sum of the amounts is 6 lb.   Amount of $6 coffee: x
                                         Amount of $3 coffee: $6 - x$

TAKE NOTE

Use the information given in the problem to fill in the amount and unit cost columns of the table. Fill in the value column by multiplying the two expressions you wrote in each row. Use the expressions in the last column to write the equation.

	Amount, A	·	Unit Cost, C	=	Value, V
$6 grade	x	·	$6	=	$6x$
$3 grade	$6 - x$	·	$3	=	$3(6 - x)$
$5 blend	6	·	$5	=	$5(6)$

> 2. Determine how the values of each ingredient are related. Use the fact that the sum of the values of all the ingredients is equal to the value of the blend.

The sum of the values of the $6 grade and the $3 grade is equal to the value of the $5 blend.

$$6x + 3(6 - x) = 5(6)$$
$$6x + 18 - 3x = 30$$
$$3x + 18 = 30$$
$$3x = 12$$
$$x = 4$$

$$6 - x = 6 - 4 = 2$$

The merchant must use 4 lb of the $6 coffee and 2 lb of the $3 coffee.

Example 1

How many ounces of a silver alloy that costs $4 an ounce must be mixed with 10 oz of an alloy that costs $6 an ounce to make a mixture that costs $4.32 an ounce?

You Try It 1

A gardener has 20 lb of a lawn fertilizer that costs $.80 per pound. How many pounds of a fertilizer that costs $.55 per pound should be mixed with this 20 lb of lawn fertilizer to produce a mixture that costs $.75 per pound?

Strategy

Your strategy

- Ounces of $4 alloy: x

	Amount	Cost	Value
$4 alloy	x	$4	$4x$
$6 alloy	10	$6	6(10)
$4.32 mixture	$10 + x$	$4.32	$4.32(10 + x)$

- The sum of the values before mixing equals the value after mixing.

Solution

$$4x + 6(10) = 4.32(10 + x)$$

$$4x + 60 = 43.2 + 4.32x$$

$$-0.32x + 60 = 43.2$$

$$-0.32x = -16.8$$

$$x = 52.5$$

52.5 oz of the $4 silver alloy must be used.

Your solution

Solution on p. S7

Objective B   To solve percent mixture problems ....

The amount of a substance in a solution can be given as a percent of the total solution. For example, a 5% salt water solution means that 5% of the total solution is salt. The remaining 95% is water.

Solving a percent mixture problem can be done using the equation $Ar = Q$, where A is the amount of a solution, r is the percent concentration of a substance in the solution, and Q is the quantity of the substance in the solution.

For example, a 500-milliliter bottle is filled with a 4% solution of hydrogen peroxide.

$$Ar = Q$$
$$500(0.04) = Q$$
$$20 = Q$$

The bottle contains 20 ml of hydrogen peroxide.

➡ How many gallons of a 20% salt solution must be mixed with 6 gal of a 30% salt solution to make a 22% salt solution?

> **Strategy for Solving a Percent Mixture Problem**
>
> 1. For each solution, write a numerical or variable expression for the amount of solution, the percent concentration, and the quantity of the substance in the solution. The results can be recorded in a table.

The unknown quantity of 20% solution: x

	Amount of Solution, A	·	Percent Concentration, r	=	Quantity of Substance, Q
20% solution	x	·	0.20	=	$0.20x$
30% solution	6	·	0.30	=	$0.30(6)$
22% solution	$x + 6$	·	0.22	=	$0.22(x + 6)$

> 2. Determine how the quantities of the substances in each solution are related. Use the fact that the sum of the quantities of the substances being mixed is equal to the quantity of the substance after mixing.

The sum of the quantities of the substances in the 20% solution and the 30% solution is equal to the quantity of the substance in the 22% solution.

$$0.20x + 0.30(6) = 0.22(x + 6)$$
$$0.20x + 1.80 = 0.22x + 1.32$$
$$-0.02x + 1.80 = 1.32$$
$$-0.02x = -0.48$$
$$x = 24$$

24 gal of the 20% solution are required.

Example 2

A chemist wishes to make 2 L of an 8% acid solution by mixing a 10% acid solution and a 5% acid solution. How many liters of each solution should the chemist use?

Strategy

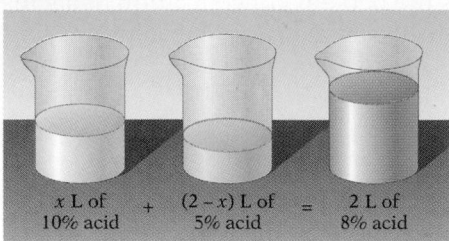

x L of 10% acid + $(2 - x)$ L of 5% acid = 2 L of 8% acid

● Liters of 10% solution: x
Liters of 5% solution: $2 - x$

	Amount	Percent	Quantity
10% solution	x	0.10	$0.10x$
5% solution	$2 - x$	0.05	$0.05(2 - x)$
8% solution	2	0.08	$0.08(2)$

● The sum of the quantities before mixing is equal to the quantity after mixing.

Solution

$$0.10x + 0.05(2 - x) = 0.08(2)$$

$$0.10x + 0.10 - 0.05x = 0.16$$

$$0.05x + 0.10 = 0.16$$

$$0.05x = 0.06$$

$$x = 1.2$$

$$2 - x = 2 - 1.2 = 0.8$$

The chemist needs 1.2 L of the 10% solution and 0.8 L of the 5% solution.

You Try It 2

A pharmacist dilutes 5 L of a 12% solution with a 6% solution. How many liters of the 6% solution are added to make an 8% solution?

Your strategy

Your solution

Solution on p. S8

Objective C   **To solve uniform motion problems** ....

A train that travels constantly in a straight line at 50 mph is in *uniform motion.* **Uniform motion** means that the speed or direction of an object does not change.

The solution of a uniform motion problem is based on the equation $rt = d$, where r is the rate of travel, t is the time spent traveling, and d is the distance traveled.

For example, a car travels 50 mph for 3 h.

$$rt = d$$
$$50 \cdot 3 = d$$
$$150 = d$$

The car travels a distance of 150 mph.

➡ A car leaves a town traveling at 40 mph. Two hours later, a second car leaves the same town, on the same road, traveling at 60 mph. In how many hours will the second car pass the first car?

> **Strategy for Solving a Uniform Motion Problem**
>
> 1. For each object, write a numerical or variable expression for the distance, rate, and time. The results can be recorded in a table.

The first car traveled 2 h longer than the second car.

Unknown time for the second car: t
Time for the first car: $t + 2$

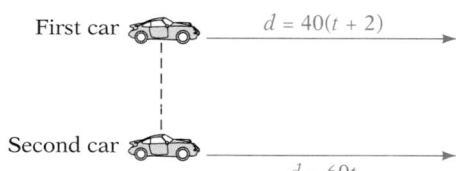

TAKE NOTE

Use the information given in the problem to fill in the rate and time columns of the table. Find the distance column by multiplying the two expressions you wrote in each row.

	Rate, r	·	Time, t	=	Distance, d
First car	40	·	$t + 2$	=	$40(t + 2)$
Second car	60	·	t	=	$60t$

> 2. Determine how the distances traveled by each object are related. For example, the total distance traveled by both objects may be known, or it may be known that the two objects traveled the same distance.

The two cars travel the same distance.

$$40(t + 2) = 60t$$
$$40t + 80 = 60t$$
$$80 = 20t$$
$$4 = t$$

The second car will pass the first car in 4 h.

Example 3

Two cars, one traveling 10 mph faster than the other car, start at the same time from the same point and travel in opposite directions. In 3 h they are 300 mi apart. Find the rate of each car.

Strategy

- Rate of 1st car: r
  Rate of 2nd car: $r + 10$

	Rate	Time	Distance
1st car	r	3	$3r$
2nd car	$r + 10$	3	$3(r + 10)$

- The total distance traveled by the two cars is 300 mi.

Solution

$$3r + 3(r + 10) = 300$$
$$3r + 3r + 30 = 300$$
$$6r + 30 = 300$$
$$6r = 270$$
$$r = 45$$

$$r + 10 = 45 + 10 = 55$$

The first car is traveling 45 mph.
The second car is traveling 55 mph.

You Try It 3

Two trains, one traveling at twice the speed of the other, start at the same time on parallel tracks from stations that are 288 mi apart and travel toward each other. In 3 h, the trains pass each other. Find the rate of each train.

Your strategy

Your solution

Example 4

How far can the members of a bicycling club ride out into the country at a speed of 12 mph and return over the same road at 8 mph if they travel a total of 10 h?

Strategy

- Time spent riding out: t
  Time spent riding back: $10 - t$

	Rate	Time	Distance
Out	12	t	$12t$
Back	8	$10 - t$	$8(10 - t)$

- The distance out equals the distance back.

Solution

$$12t = 8(10 - t)$$
$$12t = 80 - 8t$$
$$20t = 80$$
$$t = 4 \quad \text{(The time is 4 h.)}$$

The distance out $= 12t = 12(4) = 48$ mi.
The club can ride 48 mi into the country.

You Try It 4

A pilot flew out to a parcel of land and back in 5 h. The rate out was 150 mph and the rate returning was 100 mph. How far away was the parcel of land?

Your strategy

Your solution

Solutions on p. S8

3.6 Exercises

· ·

Objective A   *Application Problems*

1. An herbalist has 30 oz of herbs costing $2 per ounce. How many ounces of herbs costing $1 per ounce should be mixed with the 30 oz to produce a mixture costing $1.60 per ounce?

2. The manager of a farmer's market has 500 lb of grain that costs $1.20 per pound. How many pounds of meal costing $.80 per pound should be mixed with the 500 lb of grain to produce a mixture that costs $1.05 per pound?

3. Find the cost per pound of a meatloaf mixture made from 3 lb of ground beef costing $1.99 per pound and 1 lb of ground turkey costing $1.39 per pound.

4. Find the cost per ounce of a sunscreen made from 100 oz of a lotion that costs $2.50 per ounce and 50 oz of a lotion that costs $4.00 per ounce.

5. A snack food is made by mixing 5 lb of popcorn that costs $.80 per pound with caramel that costs $2.40 per pound. How much caramel is needed to make a mixture that costs $1.40 per pound?

6. A wild birdseed mix is made by combining 100 lb of millet seed costing $.60 per pound with sunflower seeds costing $1.10 per pound. How many pounds of sunflower seeds are needed to make a mixture that costs $.70 per pound?

7. Ten cups of a restaurant's house Italian dressing is made by blending olive oil costing $1.50 per cup with vinegar that costs $.25 per cup. How many cups of each are used if the cost of the blend is $.50 per cup?

8. A high-protein diet supplement that costs $6.75 per pound is mixed with a vitamin supplement that costs $3.25 per pound. How many pounds of each should be used to make 5 lb of a mixture that costs $4.65 per pound?

9. Find the cost per ounce of a mixture of 200 oz of a cologne that costs $5.50 per ounce and 500 oz of a cologne that costs $2.00 per ounce.

10. Find the cost per pound of a trail mix made from 40 lb of raisins that cost $4.40 per pound and 100 lb of granola that costs $2.30 per pound.

11. A 20 oz alloy of platinum that costs $220 per ounce is mixed with an alloy that costs $400 per ounce. How many ounces of the $400 alloy should be used to make an alloy that costs $300 per ounce?

12. How many liters of a blue dye that costs $1.60 per liter must be mixed with 18 L of anil that costs $2.50 per liter to make a mixture that costs $1.90 per liter?

13. The manager of a specialty food store combined almonds that cost $4.50 per pound with walnuts that cost $2.50 per pound. How many pounds of each were used to make a 100-pound mixture that costs $3.24 per pound?

14. A goldsmith combined an alloy that cost $4.30 per ounce with an alloy that cost $1.80 per ounce. How many ounces of each were used to make a mixture of 200 oz costing $2.50 per ounce?

15. Adult tickets for a play cost $6.00 and children's tickets cost $2.50. For one performance, 370 tickets were sold. Receipts for the performance were $1723. Find the number of adult tickets sold.

16. Tickets for a piano concert sold for $4.50 for each adult. Student tickets sold for $2.00 each. The total receipts for 1720 tickets were $5980. Find the number of adult tickets sold.

17. Find the cost per pound of sugar-coated breakfast cereal made from 40 lb of sugar that costs $1.00 per pound and 120 lb of corn flakes that cost $.60 per pound.

18. Find the cost per pound of a coffee mixture made from 8 lb of coffee that costs $9.20 per pound and 12 lb of coffee that costs $5.50 per pound.

Objective B   *Application Problems*

19. Forty ounces of a 30% gold alloy are mixed with 60 oz of a 20% gold alloy. Find the percent concentration of the resulting gold alloy.

20. One hundred ounces of juice that is 50% tomato juice are added to 200 oz of a vegetable juice that is 25% tomato juice. What is the percent concentration of tomato juice in the resulting mixture?

21. How many gallons of a 15% acid solution must be mixed with 5 gal of a 20% acid solution to make a 16% acid solution?

22. How many pounds of a chicken feed that is 50% corn must be mixed with 400 lb of a feed that is 80% corn to make a chicken feed that is 75% corn?

23. A rug is made by weaving 20 lb of yarn that is 50% wool with a yarn that is 25% wool. How many pounds of the yarn that is 25% wool is used if the finished rug is 35% wool?

24. Five gallons of a light green latex paint that is 20% yellow paint is combined with a darker green latex paint that is 40% yellow paint. How many gallons of the darker green paint must be used to create a green paint that is 25% yellow paint?

25. How many gallons of a plant food that is 9% nitrogen must be combined with another plant food that is 25% nitrogen to make 10 gal of a solution that is 15% nitrogen?

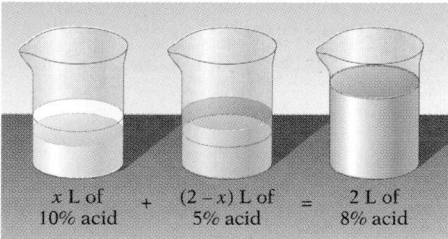

x L of   + $(2 - x)$ L of   =   2 L of
10% acid   5% acid   8% acid

26. A chemist wants to make 50 ml of a 16% acid solution by mixing a 13% acid solution and an 18% acid solution. How many milliliters of each solution should the chemist use?

27. Five grams of sugar are added to a 45-gram serving of a breakfast cereal that is 10% sugar. What is the percent concentration of sugar in the resulting mixture?

28. A goldsmith mixes 8 oz of a 30% gold alloy with 12 oz of a 25% gold alloy. What is the percent concentration of the resulting alloy?

29. How many pounds of coffee that is 40% java beans must be mixed with 80 lb of coffee that is 30% java beans to make a coffee blend that is 32% java beans?

30. The manager of a garden shop mixes grass seed that is 60% rye grass with 70 lb of grass seed that is 80% rye grass to make a mixture that is 74% rye grass. How much of the 60% rye grass is used?

31. A hair dye is made by blending a 7% hydrogen peroxide solution and a 4% hydrogen peroxide solution. How many milliliters of each are used to make a 300-milliliter solution that is 5% hydrogen peroxide?

32. A tea that is 20% jasmine is blended with a tea that is 15% jasmine. How many pounds of each tea are used to make 5 lb of tea that is 18% jasmine?

33. How many ounces of pure chocolate must be added to 150 oz of chocolate topping that is 50% chocolate to make a topping that is 75% chocolate?

34. How many ounces of pure bran flakes must be added to 50 oz of cereal that is 40% bran flakes to produce a mixture that is 50% bran flakes?

35. Thirty ounces of pure silver are added to 50 oz of a silver alloy that is 20% silver. What is the percent concentration of the resulting alloy?

36. A clothing manufacturer has some pure silk thread and some thread that is 85% silk. How many kilograms of each must be woven together to make 75 kg of cloth that is 96% silk?

Objective C   *Application Problems*

37. Two small planes start from the same point and fly in opposite directions. The first plane is flying 25 mph slower than the second plane. In 2 h, the planes are 470 mi apart. Find the rate of each plane.

38. Two cyclists start from the same point and ride in opposite directions. One cyclist rides twice as fast as the other. In 3 h, they are 81 mi apart. Find the rate of each cyclist.

39. Two planes leave an airport at 8 A.M., one flying north at 480 km/h and the other flying south at 520 km/h. At what time will they be 3000 km apart?

40. A long-distance runner started on a course running at an average speed of 6 mph. One-half hour later, a second runner began the same course at an average speed of 7 mph. How long after the second runner started will the second runner overtake the first runner?

41. A motorboat leaves a harbor and travels at an average speed of 9 mph toward a small island. Two hours later a cabin cruiser leaves the same harbor and travels at an average speed of 18 mph toward the same island. In how many hours after the cabin cruiser leaves will the cabin cruiser be alongside the motorboat?

42. A 555-mile, 5-hour plane trip was flown at two speeds. For the first part of the trip, the average speed was 105 mph. For the remainder of the trip, the average speed was 115 mph. For how long did the plane fly at each speed?

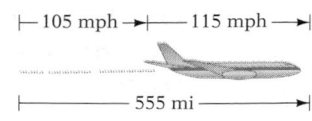

43. An executive drove from home at an average speed of 30 mph to an airport where a helicopter was waiting. The executive boarded the helicopter and flew to the corporate offices at an average speed of 60 mph. The entire distance was 150 mi. The entire trip took 3 h. Find the distance from the airport to the corporate offices.

44. After a sailboat had been on the water for 3 h, a change in the wind direction reduced the average speed of the boat by 5 mph. The entire distance sailed was 57 mi. The total time spent sailing was 6 h. How far did the sailboat travel in the first 3 h?

45. A car and a bus set out at 3 P.M. from the same point headed in the same direction. The average speed of the car is twice the average speed of the bus. In 2 h the car is 68 mi ahead of the bus. Find the rate of the car.

46. A passenger train leaves a train depot 2 h after a freight train leaves the same depot. The freight train is traveling 20 mph slower than the passenger train. Find the rate of each train if the passenger train overtakes the freight train in 3 h.

47. As part of flight training, a student pilot was required to fly to an airport and then return. The average speed on the way to the airport was 100 mph, and the average speed returning was 150 mph. Find the distance between the two airports if the total flying time was 5 h.

48. A ship traveling east at 25 mph is 10 mi from a harbor when another ship leaves the harbor traveling east at 35 mph. How long does it take the second ship to catch up to the first ship?

49. At 10 A.M. a plane leaves Boston, Massachusetts, for Seattle, Washington, a distance of 3000 mi. One hour later a plane leaves Seattle for Boston. Both planes are traveling at a speed of 500 mph. How many hours after the plane leaves Seattle will the planes pass each other?

50. At noon a train leaves Washington, D.C., headed for Charleston, South Carolina, a distance of 500 mi. The train travels at a speed of 60 mph. At 1 P.M. a second train leaves Charleston headed for Washington, D.C., traveling at 50 mph. How long after the train leaves Charleston will the two trains pass each other?

51. Two cyclists start at the same time from opposite ends of a course that is 51 mi long. One cyclist is riding at a rate of 16 mph, and the second cyclist is riding at a rate of 18 mph. How long after they begin will they meet?

52. A bus traveled on a level road for 2 h at an average speed that was 20 mph faster than its average speed on a winding road. The time spent on the winding road was 3 h. Find the average speed on the winding road if the total trip was 210 mi.

53. A bus traveling at a rate of 60 mph overtakes a car traveling at a rate of 45 mph. If the car had a 1-hour head start, how far from the starting point does the bus overtake the car?

54. A car traveling at 48 mph overtakes a cyclist who, riding at 12 mph, had a 3-hour head start. How far from the starting point does the car overtake the cyclist?

APPLYING THE CONCEPTS

55. How many grams of pure water must be added to 50 g of pure acid to make a solution that is 40% acid?

56. How many ounces of water must be evaporated from 50 oz of a 12% salt solution to produce a 15% salt solution?

57. A radiator contains 15 gal of a 20% antifreeze solution. How many gallons must be drained from the radiator and replaced by pure antifreeze so that the radiator will contain 15 gal of a 40% antifreeze solution?

58. At 10 A.M., two campers left their campsite by canoe and paddled downstream at an average speed of 12 mph. They then turned around and paddled back upstream at an average rate of 4 mph. The total trip took 1 h. At what time did the campers turn around downstream?

59. A bicyclist rides for 2 h at a speed of 10 mph and then returns at a speed of 20 mph. Find the cyclist's average speed for the trip.

60. A car travels a 1-mile track at an average speed of 30 mph. At what average speed must the car travel the next mile so that the average speed for the 2 mi is 60 mph?

Focus on Problem Solving

Trial and Error Approach to Problem Solving

The questions below require an answer of always true, sometimes true, or never true. These problems are best solved by the trial and error method. The trial and error method of arriving at a solution to a problem involves repeated tests or experiments.

For example, consider the statement

> Both sides of an equation can be divided by the same number without changing the solution of the equation.

The solution of the equation $6x = 18$ is 3. If we divide both sides of the equation by 2, the result is $3x = 9$ and the solution is still 3. So the answer "never true" has been eliminated. We still need to determine whether there is a case for which it is not true. Is there a number that we could divide both sides of the equation by and the result would be an equation for which the solution is not 3? If we divide both sides of the equation by 0, the result is $\frac{6x}{0} = \frac{18}{0}$; the solution of this equation is not 3 because the expressions on either side of the equals sign are undefined. So the statement is true for some numbers and not true for 0. The statement is sometimes true.

Determine whether the statement is always true, sometimes true, or never true.

1. Both sides of an equation can be multiplied by the same number without changing the solution of the equation.

2. For an equation of the form $ax = b$, $a \neq 0$, multiplying both sides of the equation by the reciprocal of a will result in an equation of the form $x = constant$.

3. The Multiplication Property of Equations is used to remove a term from one side of an equation.

4. Adding -3 to each side of an equation yields the same result as subtracting 3 from each side of the equation.

5. An equation contains an equals sign.

6. The same variable term can be added to both sides of an equation without changing the solution of the equation.

7. An equation of the form $ax + b = c$ cannot be solved if a is a negative number.

8. The solution of the equation $\frac{x}{0} = 0$ is 0.

9. For the diagram at the left, $\angle b = \angle d = \angle e = \angle g$.

10. In solving an equation of the form $ax + b = cx + d$, subtracting cx from each side of the equation results in an equation with only one variable term in it.

11. If a rope 8 meters long is cut into two pieces and one of the pieces has length x meters, then the length of the other piece can be represented as $(x - 8)$ meters.

12. An even integer is a multiple of 2.

13. If the first of three consecutive odd integers is n, then the second and third consecutive odd integers are represented as $n + 1$ and $n + 3$.

14. Suppose we are mixing two salt solutions. Then the variable Q in the percent mixture equation $Q = Ar$ represents the amount of salt in a solution.

15. If 100 oz of a silver alloy is 25% silver, then the alloy contains 25 oz of silver.

16. If we combine an alloy that costs $8 an ounce with an alloy that costs $5 an ounce, the cost of the resulting mixture will be greater than $8 an ounce.

17. If we combine a 9% acid solution with a solution that is 4% acid, the resulting solution will be less than 4% acid.

18. If the speed of one train is 20 mph slower than that of a second train, then the speeds of the two trains can be represented as r and $20 - r$.

Projects and Group Activities

Nielsen Ratings

Nielsen Media Research surveys television viewers to determine the number of people watching particular shows. There are an estimated 97 million television households in the United States. Each **rating point** represents 1% of that number, or 970,000 households. Therefore, for example, if *60 Minutes* receives a rating of 10 points, then 10%, or $(0.10)(97,000,000) = 9,700,000$ households, watched that program.

A rating point does not mean that 970,000 people are watching a program. A rating point refers to the number of TV sets tuned to that program; there may be more than one person watching a television set in a household.

The Nielsen Company also describes a program's share of the market. **Share** is the percentage of television sets in use that are tuned to a program. Suppose the same week that *60 Minutes* received 10 rating points, the show received a share of 20%. This would mean that 20% of all households with a television *turned on* were turned to *60 Minutes*, while 10% of all households with a television were turned to the program.

1. If *20/20* received a Nielsen rating of 11.2 and a share of 23, how many TV households watched the program that week? How many TV households were watching television during that hour?

2. Suppose that *Dateline NBC* (Tuesday) received a rating of 9.6 and a share of 18. How many TV households were watching television during that hour? How many TV households watched the program that week?

3. Suppose *Seinfeld* received a rating of 12.3 during a week that 17,100,000 people were watching the show. Find the average number of people per TV household who watched the program. Round to the nearest tenth.

The cost to advertise on a program is related to its Nielsen rating. The sponsor (the company paying for the advertisement) pays a certain number of dollars for each rating point a show receives.

4. Suppose a television network charges $25,000 per rating point for a 30-second commercial on a daytime talk show. Determine the cost for three 30-second commercials if the Nielsen rating of the show is 11.5.

Nielsen Media Research also tracks the exposure of advertisements. For example, it might be reported that commercials for McDonald's had 500,000,000 household exposures during a week when their advertisement was aired 90 times.

5. Information regarding household exposure of advertisements can be found in *USA Today* each Monday. For a recent week, find the information for the top four advertised brands. For each brand, calculate the average household exposure for each time the ad was aired.

Nielsen Media Research has a web site on the internet. You can locate the site under entertainment and television using a search engine. You will find the rating points and market share for the networks and cable stations, as well as rating points, share, and audience size for categories such as prime time and sports programming.

6. Find the top two prime-time television shows for last week. Calculate the number of TV households that watched each program. Compare these figures with the top two sports programs for last week.

Chapter Summary

Key Words An *equation* expresses the equality of two mathematical expressions.

A *solution* of an equation is a number that, when substituted for the variable, results in a true equation.

To *solve an equation* means to find a solution of the equation. The goal is to rewrite the equation in the form *variable = constant*.

To *translate* a sentence into an equation requires recognition of the words or phrases that mean "equals." Some of these phrases are *equals, is, is equal to, amounts to,* and *represents.*

Cost is the price that a business pays for a product. *Selling price* is the price for which a business sells a product to a customer. *Markup* is the difference between selling price and cost. When the markup is expressed as a percent of the retailer's cost, it is called the *markup rate.*

Discount, or *markdown,* is the amount by which a retailer reduces the regular price of a product. The percent discount is called the *discount rate.*

The *perimeter* of a geometric figure is a measure of the distance around the figure.

An *isosceles triangle* has two sides of equal measure. The three sides of an *equilateral triangle* are of equal measure.

An angle is measured in *degrees*. A 90° angle is a *right angle*. A 180° angle is a *straight angle*. One complete revolution is 360°. An *acute angle* is an angle whose measure is between 0° and 90°. An *obtuse angle* is an angle whose measure is between 90° and 180°.

Complementary angles are two angles whose measures have the sum 90°.

Supplementary angles are two angles whose measures have the sum 180°.

Parallel lines never meet; the distance between them is always the same.

Perpendicular lines are intersecting lines that form right angles.

Two angles that are on opposite sides of the intersection of two lines are *vertical angles;* vertical angles have the same measure. Two angles that share a common side are *adjacent angles;* adjacent angles of intersecting lines are supplementary angles.

A line that intersects two other lines at two different points is a *transversal*. If the lines cut by a transversal are parallel lines, equal angles are formed: *alternate interior angles, alternate exterior angles,* and *corresponding angles*.

Uniform motion means that an object, traveling at a constant speed, moves in a straight line.

Essential Rules

Addition Property of Equations

The same number can be added to each side of an equation without changing the solution of the equation.

If $a = b$, then $a + c = b + c$.

Multiplication Property of Equations

Each side of an equation can be multiplied by the same nonzero number without changing the solution of the equation.

If $a = b$ and $c \neq 0$, then $ac = bc$.

Basic Percent Equation

Percent · Base = Amount

$P \cdot B = A$

Consecutive Integers
Consecutive Even Integers
Consecutive Odd Integers

$n, n + 1, n + 2, \ldots$
$n, n + 2, n + 4, \ldots$
$n, n + 2, n + 4, \ldots$

Formulas for Perimeter

Triangle $\quad P = a + b + c$
Rectangle $\quad P = 2L + 2W$
Square $\quad\quad P = 4s$

Sum of the Angles of a Triangle

The sum of the measures of the interior angles of a triangle is 180°.
The sum of an interior and corresponding exterior angle is 180°.

$\angle a + \angle b + \angle c = 180°$

Value Mixture Equation

Amount · Unit Cost = Value

$AC = V$

Percent Mixture Equation

Amount · Percent Concentration = Quantity

$Ar = Q$

Uniform Motion Equation

Rate · Time = Distance

$rt = d$

Chapter Review

1. Solve: $x + 3 = 24$

2. Solve: $x + 5(3x - 20) = 10(x - 4)$

3. Solve: $5x - 6 = 29$

4. Is 3 a solution of $5x - 2 = 4x + 5$?

5. Solve: $\frac{3}{5}a = 12$

6. Solve: $6x + 3(2x - 1) = -27$

7. 30 is what percent of 12?

8. Solve: $5x + 3 = 10x - 17$

9. Solve: $7 - [4 + 2(x - 3)] = 11(x + 2)$

10. Solve: $-6x + 16 = -2x$

11. A furniture store uses a markup rate of 60%. The store sells a solid oak curio cabinet for $1074. Find the cost of the curio cabinet. Use the formula $S = C + rC$, where S is the selling price, C is the cost, and r is the markup rate.

12. Find the measure of $\angle x$.

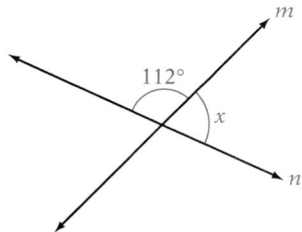

13. A lever is 12 ft long. At a distance of 2 ft from the fulcrum, a force of 120 lb is applied. How large a force must be applied to the other end so that the system will balance? Use the lever system equation $F_1 x = F_2(d - x)$.

14. A bus traveled on a level road for 2 h at an average speed of 20 mph faster than it traveled on a winding road. The time spent on the winding road was 3 h. Find the average speed on the winding road if the total trip was 200 mi.

15. A ceiling fan, which regularly sells for $60, is on sale for $40. Find the discount rate. Use the formula $S = R - rR$, where S is the sale price, R is the regular price, and r is the discount rate.

16. Given that $\angle a = 74°$ and $\angle b = 52°$, find the measures of angles x and y.

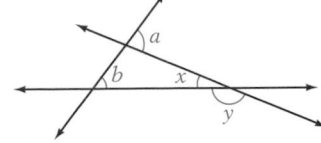

17. A health food store combined cranberry juice that cost $1.79 per quart with apple juice that cost $1.19 per quart. How many quarts of each were used to make 10 qt of cranapple juice costing $1.61 per quart?

18. Four times the second of three consecutive integers equals the sum of the first and third integers. Find the integers.

19. One angle of a triangle is 15° more than the measure of the second angle. The third angle is 15° less than the measure of the second angle. Find the measure of each angle.

20. Translate "four less than the product of five and a number is sixteen" into an equation and solve.

21. The Empire State Building is 1472 ft tall. This is 514 ft less than twice the height of the Eiffel Tower. Find the height of the Eiffel Tower.

22. The length of a rectangle is four times the width of the rectangle. The perimeter is 200 ft. Find the length and width of the rectangle.

23. A jet plane traveling at 600 mph overtakes a propeller-driven plane that had a 2-hour head start. The propeller-driven plane is traveling at 200 mph. How far from the starting point does the jet overtake the propeller-driven plane?

24. The sum of two numbers is twenty-one. Three times the smaller number is two less than twice the larger number. Find the two numbers.

25. A dairy owner mixed 5 gal of cream containing 30% butterfat with 8 gal of milk containing 4% butterfat. What is the percent of butterfat in the resulting mixture?

Chapter Test

1. Solve: $3x - 2 = 5x + 8$

2. Solve: $x - 3 = -8$

3. Solve: $3x - 5 = -14$

4. Solve: $4 - 2(3 - 2x) = 2(5 - x)$

5. Is -2 a solution of $x^2 - 3x = 2x - 6$?

6. Solve: $7 - 4x = -13$

7. What is 0.5% of 8?

8. Solve: $5x - 2(4x - 3) = 6x + 9$

9. Solve: $5x + 3 - 7x = 2x - 5$

10. Solve: $\frac{3}{4}x = -9$

11. A baker wants to make a 15-pound blend of flour that costs \$.60 per pound. The blend is made using a rye flour that costs \$.70 per pound and a wheat flour that costs \$.40 per pound. How many pounds of each flour should be used?

12. Find x.

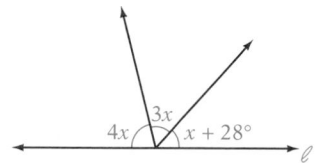

13. A television that regularly sells for \$450 is on sale for \$360. Find the discount rate. Use the formula $S = R - rR$, where S is the sale price, R is the regular price, and r is the discount rate.

14. A financial manager has determined that the cost per unit for a calculator is \$15 and that the fixed cost per month is \$2000. Find the number of calculators produced during a month in which the total cost was \$5000. Use the equation $T = U \cdot N + F$, where T is the total cost, U is the cost per unit, N is the number of units produced, and F is the fixed cost.

15. In an isosceles triangle, two angles are equal. The third angle of the triangle is 30° less than one of the equal angles. Find the measure of one of the equal angles.

16. Find three consecutive even integers whose sum is 36.

17. How many gallons of water must be mixed with 5 gal of a 20% salt solution to make a 16% salt solution?

18. Given that $\ell_1 \parallel \ell_2$, find the measures of angles a and b.

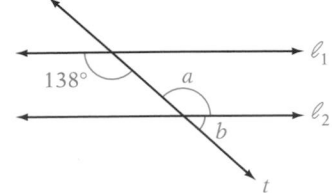

19. Translate "the difference between three times a number and fifteen is twenty-seven" into an equation and solve.

20. A cross-country skier leaves a camp to explore a wilderness area. Two hours later a friend leaves the camp in a snowmobile, traveling 4 mph faster than the skier, and meets the skier 1 h later. Find the rate of the snowmobile.

21. A company makes 140 televisions per day. Three times the number of black-and-white TVs made equals 20 less than the number of color TVs made. Find the number of color TVs made each day.

22. The sum of two numbers is eighteen. The difference between four times the smaller number and seven is equal to the sum of two times the larger number and five. Find the two numbers.

23. As part of flight training, a student pilot was required to fly to an airport and then return. The average speed to the airport was 90 mph, and the average speed returning was 120 mph. Find the distance between the two airports if the total flying time was 7 h.

24. The perimeter of a triangle is 23 ft. One side is twice the second side. The third side is 3 ft more than the second side. Find the measure of each side.

25. A chemist mixes 100 g of water at 80°C with 50 g of water at 20°C. To find the final temperature of the water after mixing, use the equation $m_1(T_1 - T) = m_2(T - T_2)$, where m_1 is the quantity of water at the hotter temperature, T_1 is the temperature of the hotter water, m_2 is the quantity of water at the cooler temperature, T_2 is the temperature of the cooler water, and T is the final temperature of the water after mixing.

Cumulative Review

1. Subtract: $-6 - (-20) - 8$

2. Multiply: $(-2)(-6)(-4)$

3. Simplify: $-\frac{5}{6} - \left(-\frac{7}{16}\right)$

4. Simplify: $-2\frac{1}{3} \div 1\frac{1}{6}$

5. Simplify: $-4^2 \cdot \left(-\frac{3}{2}\right)^3$

6. Simplify: $25 - 3\frac{(5-2)^2}{2^3+1} - (-2)$

7. Evaluate $3(a - c) - 2ab$ when $a = 2$, $b = 3$, and $c = -4$.

8. Simplify: $3x - 8x + (-12x)$

9. Simplify: $2a - (-3b) - 7a - 5b$

10. Simplify: $(16x)\left(\frac{1}{8}\right)$

11. Simplify: $-4(-9y)$

12. Simplify: $-2(-x^2 - 3x + 2)$

13. Simplify: $-2(x - 3) + 2(4 - x)$

14. Simplify: $-3[2x - 4(x - 3)] + 2$

15. Is -3 a solution of $x^2 + 6x + 9 = x + 3$?

16. Is $\frac{1}{2}$ a solution of $3 - 8x = 12x - 2$?

17. Find 32% of 60.

18. Solve: $\frac{3}{5}x = -15$

19. Solve: $7x - 8 = -29$

20. Solve: $13 - 9x = -14$

21.   Solve: $8x - 3(4x - 5) = -2x - 11$

22.   Solve: $6 - 2(5x - 8) = 3x - 4$

23.   Solve: $5x - 8 = 12x + 13$

24.   Solve: $11 - 4x = 2x + 8$

25.   A chemist mixes 300 g of water at 75°C with 100 g of water at 15°C. To find the final temperature of the water after mixing, use the equation $m_1(T_1 - T) = m_2(T - T_2)$, where m_1 is the quantity of water at the hotter temperature, T_1 is the temperature of the hotter water, m_2 is the quantity of water at the cooler temperature, T_2 is the temperature of the cooler water, and T is the final temperature of the water after mixing.

26.   Translate "the difference between twelve and the product of five and a number is negative eighteen" into an equation and solve.

27.   The area of a cement foundation of a house is 2000 ft^2. This is 200 ft^2 more than three times the area of the garage. Find the area of the garage.

28.   How many pounds of an oat flour that costs $.80 per pound must be mixed with 40 lb of a wheat flour that costs $.50 per pound to make a blend that costs $.60 per pound?

29.   How many grams of pure gold must be added to 100 g of a 20% gold alloy to make an alloy that is 36% gold?

30.   The perimeter of a rectangular office is 44 ft. The length of the office is 2 ft more than the width. Find the dimensions of the office.

31.   Find the measure of $\angle x$.

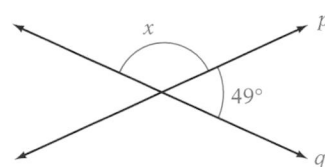

32.   In an equilateral triangle, all three angles are equal. Find the measure of one of the angles of an equilateral triangle.

33.   A sprinter ran to the end of a track at an average rate of 8 m/s and then jogged back to the starting point at an average rate of 3 m/s. The sprinter took 55 s to run to the end of the track and jog back. Find the length of the track.

4 Polynomials

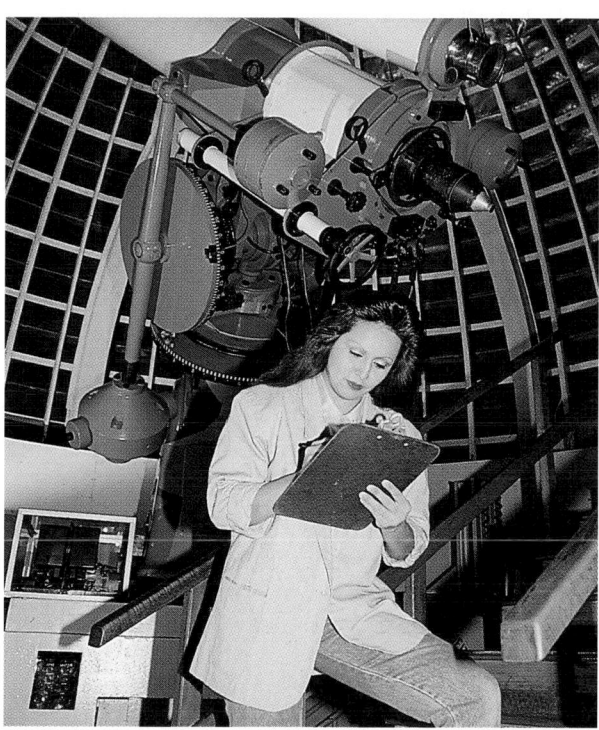

Astronomers use mathematics and physics to explore the nature of our universe. Theories pertaining to the universe are represented as mathematical equations. Astronomers analyze these theories using computers and data collected from observations of objects in space. Among the mathematical concepts that an astronomer must be knowledgeable about is scientific notation, which is presented in Section 4 of this chapter.

Objectives

Section 4.1
To add polynomials
To subtract polynomials

Section 4.2
To multiply monomials
To simplify powers of monomials

Section 4.3
To multiply a polynomial by a monomial
To multiply two polynomials
To multiply two binomials
To multiply binomials that have special products
To solve application problems

Section 4.4
To divide monomials
To write a number in scientific notation

Section 4.5
To divide a polynomial by a monomial
To divide polynomials

Early Egyptian Arithmetic Operations

The early Egyptian arithmetic processes are recorded on the Rhind Papyrus, but the underlying principles are not included. Scholars of today can only guess how these early developments were discovered.

Egyptian hieroglyphics used a base-ten system of numbers in which a vertical line represented 1, a heel bone, ∩, represented 10, and a scroll, ⟋, represented 100.

The symbols at the right represent the number 237. There are 7 vertical lines, 3 heel bones, and 2 scrolls. Thus the symbols at the right represent 7 + 30 + 200, or 237.

Addition in hieroglyphic notation does not require memorization of addition facts. Addition is done just by counting symbols.

The top example at the left shows that addition is a simple grouping operation. Write down the total of each kind of symbol. Then group 10 straight lines into one heel bone.

Subtraction in the hieroglyphic system is similar to making change. For example, what change do you get from a $1.00 bill when buying a $.55 item? 5 cannot be subtracted from 0, so a 10 is "borrowed" and 10 ones are added.

In the bottom example at the left, 5 cannot be subtracted from 3, so a 10 is "borrowed" and 10 ones are added.

Note that no zero is provided in this number system. That place value symbol is just not used. As shown at the left, the heel bone is not used when writing 208 because there are no 10's in 208.

HIEROGLYPHIC NOTATION	MODERN NOTATION
‖‖ ∩∩ ⟋⟋⟋	324
+ ‖‖‖ ∩∩∩ ⟋	+138
‖‖‖ ∩∩∩∩ ⟋⟋⟋⟋ ∩	
12 + 50 + 400 = 462	
‖ ∩∩∩∩ ⟋⟋⟋⟋ ∩∩	

‖‖ ∩∩∩ ⟋⟋⟋⟋	433
− ‖‖‖ ∩∩ ⟋⟋	−225
‖‖ ∩∩ ⟋⟋⟋⟋ ‖	4ȝ3̄
− ‖‖‖ ∩∩ ⟋⟋	−225
‖‖ ⟋⟋	208
8 + 200 = 208	

 **Addition and Subtraction of Polynomials**

Objective A   *To add polynomials* ....

A monomial is a number, a variable, or a product of numbers and variables. For instance,

7	b	$\dfrac{2}{3}a$	$12xy^2$
A number	A variable	A product of a number and a variable	A product of a number and variables

A **polynomial** is a variable expression in which the terms are monomials.

A polynomial of *one* term is a **monomial.** $-7x^2$ is a monomial.
A polynomial of *two* terms is a **binomial.** $4x + 2$ is a binomial.
A polynomial of *three* terms is a **trinomial.** $7x^2 + 5x - 7$ is a trinomial.

The terms of a polynomial in one variable are usually arranged so that the exponents of the variable decrease from left to right. This is called **descending order.**

$5x^3 - 4x^2 + 6x - 1$

$7z^4 + 4z^3 + z - 6$

$2y^4 + y^3 - 2y^2 + 4y - 1$

The **degree** of a polynomial in one variable is its largest exponent (on a variable). The degree of $4x^3 - 5x^2 + 7x - 8$ is 3; the degree of $2y^4 + y^2 - 1$ is 4.

Polynomials can be added, using either a horizontal or a vertical format, by combining like terms.

➡ Simplify $(3x^3 - 7x + 2) + (7x^2 + 2x - 7)$. Use a horizontal format.

$(3x^3 - 7x + 2) + (7x^2 + 2x - 7)$

$= 3x^3 + 7x^2 + (-7x + 2x) + (2 - 7)$ • Use the Commutative and Associative Properties of Addition to rearrange and group like terms.

$= 3x^3 + 7x^2 - 5x - 5$ • Then combine like terms.

➡ Simplify $(-4x^2 + 6x - 9) + (12 - 8x + 2x^3)$. Use a vertical format.

$$\begin{array}{r} -4x^2 + 6x - 9 \\ 2x^3 - 8x + 12 \\ \hline 2x^3 - 4x^2 - 2x + 3 \end{array}$$

• Arrange the terms of each polynomial in descending order with like terms in the same column.

• Combine the terms in each column.

Example 1

Use a horizontal format to simplify
$(8x^2 - 4x - 9) + (2x^2 + 9x - 9)$.

Solution

$(8x^2 - 4x - 9) + (2x^2 + 9x - 9)$
$= (8x^2 + 2x^2) + (-4x + 9x) + (-9 - 9)$
$= 10x^2 + 5x - 18$

You Try It 1

Use a horizontal format to simplify
$(-4x^3 + 2x^2 - 8) + (4x^3 + 6x^2 - 7x + 5)$.

Your solution

Solution on p. S8

Example 2

Use a vertical format to simplify
$(-5x^3 + 4x^2 - 7x + 9) + (2x^3 + 5x - 11)$.

Solution

$$
\begin{array}{r}
-5x^3 + 4x^2 - 7x + 9 \\
2x^3 \quad\quad + 5x - 11 \\
\hline
-3x^3 + 4x^2 - 2x - 2
\end{array}
$$

You Try It 2

Use a vertical format to simplify
$(6x^3 + 2x + 8) + (-9x^3 + 2x^2 - 12x - 8)$.

Your solution

Solution on p. S8

Objective B   To subtract polynomials ....

The **opposite** of the polynomial $(3x^2 - 7x + 8)$ is $-(3x^2 - 7x + 8)$.

To simplify the opposite of a polynomial, change the sign of each term
inside the parentheses.

$$-(3x^2 - 7x + 8) = -3x^2 + 7x - 8$$

TAKE NOTE

This is the same definition used for subtraction of integers: subtraction is addition of the opposite.

Polynomials can be subtracted using either a horizontal or a vertical format. To subtract, add the opposite of the second polynomial to the first.

➡ Simplify $(4y^2 - 6y + 7) - (2y^3 - 5y - 4)$. Use a horizontal format.

$$
\begin{aligned}
&(4y^2 - 6y + 7) - (2y^3 - 5y - 4) \\
&= (4y^2 - 6y + 7) + (-2y^3 + 5y + 4) \\
&= -2y^3 + 4y^2 + (-6y + 5y) + (7 + 4) \\
&= -2y^3 + 4y^2 - y + 11
\end{aligned}
$$

• Add the opposite of the second
  polynomial to the first.
• Combine like terms.

➡ Simplify $(9 + 4y + 3y^3) - (2y^2 + 4y - 21)$. Use a vertical format.

The opposite of $2y^2 + 4y - 21$ is $-2y^2 - 4y + 21$.

$$
\begin{array}{r}
3y^3 \quad\quad + 4y + 9 \\
-2y^2 - 4y + 21 \\
\hline
3y^3 - 2y^2 \quad\quad + 30
\end{array}
$$

• Arrange the terms of each polynomial in descending order with like terms in the same column.
• Note that $4y - 4y = 0$, but 0 is not written.

Example 3

Use a horizontal format to simplify
$(7c^2 - 9c - 12) - (9c^2 + 5c - 8)$.

Solution

$$
\begin{aligned}
&(7c^2 - 9c - 12) - (9c^2 + 5c - 8) \\
&= (7c^2 - 9c - 12) + (-9c^2 - 5c + 8) \\
&= -2c^2 - 14c - 4
\end{aligned}
$$

Example 4

Use a vertical format to simplify
$(3k^2 - 4k + 1) - (k^3 + 3k^2 - 6k - 8)$.

Solution

$$
\begin{array}{r}
3k^2 - 4k + 1 \\
-k^3 - 3k^2 + 6k + 8 \\
\hline
-k^3 \quad\quad + 2k + 9
\end{array}
$$

• Add the opposite of
  $(k^3 + 3k^2 - 6k - 8)$
  to the first polynomial.

You Try It 3

Use a horizontal format to simplify
$(-4w^3 + 8w - 8) - (3w^3 - 4w^2 - 2w - 1)$.

Your solution

You Try It 4

Use a vertical format to simplify
$(13y^3 - 6y - 7) - (4y^2 - 6y - 9)$.

Your solution

Solutions on p. S8

4.1 Exercises

· ·

Objective A

State whether the expression is a monomial.

1. 17

2. $3x^4$

3. $\dfrac{17}{\sqrt{x}}$

4. xyz

5. $\dfrac{2}{3}y$

6. $\dfrac{xy}{z}$

7. $\sqrt{5}\,x$

8. πx

State whether the expression is a monomial, binomial, trinomial, or none of these.

9. $3x + 5$

10. $2y - 3\sqrt{y}$

11. $9x^2 - x - 1$

12. $x^2 + y^2$

13. $\dfrac{2}{x} - 3$

14. $\dfrac{ab}{4}$

15. $6x^2 + 7x$

16. $12a^4 - 3a + 2$

Simplify. Use a vertical format.

17. $(x^2 + 7x) + (-3x^2 - 4x)$

18. $(3y^2 - 2y) + (5y^2 + 6y)$

19. $(y^2 + 4y) + (-4y - 8)$

20. $(3x^2 + 9x) + (6x - 24)$

21. $(2x^2 + 6x + 12) + (3x^2 + x + 8)$

22. $(x^2 + x + 5) + (3x^2 - 10x + 4)$

23. $(-7x + x^3 + 4) + (2x^2 + x - 10)$

24. $(y^2 + 3y^3 + 1) + (-4y^3 - 6y - 3)$

25. $(2a^3 - 7a + 1) + (1 - 4a - 3a^2)$

26. $(5r^3 - 6r^2 + 3r) + (-3 - 2r + r^2)$

Simplify. Use a horizontal format.

27. $(4x^2 + 2x) + (x^2 + 6x)$

28. $(-3y^2 + y) + (4y^2 + 6y)$

29. $(4x^2 - 5xy) + (3x^2 + 6xy - 4y^2)$

30. $(2x^2 - 4y^2) + (6x^2 - 2xy + 4y^2)$

31. $(2a^2 - 7a + 10) + (a^2 + 4a + 7)$

32. $(-6x^2 + 7x + 3) + (3x^2 + x + 3)$

33. $(7x + 5x^3 - 7) + (10x^2 - 8x + 3)$

34. $(4y + 3y^3 + 9) + (2y^2 + 4y - 21)$

35. $(7 - 5r + 2r^2) + (3r^3 - 6r)$

36. $(14 + 4y + 3y^3) + (-4y^2 + 21)$

Objective B

Simplify. Use a vertical format.

37. $(x^2 - 6x) - (x^2 - 10x)$

38. $(y^2 + 4y) - (y^2 + 10y)$

39. $(2y^2 - 4y) - (-y^2 + 2)$

40. $(-3a^2 - 2a) - (4a^2 - 4)$

41. $(x^2 - 2x + 1) - (x^2 + 5x + 8)$

42. $(3x^2 + 2x - 2) - (5x^2 - 5x + 6)$

43. $(4x^3 + 5x + 2) - (1 + 2x - 3x^2)$

44. $(5y^2 - y + 2) - (-3 + 3y - 2y^3)$

45. $(-2y + 6y^2 + 2y^3) - (4 + y^2 + y^3)$

46. $(4 - x - 2x^2) - (-2 + 3x - x^3)$

Simplify. Use a horizontal format.

47. $(y^2 - 10xy) - (2y^2 + 3xy)$

48. $(x^2 - 3xy) - (-2x^2 + xy)$

49. $(3x^2 + x - 3) - (4x + x^2 - 2)$

50. $(5y^2 - 2y + 1) - (-y - 2 - 3y^2)$

51. $(-2x^3 + x - 1) - (-x^2 + x - 3)$

52. $(2x^2 + 5x - 3) - (3x^3 + 2x - 5)$

53. $(1 - 2a + 4a^3) - (a^3 - 2a + 3)$

54. $(7 - 8b + b^2) - (4b^3 - 7b - 8)$

55. $(-1 - y + 4y^3) - (3 - 3y - 2y^2)$

56. $(-3 - 2x + 3x^2) - (4 - 2x^2 + 2x^3)$

APPLYING THE CONCEPTS

57. What polynomial must be added to $3x^2 - 6x + 9$ so that the sum is $4x^2 + 3x - 2$?

58. What polynomial must be subtracted from $2x^2 - x - 2$ so that the difference is $5x^2 + 3x + 1$?

59. In your own words, explain the terms monomial, binomial, trinomial, and polynomial. Give an example of each.

60. Is it possible to subtract two polynomials, each of degree 3, and have the difference be a polynomial of degree 2? If so, give an example. If not, explain why not.

61. Is it possible to add two polynomials, each of degree 3, and have the sum be a polynomial of degree 2? If so, give an example. If not, explain why not.

4.2 Multiplication of Monomials

Objective A   *To multiply monomials* ....

Recall that in an exponential expression such as x^6, x is the base and 6 is the exponent. The exponent indicates the number of times the base occurs as a factor.

The product of exponential expressions with the *same* base can be simplified by writing each expression in factored form and writing the result with an exponent.

$$x^3 \cdot x^2 = \overbrace{(x \cdot x \cdot x)}^{3 \text{ factors}} \cdot \overbrace{(x \cdot x)}^{2 \text{ factors}}$$
$$\underbrace{}_{5 \text{ factors}}$$

$$= x^5$$

Note that adding the exponents results in the same product.

$$x^3 \cdot x^2 = x^{3+2} = x^5$$

Rule for Multiplying Exponential Expressions

If *m* and *n* are positive integers, then $x^m \cdot x^n = x^{m+n}$.

➡ Simplify: $y^4 \cdot y \cdot y^3$

$$y^4 \cdot y \cdot y^3 = y^{4+1+3}$$
$$= y^8$$

- The bases are the same. Add the exponents. Recall that $y = y^1$.

➡ Simplify: $(-3a^4b^3)(2ab^4)$

$$(-3a^4b^3)(2ab^4) = (-3 \cdot 2)(a^4 \cdot a)(b^3 \cdot b^4)$$

- Use the Commutative and Associative Properties of Multiplication to rearrange and group factors.

$$= -6(a^{4+1})(b^{3+4})$$

- Multiply variables with the same base by adding their exponents.

$$= -6a^5b^7$$

- Simplify.

TAKE NOTE

The Rule for Multiplying Exponential Expressions requires the bases to be the same. The expression a^5b^7 cannot be simplified.

Example 1   Simplify: $(-5ab^3)(4a^5)$

Solution
$$(-5ab^3)(4a^5) = (-5 \cdot 4)(a \cdot a^5)b^3$$
$$= -20a^6b^3$$

You Try It 1   Simplify: $(8m^3n)(-3n^5)$

Your solution

Example 2   Simplify: $(6x^3y^2)(4x^4y^5)$

Solution
$$(6x^3y^2)(4x^4y^5) = (6 \cdot 4)(x^3 \cdot x^4)(y^2 \cdot y^5)$$
$$= 24x^7y^7$$

You Try It 2   Simplify: $(12p^4q^3)(-3p^5q^2)$

Your solution

Solutions on p. S8

Objective B **To simplify powers of monomials** ....

POINT OF INTEREST

One of the first symbolic representations of powers was given by Diophantus (c. 250 A.D.) in his book *Arithmetica.* He used Δ^Y for x^2 and κ^Y for x^3. The symbol Δ^Y was the first two letters of the Greek word *dunamis* meaning power; κ^Y was from the Greek word *kubos* meaning cube. He also combined these symbols to denote higher powers. For instance, $\Delta\kappa^Y$ was the symbol for x^5.

The power of a monomial can be simplified by writing the power in factored form and then using the Rule for Multiplying Exponential Expressions.

$$(x^4)^3 = x^4 \cdot x^4 \cdot x^4 \qquad\qquad (a^2b^3)^2 = (a^2b^3)(a^2b^3)$$
$$= x^{4+4+4} \qquad\qquad\qquad = a^{2+2}b^{3+3}$$
$$= x^{12} \qquad\qquad\qquad\qquad = a^4b^6$$

• Write in factored form.

• Use the Rule for Multiplying Exponential Expressions.

Note that multiplying each exponent inside the parentheses by the exponent outside the parentheses results in the same product.

$$(x^4)^3 = x^{4\cdot3} = x^{12} \qquad\qquad (a^2b^3)^2 = a^{2\cdot2}b^{3\cdot2} = a^4b^6$$

• Multiply each exponent inside the parentheses by the exponent outside the parentheses.

Rule for Simplifying the Power of an Exponential Expression

If m and n are positive integers, then $(x^m)^n = x^{mn}$.

Rule for Simplifying Powers of Products

If m, n, and p are positive integers, then $(x^m y^n)^p = x^{mp} y^{np}$.

➡ Simplify: $(5x^2y^3)^3$

$$(5x^2y^3)^3 = 5^{1\cdot3}x^{2\cdot3}y^{3\cdot3}$$
$$= 5^3x^6y^9$$
$$= 125x^6y^9$$

• Multiply each exponent inside the parentheses by the exponent outside the parentheses. Note that $5 = 5^1$.

• Evaluate 5^3.

Example 3   Simplify: $(-2p^3r)^4$

Solution $(-2p^3r)^4 = (-2)^{1\cdot4}p^{3\cdot4}r^{1\cdot4}$
$$= (-2)^4p^{12}r^4 = 16p^{12}r^4$$

You Try It 3   Simplify: $(-3a^4bc^2)^3$

Your solution

Example 4   Simplify: $(2a^2b)(2a^3b^2)^3$

Solution $(2a^2b)(2a^3b^2)^3$
$$= (2a^2b)(2^{1\cdot3}a^{3\cdot3}b^{2\cdot3})$$
$$= (2a^2b)(2^3a^9b^6)$$
$$= (2a^2b)(8a^9b^6) = 16a^{11}b^7$$

You Try It 4   Simplify: $(-xy^4)(-2x^3y^2)^2$

Your solution

Solutions on pp. S8–S9

4.2 Exercises

. . . .

Objective A

Simplify.

1. $(6x^2)(5x)$ **2.** $(-4y^3)(2y)$ **3.** $(7c^2)(-6c^4)$ **4.** $(-8z^5)(5z^8)$

5. $(-3a^3)(-3a^4)$ **6.** $(-5a^6)(-2a^5)$ **7.** $(x^2)(xy^4)$ **8.** $(x^2y^4)(xy^7)$

9. $(-2x^4)(5x^5y)$ **10.** $(-3a^3)(2a^2b^4)$ **11.** $(-4x^2y^4)(-3x^5y^4)$ **12.** $(-6a^2b^4)(-4ab^3)$

13. $(2xy)(-3x^2y^4)$ **14.** $(-3a^2b)(-2ab^3)$ **15.** $(x^2yz)(x^2y^4)$ **16.** $(-ab^2c)(a^2b^5)$

17. $(-a^2b^3)(-ab^2c^4)$ **18.** $(-x^2y^3z)(-x^3y^4)$ **19.** $(-5a^2b^2)(6a^3b^6)$ **20.** $(7xy^4)(-2xy^3)$

21. $(-6a^3)(-a^2b)$ **22.** $(-2a^2b^3)(-4ab^2)$ **23.** $(-5y^4z)(-8y^6z^5)$ **24.** $(3x^2y)(-4xy^2)$

25. $(x^2y)(yz)(xyz)$ **26.** $(xy^2z)(x^2y)(z^2y^2)$ **27.** $(3ab^2)(-2abc)(4ac^2)$

28. $(-2x^3y^2)(-3x^2z^2)(-5y^3z^3)$ **29.** $(4x^4z)(-yz^3)(-2x^3z^2)$ **30.** $(-a^3b^4)(-3a^4c^2)(4b^3c^4)$

31. $(-2x^2y^3)(3xy)(-5x^3y^4)$ **32.** $(4a^2b)(-3a^3b^4)(a^5b^2)$ **33.** $(3a^2b)(-6bc)(2ac^2)$

Objective B

Simplify.

34. $(z^4)^3$ **35.** $(x^3)^5$ **36.** $(y^4)^2$ **37.** $(x^7)^2$ **38.** $(-y^5)^3$

39. $(-x^2)^4$ **40.** $(-x^2)^3$ **41.** $(-y^3)^4$ **42.** $(-3y)^3$ **43.** $(-2x^2)^3$

44. $(a^3b^4)^3$ **45.** $(x^2y^3)^2$ **46.** $(2x^3y^4)^5$ **47.** $(3x^2y)^2$ **48.** $(-2ab^3)^4$

49. $(-3x^3y^2)^5$ **50.** $(3b^2)(2a^3)^4$ **51.** $(-2x)(2x^3)^2$ **52.** $(2y)(-3y^4)^3$

53. $(3x^2y)(2x^2y^2)^3$ **54.** $(a^3b)^2(ab)^3$ **55.** $(ab^2)^2(ab)^2$ **56.** $(-x^2y^3)^2(-2x^3y)^3$

57. $(-2x)^3(-2x^3y)^3$ **58.** $(-3y)(-4x^2y^3)^3$ **59.** $(-2x)(-3xy^2)^2$ **60.** $(-3y)(-2x^2y)^3$

61. $(ab^2)(-2a^2b)^3$ **62.** $(a^2b^2)(-3ab^4)^2$ **63.** $(-2a^3)(3a^2b)^3$ **64.** $(-3b^2)(2ab^2)^3$

APPLYING THE CONCEPTS

Simplify.

65. $3x^2 + (3x)^2$ **66.** $4x^2 - (4x)^2$ **67.** $2x^6y^2 + (3x^2y)^2$ **68.** $(x^2y^2)^3 + (x^3y^3)^2$

69. $(2a^3b^2)^3 - 8a^9b^6$ **70.** $4y^2z^4 - (2yz^2)^2$ **71.** $(x^2y^4)^2 + (2xy^2)^4$ **72.** $(3a^3)^2 - 4a^6 + (2a^2)^3$

For Exercises 73 to 76, answer true or false. If the answer is false, correct the right-hand side of the equation.

73. $(-a)^5 = -a^5$ **74.** $(-b)^8 = b^8$ **75.** $(x^2)^5 = x^{2+5} = x^7$ **76.** $x^3 + x^3 = 2x^{3+3} = 2x^6$

77. Evaluate $(2^3)^2$ and $2^{(3^2)}$. Are the results the same? If not, which expression has the larger value?

78. If n is a positive integer and $x^n = y^n$, does $x = y$? Explain your answer.

79. The distance a rock will fall in t seconds is $16t^2$ (neglecting air resistance). Find other examples of quantities that can be expressed in terms of an exponential expression, and explain where the expression is used.

80. Explain in your own words how to multiply monomials.

4.3 Multiplication of Polynomials

Objective A   *To multiply a polynomial by a monomial* ....

To multiply a polynomial by a monomial, use the Distributive Property and the Rule for Multiplying Exponential Expressions.

➡ Simplify: $-3a(4a^2 - 5a + 6)$

$$-3a(4a^2 - 5a + 6) = -3a(4a^2) - (-3a)(5a) + (-3a)(6)$$
$$= -12a^3 + 15a^2 - 18a$$

• **Use the Distributive Property.**

Example 1
Simplify: $(5x + 4)(-2x)$

Solution
$(5x + 4)(-2x) = -10x^2 - 8x$

Example 2
Simplify: $2a^2b(4a^2 - 2ab + b^2)$

Solution
$2a^2b(4a^2 - 2ab + b^2)$
$\quad = 8a^4b - 4a^3b^2 + 2a^2b^3$

You Try It 1
Simplify: $(-2y + 3)(-4y)$

Your solution

You Try It 2
Simplify: $-a^2(3a^2 + 2a - 7)$

Your solution

Solutions on p. S9

Objective B   *To multiply two polynomials* ....

Multiplication of two polynomials requires the repeated application of the Distributive Property.

$$(y - 2)(y^2 + 3y + 1) = (y - 2)(y^2) + (y - 2)(3y) + (y - 2)(1)$$
$$= y^3 - 2y^2 + 3y^2 - 6y + y - 2$$
$$= y^3 + y^2 - 5y - 2$$

A convenient method of multiplying two polynomials is to use a vertical format similar to that used for multiplication of whole numbers.

$$
\begin{array}{r}
y^2 + 3y + 1 \\
y - 2 \\
\hline
-2y^2 - 6y - 2 \\
y^3 + 3y^2 + \ y \\
\hline
y^3 + \ y^2 - 5y - 2
\end{array}
$$

$-2y^2 - 6y - 2 = -2(y^2 + 3y + 1)$
$y^3 + 3y^2 + y = y(y^2 + 3y + 1)$

• **Multiply by -2.**
• **Multiply by y.**
• **Add the terms in each column.**

⇒ Simplify: $(2a^3 + a - 3)(a + 5)$

$$
\begin{array}{r}
2a^3 \quad\quad + \ a - 3 \\
a + 5 \\
\hline
10a^3 \quad\quad + 5a - 15 \\
2a^4 \quad\quad\ + a^2 - 3a \\
\hline
2a^4 + 10a^3 + a^2 + 2a - 15
\end{array}
$$

• Note that spaces are provided in each product so that like terms are in the same column.

• Add the terms in each column.

Example 3
Simplify: $(2b^3 - b + 1)(2b + 3)$

Solution

$$
\begin{array}{r}
2b^3 \quad\quad - \ b + 1 \\
2b + 3 \\
\hline
6b^3 \quad\quad - 3b + 3 \\
4b^4 + \quad\quad - 2b^2 + 2b \\
\hline
4b^4 + 6b^3 - 2b^2 - \ b + 3
\end{array}
$$

You Try It 3
Simplify: $(2y^3 + 2y^2 - 3)(3y - 1)$

Your solution

Solution on p. S9

Objective C To multiply two binomials ....

It is frequently necessary to find the product of two binomials. The product can be found using a method called **FOIL**, which is based on the Distributive Property. The letters of FOIL stand for **F**irst, **O**uter, **I**nner, and **L**ast.

⇒ Simplify: $(2x + 3)(x + 5)$

Multiply the **F**irst terms.	$(2x + 3)(x + 5)$	$2x \cdot x = 2x^2$
Multiply the **O**uter terms.	$(2x + 3)(x + 5)$	$2x \cdot 5 = 10x$
Multiply the **I**nner terms.	$(2x + 3)(x + 5)$	$3 \cdot x = 3x$
Multiply the **L**ast terms.	$(2x + 3)(x + 5)$	$3 \cdot 5 = 15$

$$\qquad\qquad\qquad\qquad\qquad\quad\ \overset{\text{F}}{}\quad \overset{\text{O}}{}\quad \overset{\text{I}}{}\quad \overset{\text{L}}{}$$

Add the products.　$(2x + 3)(x + 5)$　$= 2x^2 + 10x + 3x + 15$

Combine like terms.　　　　　　　$= 2x^2 + 13x + 15$

TAKE NOTE

FOIL is not really a different way of multiplying. It is based on the Distributive Property.

$(2x + 3)(x + 5)$
$= 2x(x + 5) + 3(x + 5)$
$\quad\ \ \overset{\text{F}}{}\ \ \ \overset{\text{O}}{}\ \ \ \ \overset{\text{I}}{}\ \ \ \ \overset{\text{L}}{}$
$= 2x^2 + 10x + 3x + 15$
$= 2x^2 + 13x + 15$

⇒ Simplify: $(4x - 3)(3x - 2)$

$$(4x - 3)(3x - 2) = 4x(3x) + 4x(-2) + (-3)(3x) + (-3)(-2)$$
$$= 12x^2 - 8x - 9x + 6$$
$$= 12x^2 - 17x + 6$$

⇒ Simplify: $(3x - 2y)(x + 4y)$

$$(3x - 2y)(x + 4y) = 3x(x) + 3x(4y) + (-2y)(x) + (-2y)(4y)$$
$$= 3x^2 + 12xy - 2xy - 8y^2$$
$$= 3x^2 + 10xy - 8y^2$$

Example 4

Simplify: $(2a - 1)(3a - 2)$

Solution

$(2a - 1)(3a - 2) = 6a^2 - 4a - 3a + 2$
$\qquad\qquad\qquad = 6a^2 - 7a + 2$

You Try It 4

Simplify: $(4y - 5)(2y - 3)$

Your solution

Example 5

Simplify: $(3x - 2)(4x + 3)$

Solution

$(3x - 2)(4x + 3) = 12x^2 + 9x - 8x - 6$
$\qquad\qquad\qquad = 12x^2 + x - 6$

You Try It 5

Simplify: $(3b + 2)(3b - 5)$

Your solution

Solutions on p. S9

Objective D   *To multiply binomials that have special products* ....

Using FOIL, it is possible to find a pattern for the product of the sum and difference of two terms and for the square of a binomial.

The Sum and Difference of Two Terms

$$(a + b)(a - b) = a^2 - ab + ab - b^2$$

$$= a^2 - b^2$$

Square of first term ——————
Square of second term ——————

The Square of a Bionomial

$$(a + b)^2 = (a + b)(a + b) = a^2 + ab + ab + b^2$$

$$= a^2 + 2ab + b^2$$

Square of first term ——————
Twice the product of the two terms ——
Square of the last term ——————

➡ Simplify: $(2x + 3)(2x - 3)$

$(2x + 3)(2x - 3) = (2x)^2 - 3^2$ • This is the sum and
$\qquad\qquad\qquad = 4x^2 - 9$ difference of two terms.

➡ Simplify: $(3x - 2)^2$

$(3x - 2)^2 = (3x)^2 + 2(3x)(-2) + (-2)^2$ • This is the square of a
$\qquad\qquad = 9x^2 - 12x + 4$ binomial.

Example 6
Simplify: $(4z - 2w)(4z + 2w)$

Solution
$(4z - 2w)(4z + 2w) = 16z^2 - 4w^2$

You Try It 6
Simplify: $(2a + 5c)(2a - 5c)$

Your solution

Example 7
Simplify: $(2r - 3s)^2$

Solution
$(2r - 3s)^2 = 4r^2 - 12rs + 9s^2$

You Try It 7
Simplify: $(3x + 2y)^2$

Your solution

Solutions on p. S9

Objective E To solve application problems ··

Example 8
The length of a rectangle is $(x + 7)$ m.
The width is $(x - 4)$ m. Find the area of the
rectangle in terms of the variable x.

You Try It 8
The radius of a circle is $(x - 4)$ ft. Use the
equation $A = \pi r^2$, where r is the radius, to
find the area of the circle in terms of x.
Leave the answer in terms of π.

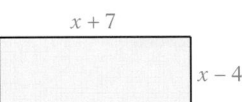

Strategy
To find the area, replace the variables L and
W in the equation $A = L \cdot W$ by the given
values and solve for A.

Your strategy

Solution
$A = L \cdot W$
$A = (x + 7)(x - 4)$
$A = x^2 - 4x + 7x - 28$
$A = x^2 + 3x - 28$

The area is $(x^2 + 3x - 28)$ m^2.

Your solution

Solution on p. S9

4.3 Exercises

· ·

Objective A

Simplify.

1. $x(x - 2)$

2. $y(3 - y)$

3. $-x(x + 7)$

4. $-y(7 - y)$

5. $3a^2(a - 2)$

6. $4b^2(b + 8)$

7. $-5x^2(x^2 - x)$

8. $-6y^2(y + 2y^2)$

9. $-x^3(3x^2 - 7)$

10. $-y^4(2y^2 - y^6)$

11. $2x(6x^2 - 3x)$

12. $3y(4y - y^2)$

13. $(2x - 4)3x$

14. $(3y - 2)y$

15. $(3x + 4)x$

16. $(2x + 1)2x$

17. $-xy(x^2 - y^2)$

18. $-x^2y(2xy - y^2)$

19. $x(2x^3 - 3x + 2)$

20. $y(-3y^2 - 2y + 6)$

21. $-a(-2a^2 - 3a - 2)$

22. $-b(5b^2 + 7b - 35)$

23. $x^2(3x^4 - 3x^2 - 2)$

24. $y^3(-4y^3 - 6y + 7)$

25. $2y^2(-3y^2 - 6y + 7)$

26. $4x^2(3x^2 - 2x + 6)$

27. $(a^2 + 3a - 4)(-2a)$

28. $(b^3 - 2b + 2)(-5b)$

29. $-3y^2(-2y^2 + y - 2)$

30. $-5x^2(3x^2 - 3x - 7)$

31. $xy(x^2 - 3xy + y^2)$

32. $ab(2a^2 - 4ab - 6b^2)$

Objective B

Simplify.

33. $(x^2 + 3x + 2)(x + 1)$

34. $(x^2 - 2x + 7)(x - 2)$

35. $(a^2 - 3a + 4)(a - 3)$

36. $(x^2 - 3x + 5)(2x - 3)$ **37.** $(-2b^2 - 3b + 4)(b - 5)$ **38.** $(-a^2 + 3a - 2)(2a - 1)$

39. $(-2x^2 + 7x - 2)(3x - 5)$ **40.** $(-a^2 - 2a + 3)(2a - 1)$ **41.** $(x^2 + 5)(x - 3)$

42. $(y^2 - 2y)(2y + 5)$ **43.** $(x^3 - 3x + 2)(x - 4)$ **44.** $(y^3 + 4y^2 - 8)(2y - 1)$

45. $(5y^2 + 8y - 2)(3y - 8)$ **46.** $(3y^2 + 3y - 5)(4y - 3)$ **47.** $(5a^3 - 5a + 2)(a - 4)$

48. $(3b^3 - 5b^2 + 7)(6b - 1)$ **49.** $(y^3 + 2y^2 - 3y + 1)(y + 2)$ **50.** $(2a^3 - 3a^2 + 2a - 1)(2a - 3)$

Objective C

Simplify.

51. $(x + 1)(x + 3)$ **52.** $(y + 2)(y + 5)$ **53.** $(a - 3)(a + 4)$ **54.** $(b - 6)(b + 3)$

55. $(y + 3)(y - 8)$ **56.** $(x + 10)(x - 5)$ **57.** $(y - 7)(y - 3)$ **58.** $(a - 8)(a - 9)$

59. $(2x + 1)(x + 7)$ **60.** $(y + 2)(5y + 1)$ **61.** $(3x - 1)(x + 4)$ **62.** $(7x - 2)(x + 4)$

63. $(4x - 3)(x - 7)$ **64.** $(2x - 3)(4x - 7)$ **65.** $(3y - 8)(y + 2)$ **66.** $(5y - 9)(y + 5)$

67. $(3x + 7)(3x + 11)$ **68.** $(5a + 6)(6a + 5)$ **69.** $(7a - 16)(3a - 5)$ **70.** $(5a - 12)(3a - 7)$

71. $(3a - 2b)(2a - 7b)$ **72.** $(5a - b)(7a - b)$ **73.** $(a - 9b)(2a + 7b)$

74. $(2a + 5b)(7a - 2b)$

75. $(10a - 3b)(10a - 7b)$

76. $(12a - 5b)(3a - 4b)$

77. $(5x + 12y)(3x + 4y)$

78. $(11x + 2y)(3x + 7y)$

79. $(2x + 15y)(7x - 4y)$

80. $(5x + 2y)(2x - 5y)$

81. $(8x - 3y)(7x - 5y)$

82. $(2x - 9y)(8x - 3y)$

Objective D

Simplify.

83. $(y - 5)(y + 5)$ **84.** $(y + 6)(y - 6)$ **85.** $(2x + 3)(2x - 3)$ **86.** $(4x - 7)(4x + 7)$

87. $(x + 1)^2$ **88.** $(y - 3)^2$ **89.** $(3a - 5)^2$ **90.** $(6x - 5)^2$

91. $(3x - 7)(3x + 7)$ **92.** $(9x - 2)(9x + 2)$ **93.** $(2a + b)^2$ **94.** $(x + 3y)^2$

95. $(x - 2y)^2$ **96.** $(2x - 3y)^2$ **97.** $(4 - 3y)(4 + 3y)$

98. $(4x - 9y)(4x + 9y)$ **99.** $(5x + 2y)^2$ **100.** $(2a - 9b)^2$

Objective E   *Application Problems*

101. The length of a rectangle is $(5x)$ ft. The width is $(2x - 7)$ ft. Find the area of the rectangle in terms of the variable x.

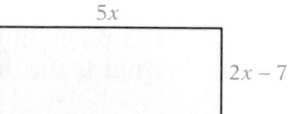

102. The width of a rectangle is $(3x + 1)$ in. The length of the rectangle is twice the width. Find the area of the rectangle in terms of the variable x.

103. The length of a side of a square is $(2x + 1)$ km. Find the area of the square in terms of the variable x.

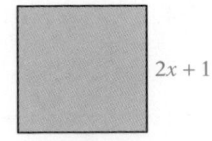

104. The radius of a circle is $(x + 4)$ cm. Find the area of the circle in terms of the variable x. Leave the answer in terms of π.

105. The base of a triangle is $(4x)$ m and the height is $(2x + 5)$ m. Find the area of the triangle in terms of the variable x.

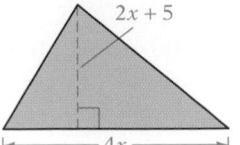

106. A softball diamond has dimensions 45 ft by 45 ft. A base-path border x feet wide lies on both the first-base side and third-base side of the diamond. Express the total area of the softball diamond and the base paths in terms of the variable x.

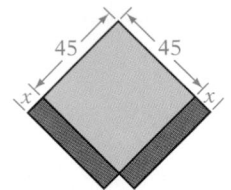

107. An athletic field has dimensions 30 yd by 100 yd. An end zone that is w yards wide borders each end of the field. Express the total area of the field and the end zones in terms of the variable w.

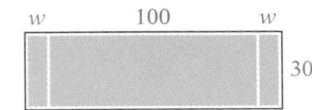

APPLYING THE CONCEPTS

Simplify.

108. $(a + b)^2 - (a - b)^2$

109. $(x^2 + x - 3)^2$

110. $(a + 3)^3$

111. What polynomial has quotient $3x - 4$ when divided by $4x + 5$?

112. Add $x^2 + 2x - 3$ to the product of $2x - 5$ and $3x + 1$.

113. Subtract $4x^2 - x - 5$ from the product of $x^2 + x + 3$ and $x - 4$.

114. If a polynomial of degree 3 is multiplied by a polynomial of degree 2, what is the degree of the resulting polynomial?

115. Is it possible to multiply a polynomial of degree 2 by a polynomial of degree 2 and have the product be a polynomial of degree 3? If so, give an example. If not, explain why not.

4.4 Integer Exponents and Scientific Notation

Objective A   *To divide monomials* ....   [CT]

The quotient of two exponential expressions with the same base can be simplified by writing each expression in factored form, dividing by the common factors, and then writing the result with an exponent.

$$\frac{x^5}{x^2} = \frac{\overset{1}{\cancel{x}} \cdot \overset{1}{\cancel{x}} \cdot x \cdot x \cdot x}{\underset{1}{\cancel{x}} \cdot \underset{1}{\cancel{x}}} = x^3$$

Note that subtracting the exponents gives the same result.

$$\frac{x^5}{x^2} = x^{5-2} = x^3$$

To divide two monomials with the same base, subtract the exponents of the like bases.

➡ Simplify: $\dfrac{a^7}{a^3}$

$$\frac{a^7}{a^3} = a^{7-3}$$ • The bases are the same. Subtract the exponents.

$$= a^4$$

➡ Simplify: $\dfrac{r^8 t^6}{r^7 t}$

$$\frac{r^8 t^6}{r^7 t} = r^{8-7} t^{6-1}$$ • Subtract the exponents of the like bases.

$$= rt^5$$

➡ Simplify: $\dfrac{p^7}{z^4}$

Because the bases are not the same, $\dfrac{p^7}{z^4}$ is already in simplest form.

Consider the expression $\dfrac{x^4}{x^4}$, $x \neq 0$. This expression can be simplified, as shown below, by subtracting exponents or by dividing by common factors.

$$\frac{x^4}{x^4} = x^{4-4} = x^0 \qquad\qquad \frac{x^4}{x^4} = \frac{\overset{1}{\cancel{x}} \cdot \overset{1}{\cancel{x}} \cdot \overset{1}{\cancel{x}} \cdot \overset{1}{\cancel{x}}}{\underset{1}{\cancel{x}} \cdot \underset{1}{\cancel{x}} \cdot \underset{1}{\cancel{x}} \cdot \underset{1}{\cancel{x}}} = 1$$

The equations $\dfrac{x^4}{x^4} = x^0$ and $\dfrac{x^4}{x^4} = 1$ suggest the following definition of x^0.

> **Definition of Zero as an Exponent**
>
> If $x \neq 0$, then $x^0 = 1$. The expression 0^0 is not defined.

➡ Simplify: $(12a^3)^0$, $a \neq 0$

$(12a^3)^0 = 1$ • **Any nonzero expression to the zero power is 1.**

➡ Simplify: $-(4x^3y^7)^0$

$-(4x^3y^7)^0 = -(1) = -1$

POINT OF INTEREST

In the 15th century, the expression $12^{2\overline{m}}$ was used to mean $12x^{-2}$. The use of $\overline{m}$ reflected an Italian influence. In Italy, *m* was used for minus and *p* was used for plus. It was understood that $2\overline{m}$ referred to an unnamed variable. Issac Newton, in the 17th century, advocated the current use of a negative exponent.

Consider the expression $\dfrac{x^4}{x^6}$, $x \neq 0$. This expression can be simplified, as shown below, by subtracting exponents or by dividing by common factors.

$$\frac{x^4}{x^6} = x^{4-6} = x^{-2} \qquad\qquad \frac{x^4}{x^6} = \frac{\overset{1}{\cancel{x}} \cdot \overset{1}{\cancel{x}} \cdot \overset{1}{\cancel{x}} \cdot \overset{1}{\cancel{x}}}{\underset{1}{\cancel{x}} \cdot \underset{1}{\cancel{x}} \cdot \underset{1}{\cancel{x}} \cdot \underset{1}{\cancel{x}} \cdot x \cdot x} = \frac{1}{x^2}$$

The equations $\dfrac{x^4}{x^6} = x^{-2}$ and $\dfrac{x^4}{x^6} = \dfrac{1}{x^2}$ suggest that $x^{-2} = \dfrac{1}{x^2}$.

Definition of a Negative Exponent

If $x \neq 0$ and *n* is a positive integer, then

$$x^{-n} = \frac{1}{x^n} \qquad \text{and} \qquad \frac{1}{x^{-n}} = x^n$$

An exponential expression is in simplest form when it is written with only positive exponents.

TAKE NOTE

Note from the example at the right that 2^{-4} is a *positive* number. A negative exponent does not change the sign of a number.

➡ Evaluate 2^{-4}.

$2^{-4} = \dfrac{1}{2^4}$ • **Use the Definition of a Negative Exponent.**

$= \dfrac{1}{16}$ • **Evaluate the expression.**

TAKE NOTE

The exponent on *n* is −5 (*negative* 5). The n^{-5} is written in the denominator as n^5. The exponent on 3 is 1 (*positive* 1). The 3 remains in the numerator.

➡ Simplify: $3n^{-5}$

$3n^{-5} = 3 \cdot \dfrac{1}{n^5} = \dfrac{3}{n^5}$ • **Use the Definition of a Negative Exponent to rewrite the expression with a positive exponent.**

➡ Simplify: $\dfrac{2}{5a^{-4}}$

$\dfrac{2}{5a^{-4}} = \dfrac{2}{5} \cdot \dfrac{1}{a^{-4}} = \dfrac{2}{5} \cdot a^4 = \dfrac{2a^4}{5}$ • **Use the Definition of a Negative Exponent to rewrite the expression with a positive exponent.**

The expression $\left(\frac{x^4}{y^3}\right)^2$, $y \neq 0$, can be simplified by squaring $\frac{x^4}{y^3}$ or by multiplying each exponent in the quotient by the exponent outside the parentheses.

$$\left(\frac{x^4}{y^3}\right)^2 = \left(\frac{x^4}{y^3}\right)\left(\frac{x^4}{y^3}\right) = \frac{x^4 \cdot x^4}{y^3 \cdot y^3} = \frac{x^{4+4}}{y^{3+3}} = \frac{x^8}{y^6} \qquad \left(\frac{x^4}{y^3}\right)^2 = \frac{x^{4 \cdot 2}}{y^{3 \cdot 2}} = \frac{x^8}{y^6}$$

Rule for Simplifying Powers of Quotients

If m, n, and q are integers and $y \neq 0$, then $\left(\dfrac{x^m}{y^n}\right)^p = \dfrac{x^{mp}}{y^{np}}$.

⮕ Simplify: $\left(\dfrac{a^3}{b^2}\right)^{-2}$

$$\left(\frac{a^3}{b^2}\right)^{-2} = \frac{a^{3(-2)}}{b^{2(-2)}}$$

- Use the Rule for Simplifying Powers of Quotients.

$$= \frac{a^{-6}}{b^{-4}} = \frac{b^4}{a^6}$$

- Use the Definition of a Negative Exponent to write the expression with positive exponents.

The example above suggests the following rule.

Rule for Negative Exponents on Fractional Expressions

If $a \neq 0$, $b \neq 0$, and n is a positive integer, then

$$\left(\frac{a}{b}\right)^{-n} = \left(\frac{b}{a}\right)^n$$

Now that zero as an exponent and negative exponents have been defined, a rule for dividing exponential expressions can be stated.

Rule for Dividing Exponential Expressions

If m and n are integers and $x \neq 0$, then $\dfrac{x^m}{x^n} = x^{m-n}$.

⮕ Evaluate $\dfrac{5^{-2}}{5}$.

$$\frac{5^{-2}}{5} = 5^{-2-1} = 5^{-3}$$

- Use the Rule for Dividing Exponential Expressions.

$$= \frac{1}{5^3} = \frac{1}{125}$$

- Use the Definition of a Negative Exponent to rewrite the expression with a positive exponent. Then evaluate.

➡ Simplify: $\dfrac{x^4}{x^9}$

$\dfrac{x^4}{x^9} = x^{4-9}$

• Use the Rule for Dividing Exponential Expressions.

$\quad = x^{-5}$

• Subtract the exponents.

$\quad = \dfrac{1}{x^5}$

• Use the Definition of a Negative Exponent to rewrite the expression with a positive exponent.

The rules for simplifying exponential expressions and powers of exponential expressions are true for all integers. These rules are restated here along with the rules for dividing exponential expressions.

Rules of Exponents

If *m*, *n*, and *p* are integers, then

$x^m \cdot x^n = x^{m+n} \qquad (x^m)^n = x^{mn} \qquad (x^m y^n)^p = x^{mp} y^{np}$

$\dfrac{x^m}{x^n} = x^{m-n}, x \neq 0 \qquad \left(\dfrac{x^m}{y^n}\right)^p = \dfrac{x^{mp}}{y^{np}}, y \neq 0 \qquad x^{-n} = \dfrac{1}{x^n}, x \neq 0$

$x^0 = 1, x \neq 0$

➡ Simplify: $(3ab^{-4})(-2a^{-3}b^7)$

$(3ab^{-4})(-2a^{-3}b^7) = [3 \cdot (-2)](a^{1+(-3)}b^{-4+7})$

• When multiplying expressions, add the exponents on like bases.

$\quad = -6a^{-2}b^3$

$\quad = -\dfrac{6b^3}{a^2}$

➡ Simplify: $\left[\dfrac{6m^2n^3}{8m^7n^2}\right]^{-3}$

$\left[\dfrac{6m^2n^3}{8m^7n^2}\right]^{-3} = \left[\dfrac{3m^{2-7}n^{3-2}}{4}\right]^{-3}$

• Simplify inside the brackets.

$\quad = \left[\dfrac{3m^{-5}n}{4}\right]^{-3}$

• Subtract the exponents.

$\quad = \dfrac{3^{-3}m^{15}n^{-3}}{4^{-3}}$

• Use the Rule for Simplifying Powers of Quotients.

$\quad = \dfrac{4^3m^{15}}{3^3n^3} = \dfrac{64m^{15}}{27n^3}$

• Use the Definition of a Negative Exponent to rewrite the expression with positive exponents. Then simplify.

➡ Simplify: $\dfrac{4a^{-2}b^5}{6a^5b^2}$

$\dfrac{4a^{-2}b^5}{6a^5b^2} = \dfrac{2a^{-2}b^5}{3a^5b^2}$

• Divide the coefficients by their common factor.

$= \dfrac{2a^{-2-5}b^{5-2}}{3}$

• Use the Rule for Dividing Exponential Expressions.

$= \dfrac{2a^{-7}b^3}{3} = \dfrac{2b^3}{3a^7}$

• Use the Definition of a Negative Exponent to rewrite the expression with positive exponents.

Example 1 Simplify: $(-2x)(3x^{-2})^{-3}$

Solution $(-2x)(3x^{-2})^{-3} = (-2x)(3^{-3}x^6)$

$= \dfrac{-2x^{1+6}}{3^3}$

$= -\dfrac{2x^7}{27}$

You Try It 1 Simplify: $(-2x^2)(x^{-3}y^{-4})^{-2}$

Your solution

Example 2 Simplify: $\dfrac{(2r^2t^{-1})^{-3}}{(r^{-3}t^4)^2}$

Solution $\dfrac{(2r^2t^{-1})^{-3}}{(r^{-3}t^4)^2} = \dfrac{2^{-3}r^{-6}t^3}{r^{-6}t^8}$

$= 2^{-3}r^{-6-(-6)}t^{3-8}$

$= 2^{-3}r^0t^{-5}$

$= \dfrac{1}{2^3t^5}$

$= \dfrac{1}{8t^5}$

You Try It 2 Simplify: $\dfrac{(6a^{-2}b^3)^{-1}}{(4a^3b^{-2})^{-2}}$

Your solution

Example 3 Simplify: $\left[\dfrac{4a^{-2}b^3}{6a^4b^{-2}}\right]^{-3}$

Solution $\left[\dfrac{4a^{-2}b^3}{6a^4b^{-2}}\right]^{-3} = \left[\dfrac{2a^{-6}b^5}{3}\right]^{-3}$

$= \dfrac{2^{-3}a^{18}b^{-15}}{3^{-3}}$

$= \dfrac{27a^{18}}{8b^{15}}$

You Try It 3 Simplify: $\left[\dfrac{6r^3s^{-3}}{9r^3s^{-1}}\right]^{-2}$

Your solution

Solutions on p. S9

Objective B *To write a number in scientific notation* ·· CT

Very large and very small numbers abound in the natural sciences. For example, the mass of an electron is 0.00000000000000000000000000000911 kg. Numbers such as this are difficult to read, so a more convenient system called **scientific notation** is used. In scientific notation, a number is expressed as the product of two factors, one a number between 1 and 10, and the other a power of 10.

To express a number in scientific notation, write it in the form $a \times 10^n$, where a is a number between 1 and 10, and n is an integer.

For numbers greater than or equal to 10, move the decimal point to the right of the first digit. The exponent n is positive and equal to the number of places the decimal point has been moved.

$$240,000 = 2.4 \times 10^5$$
$$93,000,000 = 9.3 \times 10^7$$

For numbers less than 1, move the decimal point to the right of the first nonzero digit. The exponent n is negative. The absolute value of the exponent is equal to the number of places the decimal point has been moved.

$$0.0003 = 3.0 \times 10^{-4}$$
$$0.0000832 = 8.32 \times 10^{-5}$$

Changing a number written in scientific notation to decimal notation also requires moving the decimal point.

When the exponent is positive, move the decimal point to the right the same number of places as the exponent.

$$3.45 \times 10^6 = 3,450,000$$
$$2.3 \times 10^8 = 230,000,000$$

When the exponent is negative, move the decimal point to the left the same number of places as the absolute value of the exponent.

$$8.1 \times 10^{-3} = 0.0081$$
$$6.34 \times 10^{-7} = 0.000000634$$

Example 4 Write the number 824,300,000 in scientific notation.

Solution $824,300,000 = 8.243 \times 10^8$

You Try It 4 Write the number 0.000000961 in scientific notation.

Your solution

Example 5 Write the number 6.8×10^{-10} in decimal notation.

Solution $6.8 \times 10^{-10} = 0.00000000068$

You Try It 5 Write the number 7.329×10^6 in decimal notation.

Your solution

Solutions on p. S9

4.4 Exercises

$\cdot$ $\cdot$ $\cdot$ $\cdot$ $\cdot$ $\cdot$ $\cdot$ $\cdot$ $\cdot$ $\cdot$ $\cdot$ $\cdot$ $\cdot$ $\cdot$ $\cdot$ $\cdot$ $\cdot$ $\cdot$ $\cdot$ $\cdot$ $\cdot$ $\cdot$ $\cdot$ $\cdot$ $\cdot$ $\cdot$ $\cdot$ $\cdot$ $\cdot$ $\cdot$ $\cdot$ $\cdot$ $\cdot$ $\cdot$ $\cdot$ $\cdot$ $\cdot$ $\cdot$ $\cdot$ $\cdot$

Objective A

Evaluate.

1. 5^{-2} **2.** 3^{-3} **3.** $\dfrac{1}{8^{-2}}$ **4.** $\dfrac{1}{12^{-1}}$

5. $\dfrac{3^{-2}}{3}$ **6.** $\dfrac{5^{-3}}{5}$ **7.** $\dfrac{2^{-2}}{2^{-3}}$ **8.** $\dfrac{3^2}{3^2}$

Simplify.

9. x^{-2} **10.** y^{-10} **11.** $\dfrac{1}{a^{-6}}$ **12.** $\dfrac{1}{b^{-4}}$

13. $4x^{-7}$ **14.** $-6y^{-1}$ **15.** $\dfrac{2}{3}z^{-2}$ **16.** $\dfrac{4}{5}a^{-4}$

17. $\dfrac{5}{b^{-8}}$ **18.** $\dfrac{-3}{v^{-3}}$ **19.** $\dfrac{1}{3x^{-2}}$ **20.** $\dfrac{2}{5c^{-6}}$

21. $(ab^5)^0$ **22.** $(32x^3y^4)^0$ **23.** $-(3p^2q^5)^0$ **24.** $-\left(\dfrac{2}{3}xy\right)^0$

25. $\dfrac{y^7}{y^3}$ **26.** $\dfrac{z^9}{z^2}$ **27.** $\dfrac{a^8}{a^5}$ **28.** $\dfrac{c^{12}}{c^5}$

29. $\dfrac{p^5}{p}$ **30.** $\dfrac{w^9}{w}$ **31.** $\dfrac{4x^8}{2x^5}$ **32.** $\dfrac{12z^7}{4z^3}$

33. $\dfrac{22k^5}{11k^4}$ **34.** $\dfrac{14m^{11}}{7m^{10}}$ **35.** $\dfrac{m^9n^7}{m^4n^5}$ **36.** $\dfrac{y^5z^6}{yz^3}$

37. $\dfrac{6r^4}{4r^2}$ **38.** $\dfrac{8x^9}{12x^6}$ **39.** $\dfrac{-16a^7}{24a^6}$ **40.** $\dfrac{-18b^5}{27b^4}$

41. $\dfrac{y^3}{y^8}$ **42.** $\dfrac{z^4}{z^6}$ **43.** $\dfrac{a^5}{a^{11}}$ **44.** $\dfrac{m}{m^7}$

45. $\dfrac{4x^2}{12x^5}$

46. $\dfrac{6y^8}{8y^9}$

47. $\dfrac{-12x}{-18x^6}$

48. $\dfrac{-24c^2}{-36c^{11}}$

49. $\dfrac{x^6y^5}{x^8y}$

50. $\dfrac{a^3b^2}{a^2b^3}$

51. $\dfrac{2m^6n^2}{5m^9n^{10}}$

52. $\dfrac{5r^3t^7}{6r^5t^7}$

53. $\dfrac{pq^3}{p^4q^4}$

54. $\dfrac{a^4b^5}{a^5b^6}$

55. $\dfrac{3x^4y^5}{6x^4y^8}$

56. $\dfrac{14a^3b^6}{21a^5b^6}$

57. $\dfrac{14x^4y^6z^2}{16x^3y^9z}$

58. $\dfrac{24a^2b^7c^9}{36a^7b^5c}$

59. $\dfrac{15mn^9p^3}{30m^4n^9p}$

60. $\dfrac{25x^4y^7z^2}{20x^5y^9z^{11}}$

61. $(-2xy^{-2})^3$

62. $(-3x^{-1}y^2)^2$

63. $(3x^{-1}y^{-2})^2$

64. $(5xy^{-3})^{-2}$

65. $(2x^{-1})(x^{-3})$

66. $(-2x^{-5})x^7$

67. $(-5a^2)(a^{-5})^2$

68. $(2a^{-3})(a^7b^{-1})^3$

69. $(-2ab^{-2})(4a^{-2}b)^{-2}$

70. $(3ab^{-2})(2a^{-1}b)^{-3}$

71. $(-5x^{-2}y)(-2x^{-2}y^2)$

72. $\dfrac{a^{-3}b^{-4}}{a^2b^2}$

73. $\dfrac{3x^{-2}y^2}{6xy^2}$

74. $\dfrac{2x^{-2}y}{8xy}$

75. $\dfrac{3x^{-2}y}{xy}$

76. $\dfrac{2x^{-1}y^4}{x^2y^3}$

77. $\dfrac{2x^{-1}y^{-4}}{4xy^2}$

78. $\dfrac{(x^{-1}y)^2}{xy^2}$

79. $\dfrac{(x^{-2}y)^2}{x^2y^3}$

80. $\dfrac{(x^{-3}y^{-2})^2}{x^6y^8}$

81. $\dfrac{(a^{-2}y^3)^{-3}}{a^2y}$

82. $\dfrac{12a^2b^3}{-27a^2b^2}$

83. $\dfrac{-16xy^4}{96x^4y^4}$

84. $\dfrac{-8x^2y^4}{44y^2z^5}$

85. $\dfrac{22a^2b^4}{-132b^3c^2}$

86. $\dfrac{-(8a^2b^4)^3}{64a^3b^8}$

87. $\dfrac{-(14ab^4)^2}{28a^4b^2}$

88. $\dfrac{(2a^{-2}b^3)^{-2}}{(4a^2b^{-4})^{-1}}$

89. $\dfrac{(3^{-1}r^4s^{-3})^{-2}}{(6r^2s^{-1}t^{-2})^2}$

90. $\left(\dfrac{6x^{-4}yz^{-1}}{14xy^{-4}z^2}\right)^{-3}$

91. $\left(\dfrac{15m^3n^{-2}p^{-1}}{25m^{-2}n^{-4}}\right)^{-3}$

92. $\left(\dfrac{18a^4b^{-2}c^4}{12ab^{-3}d^2}\right)^{-2}$

Objective B

Write in scientific notation.

93. 0.00000000324

94. 0.00000012

95. 0.000000000000000003

96. 1,800,000,000

97. 32,000,000,000,000,000

98. 76,700,000,000,000

99. 0.000000000000000000122

100. 0.00137

101. 547,000,000

Write in decimal notation.

102. 2.3×10^{-12}

103. 1.67×10^{-4}

104. 2×10^{15}

105. 6.8×10^7

106. 9×10^{-21}

107. 3.05×10^{-5}

108. 9.05×10^{11}

109. 1.02×10^{-9}

110. 7.2×10^{-3}

111. Avogadro's number is used in chemistry, and its value is approximately 602,300,000,000,000,000,000,000. Express this number in scientific notation.

112. 5,980,000,000,000,000,000,000,000 kg is the aproximate mass of the earth. Write the mass of the earth in scientific notation.

113. The length of an infrared light wave is approximately 0.0000037 m. Write this number in scientific notation.

114. Light travels approximately 16,000,000,000 mi in one day. Write this number in scientific notation.

115. One unit used to measure the speed of a computer is the picosecond. One picosecond is 0.000000001 s. Write this number in scientific notation.

116. One light-year is the distance traveled by light in 1 year. One light-year is 5,880,000,000,000 mi. Write this number in scientific notation.

117. The electric charge on an electron is 0.00000000000000000016 coulomb. Write this number in scientific notation.

118. Approximately 35 teragrams (3.5×10^{13} g) of sulfur in the atmosphere is converted to sulfate each year. Write this number in decimal notation.

APPLYING THE CONCEPTS

119. Evaluate 2^x when $x = -2, -1, 0, 1,$ and 2.

120. Evaluate 3^x when $x = -2, -1, 0, 1,$ and 2.

121. Evaluate 2^{-x} when $x = -2, -1, 0, 1,$ and 2.

122. Evaluate 3^{-x} when $x = -2, -1, 0, 1,$ and 2.

Determine whether each equation for Exercises 123 to 125 is true or false. If the equation is false, change the right-hand side of the equation to make a true equation.

123. $(2a)^{-3} = \dfrac{2}{a^3}$

124. $\dfrac{x^{-3}}{y^{-3}} = \left(\dfrac{x}{y}\right)^{-3}$

125. $(2 + 3)^{-1} = 2^{-1} + 3^{-1}$

126. Simplify: $\left(\dfrac{6x^4yz^3}{2x^2y^3}\right)\left(\dfrac{2x^2z^3}{4y^2z}\right) \div \left(\dfrac{6x^2y^3}{x^4y^2z}\right)$

127. If x is a nonzero real number, is x^{-2} always positive, always negative, or positive or negative depending on whether x is positive or negative? Explain your answer.

4.5 Division of Polynomials

Objective A   *To divide a polynomial by a monomial* ....

To divide a polynomial by a monomial, divide each term in the numerator by the denominator and write the sum of the quotients.

➡ Simplify: $\dfrac{6x^3 - 3x^2 + 9x}{3x}$

$$\frac{6x^3 - 3x^2 + 9x}{3x} = \frac{6x^3}{3x} - \frac{3x^2}{3x} + \frac{9x}{3x}$$

 • Divide each term of the polynomial by the monomial.

$$= 2x^2 - x + 3$$

 • Simplify each expression.

Example 1   Simplify: $\dfrac{12x^2y - 6xy + 4x^2}{2xy}$

Solution

$$\frac{12x^2y - 6xy + 4x^2}{2xy} = \frac{12x^2y}{2xy} - \frac{6xy}{2xy} + \frac{4x^2}{2xy} = 6x - 3 + \frac{2x}{y}$$

You Try It 1   Simplify: $\dfrac{24x^2y^2 - 18xy + 6y}{6xy}$

Your solution

Solution on p. S9

Objective B   *To divide polynomials* ....

The procedure for dividing two polynomials is similar to the one for dividing whole numbers. The same equation used to check division of whole numbers is used to check polynomial division.

(Quotient × divisor) + remainder = dividend

➡ Simplify: $(x^2 - 5x + 8) \div (x - 3)$

Step 1

$$\begin{array}{r} x \phantom{{}-5x+8} \\ x - 3 \overline{) x^2 - 5x + 8} \\ \underline{x^2 - 3x} \\ -2x + 8 \end{array}$$

 • Think: $x\overline{)x^2} = \dfrac{x^2}{x} = x$

 • Multiply: $x(x - 3) = x^2 - 3x$

 • Subtract: $(x^2 - 5x) - (x^2 - 3x) = -2x$
   Bring down the 8.

Step 2

$$\begin{array}{r} x - 2 \\ x - 3 \overline{) x^2 - 5x + 8} \\ \underline{x^2 - 3x} \\ -2x + 8 \\ \underline{-2x + 6} \\ 2 \end{array}$$

 • Think: $x\overline{)-2x} = \dfrac{-2x}{x} = -2$

 • Multiply: $-2(x - 3) = -2x + 6$

 • Subtract: $(-2x + 8) - (-2x + 6) = 2$
 • The remainder is 2.

Check: $(x - 2)(x - 3) + 2 = x^2 - 5x + 6 + 2 = x^2 - 5x + 8$

$$(x^2 - 5x + 8) \div (x - 3) = x - 2 + \frac{2}{x - 3}$$

If a term is missing from the dividend, a zero can be inserted for that term. This helps keep like terms in the same column.

➡ Simplify: $(6x + 26 + 2x^3) \div (2 + x)$

$(2x^3 + 6x + 26) \div (x + 2)$

$$
\begin{array}{r}
2x^2 - 4x + 14 \\
x + 2 \overline{)2x^3 + 0 \quad + 6x + 26} \\
\underline{2x^3 + 4x^2} \\
-4x^2 + 6x \\
\underline{-4x^2 - 8x} \\
14x + 26 \\
\underline{14x + 28} \\
-2
\end{array}
$$

- Arrange the terms of each polynomial in descending order.

- There is no x^2 term in $2x^3 + 6x + 26$. Insert a zero for the missing term.

Check:
$(2x^2 - 4x + 14)(x + 2) + (-2) = (2x^3 + 6x + 28) + (-2) = 2x^3 + 6x + 26$

$(2x^3 + 6x + 26) \div (x + 2) = 2x^2 - 4x + 14 - \dfrac{2}{x + 2}$

Example 2
Simplify: $(8x^2 + 4x^3 + x - 4) \div (2x + 3)$

Solution

$$
\begin{array}{r}
2x^2 + \;\; x - 1 \\
2x + 3 \overline{)4x^3 + 8x^2 + \;\; x - 4} \\
\underline{4x^3 + 6x^2} \\
2x^2 + \;\; x \\
\underline{2x^2 + 3x} \\
-2x - 4 \\
\underline{-2x - 3} \\
-1
\end{array}
$$

- Write the dividend in descending powers of x.

$(4x^3 + 8x^2 + x - 4) \div (2x + 3)$

$\quad = 2x^2 + x - 1 - \dfrac{1}{2x + 3}$

You Try It 2
Simplify: $(2x^3 + x^2 - 8x - 3) \div (2x - 3)$

Your solution

Example 3
Simplify: $(x^2 - 1) \div (x + 1)$

Solution

$$
\begin{array}{r}
x - 1 \\
x + 1 \overline{)x^2 + 0 - 1} \\
\underline{x^2 + x} \\
-x - 1 \\
\underline{-x - 1} \\
0
\end{array}
$$

- Insert a zero for the missing term.

$(x^2 - 1) \div (x + 1) = x - 1$

You Try It 3
Simplify: $(x^3 - 2x + 1) \div (x - 1)$

Your solution

Solutions on p. S9

4.5 Exercises

. . . .

Objective A

Simplify.

1. $\dfrac{10a - 25}{5}$

2. $\dfrac{16b - 40}{8}$

3. $\dfrac{6y^2 + 4y}{y}$

4. $\dfrac{4b^3 - 3b}{b}$

5. $\dfrac{3x^2 - 6x}{3x}$

6. $\dfrac{10y^2 - 6y}{2y}$

7. $\dfrac{5x^2 - 10x}{-5x}$

8. $\dfrac{3y^2 - 27y}{-3y}$

9. $\dfrac{x^3 + 3x^2 - 5x}{x}$

10. $\dfrac{a^3 - 5a^2 + 7a}{a}$

11. $\dfrac{x^6 - 3x^4 - x^2}{x^2}$

12. $\dfrac{a^8 - 5a^5 - 3a^3}{a^2}$

13. $\dfrac{5x^2y^2 + 10xy}{5xy}$

14. $\dfrac{8x^2y^2 - 24xy}{8xy}$

15. $\dfrac{9y^6 - 15y^3}{-3y^3}$

16. $\dfrac{4x^4 - 6x^2}{-2x^2}$

17. $\dfrac{3x^2 - 2x + 1}{x}$

18. $\dfrac{8y^2 + 2y - 3}{y}$

19. $\dfrac{-3x^2 + 7x - 6}{x}$

20. $\dfrac{2y^2 - 6y + 9}{y}$

21. $\dfrac{16a^2b - 20ab + 24ab^2}{4ab}$

22. $\dfrac{22a^2b - 11ab - 33ab^2}{11ab}$

23. $\dfrac{9x^2y + 6xy - 3xy^2}{xy}$

24. $\dfrac{5a^2b - 15ab + 30ab^2}{5ab}$

Objective B

Simplify.

25. $(b^2 - 14b + 49) \div (b - 7)$

26. $(x^2 - x - 6) \div (x - 3)$

27. $(y^2 + 2y - 35) \div (y + 7)$

28. $(2x^2 + 5x + 2) \div (x + 2)$

29. $(2y^2 - 13y + 21) \div (y - 3)$

30. $(4x^2 - 16) \div (2x + 4)$

31. $(2y^2 + 7) \div (y - 3)$

32. $(x^2 + 1) \div (x - 1)$

33. $(x^2 + 4) \div (x + 2)$

34. $(6x^2 - 7x) \div (3x - 2)$

35. $(6y^2 + 2y) \div (2y + 4)$

36. $(5x^2 + 7x) \div (x - 1)$

37. $(6x^2 - 5) \div (x + 2)$

38. $(a^2 + 5a + 10) \div (a + 2)$

39. $(b^2 - 8b - 9) \div (b - 3)$

40. $(2y^2 - 9y + 8) \div (2y + 3)$

41. $(3x^2 + 5x - 4) \div (x - 4)$

42. $(8x + 3 + 4x^2) \div (2x - 1)$

43. $(10 + 21y + 10y^2) \div (2y + 3)$

44. $(15a^2 - 8a - 8) \div (3a + 2)$

45. $(12a^2 - 25a - 7) \div (3a - 7)$

46. $(5 - 23x + 12x^2) \div (4x - 1)$

47. $(24 + 6a^2 + 25a) \div (3a - 1)$

48. $(x^3 + 3x^2 + 5x + 3) \div (x + 1)$

49. $(x^3 - 6x^2 + 7x - 2) \div (x - 1)$

50. $(x^4 - x^2 - 6) \div (x^2 + 2)$

51. $(x^4 + 3x^2 - 10) \div (x^2 - 2)$

APPLYING THE CONCEPTS

52. In your own words, explain how to divide exponential expressions.

53. The product of a monomial and $4b$ is $12ab^2$. Find the monomial.

Focus on Problem Solving

Dimensional Analysis

In solving application problems, it may be useful to include the units in order to organize the problem so that the answer is in the proper units. Using units to organize and check the correctness of an application is called **dimensional analysis.** We use the operations of multiplying units and dividing units in applying dimensional analysis to application problems.

The Rule for Multiplying Exponential Expressions states that we multiply two expressions with the same base by adding the exponents.

$$x^4 \cdot x^6 = x^{4+6} = x^{10}$$

In calculations that involve quantities, the units are operated on algebraically.

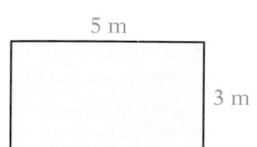

➡ A rectangle measures 3 m by 5 m. Find the area of the rectangle.

$A = LW = (3 \text{ m})(5 \text{ m}) = (3 \cdot 5)(\text{m} \cdot \text{m}) = 15 \text{ m}^2$

The area of the rectangle is 15 m² (square meters).

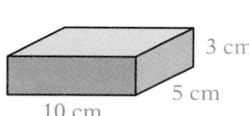

➡ A box measures 10 cm by 5 cm by 3 cm. Find the volume of the box.

$V = LWH = (10 \text{ cm})(5 \text{ cm})(3 \text{ cm}) = (10 \cdot 5 \cdot 3)(\text{cm} \cdot \text{cm} \cdot \text{cm}) = 150 \text{ cm}^3$

The volume of the box is 150 cm³ (cubic centimeters).

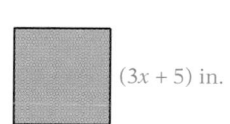

➡ Find the area of a square whose side measures $(3x + 5)$ in.

$A = s^2 = [(3x + 5) \text{ in.}]^2 = (3x + 5)^2 \text{ in}^2 = (9x^2 + 30x + 25) \text{ in}^2$

The area of the square is $(9x^2 + 30x + 25)$ in² (square inches).

Dimensional analysis is used in the conversion of units.

The following example converts the unit miles to feet. The equivalent measures 1 mi = 5280 ft are used to form the following rates, which are called conversion factors: $\dfrac{1 \text{ mi}}{5280 \text{ ft}}$ and $\dfrac{5280 \text{ ft}}{1 \text{ mi}}$. Because 1 mi = 5280 ft, both of the conversion factors

$\dfrac{1 \text{ mi}}{5280 \text{ ft}}$ and $\dfrac{5280 \text{ ft}}{1 \text{ mi}}$ are equal to 1.

To convert 3 mi to feet, multiply 3 mi by the conversion factor $\dfrac{5280 \text{ ft}}{1 \text{ mi}}$.

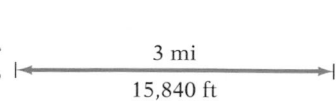

$$3 \text{ mi} = 3 \text{ mi} \cdot \boxed{1} = \frac{3 \text{ mi}}{1} \cdot \boxed{\frac{5280 \text{ ft}}{1 \text{ mi}}} = \frac{3 \text{ mi} \cdot 5280 \text{ ft}}{1 \text{ mi}} = 3 \cdot 5280 \text{ ft} = 15{,}840 \text{ ft}$$

There are two important points in the above illustration. First, you can think of dividing the numerator and denominator by the common unit "mile" just as you would divide the numerator and denominator of a fraction by a common factor. Second, the conversion factor $\dfrac{5280 \text{ ft}}{1 \text{ mi}}$ is equal to 1, and multiplying an expression by 1 does not change the value of the expression.

In the application problem that follows, the units are kept in the problem while the problem is worked.

In 1980, a horse named Fiddle Isle ran a 1.5-mile race in 2.38 min. Find Fiddle Isle's average speed for that race in miles per hour. Round to the nearest tenth.

Strategy   To find the average speed, use the formula $r = \dfrac{d}{t}$, where r is the speed, d is the distance, and t is the time. Use the conversion factor $\dfrac{60 \text{ min}}{1 \text{ h}}$.

Solution $r = \dfrac{d}{t} = \dfrac{1.5 \text{ mi}}{2.38 \text{ min}} = \dfrac{1.5 \text{ mi}}{2.38 \text{ min}} \cdot \dfrac{60 \text{ min}}{1 \text{ h}}$

$= \dfrac{90 \text{ mi}}{2.38 \text{ h}} \approx 37.8 \text{ mph}$

Fiddle Isle's average speed was 37.8 mph.

Try each of the following problems. Round to the nearest tenth.

1. Convert 88 ft/s to miles per hour.

2. Convert 8 m/s to kilometers per hour (1 km = 1000 m).

3. A carpet is to be placed in a meeting hall that is 36 ft wide and 80 ft long. At $21.50 per square yard, how much will it cost to carpet the meeting hall?

4. A carpet is to be placed in a room that is 20 ft wide and 30 ft long. At $22.25 per square yard, how much will it cost to carpet the area?

5. Find the number of gallons of water in a fish tank that is 36 in. long and 24 in. wide and is filled to a depth of 16 in. (1 gal = 231 in³).

6. Find the number of gallons of water in a fish tank that is 24 in. long and 18 in. wide and is filled to a depth of 12 in. (1 gal = 231 in³).

7. A $\frac{1}{4}$-acre commercial lot is on sale for $2.15 per square foot. Find the sale price of the commercial lot (1 acre = 43,560 ft²).

8. A 0.75-acre industrial parcel was sold for $98,010. Find the parcel's price per square foot (1 acre = 43,560 ft²).

9. A new driveway will require 800 ft³ of concrete. Concrete is ordered by the cubic yard. How much concrete should be ordered?

10. A piston-engined dragster traveled 440 yd in 4.936 s at Ennis, Texas, on October 9, 1988. Find the average speed of the dragster in miles per hour.

11. The Marianas Trench in the Pacific Ocean is the deepest part of the ocean. The depth is 6.85 mi. The speed of sound under water is 4700 ft/s. Find the time it takes sound to travel from the surface to the bottom of the Marianas Trench and back.

Projects and Group Activities

Pascal's Triangle

Simplifying the power of a binomial is called *expanding the binomial*. The expansion of the first three powers of a binomial is shown below.

$$(a + b)^1 = a + b$$

$$(a + b)^2 = (a + b)(a + b) = a^2 + 2ab + b^2$$

$$(a + b)^3 = (a + b)^2(a + b) = (a^2 + 2ab + b^2)(a + b) = a^3 + 3a^2b + 3ab^2 + b^3$$

POINT OF INTEREST

Pascal did not invent the triangle of numbers known as Pascal's Triangle. It was known to mathematicians in China probably as early as 1050 A.D. But Pascal's *Traite du triangle arithmetique* (*Treatise Concerning the Arithmetical Triangle*) brought together all the different aspects of the numbers for the first time.

Find $(a + b)^4$. [*Hint*: $(a + b)^4 = (a + b)^3(a + b)$]

Find $(a + b)^5$. [*Hint*: $(a + b)^5 = (a + b)^4(a + b)$]

If we continue in this way, the results for $(a + b)^6$ are

$$(a + b)^6 = a^6 + 6a^5b + 15a^4b^2 + 20a^3b^3 + 15a^2b^4 + 6ab^5 + b^6$$

Now expand $(a + b)^8$. Before you begin, see if you can find a pattern that will assist in writing the expansion of $(a + b)^8$ without having to multiply it out. Here are some hints.

1. Write out the variable terms of each binomial expansion from $(a + b)^1$ through $(a + b)^6$. Observe how the exponents on the variables change.
2. Write out the coefficients of all the terms without the variable parts. It will be helpful to make a triangular arrangement as shown at the left. Note that each row begins and ends with a 1. Also note in the two shaded regions that any number in a row is the sum of the two closest numbers above it. For instance, $1 + 5 = 6$ and $6 + 4 = 10$.

1 1
1 2 1
1 3 3 1
1 4 6 4 1
1 5 10 10 5 1
1 6 15 20 15 6 1

The triangle of numbers shown at the left is called Pascal's Triangle. To find the expansion of $(a + b)^8$, you need to find the eighth row of Pascal's Triangle. First find row seven. Then find row eight and use the patterns you have observed to write the expansion $(a + b)^8$.

Pascal's Triangle has been the subject of extensive analysis, and many patterns have been found. See if you can find some of them.

Chapter Summary

Key Words

A *monomial* is a number, a variable, or a product of a number and variables.

A *polynomial* is a variable expression in which the terms are monomials. A polynomial of one term is a *monomial*. A polynomial of two terms is a *binomial*. A polynomial of three terms is a *trinomial*.

The *degree of a polynomial* in one variable is the greatest of the degrees of any of its terms.

The *opposite of a polynomial* is the polynomial with the sign of every term changed.

A number written in *scientific notation* is a number written in the form $a \times 10^n$, where $1 \leq a < 10$ and n is an integer.

Essential Rules

Rule for Multiplying Exponential Expressions

$$x^m \cdot x^n = x^{m+n}$$

Rule for Simplifying the Power of an Exponential Expression

$$(x^m)^n = x^{mn}$$

Rule for Simplifying Powers of Products

$$(x^m y^n)^p = x^{mp} y^{np}$$

Definition of Zero as an Exponent

For $x \neq 0$, $x^0 = 1$.

Definition of a Negative Exponent

For $x \neq 0$, $x^{-n} = \dfrac{1}{x^n}$ and $\dfrac{1}{x^{-n}} = x^n$.

Rule for Simplifying Powers of Quotients

For $y \neq 0$, $\left(\dfrac{x^m}{y^n}\right)^p = \dfrac{x^{mp}}{y^{np}}$.

Rule for Negative Exponents on Fractional Expressions

For $a \neq 0$, $b \neq 0$, $\left(\dfrac{a}{b}\right)^{-n} = \left(\dfrac{b}{a}\right)^n$.

Rule for Dividing Exponential Expressions

For $x \neq 0$, $\dfrac{x^m}{x^n} = x^{m-n}$.

The Sum and Difference of Two Terms

$$(a + b)(a - b) = a^2 - b^2$$

The Square of a Binomial

$$(a + b)^2 = a^2 + 2ab + b^2$$
$$(a - b)^2 = a^2 - 2ab + b^2$$

Addition of Polynomials

To add polynomials, add the coefficients of the like terms.

Subtraction of Polynomials

To subtract two polynomials, add the opposite of the second polynomial to the first.

The FOIL Method

Add the products of the **F**irst terms, the **O**uter terms, the **I**nner terms, and the **L**ast terms.

Scientific Notation

To express a number in scientific notation, write it in the form $a \times 10^n$, where a is a number between 1 and 10, and n is an integer. If the number is greater than 10, the exponent on 10 will be positive. If the number is less than 1, the exponent on 10 will be negative.

$$367{,}000{,}000 = 3.67 \times 10^8$$

$$0.0000059 = 5.9 \times 10^{-6}$$

To change a number written in scientific notation to decimal notation, move the decimal point to the right if the exponent on 10 is positive and to the left if the exponent on 10 is negative. Move the decimal point the same number of places as the absolute value of the exponent on 10.

$$2.418 \times 10^7 = 24{,}180{,}000$$

$$9.06 \times 10^{-5} = 0.0000906$$

Chapter Review

1. Simplify: $(2b - 3)(4b + 5)$

2. Simplify: $(12y^2 + 17y - 4) + (9y^2 - 13y + 3)$

3. Simplify: $(b^3 - 2b^2 - 33b - 7) \div (b - 7)$

4. Simplify: $(xy^5z^3)(x^3y^3z)$

5. Simplify: $-2x(4x^2 + 7x - 9)$

6. Simplify: $\dfrac{(4a^{-2}b^{-3})^2}{(2a^{-1}b^{-2})^4}$

7. Simplify: $(2^3)^2$

8. Simplify: $(5x^2 - 2x - 1) - (3x^2 - 5x + 7)$

9. Simplify: $\dfrac{8x^{12}}{12x^9}$

10. Simplify: $(5y - 7)^2$

11. Simplify: $(5a^7b^6)^2(4ab)$

12. Simplify: $\dfrac{12b^7 + 36b^5 - 3b^3}{3b^3}$

13. Simplify: $(13y^3 - 7y - 2) - (12y^2 - 2y - 1)$

14. Simplify: $(5a^2 + 6a - 11) + (5a^2 + 6a - 11)$

15. Simplify: $(3y^2 + 4y - 7)(2y + 3)$

16. Simplify: $\dfrac{-18a^6b}{27a^3b^4}$

17. Simplify: $2ab^3(4a^2 - 2ab + 3b^2)$

18. Simplify: $(6y^2 + 2y + 7) - (8y^2 + y + 12)$

19. Simplify: $(-3x^2y^3)^2$

20. Simplify: $(6b^3 - 2b^2 - 5)(2b^2 - 1)$

21. Simplify: $(2x^3 + 7x^2 + x) + (2x^2 - 4x - 12)$

22. Simplify: $\dfrac{16y^2 - 32y}{-4y}$

23. Simplify: $(a + 7)(a - 7)$

24. Simplify: $(2a^{12}b^3)(-9b^2c^6)(3ac)$

25. Simplify: $(6y^2 - 35y + 36) \div (3y - 4)$

26. Simplify: $(-3x^{-2}y^{-3})^{-2}$

27. Simplify: $(5xy^2)(-4x^2y^3)$

28. Simplify: $(5a - 7)(2a + 9)$

29. Write 0.000000127 in scientific notation.

30. Write 3.2×10^{-12} in decimal notation.

31. The length of a Ping-Pong table is 1 ft less than twice the width of the table. Let w represent the width of the Ping-Pong table. Express the area of the table in terms of the variable w.

32. The side of a checkerboard is $(3x - 2)$ in. Express the area of the checker-board in terms of the variable x.

Chapter Test

1. Simplify: $2x(2x^2 - 3x)$

2. Simplify: $\dfrac{12x^3 - 3x^2 + 9}{3x^2}$

3. Simplify: $\dfrac{12x^2}{-3x^8}$

4. Simplify: $(-2xy^2)(3x^2y^4)$

5. Simplify: $(x^2 + 1) \div (x + 1)$

6. Simplify: $(x - 3)(x^2 - 4x + 5)$

7. Simplify: $(-2a^2b)^3$

8. Simplify: $\dfrac{(3x^{-2}y^3)^3}{3x^4y^{-1}}$

9. Simplify: $(a - 2b)(a + 5b)$

10. Simplify: $\dfrac{16x^5 - 8x^3 + 20x}{4x}$

11. Simplify: $(x^2 + 6x - 7) \div (x - 1)$

12. Simplify: $-3y^2(-2y^2 + 3y - 6)$

13. Simplify: $(-2x^3 + x^2 - 7)(2x - 3)$

14. Simplify: $(4y - 3)(4y + 3)$

15. Simplify: $(ab^2)(a^3b^5)$

16. Simplify: $\dfrac{2a^{-1}b}{2^{-2}a^{-2}b^{-3}}$

17. Simplify: $\dfrac{20a - 35}{5}$

18. Simplify: $(3a^2 - 2a - 7) - (5a^3 + 2a - 10)$

19. Simplify: $(2x - 5)^2$

20. Simplify: $(4x^2 - 7) \div (2x - 3)$

21. Simplify: $\dfrac{-(2x^2y)^3}{4x^3y^3}$

22. Simplify: $(2x - 7y)(5x - 4y)$

23. Simplify: $(3x^3 - 2x^2 - 4) + (8x^2 - 8x + 7)$

24. Write 0.00000000302 in scientific notation.

25. The radius of a circle is $(x - 5)$ m. Use the equation $A = \pi r^2$, where r is the radius, to find the area of the circle in terms of the variable x. Leave the answer in terms of π.

Cumulative Review

1. Simplify: $\frac{3}{16} \cdot \left(-\frac{5}{8}\right) - \frac{7}{9}$

2. Evaluate $-3^2 \cdot \left(\frac{2}{3}\right)^3 \cdot \left(-\frac{5}{8}\right)$.

3. Simplify: $\left(-\frac{1}{2}\right)^3 \div \left(\frac{3}{8} - \frac{5}{6}\right) + 2$

4. Evaluate $\frac{b - (a - b)^2}{b^2}$ when $a = -2$ and $b = 3$.

5. Simplify: $-2x - (-xy) + 7x - 4xy$

6. Simplify: $(12x)\left(-\frac{3}{4}\right)$

7. Simplify: $-2[3x - 2(4 - 3x) + 2]$

8. Solve: $12 = -\frac{3}{4}x$

9. Solve: $2x - 9 = 3x + 7$

10. Solve: $2 - 3(4 - x) = 2x + 5$

11. 35.2 is what percent of 160?

12. Simplify: $(4b^3 - 7b^2 - 7) + (3b^2 - 8b + 3)$

13. Simplify: $(3y^3 - 5y + 8) - (-2y^2 + 5y + 8)$

14. Simplify: $(a^3b^5)^3$

15. Simplify: $(4xy^3)(-2x^2y^3)$

16. Simplify: $-2y^2(-3y^2 - 4y + 8)$

17. Simplify: $(2a - 7)(5a^2 - 2a + 3)$

18. Simplify: $(3b - 2)(5b - 7)$

19. Simplify: $\dfrac{(-2a^2b^3)^2}{8a^4b^8}$

20. Simplify: $(a^2 - 4a - 21) \div (a + 3)$

21. Write 6.09×10^{-5} in decimal notation.

22. Translate "the difference between eight times a number and twice the number is eighteen" into an equation and solve.

23. Fifty ounces of orange juice are added to 200 oz of a fruit punch that is 10% orange juice. What is the percent concentration of orange juice in the resulting mixture?

24. A car traveling at 50 mph overtakes a cyclist who, riding at 10 mph, has had a two hour head start. How far from the starting point does the car overtake the cyclist?

25. The width of a rectangle is 40% of the length. The perimeter of the rectangle is 42 m. Find the length and width of the rectangle.

5

Factoring

Objectives

Section 5.1
To factor a monomial from a polynomial
To factor by grouping

Section 5.2
To factor a trinomial of the form $x^2 + bx + c$
To factor completely

Section 5.3
To factor a trinomial of the form $ax^2 + bx + c$
  by using trial factors
To factor a trinomial of the form $ax^2 + bx + c$
  by grouping

Section 5.4
To factor the difference of two squares and
  perfect-square trinomials
To factor completely

Section 5.5
To solve equations by factoring
To solve application problems

Technical writers translate technological information into easily understood language for use in training manuals, public relations brochures, and the like. The computer industry uses software technical writers to explain the programs that computers run. Generally these technical writers need to learn from programmers how things work before they write the descriptions. It is common for software technical writers to have a liberal arts degree with some courses in mathematics and science, which enable them to better understand technical instructions.

Algebra from Geometry

The early Babylonians made substantial progress in both algebra and geometry. Often the progress they made in algebra was based on geometric concepts.

Here are some geometric proofs of algebraic identities the Babylonians understood.

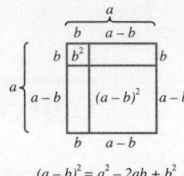

$$(a-b)^2 = a^2 - 2ab + b^2$$

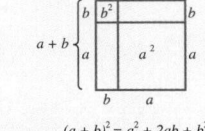

$$(a+b)^2 = a^2 + 2ab + b^2$$

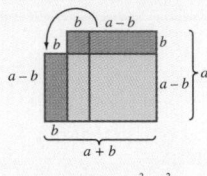

$$(a-b)(a+b) = a^2 - b^2$$

5.1   **Common Factors**

Objective A   ***To factor a monomial from a polynomial*** ....

The **greatest common factor (GCF)** of two or more monomials is the product of the GCF of the coefficients and the common variable factors.

$$6x^3y = 2 \cdot 3 \cdot x \cdot x \cdot x \cdot y$$
$$8x^2y^2 = 2 \cdot 2 \cdot 2 \cdot x \cdot x \cdot y \cdot y$$
$$\text{GCF} = 2 \cdot x \cdot x \cdot y = 2x^2y$$

Note that the exponent of each variable in the GCF is the same as the *smallest* exponent of that variable in either of the monomials.

The GCF of $6x^3y$ and $8x^2y^2$ is $2x^2y$.

➡ Find the GCF of $12a^4b$ and $18a^2b^2c$.

The common variable factors are a^2 and b. c is not a common variable factor.

$$12a^4b = 2 \cdot 2 \cdot 3 \cdot a^4 \cdot b$$
$$18a^2b^2c = 2 \cdot 3 \cdot 3 \cdot a^2 \cdot b^2 \cdot c$$
$$\text{GCF} = 2 \cdot 3 \cdot a^2 \cdot b = 6a^2b$$

To **factor** a polynomial means to write the polynomial as a product of other polynomials.

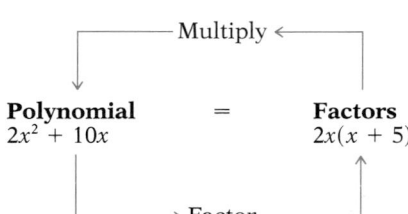

In the example above, $2x$ is the GCF of the terms $2x^2$ and $10x$. It is a **common factor** of the terms.

➡ Factor: $5x^3 - 35x^2 + 10x$

Find the GCF of the terms of the polynomial.

$$5x^3 = 5 \cdot x^3$$
$$35x^2 = 5 \cdot 7 \cdot x^2$$
$$10x = 2 \cdot 5 \cdot x$$

The GCF is $5x$.

Rewrite the polynomial, expressing each term as a product with the GCF as one of the factors.

$$5x^3 - 35x^2 + 10x = 5x(x^2) + 5x(-7x) + 5x(2)$$
$$= 5x(x^2 - 7x + 2)$$

• **Use the Distributive Property to write the polynomial as a product of factors.**

TAKE NOTE

At the right, the factors in parentheses are determined by dividing each term of the trinomial by the GCF, 5x.

$$\frac{5x^3}{5x} = x^2,$$

$$\frac{-35x^2}{5x} = -7x, \text{ and}$$

$$\frac{10x}{5x} = 2$$

➡ Factor: $21x^2y^3 - 6xy^5 + 15x^4y^2$

Find the GCF of the terms of the polynomial.

$$21x^2y^3 = 3 \cdot 7 \cdot x^2 \cdot y^3$$

$$6xy^5 = 2 \cdot 3 \cdot x \cdot y^5$$

$$15x^4y^2 = 3 \cdot 5 \cdot x^4 \cdot y^2$$

The GCF is $3xy^2$.

Rewrite the polynomial, expressing each term as a product with the GCF as one of the factors.

$$21x^2y^3 - 6xy^5 + 15x^4y^2 = 3xy^2(7xy) + 3xy^2(-2y^3) + 3xy^2(5x^3)$$

$$= 3xy^2(7xy - 2y^3 + 5x^3)$$

• **Use the Distributive Property to write the polynomial as a product of factors.**

Example 1

Factor: $8x^2 + 2xy$

Solution

The GCF is $2x$.

$$8x^2 + 2xy = 2x(4x) + 2x(y) = 2x(4x + y)$$

You Try It 1

Factor: $14a^2 - 21a^4b$

Your solution

Example 2

Factor: $n^3 - 5n^2 + 2n$

Solution

The GCF is n.

$$n^3 - 5n^2 + 2n = n(n^2) + n(-5n) + n(2)$$
$$= n(n^2 - 5n + 2)$$

You Try It 2

Factor: $27b^2 + 18b + 9$

Your solution

Example 3

Factor: $16x^2y + 8x^4y^2 - 12x^4y^5$

Solution

The GCF is $4x^2y$.

$$16x^2y + 8x^4y^2 - 12x^4y^5$$
$$= 4x^2y(4) + 4x^2y(2x^2y) + 4x^2y(-3x^2y^4)$$
$$= 4x^2y(4 + 2x^2y - 3x^2y^4)$$

You Try It 3

Factor: $6x^4y^2 - 9x^3y^2 + 12x^2y^4$

Your solution

Solutions on p. S10

Objective B   ***To factor by grouping*** ·······································

In the examples at the right, the binomials in parentheses are called **binomial factors.**

$$2a(a + b)^2$$
$$3xy(x - y)$$

The Distributive Property is used to factor a common binomial factor from an expression.

The common binomial factor of the expression $6x(x - 3) + y^2(x - 3)$ is $(x - 3)$. To factor that expression, use the Distributive Property to write the expression as a product of factors.

$$6x(x - 3) + y^2(x - 3) = (x - 3)(6x + y^2)$$

Consider the following simplification of $-(a - b)$.

$$-(a - b) = -1(a - b) = -a + b = b - a$$

Thus, $b - a = -(a - b)$

This equation is sometimes used to factor a common binomial from an expression.

➡ Factor: $2x(x - y) + 5(y - x)$

$$
\begin{aligned}
2x(x - y) + 5(y - x) &= 2x(x - y) - 5(x - y) \\
&= (x - y)(2x - 5)
\end{aligned}
$$

- $5(y - x) = 5[(-1)(x - y)]$
  $= -5(x - y)$

Some polynomials can be factored by grouping terms in such a way that a common binomial factor is found.

➡ Factor: $ax + bx - ay - by$

$$ax + bx - ay - by = (ax + bx) - (ay + by)$$

- **Group the first two terms and the last two terms. Note that** $-ay - by = -(ay + by)$.

$$
\begin{aligned}
&= x(a + b) - y(a + b) \\
&= (a + b)(x - y)
\end{aligned}
$$

- **Factor the GCF,** $(a + b)$, **from each group.**

➡ Factor: $6x^2 - 9x - 4xy + 6y$

$$6x^2 - 9x - 4xy + 6y = (6x^2 - 9x) - (4xy - 6y)$$

- **Group the first two terms and the last two terms. Note that** $-4xy + 6y = -(4xy - 6y)$.

$$
\begin{aligned}
&= 3x(2x - 3) - 2y(2x - 3) \\
&= (2x - 3)(3x - 2y)
\end{aligned}
$$

- **Factor the GCF,** $(2x - 3)$, **from each group.**

Example 4

Factor: $4x(3x - 2) - 7(3x - 2)$

Solution

$4x(3x - 2) - 7(3x - 2)$

$\quad = (3x - 2)(4x - 7)$

You Try It 4

Factor: $2y(5x - 2) - 3(2 - 5x)$

Your solution

Example 5

Factor: $9x^2 - 15x - 6xy + 10y$

Solution

$9x^2 - 15x - 6xy + 10y$

$\quad = (9x^2 - 15x) - (6xy - 10y)$

$\quad = 3x(3x - 5) - 2y(3x - 5)$

$\quad = (3x - 5)(3x - 2y)$

You Try It 5

Factor: $a^2 - 3a + 2ab - 6b$

Your solution

Example 6

Factor: $3x^2y - 4x - 15xy + 20$

Solution

$3x^2y - 4x - 15xy + 20$

$\quad = (3x^2y - 4x) - (15xy - 20)$

$\quad = x(3xy - 4) - 5(3xy - 4)$

$\quad = (3xy - 4)(x - 5)$

You Try It 6

Factor: $2mn^2 - n + 8mn - 4$

Your solution

Example 7

Factor: $4ab - 6 + 3b - 2ab^2$

Solution

$4ab - 6 + 3b - 2ab^2$

$\quad = (4ab - 6) + (3b - 2ab^2)$

$\quad = 2(2ab - 3) + b(3 - 2ab)$

$\quad = 2(2ab - 3) - b(2ab - 3)$

$\quad = (2ab - 3)(2 - b)$

You Try It 7

Factor: $2xy - 6y - 12 + 4x$

Your solution

Solutions on p. S10

5.1 Exercises

· ·

Objective A

Factor.

1. $5a + 5$ **2.** $7b - 7$ **3.** $16 - 8a^2$ **4.** $12 + 12y^2$ **5.** $8x + 12$

6. $16a - 24$ **7.** $30a - 6$ **8.** $20b + 5$ **9.** $7x^2 - 3x$ **10.** $12y^2 - 5y$

11. $3a^2 + 5a^5$ **12.** $9x - 5x^2$ **13.** $14y^2 + 11y$ **14.** $6b^3 - 5b^2$ **15.** $2x^4 - 4x$

16. $3y^4 - 9y$ **17.** $10x^4 - 12x^2$ **18.** $12a^5 - 32a^2$ **19.** $8a^8 - 4a^5$ **20.** $16y^4 - 8y^7$

21. $x^2y^2 - xy$ **22.** $a^2b^2 + ab$ **23.** $3x^2y^4 - 6xy$ **24.** $12a^2b^5 - 9ab$ **25.** $x^2y - xy^3$

26. $3x^3 + 6x^2 + 9x$ **27.** $5y^3 - 20y^2 + 10y$ **28.** $2x^4 - 4x^3 + 6x^2$ **29.** $3y^4 - 9y^3 - 6y^2$

30. $2x^3 + 6x^2 - 14x$ **31.** $3y^3 - 9y^2 + 24y$ **32.** $2y^5 - 3y^4 + 7y^3$ **33.** $6a^5 - 3a^3 - 2a^2$

34. $x^3y - 3x^2y^2 + 7xy^3$ **35.** $2a^2b - 5a^2b^2 + 7ab^2$ **36.** $5y^3 + 10y^2 - 25y$

37. $4b^5 + 6b^3 - 12b$ **38.** $3a^2b^2 - 9ab^2 + 15b^2$ **39.** $8x^2y^2 - 4x^2y + x^2$

Objective B

Factor.

40. $x(b + 4) + 3(b + 4)$ **41.** $y(a + z) + 7(a + z)$ **42.** $a(y - x) - b(y - x)$

43. $3r(a - b) + s(a - b)$ **44.** $x(x - 2) + y(2 - x)$ **45.** $t(m - 7) + 7(7 - m)$

46. $2x(7 + b) - y(b + 7)$

47. $2y(4a - b) - (b - 4a)$

48. $8c(2m - 3n) + (3n - 2m)$

49. $x^2 + 2x + 2xy + 4y$

50. $x^2 - 3x + 4ax - 12a$

51. $p^2 - 2p - 3rp + 6r$

52. $t^2 + 4t - st - 4s$

53. $ab + 6b - 4a - 24$

54. $xy - 5y - 2x + 10$

55. $2z^2 - z + 2yz - y$

56. $2y^2 - 10y + 7xy - 35x$

57. $8v^2 - 12vy + 14v - 21y$

58. $21x^2 + 6xy - 49x - 14y$

59. $2x^2 - 5x - 6xy + 15y$

60. $4a^2 + 5ab - 10b - 8a$

61. $3y^2 - 6y - ay + 2a$

62. $2ra + a^2 - 2r - a$

63. $3xy - y^2 - y + 3x$

64. $2ab - 3b^2 - 3b + 2a$

65. $3st + t^2 - 2t - 6s$

66. $4x^2 + 3xy - 12y - 16x$

APPLYING THE CONCEPTS

67. Factor: **a.** $2x^2 + 6x + 5x + 15$ **b.** $2x^2 + 5x + 6x + 15$

68. Look at parts a and b of Exercise 67. Do different groupings of the terms in a polynomial affect the binomial factors?

A natural number is a perfect number if it is the sum of all its factors less than itself. For example, 6 is a perfect number because all the factors of 6 that are less than 6 are 1, 2, and 3, and $1 + 2 + 3 = 6$.

69. Find the one perfect number between 20 and 30.

70. Find the one perfect number between 490 and 500.

71. In the equation $P = 2L + 2W$, what is the effect on P when the quantity $L + W$ doubles?

72. Write an expression in factored form for each of the shaded portions in the following diagrams. (Use the equation for the area of a rectangle $A = bh$ and the equation for the area of a circle $A = \pi r^2$.)

a.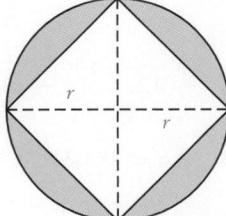

b.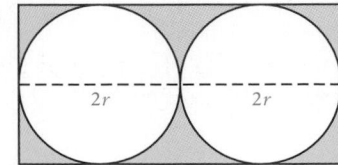

c.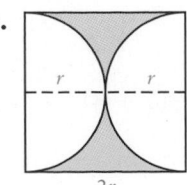

5.2 Factoring Polynomials of the Form $x^2 + bx + c$

Objective A   **To factor a trinomial of the form $x^2 + bx + c$** ....

Trinomials of the form $x^2 + bx + c$, where b and c are integers, are shown at the right.

$$x^2 + 8x + 12; b = 8, c = 12$$
$$x^2 - 7x + 12; b = -7, c = 12$$
$$x^2 - 2x - 15; b = -2, c = -15$$

To factor a trinomial of this form means to express the trinomial as the product of two binomials.

Trinomials expressed as the product of binomials are shown at the right.

$$x^2 + 8x + 12 = (x + 6)(x + 2)$$
$$x^2 - 7x + 12 = (x - 3)(x - 4)$$
$$x^2 - 2x - 15 = (x + 3)(x - 5)$$

The method by which factors of a trinomial are found is based on FOIL. Consider the following binomial products, noting the relationship between the constant terms of the binomials and the terms of the trinomials.

Signs in the binomials are the same.

$$(x + 6)(x + 2) = x^2 + 2x + 6x + (6)(2) = x^2 + 8x + 12$$
Sum of 6 and 2
Product of 6 and 2

$$(x - 3)(x - 4) = x^2 - 4x - 3x + (-3)(-4) = x^2 - 7x + 12$$
Sum of -3 and -4
Product of -3 and -4

Signs in the binomials are opposite.

$$(x + 3)(x - 5) = x^2 - 5x + 3x + (3)(-5) = x^2 - 2x - 15$$
Sum of 3 and -5
Product of 3 and -5

$$(x - 4)(x + 6) = x^2 + 6x - 4x + (-4)(6) = x^2 + 2x - 24$$
Sum of -4 and 6
Product of -4 and 6

IMPORTANT RELATIONSHIPS

1. When the constant term of the trinomial is positive, the constant terms of the binomials have the same sign. They are both positive when the coefficient of the x term in the trinomial is positive. They are both negative when the coefficient of the x term in the trinomial is negative.

2. When the constant term of the trinomial is negative, the constant terms of the binomials have opposite signs.

3. In the trinomial, the coefficient of x is the sum of the constant terms of the binomials.

4. In the trinomial, the constant term is the product of the constant terms of the binomials.

➡ Factor: $x^2 - 7x + 10$

Because the constant term is positive and the coefficient of x is negative, the binomial constants will be negative. Find two negative factors of 10 whose sum is -7. The results can be recorded in a table.

Negative Factors of 10	Sum
$-1, -10$	-11
$-2, -5$	-7

● These are the correct factors.

$x^2 - 7x + 10 = (x - 2)(x - 5)$ ● Write the trinomial as a product of its factors.

You can check the proposed factorization by multiplying the two binomials.

Check: $(x - 2)(x - 5) = x^2 - 5x - 2x + 10$
$$= x^2 - 7x + 10$$

TAKE NOTE

Always check your proposed factorization to ensure accuracy.

➡ Factor: $x^2 - 9x - 36$

The constant term is negative. The binomial constants will have opposite signs. Find two factors of -36 whose sum is -9.

Factors of -36	Sum
$+1, -36$	-35
$-1, +36$	35
$+2, -18$	-16
$-2, +18$	16
$+3, -12$	-9

● Once the correct factors are found, it is not necessary to try the remaining factors.

$x^2 - 9x - 36 = (x + 3)(x - 12)$

● Write the trinomial as a product of its factors.

➡ Factor: $x^2 + 7x + 8$

Because the constant term is positive and the coefficient of x is positive, the binomial constants will be positive. Find two positive factors of 8 whose sum is 7.

Positive Factors of 8	Sum
$1, 8$	9
$2, 4$	6

There are no positive integer factors of 8 whose sum is 7. The trinomial $x^2 + 7x + 8$ is said to be **nonfactorable over the integers.**

Just as 17 is a prime number, $x^2 + 7x + 8$ is a **prime polynomial.** Binomials of the form $x - a$ and $x + a$ are also prime polynomials.

Example 1
Factor: $x^2 - 8x + 15$

Solution
Find two negative factors of 15 whose sum is -8.

Factors	Sum
$-1, -15$	-16
$-3, -5$	-8

$x^2 - 8x + 15 = (x - 3)(x - 5)$

You Try It 1
Factor: $x^2 + 9x + 20$

Your solution

Solution on p. S10

Example 2

Factor: $x^2 + 6x - 27$

Solution

Find two factors of -27 whose sum is 6.

Factors	Sum
$+1, -27$	-26
$-1, +27$	26
$+3, -9$	-6
$-3, +9$	6

$x^2 + 6x - 27 = (x - 3)(x + 9)$

You Try It 2

Factor: $x^2 + 7x - 18$

Your solution

Solution on p. S10

Objective B   **To factor completely** ....

A polynomial is factored completely when it is written as a product of factors that are nonfactorable over the integers.

➡ Factor: $4y^3 - 4y^2 - 24y$

$$4y^3 - 4y^2 - 24y = 4y(y^2) - 4y(y) - 4y(6)$$ • The GCF is $4y$.

$$= 4y(y^2 - y - 6)$$ • Use the Distributive Property to factor out the GCF.

$$= 4y(y + 2)(y - 3)$$ • Factor $y^2 - y - 6$. The two factors of -6 whose sum is -1 are 2 and -3.

TAKE NOTE

The first step in *any* factoring problem is to determine whether the terms of the polynomial have a **common factor.** If they do, factor it out first.

It is always possible to check the proposed factorization by multiplying the polynomials. Here is the check for the last example.

Check: $4y(y + 2)(y - 3) = 4y(y^2 - 3y + 2y - 6)$

$$= 4y(y^2 - y - 6)$$

$$= 4y^3 - 4y^2 - 24y$$ • This is the original polynomial.

➡ Factor: $5x^2 + 60xy + 100y^2$

$$5x^2 + 60xy + 100y^2 = 5(x^2) + 5(12xy) + 5(20y^2)$$ • The GCF is 5.

$$= 5(x^2 + 12xy + 20y^2)$$ • Use the Distributive Property to factor out the GCF.

$$= 5(x + 2y)(x + 10y)$$ • Factor $x^2 + 12xy + 20y^2$. The two factors of 20 whose sum is 12 are 2 and 10.

TAKE NOTE

$2y$ and $10y$ are placed in the binomials. This is necessary so that the middle term contains xy and the last term contains y^2.

Note that $2y$ and $10y$ were placed in the binomials. The following check shows that was necessary.

Check: $5(x + 2y)(x + 10y) = 5(x^2 + 10xy + 2xy + 20y^2)$

$$= 5(x^2 + 12xy + 20y^2)$$

$$= 5x^2 + 60xy + 100y^2$$ • This is the original polynomial.

➡ Factor: $15 - 2x - x^2$

Because the coefficient of x^2 is -1, factor -1 from the trinomial and then write the resulting trinomial in descending order.

$$15 - 2x - x^2 = -(x^2 + 2x - 15)$$

$$= -(x + 5)(x - 3)$$

- $15 - 2x - x^2 = -1(-15 + 2x + x^2)$
  $$= -(x^2 + 2x - 15)$$
- Factor $x^2 + 2x - 15$. The two factors of -15 whose sum is 2 are 5 and -3.

Check: $-(x + 5)(x - 3) = -(x^2 + 2x - 15)$
$$= -x^2 - 2x + 15$$
$$= 15 - 2x - x^2$$

- This is the original polynomial.

Example 3
Factor: $-3x^3 + 9x^2 + 12x$

Solution
The GCF is $-3x$.
$-3x^3 + 9x^2 + 12x = -3x(x^2 - 3x - 4)$
Factor the trinomial $x^2 - 3x - 4$. Find two factors of -4 whose sum is -3.

Factors	Sum
$-2, +2$	0
$+1, -4$	-3

$-3x^3 + 9x^2 + 12x = -3x(x + 1)(x - 4)$

You Try It 3
Factor: $-2x^3 + 14x^2 - 12x$

Your solution

Example 4
Factor: $4x^2 - 40xy + 84y^2$

Solution
The GCF is 4.
$4x^2 - 40xy + 84y^2 = 4(x^2 - 10xy + 21y^2)$
Factor the trinomial $x^2 - 10xy + 21y^2$. Find two negative factors of 21 whose sum is -10.

Factors	Sum
$-1, -21$	-22
$-3, -7$	-10

$4x^2 - 40xy + 84y^2 = 4(x - 3y)(x - 7y)$

You Try It 4
Factor: $3x^2 - 9xy - 12y^2$

Your solution

Solutions on p. S10

5.2 Exercises

. . . .

Objective A

Factor.

1. $x^2 + 3x + 2$

2. $x^2 + 5x + 6$

3. $x^2 - x - 2$

4. $x^2 + x - 6$

5. $a^2 + a - 12$

6. $a^2 - 2a - 35$

7. $a^2 - 3a + 2$

8. $a^2 - 5a + 4$

9. $a^2 + a - 2$

10. $a^2 - 2a - 3$

11. $b^2 - 6b + 9$

12. $b^2 + 8b + 16$

13. $b^2 + 7b - 8$

14. $y^2 - y - 6$

15. $y^2 + 6y - 55$

16. $z^2 - 4z - 45$

17. $y^2 - 5y + 6$

18. $y^2 - 8y + 15$

19. $z^2 - 14z + 45$

20. $z^2 - 14z + 49$

21. $z^2 - 12z - 160$

22. $p^2 + 2p - 35$

23. $p^2 + 12p + 27$

24. $p^2 - 6p + 8$

25. $x^2 + 20x + 100$

26. $x^2 + 18x + 81$

27. $b^2 + 9b + 20$

28. $b^2 + 13b + 40$

29. $x^2 - 11x - 42$

30. $x^2 + 9x - 70$

31. $b^2 - b - 20$

32. $b^2 + 3b - 40$

33. $y^2 - 14y - 51$

34. $y^2 - y - 72$

35. $p^2 - 4p - 21$

36. $p^2 + 16p + 39$

37. $y^2 - 8y + 32$

38. $y^2 - 9y + 81$

39. $x^2 - 20x + 75$

40. $x^2 - 12x + 11$

41. $p^2 + 24p + 63$

42. $x^2 - 15x + 56$

43. $x^2 + 21x + 38$

44. $x^2 + x - 56$

45. $x^2 + 5x - 36$

46. $a^2 - 21a - 72$

47. $a^2 - 7a - 44$

48. $a^2 - 15a + 36$

49. $a^2 - 21a + 54$

50. $z^2 - 9z - 136$

51. $z^2 + 14z - 147$

52. $c^2 - c - 90$

53. $c^2 - 3c - 180$

54. $z^2 + 15z + 44$

55. $p^2 + 24p + 135$

56. $c^2 + 19c + 34$

57. $c^2 + 11c + 18$

58. $x^2 - 4x - 96$

59. $x^2 + 10x - 75$

60. $x^2 - 22x + 112$

61. $x^2 + 21x - 100$

62. $b^2 + 8b - 105$

63. $b^2 - 22b + 72$

64. $a^2 - 9a - 36$

65. $a^2 + 42a - 135$

66. $b^2 - 23b + 102$

67. $b^2 - 25b + 126$

68. $a^2 + 27a + 72$

69. $z^2 + 24z + 144$

70. $x^2 + 25x + 156$

71. $x^2 - 29x + 100$

72. $x^2 - 10x - 96$

73. $x^2 + 9x - 112$

Objective B

Factor.

74. $2x^2 + 6x + 4$

75. $3x^2 + 15x + 18$

76. $18 + 7x - x^2$

77. $12 - 4x - x^2$

78. $ab^2 + 2ab - 15a$

79. $ab^2 + 7ab - 8a$

80. $xy^2 - 5xy + 6x$

81. $xy^2 + 8xy + 15x$

82. $z^3 - 7z^2 + 12z$

83. $-2a^3 - 6a^2 - 4a$

84. $-3y^3 + 15y^2 - 18y$

85. $4y^3 + 12y^2 - 72y$

86. $3x^2 + 3x - 36$

87. $2x^3 - 2x^2 + 4x$

88. $5z^2 - 15z - 140$

89. $6z^2 + 12z - 90$

90. $2a^3 + 8a^2 - 64a$

91. $3a^3 - 9a^2 - 54a$

92. $x^2 - 5xy + 6y^2$

93. $x^2 + 4xy - 21y^2$

94. $a^2 - 9ab + 20b^2$

95. $a^2 - 15ab + 50b^2$

96. $x^2 - 3xy - 28y^2$

97. $s^2 + 2st - 48t^2$

98. $y^2 - 15yz - 41z^2$

99. $y^2 + 85xy + 36z^2$

100. $z^4 - 12z^3 + 35z^2$

101. $z^4 + 2z^3 - 80z^2$

102. $b^4 - 22b^3 + 120b^2$

103. $b^4 - 3b^3 - 10b^2$

104. $2y^4 - 26y^3 - 96y^2$

105. $3y^4 + 54y^3 + 135y^2$

106. $-x^4 - 7x^3 + 8x^2$

107. $-x^4 + 11x^3 + 12x^2$

108. $4x^2y + 20xy - 56y$

109. $3x^2y - 6xy - 45y$

110. $c^3 + 18c^2 - 40c$

111. $-3x^3 + 36x^2 - 81x$

112. $-4x^3 - 4x^2 + 24x$

113. $x^2 - 8xy + 15y^2$

114. $y^2 - 7xy - 8x^2$

115. $a^2 - 13ab + 42b^2$

116. $y^2 + 4yz - 21z^2$

117. $y^2 + 8yz + 7z^2$

118. $y^2 - 16yz + 15z^2$

119. $3x^2y + 60xy - 63y$

120. $4x^2y - 68xy - 72y$

121. $3x^3 + 3x^2 - 36x$

122. $4x^3 + 12x^2 - 160x$

123. $4z^3 + 32z^2 - 132z$

124. $5z^3 - 50z^2 - 120z$

125. $4x^3 + 8x^2 - 12x$

126. $5x^3 + 30x^2 + 40x$

127. $5p^2 + 25p - 420$

128. $4p^2 - 28p - 480$

129. $p^4 + 9p^3 - 36p^2$

130. $p^4 + p^3 - 56p^2$

131. $t^2 - 12ts + 35s^2$

132. $a^2 - 10ab + 25b^2$

133. $a^2 - 8ab - 33b^2$

APPLYING THE CONCEPTS

Factor.

134. $2 + c^2 + 9c$

135. $x^2y - 54y - 3xy$

136. $45a^2 + a^2b^2 - 14a^2b$

Find all integers k such that the trinomial can be factored over the integers.

137. $x^2 + kx + 35$

138. $x^2 + kx + 18$

139. $x^2 + kx + 21$

Determine the positive integer values of k for which the following polynomials are factorable over the integers.

140. $y^2 + 4y + k$

141. $z^2 + 7z + k$

142. $a^2 - 6a + k$

143. $c^2 - 7c + k$

144. $x^2 - 3x + k$

145. $y^2 + 5y + k$

146. In Exercises 140 to 145, there was the stated requirement that $k > 0$. If k is allowed to be any integer, how many different values of k are possible for each polynomial?

5.3 Factoring Polynomials of the Form $ax^2 + bx + c$

Objective A *To factor a trinomial of the form $ax^2 + bx + c$ by using trial factors* ....

Trinomials of the form $ax^2 + bx + c$, where a, b, and c are integers, are shown at the right.

$3x^2 - x + 4$; $a = 3, b = -1, c = 4$
$6x^2 + 2x - 3$; $a = 6, b = 2, c = -3$

These trinomials differ from those in the previous section in that the coefficient of x^2 is not 1. There are various methods of factoring these trinomials. The method described in this objective is factoring polynomials using trial factors.

To reduce the number of trial factors that must be considered, remember the following:

1. Use the signs of the constant term and the coefficient of x in the trinomial to determine the signs of the binomial factors. If the constant term is positive, the signs of the binomial factors will be the same as the sign of the coefficient of x in the trinomial. If the sign of the constant term is negative, the constant terms in the binomials have opposite signs.

2. If the terms of the trinomial do not have a common factor, then the terms of neither of the binomial factors will have a common factor.

➡ Factor: $2x^2 - 7x + 3$

The terms have no common factor. The constant term is positive. The coefficient of x is negative. The binomial constants will be negative.

Positive Factors of 2 (coefficient of x^2)	Negative Factors of 3 (constant term)
1, 2	−1, −3

Write trial factors. Use the **O**uter and **I**nner products of FOIL to determine the middle term, $-7x$, of the trinomial.

Trial Factors	Middle Term
$(x - 1)(2x - 3)$	$-3x - 2x = -5x$
$(x - 3)(2x - 1)$	$-x - 6x = -7x$

Write the factors of the trinomial.

$2x^2 - 7x + 3 = (x - 3)(2x - 1)$

➡ Factor: $6x^2 - 13x + 6$

The terms have no common factor. The constant term is positive. The coefficient of x is negative. The binomial constants will be negative.

Positive Factors of 6 (coefficient of x^2)	Negative Factors of 6 (constant term)
2, 3	−2, −3
1, 6	−1, −6

Write trial factors. Use the **O**uter and **I**nner products of FOIL to determine the middle term, $-13x$, of the trinomial.

Trial Factors	Middle Term
$(2x - 3)(3x - 2)$	$-4x - 9x = -13x$
$(x - 6)(6x - 1)$	$-x - 36x = -37x$

Write the factors of the trinomial.

$6x^2 - 13x + 6 = (2x - 3)(3x - 2)$

➡️ Factor: $6x^3 + 14x^2 - 12x$.

Factor the GCF, $2x$, from the terms.

$$6x^3 + 14x^2 - 12x = 2x(3x^2 + 7x - 6)$$

Factor the trinomial. The constant term is negative. The binomial constants will have opposite signs.

Positive Factors of 3	Factors of -6
1, 3	$-1, \ 6$
	$1, \ -6$
	$-2, \ 3$
	$2, \ -3$

Write trial factors. Use the **O**uter and **I**nner products of FOIL to determine the middle term, $7x$, of the trinomial.

It is not necessary to test trial factors that have a common factor.

Trial Factors	Middle Term
$(x - 1)(3x + 6)$	Common factor
$(x + 6)(3x - 1)$	$-x + 18x = 17x$
$(x + 1)(3x - 6)$	Common factor
$(x - 6)(3x + 1)$	$x - 18x = -17x$
$(x - 2)(3x + 3)$	Common factor
$(x + 3)(3x - 2)$	$-2x + 9x = 7x$
$(x + 2)(3x - 3)$	Common factor
$(x - 3)(3x + 2)$	$2x - 9x = -7x$

Write the factors of the trinomial.

$$6x^3 + 14x^2 - 12x = 2x(x + 3)(3x - 2)$$

For this example, all the trial factors were listed. Once the correct factors have been found, the remaining trial factors can be omitted. For the examples and solutions in this text, all trial factors except those that have a common factor will be listed.

Example 1
Factor: $3x^2 + x - 2$

Solution
Positive factors of 3: 1, 3   Factors of -2:   1, -2 -1,   2

Trial Factors	Middle Term
$(x + 1)(3x - 2)$	$-2x + 3x = x$
$(x - 2)(3x + 1)$	$x - 6x = -5x$
$(x - 1)(3x + 2)$	$2x - 3x = -x$
$(x + 2)(3x - 1)$	$-x + 6x = 5x$

$$3x^2 + x - 2 = (x + 1)(3x - 2)$$

Example 2
Factor: $-12x^3 - 32x^2 + 12x$

Solution
The GCF is $-4x$.
$$-12x^3 - 32x^2 + 12x = -4x(3x^2 + 8x - 3)$$
Factor the trinomial.
Positive factors of 3: 1, 3   Factors of -3:   1, -3 -1,   3

Trial Factors	Middle Term
$(x - 3)(3x + 1)$	$x - 9x = -8x$
$(x + 3)(3x - 1)$	$-x + 9x = 8x$

$$-12x^3 - 32x^2 + 12x = -4x(x + 3)(3x - 1)$$

You Try It 1
Factor: $2x^2 - x - 3$

Your solution

You Try It 2
Factor: $-45y^3 + 12y^2 + 12y$

Your solution

Solutions on pp. S10–S11

Objective B   ***To factor a trinomial of the form $ax^2 + bx + c$ by grouping*** ....

In the previous objective, trinomials of the form $ax^2 + bx + c$ were factored by using trial factors. In this objective, these trinomials will be factored by grouping.

To factor $ax^2 + bx + c$, first find two factors of $a \cdot c$ whose sum is b. Then use factoring by grouping to write the factorization of the trinomial.

➡ Factor: $2x^2 + 13x + 15$

Find two positive factors of 30 ($2 \cdot 15$) whose sum is 13.

Positive Factors of 30	Sum
1, 30	31
2, 15	17
3, 10	13

• **When the required sum has been found, the remaining factors need not be checked.**

$$2x^2 + 13x + 15 = 2x^2 + 3x + 10x + 15$$

• **Use the factors of 30 whose sum is 13 to write 13x as 3x + 10x.**

$$= (2x^2 + 3x) + (10x + 15)$$
$$= x(2x + 3) + 5(2x + 3)$$
$$= (2x + 3)(x + 5)$$

• **Factor by grouping.**

Check your answer. $(2x + 3)(x + 5) = 2x^2 + 10x + 3x + 15$
$$= 2x^2 + 13x + 15$$

➡ Factor: $6x^2 - 11x - 10$

Find two factors of -60 [$6 \cdot (-10)$] whose sum is -11.

Factors of -60	Sum
1, -60	-59
-1, 60	59
2, -30	-28
-2, 30	28
3, -20	-17
-3, 20	17
4, -15	-11

$$6x^2 - 11x - 10 = 6x^2 + 4x - 15x - 10$$

• **Use the factors of -60 whose sum is -11 to write $-11x$ as 4x − 15x.**

$$= (6x^2 + 4x) - (15x + 10)$$
$$= 2x(3x + 2) - 5(3x + 2)$$
$$= (3x + 2)(2x - 5)$$

• **Factor by grouping. Recall $-15x - 10 = -(15x + 10)$.**

Check your answer. $(3x + 2)(2x - 5) = 6x^2 - 15x + 4x - 10$
$$= 6x^2 - 11x - 10$$

➡ Factor: $3x^2 - 2x - 4$

Find two factors of -12 $[3 \cdot (-4)]$ whose sum is -2.

Factors of -12	Sum
1, -12	-11
-1, 12	11
2, -6	-4
-2, 6	4
3, -4	-1
-3, 4	1

TAKE NOTE

$3x^2 - 2x - 4$ is a prime polynomial.

Because no integer factors of -12 have a sum of -2, $3x^2 - 2x - 4$ is nonfactorable over the integers.

Example 3
Factor: $2x^2 + 19x - 10$

Solution

Factors of -20 $[2(-10)]$	Sum
$-1, 20$	19

$$
\begin{aligned}
2x^2 + 19x - 10 &= 2x^2 - x + 20x - 10 \\
&= (2x^2 - x) + (20x - 10) \\
&= x(2x - 1) + 10(2x - 1) \\
&= (2x - 1)(x + 10)
\end{aligned}
$$

Example 4
Factor: $24x^2y - 76xy + 40y$

Solution
The GCF is $4y$.
$24x^2y - 76xy + 40y = 4y(6x^2 - 19x + 10)$

Negative Factors of 60 $[6(10)]$	Sum
$-1, -60$	-61
$-2, -30$	-32
$-3, -20$	-23
$-4, -15$	-19

$$
\begin{aligned}
6x^2 - 19x + 10 &= 6x^2 - 4x - 15x + 10 \\
&= (6x^2 - 4x) - (15x - 10) \\
&= 2x(3x - 2) - 5(3x - 2) \\
&= (3x - 2)(2x - 5)
\end{aligned}
$$

$$
\begin{aligned}
24x^2y - 76xy + 40y &= 4y(6x^2 - 19x + 10) \\
&= 4y(3x - 2)(2x - 5)
\end{aligned}
$$

You Try It 3
Factor: $2a^2 + 13a - 7$

Your solution

You Try It 4
Factor: $15x^3 + 40x^2 - 80x$

Your solution

Solutions on p. S11

5.3 Exercises

· ·

Objective A

Factor by using trial factors.

1. $2x^2 + 3x + 1$

2. $5x^2 + 6x + 1$

3. $2y^2 + 7y + 3$

4. $3y^2 + 7y + 2$

5. $2a^2 - 3a + 1$

6. $3a^2 - 4a + 1$

7. $2b^2 - 11b + 5$

8. $3b^2 - 13b + 4$

9. $2x^2 + x - 1$

10. $4x^2 - 3x - 1$

11. $2x^2 - 5x - 3$

12. $3x^2 + 5x - 2$

13. $2t^2 - t - 10$

14. $2t^2 + 5t - 12$

15. $3p^2 - 16p + 5$

16. $6p^2 + 5p + 1$

17. $12y^2 - 7y + 1$

18. $6y^2 - 5y + 1$

19. $6z^2 - 7z + 3$

20. $9z^2 + 3z + 2$

21. $6t^2 - 11t + 4$

22. $10t^2 + 11t + 3$

23. $8x^2 + 33x + 4$

24. $7x^2 + 50x + 7$

25. $5x^2 - 62x - 7$

26. $9x^2 - 13x - 4$

27. $12y^2 + 19y + 5$

28. $5y^2 - 22y + 8$

29. $7a^2 + 47a - 14$

30. $11a^2 - 54a - 5$

31. $3b^2 - 16b + 16$

32. $6b^2 - 19b + 15$

33. $2z^2 - 27z - 14$

34. $4z^2 + 5z - 6$

35. $3p^2 + 22p - 16$

36. $7p^2 + 19p + 10$

37. $4x^2 + 6x + 2$

38. $12x^2 + 33x - 9$

39. $15y^2 - 50y + 35$

40. $30y^2 + 10y - 20$

41. $2x^3 - 11x^2 + 5x$

42. $2x^3 - 3x^2 - 5x$

43. $3a^2b - 16ab + 16b$

44. $2a^2b - ab - 21b$

45. $3z^2 + 95z + 10$

46. $8z^2 - 36z + 1$

47. $36x - 3x^2 - 3x^3$

48. $-2x^3 + 2x^2 + 4x$

49. $80y^2 - 36y + 4$

50. $24y^2 - 24y - 18$

51. $8z^3 + 14z^2 + 3z$

52. $6z^3 - 23z^2 + 20z$

53. $6x^2y - 11xy - 10y$

54. $8x^2y - 27xy + 9y$

55. $10t^2 - 5t - 50$

56. $16t^2 + 40t - 96$

57. $3p^3 - 16p^2 + 5p$

58. $6p^3 + 5p^2 + p$

59. $26z^2 + 98z - 24$

60. $30z^2 - 87z + 30$

61. $10y^3 - 44y^2 + 16y$

62. $14y^3 + 94y^2 - 28y$

63. $4yz^3 + 5yz^2 - 6yz$

64. $12a^3 + 14a^2 - 48a$

65. $42a^3 + 45a^2 - 27a$

66. $36p^2 - 9p^3 - p^4$

67. $9x^2y - 30xy^2 + 25y^3$

68. $8x^2y - 38xy^2 + 35y^3$

69. $9x^3y - 24x^2y^2 + 16xy^3$

70. $9x^3y + 12x^2y + 4xy$

Objective B

Factor by grouping.

71. $6x^2 - 17x + 12$ **72.** $15x^2 - 19x + 6$ **73.** $5b^2 + 33b - 14$ **74.** $8x^2 - 30x + 25$

75. $6a^2 + 7a - 24$ **76.** $14a^2 + 15a - 9$ **77.** $4z^2 + 11z + 6$ **78.** $6z^2 - 25z + 14$

79. $22p^2 + 51p - 10$ **80.** $14p^2 - 41p + 15$ **81.** $8y^2 + 17y + 9$ **82.** $12y^2 - 145y + 12$

83. $18t^2 - 9t - 5$ **84.** $12t^2 + 28t - 5$ **85.** $6b^2 + 71b - 12$ **86.** $8b^2 + 65b + 8$

87. $9x^2 + 12x + 4$ **88.** $25x^2 - 30x + 9$ **89.** $6b^2 - 13b + 6$ **90.** $20b^2 + 37b + 15$

91. $33b^2 + 34b - 35$ **92.** $15b^2 - 43b + 22$ **93.** $18y^2 - 39y + 20$ **94.** $24y^2 + 41y + 12$

95. $15a^2 + 26a - 21$ **96.** $6a^2 + 23a + 21$ **97.** $8y^2 - 26y + 15$ **98.** $18y^2 - 27y + 4$

99. $8z^2 + 2z - 15$ **100.** $10z^2 + 3z - 4$ **101.** $15x^2 - 82x + 24$ **102.** $13z^2 + 49z - 8$

103. $10z^2 - 29z + 10$ **104.** $15z^2 - 44z + 32$ **105.** $36z^2 + 72z + 35$ **106.** $16z^2 + 8z - 35$

107. $3x^2 + xy - 2y^2$ **108.** $6x^2 + 10xy + 4y^2$ **109.** $3a^2 + 5ab - 2b^2$ **110.** $2a^2 - 9ab + 9b^2$

111. $4y^2 - 11yz + 6z^2$ **112.** $2y^2 + 7yz + 5z^2$ **113.** $28 + 3z - z^2$ **114.** $15 - 2z - z^2$

115. $8 - 7x - x^2$ **116.** $12 + 11x - x^2$ **117.** $9x^2 + 33x - 60$ **118.** $16x^2 - 16x - 12$

119. $24x^2 - 52x + 24$ **120.** $60x^2 + 95x + 20$ **121.** $35a^4 + 9a^3 - 2a^2$

122. $15a^4 + 26a^3 + 7a^2$ **123.** $15b^2 - 115b + 70$ **124.** $25b^2 + 35b - 30$

125. $3x^2 - 26xy + 35y^2$ **126.** $4x^2 + 16xy + 15y^2$ **127.** $216y^2 - 3y - 3$

128. $360y^2 + 4y - 4$ **129.** $21 - 20x - x^2$ **130.** $18 + 17x - x^2$

APPLYING THE CONCEPTS

131. In your own words, explain how the signs of the last terms of the two binomial factors of a trinomial are determined.

Factor.

132. $(x + 1)^2 - (x + 1) - 6$ **133.** $(x - 2)^2 + 3(x - 2) + 2$ **134.** $(y + 3)^2 - 5(y + 3) + 6$

135. $2(y + 2)^2 - (y + 2) - 3$ **136.** $3(a + 2)^2 - (a + 2) - 4$ **137.** $4(y - 1)^2 - 7(y - 1) - 2$

Find all integers k such that the trinomial can be factored over the integers.

138. $2x^2 + kx + 3$ **139.** $2x^2 + kx - 3$ **140.** $3x^2 + kx + 2$

141. $3x^2 + kx - 2$ **142.** $2x^2 + kx + 5$ **143.** $2x^2 + kx - 5$

5.4   Special Factoring

Objective A   To factor the difference of two squares and perfect-square trinomials ....

Recall that the product of the sum and difference of the same terms equals the square of the first term minus the square of the second term.

Sum and difference of two terms		**Difference of two squares**
$(a + b)(a - b)$	$=$	$a^2 - b^2$

This suggests that the difference of two squares can be factored as

$$a^2 - b^2 = (a + b)(a - b)$$

Note that the polynomial $x^2 + y^2$ is the *sum* of two squares. The sum of two squares is nonfactorable over the integers.

⇒ Factor: $x^2 - 16$

$x^2 - 16 = (x)^2 - (4)^2$ • Write $x^2 - 16$ as the difference of two squares. Then factor.

$= (x - 4)(x + 4)$

Check: $(x - 4)(x + 4) = x^2 + 4x - 4x - 16$

$= x^2 - 16$

⇒ Factor: $8x^3 - 18x$

$8x^3 - 18x = 2x(4x^2 - 9)$ • The GCF is $2x$.

$= 2x[(2x)^2 - 3^2]$ • Factor the difference of two squares.

$= 2x(2x - 3)(2x + 3)$

You should check the factorization.

⇒ Factor: $x^2 - 10$

Because 10 cannot be written as the square of an integer, $x^2 - 10$ is nonfactorable over the integers.

Recall from an earlier discussion the pattern for finding the square of a binomial. The result is a **perfect-square trinomial.**

The Square of a Binomial

$$(\boldsymbol{a + b})^2 = (a + b)(a + b) = a^2 + ab + ab + b^2$$
$$= \boldsymbol{a^2 + 2ab + b^2}$$

Square of first term ─────────────┘ | |
Twice the product of the two terms ─────────┘ |
Square of the last term ─────────────────────────────┘

This pattern is used to factor a perfect-square trinomial.

→ Factor: $4x^2 - 20x + 25$

Because the first and last terms are squares $[(2x)^2 = 4x^2; 5^2 = 25]$, try to factor this as the square of a binomial. Check the factorization.

$$4x^2 - 20x + 25 = (2x - 5)^2$$

Check: $(2x - 5)^2 = (2x)^2 + 2(2x)(-5) + 5^2$
$$= 4x^2 - 20x + 25$$

• **The factorization is correct.**

$$4x^2 - 20x + 25 = (2x - 5)^2$$

→ Factor: $4x^2 + 37x + 9$

Because the first and last terms are squares $[(2x)^2 = 4x^2; 3^2 = 9]$, try to factor this as the square of a binomial. Check the proposed factorization.

$$4x^2 + 37x + 9 = (2x + 3)^2$$

Check: $(2x + 3)^2 = (2x)^2 + 2(2x)(3) + 3^2$
$$= 4x^2 + 12x + 9$$

Because $4x^2 + 12x + 9 \neq 4x^2 + 37x + 9$, the proposed factorization is not correct. In this case, the polynomial is not a perfect-square trinomial. It may, however, still factor. In fact, $4x^2 + 37x + 9 = (4x + 1)(x + 9)$.

Example 1
Factor: $16x^2 - y^2$

Solution
$16x^2 - y^2 = (4x)^2 - y^2 = (4x + y)(4x - y)$

You Try It 1
Factor: $25a^2 - b^2$

Your solution

Example 2
Factor: $z^4 - 16$

Solution
$z^4 - 16 = (z^2)^2 - 4^2 = (z^2 + 4)(z^2 - 4)$
$\quad\quad = (z^2 + 4)(z - 2)(z + 2)$

You Try It 2
Factor: $n^4 - 81$

Your solution

Example 3
Factor: $9x^2 - 30x + 25$

Solution
$9x^2 = (3x)^2$, $25 = (5)^2$
$9x^2 - 30x + 25 = (3x - 5)^2$

Check: $(3x - 5)^2 = (3x)^2 + 2(3x)(-5) + 5^2$
$$= 9x^2 - 30x + 25$$

You Try It 3
Factor: $16y^2 + 8y + 1$

Your solution

Solutions on p. S11

Example 4
Factor: $9x^2 + 40x + 16$

Solution
Because $9x^2 = (3x)^2$, $16 = 4^2$, and $40x \neq 2(3x)(4)$, the trinomial is not a perfect-square trinomial.

Try to factor by another method.

$9x^2 + 40x + 16 = (9x + 4)(x + 4)$

You Try It 4
Factor: $x^2 + 15x + 36$

Your solution

Example 5
Factor: $(r + 2)^2 - 4$

Solution
$$\begin{aligned}(r + 2)^2 - 4 &= (r + 2)^2 - 2^2 \\ &= (r + 2 - 2)(r + 2 + 2) \\ &= r(r + 4)\end{aligned}$$

You Try It 5
Factor: $(x^2 - 6x + 9) - y^2$

Your solution

Solutions on p. S11

Objective B   *To factor completely* ·· CT

When factoring a polynomial completely, ask the following questions about the polynomial.

1. Is there a common factor? If so, factor out the common factor.
2. Is the polynomial the difference of two perfect squares? If so, factor.
3. Is the polynomial a perfect-square trinomial? If so, factor.
4. Is the polynomial a trinomial that is the product of two binomials? If so, factor.
5. Does the polynomial contain four terms? If so, try factoring by grouping.
6. Is each binomial factor a prime polynomial over the integers? If not, factor.

➡ Factor: $z^3 + 4z^2 - 9z - 36$

$$\begin{aligned}z^3 + 4z^2 - 9z - 36 &= (z^3 + 4z^2) - (9z + 36) \\ &= z^2(z + 4) - 9(z + 4) \\ &= (z + 4)(z^2 - 9) \\ &= (z + 4)(z + 3)(z - 3)\end{aligned}$$

• Factor by grouping. Recall $-9z - 36 = -(9z + 36)$.
• $z^3 + 4z^2 = z^2(z + 4)$
  $9z + 36 = 9(z + 4)$
• Factor out the common binomial factor $(z + 4)$.
• Factor the difference of squares.

Example 6

Factor: $3x^2 - 48$

Solution

The GCF is 3.

$3x^2 - 48 = 3(x^2 - 16)$
$\qquad\qquad = 3(x + 4)(x - 4)$

$3x^2 - 48 = 3(x + 4)(x - 4)$

You Try It 6

Factor: $12x^3 - 75x$

Your solution

Example 7

Factor: $x^3 - 3x^2 - 4x + 12$

Solution

Factor by grouping.

$x^3 - 3x^2 - 4x + 12 = (x^3 - 3x^2) - (4x - 12)$
$\qquad\qquad\qquad\qquad = x^2(x - 3) - 4(x - 3)$
$\qquad\qquad\qquad\qquad = (x - 3)(x^2 - 4)$
$\qquad\qquad\qquad\qquad = (x - 3)(x + 2)(x - 2)$

$x^3 - 3x^2 - 4x + 12 = (x - 3)(x + 2)(x - 2)$

You Try It 7

Factor: $a^2b - 7a^2 - b + 7$

Your solution

Example 8

Factor: $4x^2y^2 + 12xy^2 + 9y^2$

Solution

The GCF is y^2.

$4x^2y^2 + 12xy^2 + 9y^2 = y^2(4x^2 + 12x + 9)$
$\qquad\qquad\qquad\qquad\quad = y^2(2x + 3)^2$

$4x^2y^2 + 12xy^2 + 9y^2 = y^2(2x + 3)^2$

You Try It 8

Factor: $4x^3 + 28x^2 - 120x$

Your solution

Solutions on p. S11

5.4 Exercises

· ·

Objective A

Factor.

1. $x^2 - 4$ **2.** $x^2 - 9$ **3.** $a^2 - 81$ **4.** $a^2 - 49$

5. $y^2 + 2y + 1$ **6.** $y^2 + 14y + 49$ **7.** $a^2 - 2a + 1$ **8.** $x^2 - 12x + 36$

9. $4x^2 - 1$ **10.** $9x^2 - 16$ **11.** $x^6 - 9$ **12.** $y^{12} - 4$

13. $x^2 + 8x - 16$ **14.** $z^2 - 18z - 81$ **15.** $x^2 + 2xy + y^2$ **16.** $x^2 + 6xy + 9y^2$

17. $4a^2 + 4a + 1$ **18.** $25x^2 + 10x + 1$ **19.** $9x^2 - 1$ **20.** $1 - 49x^2$

21. $1 - 64x^2$ **22.** $t^2 + 36$ **23.** $x^2 + 64$ **24.** $64a^2 - 16a + 1$

25. $9a^2 + 6a + 1$ **26.** $x^4 - y^2$ **27.** $b^4 - 16a^2$ **28.** $16b^2 + 8b + 1$

29. $4a^2 - 20a + 25$ **30.** $4b^2 + 28b + 49$ **31.** $9a^2 - 42a + 49$ **32.** $9x^2 - 16y^2$

33. $25z^2 - y^2$ **34.** $x^2y^2 - 4$ **35.** $a^2b^2 - 25$ **36.** $16 - x^2y^2$

37. $25x^2 - 1$

38. $25a^2 + 30ab + 9b^2$

39. $4a^2 - 12ab + 9b^2$

40. $49x^2 + 28xy + 4y^2$

41. $4y^2 - 36yz + 81z^2$

42. $64y^2 - 48yz + 9z^2$

43. $\dfrac{1}{x^2} - 4$

44. $\dfrac{9}{a^2} - 16$

45. $9a^2b^2 - 6ab + 1$

46. $16x^2y^2 - 24xy + 9$

Objective B

Factor.

47. $8y^2 - 2$

48. $12n^2 - 48$

49. $3a^3 + 6a^2 + 3a$

50. $4rs^2 - 4rs + r$

51. $m^4 - 256$

52. $81 - t^4$

53. $9x^2 + 13x + 4$

54. $x^2 + 10x + 16$

55. $16y^4 + 48y^3 + 36y^2$

56. $36c^4 - 48c^3 + 16c^2$

57. $y^8 - 81$

58. $32s^4 - 2$

59. $25 - 20p + 4p^2$

60. $9 + 24a + 16a^2$

61. $(4x - 3)^2 - y^2$

62. $(2x + 5)^2 - 25$

63. $(x^2 - 4x + 4) - y^2$

64. $(4x^2 + 12x + 9) - 4y^2$

65. $5x^2 - 5$

66. $2x^2 - 18$

67. $x^3 + 4x^2 + 4x$

68. $y^3 - 10y^2 + 25y$

69. $x^4 + 2x^3 - 35x^2$

70. $a^4 - 11a^3 + 24a^2$

71. $5b^2 + 75b + 180$

72. $6y^2 - 48y + 72$

73. $3a^2 + 36a + 10$

74. $5a^2 - 30a + 4$

75. $2x^2y + 16xy - 66y$

76. $3a^2b + 21ab - 54b$

77. $x^3 - 6x^2 - 5x$

78. $b^3 - 8b^2 - 7b$

79. $3y^2 - 36$

80. $3y^2 - 147$

81. $20a^2 + 12a + 1$

82. $12a^2 - 36a + 27$

83. $x^2y^2 - 7xy^2 - 8y^2$

84. $a^2b^2 + 3a^2b - 88a^2$

85. $10a^2 - 5ab - 15b^2$

86. $16x^2 - 32xy + 12y^2$

87. $50 - 2x^2$

88. $72 - 2x^2$

89. $a^2b^2 - 10ab^2 + 25b^2$

90. $a^2b^2 + 6ab^2 + 9b^2$

91. $12a^3b - a^2b^2 - ab^3$

92. $2x^3y - 7x^2y^2 + 6xy^3$

93. $12a^3 - 12a^2 + 3a$

94. $18a^3 + 24a^2 + 8a$

95. $243 + 3a^2$

96. $75 + 27y^2$

97. $12a^3 - 46a^2 + 40a$

98. $24x^3 - 66x^2 + 15x$

99. $4a^3 + 20a^2 + 25a$

100. $2a^3 - 8a^2b + 8ab^2$

101. $27a^2b - 18ab + 3b$ **102.** $a^2b^2 - 6ab^2 + 9b^2$ **103.** $48 - 12x - 6x^2$

104. $21x^2 - 11x^3 - 2x^4$ **105.** $x^4 - x^2y^2$ **106.** $b^4 - a^2b^2$

107. $18a^3 + 24a^2 + 8a$ **108.** $32xy^2 - 48xy + 18x$ **109.** $2b + ab - 6a^2b$

110. $15y^2 - 2xy^2 - x^2y^2$ **111.** $4x^4 - 38x^3 + 48x^2$ **112.** $3x^2 - 27y^2$

113. $x^4 - 25x^2$ **114.** $y^3 - 9y$ **115.** $a^4 - 16$

116. $15x^4y^2 - 13x^3y^3 - 20x^2y^4$ **117.** $45y^2 - 42y^3 - 24y^4$ **118.** $a(2x - 2) + b(2x - 2)$

119. $4a(x - 3) - 2b(x - 3)$ **120.** $x^2(x - 2) - (x - 2)$ **121.** $y^2(a - b) - (a - b)$

122. $a(x^2 - 4) + b(x^2 - 4)$ **123.** $x(a^2 - b^2) - y(a^2 - b^2)$ **124.** $4(x - 5) - x^2(x - 5)$

APPLYING THE CONCEPTS

Find all integers k such that the trinomial is a perfect-square trinomial.

125. $4x^2 - kx + 9$ **126.** $x^2 + 6x + k$ **127.** $64x^2 + kxy + y^2$

128. $x^2 - 2x + k$ **129.** $25x^2 - kx + 1$ **130.** $x^2 + 10x + k$

131. Select any odd integer greater than 1, square it, and then subtract 1. Is the result evenly divisible by 8? Prove that this procedure always produces a number divisible by 8. (*Suggestion:* Any odd integer greater than 1 can be expressed as $2n + 1$, where n is a natural number.)

5.5 Solving Equations

Objective A *To solve equations by factoring* ....

The Multiplication Property of Zero states that the product of a number and zero is zero. This property is stated below.

$$\text{If } a \text{ is a real number, then } a \cdot 0 = 0 \cdot a = 0.$$

Now consider $x \cdot y = 0$. For this to be a true equation, then either $x = 0$ or $y = 0$.

Principle of Zero Products

If the product of two factors is zero, then at least one of the factors must be zero.

$$\text{If } a \cdot b = 0, \text{ then } a = 0 \text{ or } b = 0.$$

The Principle of Zero Products is used to solve some equations.

➡ Solve: $(x - 2)(x - 3) = 0$

$(x - 2)(x - 3) = 0$
$x - 2 = 0 \quad x - 3 = 0$

- Let each factor equal zero (the Principle of Zero Products).

$\qquad x = 2 \qquad x = 3$

- Rewrite each equation in the form *variable = constant*.

Check:

$(x - 2)(x - 3) = 0$ $(x - 2)(x - 3) = 0$
$\overline{(2 - 2)(2 - 3)} \,\big|\, 0$ $\overline{(3 - 2)(3 - 3)} \,\big|\, 0$
$\qquad\quad 0(-1) \,\big|\, 0$ $\qquad\quad (1)(0) \,\big|\, 0$
$\qquad\qquad 0 = 0$ $\qquad\qquad 0 = 0$

A true equation   A true equation

The solutions are 2 and 3.

An equation of the form $ax^2 + bx + c = 0$, $a \neq 0$, is a **quadratic equation.** A quadratic equation is in **standard form** when the polynomial is in descending order and equal to zero. The quadratic equations at the right are in standard form.

$3x^2 + 2x + 1 = 0$

$4x^2 - 3x + 2 = 0$

➡ Solve: $2x^2 + x = 6$

$$2x^2 + x = 6$$

$$2x^2 + x - 6 = 0$$ • Write the equation in standard form.

$$(2x - 3)(x + 2) = 0$$ • Factor.

$$2x - 3 = 0 \qquad x + 2 = 0$$ • Use the Principle of Zero Products.

$$2x = 3 \qquad\qquad x = -2$$ • Rewrite each equation in the form *variable = constant.*

$$x = \frac{3}{2}$$

Check: $\frac{3}{2}$ and -2 check as solutions.

The solutions are $\frac{3}{2}$ and -2.

Example 1
Solve: $x(x - 3) = 0$

Solution
$x(x - 3) = 0$

$x = 0 \qquad\qquad x - 3 = 0$
$\qquad\qquad\qquad x = 3$

The solutions are 0 and 3.

You Try It 1
Solve: $2x(x + 7) = 0$

Your solution

Example 2
Solve: $2x^2 - 50 = 0$

Solution
$$2x^2 - 50 = 0$$
$$2(x^2 - 25) = 0$$
$$2(x + 5)(x - 5) = 0$$
$$x + 5 = 0 \qquad x - 5 = 0$$
$$x = -5 \qquad\quad x = 5$$

The solutions are -5 and 5.

You Try It 2
Solve: $4x^2 - 9 = 0$

Your solution

Example 3
Solve: $(x - 3)(x - 10) = -10$

Solution
$$(x - 3)(x - 10) = -10$$
$$x^2 - 13x + 30 = -10$$ • Multiply $(x - 3)(x - 10)$.
$$x^2 - 13x + 40 = 0$$ • Add 10 to each side of
$$(x - 8)(x - 5) = 0$$ the equation. The equation
$$x - 8 = 0 \qquad x - 5 = 0$$ is now in standard form.
$$x = 8 \qquad\quad x = 5$$

The solutions are 8 and 5.

You Try It 3
Solve: $(x + 2)(x - 7) = 52$

Your solution

Solutions on pp. S11–S12

Objective B   To solve application problems .... ‹18› [CT]

Example 4

The sum of the squares of two consecutive positive even integers is equal to 100. Find the two integers.

You Try It 4

The sum of the squares of two consecutive positive integers is 61. Find the two integers.

Strategy

First positive even integer: n
Second positive even integer: $n + 2$

The sum of the square of the first positive even integer and the square of the second positive even integer is 100.

Your strategy

Solution

$$n^2 + (n + 2)^2 = 100$$
$$n^2 + n^2 + 4n + 4 = 100$$
$$2n^2 + 4n + 4 = 100$$
$$2n^2 + 4n - 96 = 0$$
$$2(n^2 + 2n - 48) = 0$$
$$2(n - 6)(n + 8) = 0$$

$$n - 6 = 0 \qquad n + 8 = 0$$
$$n = 6 \qquad\quad n = -8$$

Because -8 is not a positive even integer, it is not a solution.

$$n = 6$$
$$n + 2 = 6 + 2 = 8$$

The two integers are 6 and 8.

Your solution

Solution on p. S12

Example 5

A stone is thrown into a well with an initial speed of 4 ft/s. The well is 420 ft deep. How many seconds later will the stone hit the bottom of the well? Use the equation $d = vt + 16t^2$, where d is the distance in feet, v is the initial speed in feet per second, and t is the time in seconds.

Strategy

To find the time for the stone to drop to the bottom of the well, replace the variables d and v by their given values and solve for t.

Solution

$$d = vt + 16t^2$$
$$420 = 4t + 16t^2$$
$$0 = -420 + 4t + 16t^2$$
$$0 = 16t^2 + 4t - 420$$
$$0 = 4(4t^2 + t - 105)$$
$$0 = 4(4t + 21)(t - 5)$$

$$4t + 21 = 0 \qquad t - 5 = 0$$
$$4t = -21 \qquad\quad t = 5$$
$$t = -\frac{21}{4}$$

Because the time cannot be a negative number, $-\frac{21}{4}$ is not a solution.

The time is 5 s.

You Try It 5

The length of a rectangle is 4 in. longer than twice the width. The area of the rectangle is 96 in². Find the length and width of the rectangle.

Your strategy

Your solution

Solution on p. S12

5.5 Exercises

. . . .

Objective A

Solve.

1. $(y + 3)(y + 2) = 0$ **2.** $(y - 3)(y - 5) = 0$ **3.** $(z - 7)(z - 3) = 0$ **4.** $(z + 8)(z - 9) = 0$

5. $x(x - 5) = 0$ **6.** $x(x + 2) = 0$ **7.** $a(a - 9) = 0$ **8.** $a(a + 12) = 0$

9. $y(2y + 3) = 0$ **10.** $t(4t - 7) = 0$ **11.** $2a(3a - 2) = 0$ **12.** $4b(2b + 5) = 0$

13. $(b + 2)(b - 5) = 0$ **14.** $(b - 8)(b + 3) = 0$ **15.** $x^2 - 81 = 0$ **16.** $x^2 - 121 = 0$

17. $4x^2 - 49 = 0$ **18.** $16x^2 - 1 = 0$ **19.** $9x^2 - 1 = 0$ **20.** $16x^2 - 49 = 0$

21. $x^2 + 6x + 8 = 0$ **22.** $x^2 - 8x + 15 = 0$ **23.** $z^2 + 5z - 14 = 0$ **24.** $z^2 + z - 72 = 0$

25. $2a^2 - 9a - 5 = 0$ **26.** $3a^2 + 14a + 8 = 0$ **27.** $6z^2 + 5z + 1 = 0$ **28.** $6y^2 - 19y + 15 = 0$

29. $x^2 - 3x = 0$ **30.** $a^2 - 5a = 0$ **31.** $x^2 - 7x = 0$ **32.** $2a^2 - 8a = 0$

33. $a^2 + 5a = -4$ **34.** $a^2 - 5a = 24$ **35.** $y^2 - 5y = -6$ **36.** $y^2 - 7y = 8$

37. $2t^2 + 7t = 4$ **38.** $3t^2 + t = 10$ **39.** $3t^2 - 13t = -4$ **40.** $5t^2 - 16t = -12$

41. $x(x - 12) = -27$ **42.** $x(x - 11) = 12$ **43.** $y(y - 7) = 18$ **44.** $y(y + 8) = -15$

45. $p(p + 3) = -2$ **46.** $p(p - 1) = 20$ **47.** $y(y + 4) = 45$ **48.** $y(y - 8) = -15$

49. $x(x + 3) = 28$ **50.** $p(p - 14) = 15$ **51.** $(x + 8)(x - 3) = -30$ **52.** $(x + 4)(x - 1) = 14$

53. $(z - 5)(z + 4) = 52$ **54.** $(z - 8)(z + 4) = -35$ **55.** $(z - 6)(z + 1) = -10$

56. $(a + 3)(a + 4) = 72$ **57.** $(a - 4)(a + 7) = -18$ **58.** $(2x + 5)(x + 1) = -1$

Objective B   *Application Problems*

Solve.

59. The square of a positive number is six more than five times the positive number. Find the number.

60. The square of a negative number is fifteen more than twice the negative number. Find the number.

61. The sum of two numbers is six. The sum of the squares of the two numbers is twenty. Find the two numbers.

62. The sum of two numbers is eight. The sum of the squares of the two numbers is thirty-four. Find the two numbers.

63. The sum of the squares of two consecutive positive integers is forty-one. Find the two integers.

64. The sum of the squares of two consecutive positive even integers is one hundred. Find the two integers.

65. The sum of two numbers is ten. The product of the two numbers is twenty-one. Find the two numbers.

66. The sum of two numbers is thirteen. The product of the two numbers is forty. Find the two numbers.

The formula $S = \dfrac{n^2 + n}{2}$ gives the sum, S, of the first n natural numbers. Use this formula for Exercises 67 and 68.

67. How many consecutive natural numbers beginning with 1 will give a sum of 78?

68. How many consecutive natural numbers beginning with 1 will give a sum of 171?

The formula $N = \dfrac{t^2 - t}{2}$ gives the number, N, of football games that must be scheduled in a league with t teams if each team is to play every other team once. Use this formula for Exercises 69 and 70.

69. How many teams are in a league that schedules 15 games in such a way that each team plays every other team once?

70. How many teams are in a league that schedules 45 games in such a way that each team plays every other team once?

The distance, s, in feet, that an object will fall (neglecting air resistance) in t seconds is given by $s = vt + 16t^2$, where v is the initial velocity of the object in feet per second. Use this formula for Exercises 71 and 72.

71. An object is released from the top of a building 192 ft high. The initial velocity is 16 ft/s, and air resistance is neglected. How many seconds later will the object hit the ground?

72. An object is released from the top of a building 320 ft high. The initial velocity is 16 ft/s, and air resistance is neglected. How many seconds later will the object hit the ground?

The height, h, in feet, an object will attain (neglecting air resistance) in t seconds is given by $h = vt - 16t^2$, where v is the initial velocity of the object in feet per second. Use this formula for Exercises 73 and 74.

73. A golf ball is thrown onto a cement surface and rebounds straight up. The initial velocity of the rebound is 60 ft/s. How many seconds later will the golf ball return to the ground?

74. A foul ball leaves a bat and travels straight up with an initial velocity of 64 ft/s. How many seconds later will the ball be 64 ft above the ground?

75. The length of a rectangle is 5 in. more than twice its width. Its area is 75 in². Find the length and width of the rectangle.

76. The width of a rectangle is 5 ft less than the length. The area of the rectangle is 176 ft². Find the length and width of the rectangle.

77. The height of a triangle is 4 m more than twice the length of the base. The area of the triangle is 35 m². Find the height of the triangle.

78. The length of each side of a square is extended 5 in. The area of the resulting square is 64 in². Find the length of a side of the original square.

79. The page of a book measures 6 in. by 9 in. A uniform border around the page leaves 28 in² for type. What are the dimensions of the type area?

80. A small garden measures 8 ft by 10 ft. A uniform border around the garden increases the total area to 143 ft². What is the width of the border?

81. The radius of a circle is increased by 3 in.; this increases the area by 100 in². Find the radius of the original circle. Round to the nearest hundredth.

82. A circle has a radius of 10 in. Find the increase in area that occurs when the radius is increased by 2 in. Round to the nearest hundredth.

APPLYING THE CONCEPTS

83. In your own words, what is the Principle of Zero Products?

84. Explain the error made in solving the equation at the right. Solve the equation correctly.

$$(x + 2)(x - 3) = 6$$
$$x + 2 = 6 \quad x - 3 = 6$$
$$x = 4 \qquad x = 9$$

85. Explain the error made in solving the equation at the right. Solve the equation correctly.

$$x^2 = x$$
$$\frac{x^2}{x} = \frac{x}{x}$$
$$x = 1$$

86. Find $3n^2$ if $n(n + 5) = -4$.

87. Find $2n^2$ if $n(n + 3) = 4$.

Solve.

88. $2y(y + 4) = -5(y + 3)$

89. $(b + 5)^2 = 16$

90. $p^3 = 9p^2$

91. $(x + 3)(2x - 1) = (3 - x)(5 - 3x)$

Focus on Problem Solving

Making a Table

Sometimes a table can be used in organizing information so that it is in a useful form. In the chapter Solving Equations, we used tables in the applications to organize the data. Tables are also useful in applications that require you to find all possible combinations to a given situation.

A basketball player scored 11 points in a game. The player can score 1 point for making a free throw, 2 points for making a field goal within the three-point line, and 3 points for making a field goal outside the three-point line. Find the possible combinations in which the player can score the 11 points.

The following table lists the possible combinations of scoring the 11 points.

Free throws	0	2	1	3	5	0	2	4	6	8	1	3	5	7	9	11
2-point field goal	1	0	2	1	0	4	3	2	1	0	5	4	3	2	1	0
3-point field goal	3	3	2	2	2	1	1	1	1	1	0	0	0	0	0	0
Total Points	11	11	11	11	11	11	11	11	11	11	11	11	11	11	11	11

There are 16 possible ways in which the basketball player could have scored 11 points.

1. A football team scores 17 points. A touchdown counts 6 points, an extra point scores 1 point, a field goal scores 3 points, and a safety scores 2 points. Find the possible combinations in which the team can score 17 points. Remember that the number of extra points cannot exceed the number of touchdowns scored.

2. Repeat Exercise 1. Assume that no safety was scored.

3. Repeat Exercise 1. Assume that no safety was scored and that the team scored two field goals.

4. Find the number of possible combinations of nickels, dimes, and quarters when receiving $.85 in change.

5. Repeat Exercise 4. Assume no combination contains coins that could be exchanged for a larger coin. That is, the combination of three quarters and two nickels would not be allowed as the two nickels could be exchanged for a dime.

6. Find the number of possible combinations of $1, $5, $10, and $20 bills when receiving $33 in change.

Projects and Group Activities

Evaluating Polynomials Using a Calculator

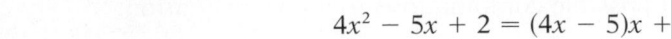

One way to evaluate a polynomial is first to express the polynomial in a form that suggests a sequence of steps on a calculator. To illustrate this method, consider the polynomial $4x^2 - 5x + 2$. First the polynomial is rewritten as

$$4x^2 - 5x + 2 = (4x - 5)x + 2$$

To evaluate the polynomial, work through the rewritten expression from left to right, substituting the appropriate value for x.

Here are some examples.

Evaluate $5x^2 - 2x + 4$ when $x = 3$.

Rewrite the polynomial. $5x^2 - 2x + 4 = (5x - 2)x + 4$

Replace x in the rewritten expression by the given value. $(5 \cdot 3 - 2) \cdot 3 + 4$

Work through the expression $\boxed{(}\ 5\ \boxed{\times}\ 3\ \boxed{-}\ 2\ \boxed{)}\ \boxed{\times}\ 3\ \boxed{+}\ 4\ \boxed{=}$
from left to right.

The result in the display should be 43.

Evaluate $2x^3 - 4x^2 + 7x - 12$ when $x = 4$.

Rewrite the polynomial. $2x^3 - 4x^2 + 7x - 12 = [(2x - 4)x + 7]x - 12$

Replace x in the rewritten expression by the given value. $[(2 \cdot 4 - 4) \cdot 4 + 7] \cdot 4 - 12$

Work through the expression from left to right.

$\boxed{(}\ \boxed{(}\ 2\ \boxed{\times}\ 4\ \boxed{-}\ 4\ \boxed{)}\ \boxed{\times}\ 4\ \boxed{+}\ 7\ \boxed{)}\ \boxed{\times}\ 4\ \boxed{-}\ 12\ \boxed{=}$

The result in the display should be 80.

Evaluate $4x^2 - 3x + 5$ when $x = -2$.

Rewrite the polynomial. $4x^2 - 3x + 5 = (4x - 3)x + 5$

Replace x in the given expression by the given value. $[4 \cdot (-2) - 3] \cdot (-2) + 5$

Work through the expression from left to right.

$\boxed{(}\ 4\ \boxed{\times}\ 2\ \boxed{+/-}\ \boxed{-}\ 3\ \boxed{)}\ \boxed{\times}\ 2\ \boxed{+/-}\ \boxed{+}\ 5\ \boxed{=}$

The result in the display should be 27.

Here are some practice exercises. Evaluate for the given value.

1. $2x^2 - 3x + 7; x = 4$ 2. $3x^2 + 7x - 12; x = -3$
3. $3x^3 - 2x^2 + 6x - 8; x = 3$ 4. $2x^3 + 4x^2 - x - 2; x = -2$
5. $x^4 - 3x^3 + 6x^2 + 5x - 1;$ 6. $2x^3 - 4x + 8; x = 2$
   $x = 2$ *Hint:* $2x^3 - 4x + 8 = 2x^3 + 0x^2 - 4x + 8$

Search the World Wide Web

At the address http://www.utm.edu/research/primes/mersenne.shtml#hist, you can find the history, theorems, and lists of Mersenne Primes. When $2^n - 1$ is prime, it is said to be a Mersenne Prime. An interesting note is that the 25th and 26th Mersenne Primes were found by high school students Laura Nickel and Curt Noll.

Would you like to find the answer to questions such as these?

1. What good are perfect numbers?
2. Is zero prime, composite, or neither?
3. What is the difference between zero and nothing?
4. When something is divided by zero, why is the answer undefined?
5. What is infinity plus one?
6. Is infinity positive or negative?

These and many other questions are answered at the address

http://forum.swarthmore.edu/dr.math/problems/purpose_zero.html

The answers to these questions are presented in a clever and interesting fashion. The answer to the question "What is the purpose of the number zero?" is given below.

The invention of zero was one of the most important breakthroughs in the history of civilization. More important, in my opinion, than the invention of the wheel. I think that it's a fairly deep concept.

One crucial purpose that zero holds is as a placeholder in our system of notation. When we write the number 408, we're really using a shorthand notation. What we really mean by 408 is "4 times 100, plus 0 times 10, plus 8 times 1." Without the number zero, we wouldn't be able to tell the numbers 408, 48, 480, 408,000, and 4800 apart. So yes, zero is important.

Another crucial role that zero plays in mathematics is that of an "additive identity element." What this means is that when you add zero to any number, you get the number that you started with. For instance, $5 + 0 = 5$. That may seem obvious and trivial, but it's actually quite important to have such a number. For instance, when you're manipulating some numerical quantity and you want to change its form but not its value, you might add some fancy version of zero to it, like this:

$$x^2 + y^2 = x^2 + y^2 + 2xy - 2xy$$
$$= x^2 + 2xy + y^2 - 2xy$$
$$= (x + y)^2 - 2xy$$

Now if we wanted to, we could use this as a proof that $(x + y)^2$ is always greater than $2xy$; the expression we started with was positive, so the one we ended up with must be positive, too. Therefore, subtracting $2xy$ from $(x + y)^2$ must leave us with a positive number. Neat stuff.*

*Ask Dr. Math. Copyright © 1994–1997 *The Math Forum.* Used by permission.

The internet is a good source for the history of and interesting facts about mathematical concepts. You can use the address

http://www-groups.dcs.st-and.ac.uk/~history/HistTopics/Prime_numbers.html

to find the history of prime numbers. This Web address also contains a list of unsolved problems on prime numbers.

There is an on-line mathematics dictionary at the address

http://www.mathpro.com/math/glossary/glossary.html

This site contains several hundred mathematical definitions as well as an on-line glossary of technical notation for unfamiliar mathematical notation.

Chapter Summary

Key Words
The *greatest common factor* (GCF) of two or more monomials is the product of the GCF of the coefficients and the common variable factors.

To *factor* a polynomial means to write the polynomial as a product of other polynomials.

To *factor* a trinomial of the form $ax^2 + bx + c$ means to express the trinomial as the product of two binomials.

A *polynomial* that does not factor using only integers is *nonfactorable over the integers*.

An equation of the form $ax^2 + bx + c = 0$ is a *quadratic equation*. A quadratic equation is in *standard form* when the polynomial is in descending order and equal to zero. The quadratic equation $ax^2 + bx + c = 0$ is in standard form.

Essential Rules
Sum and Difference of Two Terms = Difference of Two Squares
$$(a + b)(a - b) = a^2 - b^2$$

Square of a binomial = Perfect-Square Trinomial
$$(a + b)^2 = a^2 + 2ab + b^2$$

Principle of Zero Products
If the product of two factors is zero, then at least one of the factors must be zero.

If $a \cdot b = 0$, then $a = 0$ or $b = 0$.

General Factoring Strategy

1. Is there a common factor? If so, factor out the common factor.
2. Is the polynomial the difference of two perfect squares? If so, factor.
3. Is the polynomial a perfect-square trinomial? If so, factor.
4. Is the polynomial a trinomial that is the product of two binomials? If so, factor.
5. Does the polynomial contain four terms? If so, try factoring by grouping.
6. Is each binomial factor a prime polynomial over the integers? If not, factor.

Chapter Review

1. Factor: $b^2 - 13b + 30$

2. Factor: $4x(x - 3) - 5(3 - x)$

3. Factor $2x^2 - 5x + 6$ by using trial factors.

4. Factor: $5x^3 + 10x^2 + 35x$

5. Factor: $14y^9 - 49y^6 + 7y^3$

6. Factor: $y^2 + 5y - 36$

7. Factor $6x^2 - 29x + 28$ by using trial factors.

8. Factor: $12a^2b + 3ab^2$

9. Factor: $a^6 - 100$

10. Factor: $n^4 - 2n^3 - 3n^2$

11. Factor $12y^2 + 16y - 3$ by using trial factors.

12. Factor: $12b^3 - 58b^2 + 56b$

13. Factor: $9y^4 - 25z^2$

14. Factor: $c^2 + 8c + 12$

15. Factor $18a^2 - 3a - 10$ by grouping.

16. Solve: $4x^2 + 27x = 7$

17. Factor: $4x^3 - 20x^2 - 24x$

18. Factor: $3a^2 - 15a - 42$

19. Factor $2a^2 - 19a - 60$ by grouping.

20. Solve: $(x + 1)(x - 5) = 16$

21. Factor: $21ax - 35bx - 10by + 6ay$

22. Factor: $a^2b^2 - 1$

23. Factor: $10x^2 + 25x + 4xy + 10y$

24. Factor: $5x^2 - 5x - 30$

25. Factor: $3x^2 + 36x + 108$

26. Factor $3x^2 - 17x + 10$ by grouping.

27. The length of a hockey field is 20 yd less than twice the width of the hockey field. The area of the hockey field is 6000 yd². Find the length and width of the hockey field.

28. The size, S, of an image from a slide projector depends on the distance, d, of the screen from the projector and is given by $S = d^2$. Find the distance between the projector and the screen when the size of the picture is 400 ft².

29. A rectangular photograph has dimensions 15 in. by 12 in. A picture frame around the photograph increases the total area to 270 in². What is the width of the frame?

30. The length of each side of a square garden plot is extended 4 ft. The area of the resulting square is 576 ft². Find the length of a side of the original garden plot.

Chapter Test

1. Factor: $ab + 6a - 3b - 18$

2. Factor: $2y^4 - 14y^3 - 16y^2$

3. Factor $8x^2 + 20x - 48$ by grouping.

4. Factor $6x^2 + 19x + 8$ by using trial factors.

5. Factor: $a^2 - 19a + 48$

6. Factor: $6x^3 - 8x^2 + 10x$

7. Factor: $x^2 + 2x - 15$

8. Solve: $4x^2 - 1 = 0$

9. Factor: $5x^2 - 45x - 15$

10. Factor: $p^2 + 12p + 36$

11. Solve: $x(x - 8) = -15$

12. Factor: $3x^2 + 12xy + 12y^2$

13. Factor: $b^2 - 16$

14. Factor $6x^2y^2 + 9xy^2 + 3y^2$ by grouping.

15. Factor: $p^2 + 5p + 6$

16. Factor: $a(x - 2) + b(x - 2)$

17. Factor: $x(p + 1) - (p + 1)$

18. Factor: $3a^2 - 75$

19. Factor $2x^2 + 4x - 5$ by using trial factors.

20. Factor: $x^2 - 9x - 36$

21. Factor: $4a^2 - 12ab + 9b^2$

22. Factor: $4x^2 - 49y^2$

23. Solve: $(2a - 3)(a + 7) = 0$

24. The sum of two numbers is ten. The sum of the squares of the two numbers is fifty-eight. Find the two numbers.

25. The length of a rectangle is 3 cm longer than twice its width. The area of the rectangle is 90 cm². Find the length and width of the rectangle.

Cumulative Review

1. Subtract: $-2 - (-3) - 5 - (-11)$

2. Simplify: $(3 - 7)^2 \div (-2) - 3 \cdot (-4)$

3. Evaluate $-2a^2 \div (2b) - c$ when $a = -4$, $b = 2$, and $c = -1$.

4. Simplify: $-\frac{3}{4}(-20x^2)$

5. Simplify: $-2[4x - 2(3 - 2x) - 8x]$

6. Solve: $-\frac{5}{7}x = -\frac{10}{21}$

7. Solve: $3x - 2 = 12 - 5x$

8. Solve: $-2 + 4[3x - 2(4 - x) - 3] = 4x + 2$

9. 120% of what number is 54?

10. Simplify: $(-3a^3b^2)^2$

11. Simplify: $(x + 2)(x^2 - 5x + 4)$

12. Simplify: $(8x^2 + 4x - 3) \div (2x - 3)$

13. Simplify: $(x^{-4}y^3)^2$

14. Factor: $3a - 3b - ax + bx$

15. Factor: $15xy^2 - 20xy^4$

16. Factor: $x^2 - 5xy - 14y^2$

17. Factor: $p^2 - 9p - 10$

18. Factor: $18a^3 + 57a^2 + 30a$

19. Factor: $36a^2 - 49b^2$

20. Factor: $4x^2 + 28xy + 49y^2$

21. Factor: $9x^2 + 15x - 14$

22. Factor: $18x^2 - 48xy + 32y^2$

23. Factor: $3y(x - 3) - 2(x - 3)$

24. Solve: $3x^2 + 19x - 14 = 0$

25. A board 10 ft long is cut into two pieces. Four times the length of the shorter piece is 2 ft less than three times the length of the longer piece. Find the length of each piece.

26. A stereo that regularly sells for \$165 is on sale for \$99. Find the discount rate. Use the formula $S = R - rR$.

27. Given that lines ℓ_1 and ℓ_2 are parallel, find the measures of angles a and b.

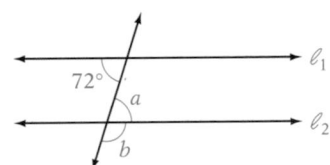

28. A family drove to a resort at an average speed of 42 mph and later returned over the same road at an average speed of 56 mph. Find the distance to the resort if the total driving time was 7 h.

29. Find three consecutive even integers such that five times the middle integer is twelve more than twice the sum of the first and third.

30. The length of the base of a triangle is three times the height. The area of the triangle is 24 in². Find the length of the base of the triangle.

CHAPTER

6

Rational Expressions

Carpentry requires the application of geometric concepts. A cabinet, for instance, has sides that must lie in parallel planes and doors that are in the shape of rectangles. A carpenter also applies the geometric principles of congruence and similarity; for example, the drawers in a dresser may be the same size and shape, or they may be the same shape but different sizes. Similar objects are a topic in Section 6 of this chapter.

Objectives

Section 6.1
To simplify a rational expression
To multiply rational expressions
To divide rational expressions

Section 6.2
To find the least common multiple (LCM) of two or more polynomials
To express two fractions in terms of the LCM of their denominators

Section 6.3
To add or subtract rational expressions with the same denominators
To add or subtract rational expressions with different denominators

Section 6.4
To simplify a complex fraction

Section 6.5
To solve an equation containing fractions

Section 6.6
To solve a proportion
To solve application problems
To solve problems involving similar triangles

Section 6.7
To solve a literal equation for one of the variables

Section 6.8
To solve work problems
To solve uniform motion problems

$$\frac{7\frac{1}{2}°}{360°} = \frac{520 \text{ mi}}{C}$$

C = 24,960 miles

Measurement of the Circumference of the Earth

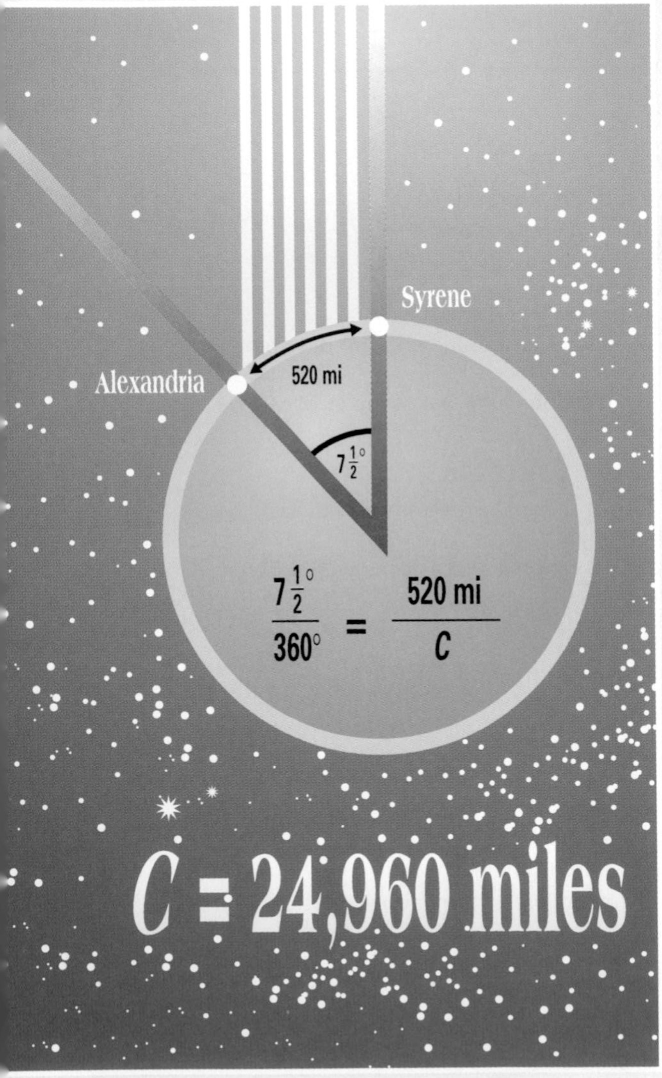

Distances on the earth, the circumference of the earth, and the distance to the moon and stars are known to great precision. Eratosthenes, the fifth librarian of Alexandria (230 B.C.), laid the foundation of scientific geography with his determination of the circumference of the earth.

Eratosthenes was familiar with certain astronomical data that enabled him to calculate the circumference of the earth by using a proportion statement.

Eratosthenes knew that on a midsummer day, the sun was directly overhead at Syrene, as shown in the diagram. At the same time, at Alexandria the sun was at a $7\frac{1}{2}°$ angle from the zenith. The distance from Syrene to Alexandria was 5000 stadia (about 520 mi).

Knowing that the ratio of the $7\frac{1}{2}°$ angle to one revolution (360°) is equal to the ratio of the arc length (520 mi) to the circumference, Eratosthenes was able to write and solve a proportion.

This result, calculated over 2000 years ago is very close to the accepted value of 24,800 miles.

6.1 Multiplication and Division of Rational Expressions

Objective A *To simplify a rational expression* ....

A fraction in which the numerator or denominator is a polynomial is called a **rational expression.** Examples of rational expressions are shown at the right.

$$\frac{5}{z}, \quad \frac{x^2 + 1}{2x - 1}, \quad \frac{y^2 + y - 1}{4y^2 + 1}$$

Care must be exercised with a rational expression to ensure that when the variables are replaced with numbers, the resulting denominator is not zero.

Consider the rational expression at the right. The value of x cannot be 3 because the denominator would then be zero.

$$\frac{4x^2 - 9}{2x - 6}$$

$$\frac{4(3)^2 - 9}{2(3) - 6} = \frac{27}{0} \quad \text{Not a real number}$$

A rational expression is in **simplest form** when the numerator and denominator have no common factors. The Multiplication Property of One is used to write a rational expression in simplest form.

➡ Simplify: $\frac{x^2 - 4}{x^2 - 2x - 8}$

$$\frac{x^2 - 4}{x^2 - 2x - 8} = \frac{(x - 2)(x + 2)}{(x - 4)(x + 2)}$$

- Factor the numerator and denominator.

$$= \frac{x - 2}{x - 4} \cdot \boxed{\frac{x + 2}{x + 2}} = \frac{x - 2}{x - 4} \cdot 1$$

$$= \frac{x - 2}{x - 4}, x \neq -2, 4$$

- The restrictions, $x \neq -2$ or 4, are necessary to prevent division by zero.

This simplification is usually shown with slashes through the common factors. The last simplification would be shown as

$$\frac{x^2 - 4}{x^2 - 2x - 8} = \frac{(x - 2)\overset{1}{\cancel{(x + 2)}}}{(x - 4)\underset{1}{\cancel{(x + 2)}}}$$

- Factor the numerator and denominator.

$$= \frac{x - 2}{x - 4}, x \neq -2, 4$$

- Divide by the common factors. The restrictions, $x \neq -2$ or 4, are necessary to prevent division by zero.

➡ Simplify: $\frac{10 + 3x - x^2}{x^2 - 4x - 5}$

$$\frac{10 + 3x - x^2}{x^2 - 4x - 5} = \frac{(5 - x)(2 + x)}{(x - 5)(x + 1)}$$

- Factor the numerator and denominator.

$$= \frac{\overset{-1}{\cancel{(5 - x)}}(2 + x)}{\underset{1}{\cancel{(x - 5)}}(x + 1)}$$

- Recall that $5 - x = -(x - 5)$. Therefore, $\dfrac{5 - x}{x - 5} = \dfrac{-(x - 5)}{x - 5} = \dfrac{-1}{1} = -1.$

$$= -\frac{x + 2}{x + 1}, x \neq -1, 5$$

For the remaining examples, we will omit the restrictions on the variables that prevent division by zero and assume the values of the variables are such that division by zero is not possible.

Example 1

Simplify: $\dfrac{4x^3y^4}{6x^4y}$

Solution

$\dfrac{4x^3y^4}{6x^4y} = \dfrac{2y^3}{3x}$ • Use rules of exponents.

You Try It 1

Simplify: $\dfrac{6x^5y}{12x^2y^3}$

Your solution

Example 2

Simplify: $\dfrac{9 - x^2}{x^2 + x - 12}$

Solution

$\dfrac{9 - x^2}{x^2 + x - 12} = \dfrac{\overset{-1}{\cancel{(3 - x)}}(3 + x)}{\underset{1}{\cancel{(x - 3)}}(x + 4)} = -\dfrac{x + 3}{x + 4}$

You Try It 2

Simplify: $\dfrac{x^2 + 2x - 24}{16 - x^2}$

Your solution

Example 3

Simplify: $\dfrac{x^2 + 2x - 15}{x^2 - 7x + 12}$

Solution

$\dfrac{x^2 + 2x - 15}{x^2 - 7x + 12} = \dfrac{(x + 5)\overset{1}{\cancel{(x - 3)}}}{\underset{1}{\cancel{(x - 3)}}(x - 4)} = \dfrac{x + 5}{x - 4}$

You Try It 3

Simplify: $\dfrac{x^2 + 4x - 12}{x^2 - 3x + 2}$

Your solution

Solutions on p. S12

Objective B **To multiply rational expressions** ....

The product of two fractions is a fraction whose numerator is the product of the numerators of the two fractions and whose denominator is the product of the denominators of the two fractions.

> **Rule for Multiplying Fractions**
>
> If $\dfrac{a}{b}$ and $\dfrac{c}{d}$ are fractions and $b \neq 0$, $d \neq 0$, then $\dfrac{a}{b} \cdot \dfrac{c}{d} = \dfrac{ac}{bd}$.

$$\dfrac{2}{3} \cdot \dfrac{4}{5} = \dfrac{8}{15} \qquad \dfrac{3x}{y} \cdot \dfrac{2}{z} = \dfrac{6x}{yz} \qquad \dfrac{x + 2}{x} \cdot \dfrac{3}{x - 2} = \dfrac{3x + 6}{x^2 - 2x}$$

➡️ Simplify: $\dfrac{x^2 + 3x}{x^2 - 3x - 4} \cdot \dfrac{x^2 - 5x + 4}{x^2 + 2x - 3}$

$$\dfrac{x^2 + 3x}{x^2 - 3x - 4} \cdot \dfrac{x^2 - 5x + 4}{x^2 + 2x - 3}$$

$$= \dfrac{x(x + 3)}{(x - 4)(x + 1)} \cdot \dfrac{(x - 4)(x - 1)}{(x + 3)(x - 1)}$$

• Factor the numerator and denominator of each fraction.

$$= \dfrac{x\cancel{(x + 3)}\cancel{(x - 4)}\cancel{(x - 1)}}{\cancel{(x - 4)}(x + 1)\cancel{(x + 3)}\cancel{(x - 1)}}$$

• Multiply.

$$= \dfrac{x}{x + 1}$$

• Write the answer in simplest form.

Example 4

Simplify: $\dfrac{10x^2 - 15x}{12x - 8} \cdot \dfrac{3x - 2}{20x - 25}$

Solution

$$\dfrac{10x^2 - 15x}{12x - 8} \cdot \dfrac{3x - 2}{20x - 25}$$

$$= \dfrac{5x(2x - 3)}{4(3x - 2)} \cdot \dfrac{(3x - 2)}{5(4x - 5)}$$

$$= \dfrac{\cancel{5}x(2x - 3)\cancel{(3x - 2)}}{4\cancel{(3x - 2)}\cancel{5}(4x - 5)} = \dfrac{x(2x - 3)}{4(4x - 5)}$$

You Try It 4

Simplify: $\dfrac{12x^2 + 3x}{10x - 15} \cdot \dfrac{8x - 12}{9x + 18}$

Your solution

Example 5

Simplify: $\dfrac{x^2 + x - 6}{x^2 + 7x + 12} \cdot \dfrac{x^2 + 3x - 4}{4 - x^2}$

Solution

$$\dfrac{x^2 + x - 6}{x^2 + 7x + 12} \cdot \dfrac{x^2 + 3x - 4}{4 - x^2}$$

$$= \dfrac{(x + 3)(x - 2)}{(x + 3)(x + 4)} \cdot \dfrac{(x + 4)(x - 1)}{(2 - x)(2 + x)}$$

$$= \dfrac{\cancel{(x + 3)}\cancel{(x - 2)}\cancel{(x + 4)}(x - 1)}{\cancel{(x + 3)}\cancel{(x + 4)}\cancel{(2 - x)}(2 + x)} = -\dfrac{x - 1}{x + 2}$$

You Try It 5

Simplify: $\dfrac{x^2 + 2x - 15}{9 - x^2} \cdot \dfrac{x^2 - 3x - 18}{x^2 - 7x + 6}$

Your solution

Solutions on p. S12

Objective C   **To divide rational expressions** ·································

The reciprocal of a fraction is a fraction with the numerator and denominator interchanged.

$$\text{Fraction} \left\{ \begin{array}{cc} \dfrac{a}{b} & \dfrac{b}{a} \\[2mm] x^2 = \dfrac{x^2}{1} & \dfrac{1}{x^2} \\[2mm] \dfrac{x+2}{x} & \dfrac{x}{x+2} \end{array} \right\} \text{Reciprocal}$$

Rule for Dividing Fractions

Divide fractions by multiplying the dividend by the reciprocal of the divisor.

$$\frac{a}{b} \div \frac{c}{d} = \frac{a}{b} \cdot \frac{d}{c} = \frac{ad}{bc}$$

$$\frac{4}{x} \div \frac{y}{5} = \frac{4}{x} \cdot \frac{5}{y} = \frac{20}{xy}$$

$$\frac{x+4}{x} \div \frac{x-2}{4} = \frac{x+4}{x} \cdot \frac{4}{x-2} = \frac{4(x+4)}{x(x-2)}$$

The basis for the division rule is shown at the right.

$$\frac{a}{b} \div \frac{c}{d} = \frac{\dfrac{a}{b}}{\dfrac{c}{d}} = \frac{\dfrac{a}{b} \cdot \dfrac{d}{c}}{\dfrac{c}{d} \cdot \dfrac{d}{c}} = \frac{\dfrac{a}{b} \cdot \dfrac{d}{c}}{1} = \frac{a}{b} \cdot \frac{d}{c}$$

Example 6

Simplify: $\dfrac{xy^2 - 3x^2y}{z^2} \div \dfrac{6x^2 - 2xy}{z^3}$

Solution

$$\frac{xy^2 - 3x^2y}{z^2} \div \frac{6x^2 - 2xy}{z^3}$$

$$= \frac{xy^2 - 3x^2y}{z^2} \cdot \frac{z^3}{6x^2 - 2xy}$$

$$= \frac{xy\overset{-1}{\cancel{(y - 3x)}} \cdot z^3}{z^2 \cdot 2x\underset{1}{\cancel{(3x - y)}}} = -\frac{yz}{2}$$

You Try It 6

Simplify: $\dfrac{a^2}{4bc^2 - 2b^2c} \div \dfrac{a}{6bc - 3b^2}$

Your solution

Example 7

Simplify: $\dfrac{2x^2 + 5x + 2}{2x^2 + 3x - 2} \div \dfrac{3x^2 + 13x + 4}{2x^2 + 7x - 4}$

Solution

$$\frac{2x^2 + 5x + 2}{2x^2 + 3x - 2} \div \frac{3x^2 + 13x + 4}{2x^2 + 7x - 4}$$

$$= \frac{2x^2 + 5x + 2}{2x^2 + 3x - 2} \cdot \frac{2x^2 + 7x - 4}{3x^2 + 13x + 4}$$

$$= \frac{(2x+1)\overset{1}{\cancel{(x+2)}} \cdot \overset{1}{\cancel{(2x-1)}}\overset{1}{\cancel{(x+4)}}}{\underset{1}{\cancel{(2x-1)}}\underset{1}{\cancel{(x+2)}} \cdot (3x+1)\underset{1}{\cancel{(x+4)}}} = \frac{2x+1}{3x+1}$$

You Try It 7

Simplify: $\dfrac{3x^2 + 26x + 16}{3x^2 - 7x - 6} \div \dfrac{2x^2 + 9x - 5}{x^2 + 2x - 15}$

Your solution

Solutions on p. S13

6.1 Exercises

· ·

Objective A

Simplify.

1. $\dfrac{9x^3}{12x^4}$

2. $\dfrac{16x^2y}{24xy^3}$

3. $\dfrac{(x+3)^2}{(x+3)^3}$

4. $\dfrac{(2x-1)^5}{(2x-1)^4}$

5. $\dfrac{3n-4}{4-3n}$

6. $\dfrac{5-2x}{2x-5}$

7. $\dfrac{6y(y+2)}{9y^2(y+2)}$

8. $\dfrac{12x^2(3-x)}{18x(3-x)}$

9. $\dfrac{6x(x-5)}{8x^2(5-x)}$

10. $\dfrac{14x^3(7-3x)}{21x(3x-7)}$

11. $\dfrac{a^2+4a}{ab+4b}$

12. $\dfrac{x^2-3x}{2x-6}$

13. $\dfrac{4-6x}{3x^2-2x}$

14. $\dfrac{5xy-3y}{9-15x}$

15. $\dfrac{y^2-3y+2}{y^2-4y+3}$

16. $\dfrac{x^2+5x+6}{x^2+8x+15}$

17. $\dfrac{x^2+3x-10}{x^2+2x-8}$

18. $\dfrac{a^2+7a-8}{a^2+6a-7}$

19. $\dfrac{x^2+x-12}{x^2-6x+9}$

20. $\dfrac{x^2+8x+16}{x^2-2x-24}$

21. $\dfrac{x^2-3x-10}{25-x^2}$

22. $\dfrac{4-y^2}{y^2-3y-10}$

23. $\dfrac{2x^3+2x^2-4x}{x^3+2x^2-3x}$

24. $\dfrac{3x^3-12x}{6x^3-24x^2+24x}$

25. $\dfrac{6x^2-7x+2}{6x^2+5x-6}$

26. $\dfrac{2n^2-9n+4}{2n^2-5n-12}$

27. $\dfrac{x^2+3x-28}{24-2x-x^2}$

Objective B

Simplify.

28. $\dfrac{8x^2}{9y^3} \cdot \dfrac{3y^2}{4x^3}$

29. $\dfrac{14a^2b^3}{15x^5y^2} \cdot \dfrac{25x^3y}{16ab}$

30. $\dfrac{12x^3y^4}{7a^2b^3} \cdot \dfrac{14a^3b^4}{9x^2y^2}$

31. $\dfrac{18a^4b^2}{25x^2y^3} \cdot \dfrac{50x^5y^6}{27a^6b^2}$

32. $\dfrac{3x-6}{5x-20} \cdot \dfrac{10x-40}{27x-54}$

33. $\dfrac{8x-12}{14x+7} \cdot \dfrac{42x+21}{32x-48}$

34. $\dfrac{3x^2+2x}{2xy-3y} \cdot \dfrac{2xy^3-3y^3}{3x^3+2x^2}$

35. $\dfrac{4a^2x-3a^2}{2by+5b} \cdot \dfrac{2b^3y+5b^3}{4ax-3a}$

36. $\dfrac{x^2+5x+4}{x^3y^2} \cdot \dfrac{x^2y^3}{x^2+2x+1}$

37. $\dfrac{x^2+x-2}{xy^2} \cdot \dfrac{x^3y}{x^2+5x+6}$

38. $\dfrac{x^4y^2}{x^2+3x-28} \cdot \dfrac{x^2-49}{xy^4}$

39. $\dfrac{x^5y^3}{x^2+13x+30} \cdot \dfrac{x^2+2x-3}{x^7y^2}$

40. $\dfrac{2x^2-5x}{2xy+y} \cdot \dfrac{2xy^2+y^2}{5x^2-2x^3}$

41. $\dfrac{3a^3+4a^2}{5ab-3b} \cdot \dfrac{3b^3-5ab^3}{3a^2+4a}$

42. $\dfrac{x^2-2x-24}{x^2-5x-6} \cdot \dfrac{x^2+5x+6}{x^2+6x+8}$

43. $\dfrac{x^2-8x+7}{x^2+3x-4} \cdot \dfrac{x^2+3x-10}{x^2-9x+14}$

44. $\dfrac{x^2+2x-35}{x^2+4x-21} \cdot \dfrac{x^2+3x-18}{x^2+9x+18}$

45. $\dfrac{y^2+y-20}{y^2+2y-15} \cdot \dfrac{y^2+4y-21}{y^2+3y-28}$

46. $\dfrac{x^2 - 3x - 4}{x^2 + 6x + 5} \cdot \dfrac{x^2 + 5x + 6}{8 + 2x - x^2}$

47. $\dfrac{25 - n^2}{n^2 - 2n - 35} \cdot \dfrac{n^2 - 8n - 20}{n^2 - 3n - 10}$

48. $\dfrac{12x^2 - 6x}{x^2 + 6x + 5} \cdot \dfrac{2x^4 + 10x^3}{4x^2 - 1}$

49. $\dfrac{8x^3 + 4x^2}{x^2 - 3x + 2} \cdot \dfrac{x^2 - 4}{16x^2 + 8x}$

50. $\dfrac{16 + 6x - x^2}{x^2 - 10x - 24} \cdot \dfrac{x^2 - 6x - 27}{x^2 - 17x + 72}$

51. $\dfrac{x^2 - 11x + 28}{x^2 - 13x + 42} \cdot \dfrac{x^2 + 7x + 10}{20 - x - x^2}$

52. $\dfrac{2x^2 + 5x + 2}{2x^2 + 7x + 3} \cdot \dfrac{x^2 - 7x - 30}{x^2 - 6x - 40}$

53. $\dfrac{x^2 - 4x - 32}{x^2 - 8x - 48} \cdot \dfrac{3x^2 + 17x + 10}{3x^2 - 22x - 16}$

Objective C

Simplify.

54. $\dfrac{4x^2y^3}{15a^2b^3} \div \dfrac{6xy}{5a^3b^5}$

55. $\dfrac{9x^3y^4}{16a^4b^2} \div \dfrac{45x^4y^2}{14a^7b}$

56. $\dfrac{6x - 12}{8x + 32} \div \dfrac{18x - 36}{10x + 40}$

57. $\dfrac{28x + 14}{45x - 30} \div \dfrac{14x + 7}{30x - 20}$

58. $\dfrac{6x^3 + 7x^2}{12x - 3} \div \dfrac{6x^2 + 7x}{36x - 9}$

59. $\dfrac{5a^2y + 3a^2}{2x^3 + 5x^2} \div \dfrac{10ay + 6a}{6x^3 + 15x^2}$

60. $\dfrac{x^2 + 4x + 3}{x^2y} \div \dfrac{x^2 + 2x + 1}{xy^2}$

61. $\dfrac{x^3y^2}{x^2 - 3x - 10} \div \dfrac{xy^4}{x^2 - x - 20}$

62. $\dfrac{x^2 - 49}{x^4y^3} \div \dfrac{x^2 - 14x + 49}{x^4y^3}$

63. $\dfrac{x^2y^5}{x^2 - 11x + 30} \div \dfrac{xy^6}{x^2 - 7x + 10}$

64. $\dfrac{4ax - 8a}{c^2} \div \dfrac{2y - xy}{c^3}$

65. $\dfrac{3x^2y - 9xy}{a^2b} \div \dfrac{3x^2 - x^3}{ab^2}$

66. $\dfrac{x^2 - 5x + 6}{x^2 - 9x + 18} \div \dfrac{x^2 - 6x + 8}{x^2 - 9x + 20}$

67. $\dfrac{x^2 + 3x - 40}{x^2 + 2x - 35} \div \dfrac{x^2 + 2x - 48}{x^2 + 3x - 18}$

68. $\dfrac{x^2 + 2x - 15}{x^2 - 4x - 45} \div \dfrac{x^2 + x - 12}{x^2 - 5x - 36}$

69. $\dfrac{y^2 - y - 56}{y^2 + 8y + 7} \div \dfrac{y^2 - 13y + 40}{y^2 - 4y - 5}$

70. $\dfrac{8 + 2x - x^2}{x^2 + 7x + 10} \div \dfrac{x^2 - 11x + 28}{x^2 - x - 42}$

71. $\dfrac{x^2 - x - 2}{x^2 - 7x + 10} \div \dfrac{x^2 - 3x - 4}{40 - 3x - x^2}$

72. $\dfrac{2x^2 - 3x - 20}{2x^2 - 7x - 30} \div \dfrac{2x^2 - 5x - 12}{4x^2 + 12x + 9}$

73. $\dfrac{6n^2 + 13n + 6}{4n^2 - 9} \div \dfrac{6n^2 + n - 2}{4n^2 - 1}$

APPLYING THE CONCEPTS

74. Given the expression $\dfrac{9}{x^2 + 1}$, choose some values of x and evaluate the expression for those values. Is it possible to choose a value of x for which the value of the expression is greater than 10? If so, what is that value of x? If not, explain why it is not possible.

75. Given the expression $\dfrac{1}{y - 3}$, choose some values of y and evaluate the expression for those values. Is it possible to choose a value of y for which the value of the expression is greater than 10,000,000? If so, what is that value of y? If not, explain why it is not possible.

For what values of x is the algebraic fraction undefined?

76. $\dfrac{x}{(x - 2)(x + 5)}$

77. $\dfrac{7}{x^2 - 25}$

78. $\dfrac{3x - 8}{3x^2 - 10x - 8}$

Simplify.

79. $\dfrac{xy}{3} \cdot \dfrac{x}{y^2} \div \dfrac{x}{4}$

80. $\left(\dfrac{y}{3}\right) \div \left(\dfrac{y}{2} \cdot \dfrac{y}{4}\right)$

81. $\left(\dfrac{x - 4}{y^2}\right)^3 \cdot \left(\dfrac{y}{4 - x}\right)^3$

82. $\dfrac{x - 2}{x + 5} \div \dfrac{x - 3}{x + 5} \cdot \dfrac{x - 3}{x - 2}$

83. $\dfrac{b + 4}{b - 1} \div \dfrac{b + 4}{b + 2} \cdot \dfrac{b - 1}{b - 5}$

6.2 Expressing Fractions in Terms of the Least Common Multiple (LCM)

Objective A *To find the least common multiple (LCM) of two or more polynomials* ....

The **least common multiple (LCM)** of two or more numbers is the smallest number that contains the prime factorization of each number.

The LCM of 12 and 18 is 36 because 36 contains the prime factors of 12 and the prime factors of 18.

$$12 = 2 \cdot 2 \cdot 3$$
$$18 = 2 \cdot 3 \cdot 3$$

$$\text{LCM} = 36 = \overbrace{2 \cdot \underbrace{2 \cdot 3}_{} \cdot 3}^{\text{Factors of 12}}$$

Factors of 18

The least common multiple of two or more polynomials is the polynomial of least degree that contains the factors of each polynomial.

To find the LCM of two or more polynomials, first factor each polynomial completely. The LCM is the product of each factor the greatest number of times it occurs in any one factorization.

$\Rightarrow$ Find the LCM of $4x^2 + 4x$ and $x^2 + 2x + 1$.

The LCM of the polynomials is the product of the LCM of the numerical coefficients and each variable factor the greatest number of times it occurs in any one factorization.

$$4x^2 + 4x = 4x(x + 1) = 2 \cdot 2 \cdot x(x + 1)$$
$$x^2 + 2x + 1 = (x + 1)(x + 1)$$

$$\text{LCM} = \overbrace{2 \cdot 2 \cdot x\underbrace{(x + 1)(x + 1)}_{\text{Factors of } x^2 + 2x + 1}}^{\text{Factors of } 4x^2 + 4x} = 4x(x + 1)(x + 1)$$

TAKE NOTE

The LCM must contain the factors of each polynomial. As shown with the braces at the right, the LCM contains the factors of $4x^2 + 4x$ and the factors of $x^2 + 2x + 1$.

Example 1

Find the LCM of $4x^2y$ and $6xy^2$.

Solution

$4x^2y = 2 \cdot 2 \cdot x \cdot x \cdot y$
$6xy^2 = 2 \cdot 3 \cdot x \cdot y \cdot y$
$\text{LCM} = 2 \cdot 2 \cdot 3 \cdot x \cdot x \cdot y \cdot y = 12x^2y^2$

Example 2

Find the LCM of $x^2 - x - 6$ and $9 - x^2$.

Solution

$x^2 - x - 6 = (x - 3)(x + 2)$
$9 - x^2 = -(x^2 - 9) = -(x + 3)(x - 3)$
$\text{LCM} = (x - 3)(x + 2)(x + 3)$

You Try It 1

Find the LCM of $8uv^2$ and $12uw$.

Your solution

You Try It 2

Find the LCM of $m^2 - 6m + 9$ and $m^2 - 2m - 3$.

Your solution

Solutions on p. S13

Objective B   **To express two fractions in terms of the LCM of their denominators** ....

When adding and subtracting fractions, it is frequently necessary to express two or more fractions in terms of a common denominator. This common denominator is the LCM of the denominators of the fractions.

⇒ Write the fractions $\frac{x+1}{4x^2}$ and $\frac{x-3}{6x^2-12x}$ in terms of the LCM of the denominators.

Find the LCM of the denominators.

The LCM is $12x^2(x-2)$.

For each fraction, multiply the numerator and denominator by the factors whose product with the denominator is the LCM.

$$\frac{x+1}{4x^2} = \frac{x+1}{4x^2} \cdot \frac{3(x-2)}{3(x-2)} = \frac{3x^2-3x-6}{12x^2(x-2)} \leftarrow$$

$$\frac{x-3}{6x^2-12x} = \frac{x-3}{6x(x-2)} \cdot \frac{2x}{2x} = \frac{2x^2-6x}{12x^2(x-2)} \leftarrow$$

LCM

Example 3

Write the fractions $\frac{x+2}{3x^2}$ and $\frac{x-1}{8xy}$ in terms of the LCM of the denominators.

Solution
The LCM is $24x^2y$.

$$\frac{x+2}{3x^2} = \frac{x+2}{3x^2} \cdot \frac{8y}{8y} = \frac{8xy+16y}{24x^2y}$$

$$\frac{x-1}{8xy} = \frac{x-1}{8xy} \cdot \frac{3x}{3x} = \frac{3x^2-3x}{24x^2y}$$

You Try It 3

Write the fractions $\frac{x-3}{4xy^2}$ and $\frac{2x+1}{9y^2z}$ in terms of the LCM of the denominators.

Your solution

Example 4

Write the fractions $\frac{2x-1}{2x-x^2}$ and $\frac{x}{x^2+x-6}$ in terms of the LCM of the denominators.

Solution

$$\frac{2x-1}{2x-x^2} = \frac{2x-1}{-(x^2-2x)} = -\frac{2x-1}{x^2-2x}$$

The LCM is $x(x-2)(x+3)$.

$$\frac{2x-1}{2x-x^2} = -\frac{2x-1}{x(x-2)} \cdot \frac{x+3}{x+3} = -\frac{2x^2+5x-3}{x(x-2)(x+3)}$$

$$\frac{x}{x^2+x-6} = \frac{x}{(x-2)(x+3)} \cdot \frac{x}{x} = \frac{x^2}{x(x-2)(x+3)}$$

You Try It 4

Write the fractions $\frac{x+4}{x^2-3x-10}$ and $\frac{2x}{25-x^2}$ in terms of the LCM of the denominators.

Your solution

Solutions on p. S13

6.2 Exercises

· ·

Objective A

Find the LCM of the expressions.

1. $8x^3y$
$12xy^2$

2. $6ab^2$
$18ab^3$

3. $10x^4y^2$
$15x^3y$

4. $12a^2b$
$18ab^3$

5. $8x^2$
$4x^2 + 8x$

6. $6y^2$
$4y + 12$

7. $2x^2y$
$3x^2 + 12x$

8. $4xy^2$
$6xy^2 + 12y^2$

9. $9x(x + 2)$
$12(x + 2)^2$

10. $8x^2(x - 1)^2$
$10x^3(x - 1)$

11. $3x + 3$
$2x^2 + 4x + 2$

12. $4x - 12$
$2x^2 - 12x + 18$

13. $(x - 1)(x + 2)$
$(x - 1)(x + 3)$

14. $(2x - 1)(x + 4)$
$(2x + 1)(x + 4)$

15. $(2x + 3)^2$
$(2x + 3)(x - 5)$

16. $(x - 7)(x + 2)$
$(x - 7)^2$

17. $x - 1$
$x - 2$
$(x - 1)(x - 2)$

18. $(x + 4)(x - 3)$
$x + 4$
$x - 3$

19. $x^2 - x - 6$
$x^2 + x - 12$

20. $x^2 + 3x - 10$
$x^2 + 5x - 14$

21. $x^2 + 5x + 4$
$x^2 - 3x - 28$

22. $x^2 - 10x + 21$
$x^2 - 8x + 15$

23. $x^2 - 2x - 24$
$x^2 - 36$

24. $x^2 + 7x + 10$
$x^2 - 25$

25. $x^2 - 7x - 30$
$x^2 - 5x - 24$

26. $2x^2 - 7x + 3$
$2x^2 + x - 1$

27. $3x^2 - 11x + 6$
$3x^2 + 4x - 4$

28. $2x^2 - 9x + 10$
$2x^2 + x - 15$

29. $6 + x - x^2$
$x + 2$
$x - 3$

30. $15 + 2x - x^2$
$x - 5$
$x + 3$

31. $5 + 4x - x^2$
$x - 5$
$x + 1$

32. $x^2 + 3x - 18$
$3 - x$
$x + 6$

33. $x^2 - 5x + 6$
$1 - x$
$x - 6$

Objective B

Write each fraction in terms of the LCM of the denominators.

34. $\dfrac{4}{x}, \dfrac{3}{x^2}$

35. $\dfrac{5}{ab^2}, \dfrac{6}{ab}$

36. $\dfrac{x}{3y^2}, \dfrac{z}{4y}$

37. $\dfrac{5y}{6x^2}, \dfrac{7}{9xy}$

38. $\dfrac{y}{x(x-3)}, \dfrac{6}{x^2}$

39. $\dfrac{a}{y^2}, \dfrac{6}{y(y+5)}$

40. $\dfrac{9}{(x-1)^2}, \dfrac{6}{x(x-1)}$

41. $\dfrac{a^2}{y(y+7)}, \dfrac{a}{(y+7)^2}$

42. $\dfrac{3}{x-3}, \dfrac{5}{x(3-x)}$

43. $\dfrac{b}{y(y-4)}, \dfrac{b^2}{4-y}$

44. $\dfrac{3}{(x-5)^2}, \dfrac{2}{5-x}$

45. $\dfrac{3}{7-y}, \dfrac{2}{(y-7)^2}$

46. $\dfrac{3}{x^2+2x}, \dfrac{4}{x^2}$

47. $\dfrac{2}{y-3}, \dfrac{3}{y^3-3y^2}$

48. $\dfrac{x-2}{x+3}, \dfrac{x}{x-4}$

49. $\dfrac{x^2}{2x-1}, \dfrac{x+1}{x+4}$

50. $\dfrac{3}{x^2+x-2}, \dfrac{x}{x+2}$

51. $\dfrac{3x}{x-5}, \dfrac{4}{x^2-25}$

52. $\dfrac{x}{x^2+x-6}, \dfrac{2x}{x^2-9}$

53. $\dfrac{x-1}{x^2+2x-15}, \dfrac{x}{x^2+6x+5}$

APPLYING THE CONCEPTS

54. When is the LCM of two expressions equal to their product?

Write each expression in terms of the LCM of the denominators.

55. $\dfrac{8}{10^3}, \dfrac{9}{10^5}$

56. $3, \dfrac{2}{n}$

57. $x, \dfrac{x}{x^2-1}$

58. $\dfrac{x^2+1}{(x-1)^3}, \dfrac{x+1}{(x-1)^2}, \dfrac{1}{x-1}$

59. $\dfrac{c}{6c^2+7cd+d^2}, \dfrac{d}{3c^2-3d^2}$

60. $\dfrac{1}{ab+3a-3b-b^2}, \dfrac{1}{ab+3a+3b+b^2}$

6.3 Addition and Subtraction of Rational Expressions

Objective A   *To add or subtract rational expressions with the same denominators* ....

When adding rational expressions in which the denominators are the same, add the numerators. The denominator of the sum is the common denominator.

> **Rule for Adding Fractions**
>
> If $\dfrac{a}{b}$ and $\dfrac{c}{b}$ are fractions and $b \neq 0$, then $\dfrac{a}{b} + \dfrac{c}{b} = \dfrac{a + c}{b}$.

$$\frac{5x}{18} + \frac{7x}{18} = \frac{5x + 7x}{18} = \frac{12x}{18} = \frac{2x}{3}$$

$$\frac{x}{x^2 - 1} + \frac{1}{x^2 - 1} = \frac{x + 1}{x^2 - 1} = \frac{\overset{1}{\cancel{(x + 1)}}}{(x - 1)\underset{1}{\cancel{(x + 1)}}} = \frac{1}{x - 1}$$

Note that the sum is written in simplest form.

When subtracting rational expressions with like denominators, subtract the numerators. The denominator of the difference is the common denominator. Write the answer in simplest form.

$$\frac{2x}{x - 2} - \frac{4}{x - 2} = \frac{2x - 4}{x - 2} = \frac{2\overset{1}{\cancel{(x - 2)}}}{\underset{1}{\cancel{x - 2}}} = 2$$

$$\frac{3x - 1}{x^2 - 5x + 4} - \frac{2x + 3}{x^2 - 5x + 4} = \frac{(3x - 1) - (2x + 3)}{x^2 - 5x + 4} = \frac{3x - 1 - 2x - 3}{x^2 - 5x + 4}$$

$$= \frac{x - 4}{x^2 - 5x + 4} = \frac{\overset{1}{\cancel{(x - 4)}}}{\underset{1}{\cancel{(x - 4)}}(x - 1)} = \frac{1}{x - 1}$$

Example 1

Simplify: $\dfrac{3x^2}{x^2 - 1} - \dfrac{x + 4}{x^2 - 1}$

Solution

$$\frac{3x^2}{x^2 - 1} - \frac{x + 4}{x^2 - 1} = \frac{3x^2 - (x + 4)}{x^2 - 1}$$

$$= \frac{3x^2 - x - 4}{x^2 - 1}$$

$$= \frac{(3x - 4)\overset{1}{\cancel{(x + 1)}}}{(x - 1)\underset{1}{\cancel{(x + 1)}}} = \frac{3x - 4}{x - 1}$$

You Try It 1

Simplify: $\dfrac{2x^2}{x^2 - x - 12} - \dfrac{7x + 4}{x^2 - x - 12}$

Your solution

Solution on p. S13

Example 2

Simplify:

$$\frac{2x^2 + 5}{x^2 + 2x - 3} - \frac{x^2 - 3x}{x^2 + 2x - 3} + \frac{x - 2}{x^2 + 2x - 3}$$

Solution

$$\frac{2x^2 + 5}{x^2 + 2x - 3} - \frac{x^2 - 3x}{x^2 + 2x - 3} + \frac{x - 2}{x^2 + 2x - 3}$$

$$= \frac{(2x^2 + 5) - (x^2 - 3x) + (x - 2)}{x^2 + 2x - 3}$$

$$= \frac{2x^2 + 5 - x^2 + 3x + x - 2}{x^2 + 2x - 3}$$

$$= \frac{x^2 + 4x + 3}{x^2 + 2x - 3} = \frac{\overset{1}{\cancel{(x + 3)}}(x + 1)}{\underset{1}{\cancel{(x + 3)}}(x - 1)} = \frac{x + 1}{x - 1}$$

You Try It 2

Simplify:

$$\frac{x^2 - 1}{x^2 - 8x + 12} - \frac{2x + 1}{x^2 - 8x + 12} + \frac{x}{x^2 - 8x + 12}$$

Your solution

Solution on p. S13

Objective B   To add or subtract rational expressions with different denominators ....

Before two fractions with unlike denominators can be added or subtracted, each fraction must be expressed in terms of a common denominator. This common denominator is the LCM of the denominators of the fractions.

➡ Simplify: $\dfrac{x - 3}{x^2 - 2x} + \dfrac{6}{x^2 - 4}$

The LCM is $x(x - 2)(x + 2)$.   • **Find the LCM of the denominators.**

$$\frac{x - 3}{x^2 - 2x} + \frac{6}{x^2 - 4} = \frac{x - 3}{x(x - 2)} \cdot \frac{x + 2}{x + 2} + \frac{6}{(x - 2)(x + 2)} \cdot \frac{x}{x}$$

• **Write each fraction in terms of the LCM.**

$$= \frac{x^2 - x - 6}{x(x - 2)(x + 2)} + \frac{6x}{x(x - 2)(x + 2)}$$

• **Multiply the factors in the numerator and then add the fractions.**

$$= \frac{(x^2 - x - 6) + 6x}{x(x - 2)(x + 2)}$$

$$= \frac{x^2 + 5x - 6}{x(x - 2)(x + 2)}$$

$$= \frac{(x + 6)(x - 1)}{x(x - 2)(x + 2)}$$

The last step is to factor the numerator to determine whether there are common factors in the numerator and denominator. For this example, there are no common factors, so the answer is in simplest form.

Example 3

Simplify: $\dfrac{y}{x} - \dfrac{4y}{3x} + \dfrac{3y}{4x}$

Solution

The LCM of the denominators is $12x$.

$\dfrac{y}{x} - \dfrac{4y}{3x} + \dfrac{3y}{4x} = \dfrac{y}{x} \cdot \dfrac{12}{12} - \dfrac{4y}{3x} \cdot \dfrac{4}{4} + \dfrac{3y}{4x} \cdot \dfrac{3}{3}$

$= \dfrac{12y}{12x} - \dfrac{16y}{12x} + \dfrac{9y}{12x}$

$= \dfrac{12y - 16y + 9y}{12x} = \dfrac{5y}{12x}$

You Try It 3

Simplify: $\dfrac{z}{8y} - \dfrac{4z}{3y} + \dfrac{5z}{4y}$

Your solution

Example 4

Simplify: $\dfrac{2x}{x-3} - \dfrac{5}{3-x}$

Solution

Remember $3 - x = -(x - 3)$.

Therefore, $\dfrac{5}{3-x} = \dfrac{5}{-(x-3)} = \dfrac{-5}{x-3}$.

$\dfrac{2x}{x-3} - \dfrac{5}{3-x} = \dfrac{2x}{x-3} - \dfrac{-5}{x-3}$

$= \dfrac{2x - (-5)}{x-3} = \dfrac{2x+5}{x-3}$

You Try It 4

Simplify: $\dfrac{5x}{x-2} - \dfrac{3}{2-x}$

Your solution

Example 5

Simplify: $\dfrac{2x}{2x-3} - \dfrac{1}{x+1}$

Solution

The LCM is $(2x - 3)(x + 1)$.

$\dfrac{2x}{2x-3} - \dfrac{1}{x+1}$

$= \dfrac{2x}{2x-3} \cdot \dfrac{x+1}{x+1} - \dfrac{1}{x+1} \cdot \dfrac{2x-3}{2x-3}$

$= \dfrac{2x^2 + 2x}{(2x-3)(x+1)} - \dfrac{2x-3}{(2x-3)(x+1)}$

$= \dfrac{(2x^2 + 2x) - (2x - 3)}{(2x-3)(x+1)} = \dfrac{2x^2 + 3}{(2x-3)(x+1)}$

You Try It 5

Simplify: $\dfrac{4x}{3x-1} - \dfrac{9}{x+4}$

Your solution

Solutions on p. S13

Example 6

Simplify: $1 + \dfrac{3}{x^2}$

Solution

The LCM is x^2.

$1 + \dfrac{3}{x^2} = 1 \cdot \dfrac{x^2}{x^2} + \dfrac{3}{x^2}$

$\quad = \dfrac{x^2}{x^2} + \dfrac{3}{x^2}$

$\quad = \dfrac{x^2 + 3}{x^2}$

You Try It 6

Simplify: $2 - \dfrac{1}{x - 3}$

Your solution

Example 7

Simplify: $\dfrac{x + 3}{x^2 - 2x - 8} + \dfrac{3}{4 - x}$

Solution

The LCM is $(x - 4)(x + 2)$.

Recall: $\dfrac{3}{4 - x} = \dfrac{-3}{x - 4}$

$\dfrac{x + 3}{x^2 - 2x - 8} + \dfrac{3}{4 - x}$

$\quad = \dfrac{x + 3}{(x - 4)(x + 2)} + \dfrac{(-3)}{x - 4}$

$\quad = \dfrac{x + 3}{(x - 4)(x + 2)} + \dfrac{(-3)}{x - 4} \cdot \dfrac{x + 2}{x + 2}$

$\quad = \dfrac{x + 3}{(x - 4)(x + 2)} + \dfrac{(-3)(x + 2)}{(x - 4)(x + 2)}$

$\quad = \dfrac{(x + 3) + (-3)(x + 2)}{(x - 4)(x + 2)}$

$\quad = \dfrac{x + 3 - 3x - 6}{(x - 4)(x + 2)} = \dfrac{-2x - 3}{(x - 4)(x + 2)}$

You Try It 7

Simplify: $\dfrac{2x - 1}{x^2 - 25} + \dfrac{2}{5 - x}$

Your solution

Example 8

Simplify: $\dfrac{3x + 2}{2x^2 - x - 1} - \dfrac{3}{2x + 1} + \dfrac{4}{x - 1}$

Solution

The LCM is $(2x + 1)(x - 1)$.

$\dfrac{3x + 2}{2x^2 - x - 1} - \dfrac{3}{2x + 1} + \dfrac{4}{x - 1}$

$\quad = \dfrac{3x + 2}{(2x + 1)(x - 1)} - \dfrac{3}{2x + 1} \cdot \dfrac{x - 1}{x - 1} + \dfrac{4}{x - 1} \cdot \dfrac{2x + 1}{2x + 1}$

$\quad = \dfrac{3x + 2}{(2x + 1)(x - 1)} - \dfrac{3x - 3}{(2x + 1)(x - 1)} + \dfrac{8x + 4}{(2x + 1)(x - 1)}$

$\quad = \dfrac{(3x + 2) - (3x - 3) + (8x + 4)}{(2x + 1)(x - 1)}$

$\quad = \dfrac{3x + 2 - 3x + 3 + 8x + 4}{(2x + 1)(x - 1)} = \dfrac{8x + 9}{(2x + 1)(x - 1)}$

You Try It 8

Simplify: $\dfrac{2x - 3}{3x^2 - x - 2} + \dfrac{5}{3x + 2} - \dfrac{1}{x - 1}$

Your solution

Solutions on p. S14

6.3 Exercises

. . . .

Objective A

Simplify.

1. $\dfrac{3}{y^2} + \dfrac{8}{y^2}$

2. $\dfrac{6}{ab} - \dfrac{2}{ab}$

3. $\dfrac{3}{x + 4} - \dfrac{10}{x + 4}$

4. $\dfrac{x}{x + 6} - \dfrac{2}{x + 6}$

5. $\dfrac{3x}{2x + 3} + \dfrac{5x}{2x + 3}$

6. $\dfrac{6y}{4y + 1} - \dfrac{11y}{4y + 1}$

7. $\dfrac{2x + 1}{x - 3} + \dfrac{3x + 6}{x - 3}$

8. $\dfrac{4x + 3}{2x - 7} + \dfrac{3x - 8}{2x - 7}$

9. $\dfrac{5x - 1}{x + 9} - \dfrac{3x + 4}{x + 9}$

10. $\dfrac{6x - 5}{x - 10} - \dfrac{3x - 4}{x - 10}$

11. $\dfrac{x - 7}{2x + 7} - \dfrac{4x - 3}{2x + 7}$

12. $\dfrac{2n}{3n + 4} - \dfrac{5n - 3}{3n + 4}$

13. $\dfrac{x}{x^2 + 2x - 15} - \dfrac{3}{x^2 + 2x - 15}$

14. $\dfrac{3x}{x^2 + 3x - 10} - \dfrac{6}{x^2 + 3x - 10}$

15. $\dfrac{2x + 3}{x^2 - x - 30} - \dfrac{x - 2}{x^2 - x - 30}$

16. $\dfrac{3x - 1}{x^2 + 5x - 6} - \dfrac{2x - 7}{x^2 + 5x - 6}$

17. $\dfrac{4y + 7}{2y^2 + 7y - 4} - \dfrac{y - 5}{2y^2 + 7y - 4}$

18. $\dfrac{x + 1}{2x^2 - 5x - 12} + \dfrac{x + 2}{2x^2 - 5x - 12}$

19. $\dfrac{2x^2 + 3x}{x^2 - 9x + 20} + \dfrac{2x^2 - 3}{x^2 - 9x + 20} - \dfrac{4x^2 + 2x + 1}{x^2 - 9x + 20}$

20. $\dfrac{2x^2 + 3x}{x^2 - 2x - 63} - \dfrac{x^2 - 3x + 21}{x^2 - 2x - 63} - \dfrac{x - 7}{x^2 - 2x - 63}$

___

Objective B

Simplify.

21. $\dfrac{4}{x} + \dfrac{5}{y}$

22. $\dfrac{7}{a} + \dfrac{5}{b}$

23. $\dfrac{12}{x} - \dfrac{5}{2x}$

24. $\dfrac{5}{3a} - \dfrac{3}{4a}$

25. $\dfrac{1}{2x} - \dfrac{5}{4x} + \dfrac{7}{6x}$

26. $\dfrac{7}{4y} + \dfrac{11}{6y} - \dfrac{8}{3y}$

27. $\dfrac{5}{3x} - \dfrac{2}{x^2} + \dfrac{3}{2x}$

28. $\dfrac{6}{y^2} + \dfrac{3}{4y} - \dfrac{2}{5y}$

29. $\dfrac{2}{x} - \dfrac{3}{2y} + \dfrac{3}{5x} - \dfrac{1}{4y}$

30. $\dfrac{5}{2a} + \dfrac{7}{3b} - \dfrac{2}{b} - \dfrac{3}{4a}$

31. $\dfrac{2x + 1}{3x} + \dfrac{x - 1}{5x}$

32. $\dfrac{4x - 3}{6x} + \dfrac{2x + 3}{4x}$

33. $\dfrac{x - 3}{6x} + \dfrac{x + 4}{8x}$

34. $\dfrac{2x - 3}{2x} + \dfrac{x + 3}{3x}$

35. $\dfrac{2x + 9}{9x} - \dfrac{x - 5}{5x}$

36. $\dfrac{3y - 2}{12y} - \dfrac{y - 3}{18y}$

37. $\dfrac{x + 4}{2x} - \dfrac{x - 1}{x^2}$

38. $\dfrac{x - 2}{3x^2} - \dfrac{x + 4}{x}$

39. $\dfrac{x - 10}{4x^2} + \dfrac{x + 1}{2x}$

40. $\dfrac{x + 5}{3x^2} + \dfrac{2x + 1}{2x}$

41. $\dfrac{4}{x + 4} - x$

42. $2x + \dfrac{1}{x}$

43. $5 - \dfrac{x - 2}{x + 1}$

44. $3 + \dfrac{x - 1}{x + 1}$

45. $\dfrac{x+3}{6x} - \dfrac{x-3}{8x^2}$

46. $\dfrac{x+2}{xy} - \dfrac{3x-2}{x^2y}$

47. $\dfrac{3x-1}{xy^2} - \dfrac{2x+3}{xy}$

48. $\dfrac{4x-3}{3x^2y} + \dfrac{2x+1}{4xy^2}$

49. $\dfrac{5x+7}{6xy^2} - \dfrac{4x-3}{8x^2y}$

50. $\dfrac{x-2}{8x^2} - \dfrac{x+7}{12xy}$

51. $\dfrac{3x-1}{6y^2} - \dfrac{x+5}{9xy}$

52. $\dfrac{4}{x-2} + \dfrac{5}{x+3}$

53. $\dfrac{2}{x-3} + \dfrac{5}{x-4}$

54. $\dfrac{6}{x-7} - \dfrac{4}{x+3}$

55. $\dfrac{3}{y+6} - \dfrac{4}{y-3}$

56. $\dfrac{2x}{x+1} + \dfrac{1}{x-3}$

57. $\dfrac{3x}{x-4} + \dfrac{2}{x+6}$

58. $\dfrac{4x}{2x-1} - \dfrac{5}{x-6}$

59. $\dfrac{6x}{x+5} - \dfrac{3}{2x+3}$

60. $\dfrac{2a}{a-7} + \dfrac{5}{7-a}$

61. $\dfrac{4x}{6-x} + \dfrac{5}{x-6}$

62. $\dfrac{x}{x^2-9} + \dfrac{3}{x-3}$

63. $\dfrac{y}{y^2-16} + \dfrac{1}{y-4}$

64. $\dfrac{2x}{x^2-x-6} - \dfrac{3}{x+2}$

65. $\dfrac{(x-1)^2}{(x+1)^2} - 1$

66. $1 - \dfrac{(y-2)^2}{(y+2)^2}$

67. $\dfrac{x}{1-x^2} - 1 + \dfrac{x}{1+x}$

68. $\dfrac{y}{x-y} + 2 - \dfrac{x}{y-x}$

69. $\dfrac{3x - 1}{x^2 - 10x + 25} - \dfrac{3}{x - 5}$

70. $\dfrac{2a + 3}{a^2 - 7a + 12} - \dfrac{2}{a - 3}$

71. $\dfrac{x + 4}{x^2 - x - 42} + \dfrac{3}{7 - x}$

72. $\dfrac{x + 3}{x^2 - 3x - 10} + \dfrac{2}{5 - x}$

73. $\dfrac{1}{x + 1} + \dfrac{x}{x - 6} - \dfrac{5x - 2}{x^2 - 5x - 6}$

74. $\dfrac{x}{x - 4} + \dfrac{5}{x + 5} - \dfrac{11x - 8}{x^2 + x - 20}$

75. $\dfrac{3x + 1}{x - 1} - \dfrac{x - 1}{x - 3} + \dfrac{x + 1}{x^2 - 4x + 3}$

76. $\dfrac{4x + 1}{x - 8} - \dfrac{3x + 2}{x + 4} - \dfrac{49x + 4}{x^2 - 4x - 32}$

77. $\dfrac{2x + 9}{3 - x} + \dfrac{x + 5}{x + 7} - \dfrac{2x^2 + 3x - 3}{x^2 + 4x - 21}$

78. $\dfrac{3x + 5}{x + 5} - \dfrac{x + 1}{2 - x} - \dfrac{4x^2 - 3x - 1}{x^2 + 3x - 10}$

APPLYING THE CONCEPTS

79. Find the sum of the following:

$$\dfrac{1}{1 \cdot 2} + \dfrac{1}{2 \cdot 3}$$

$$\dfrac{1}{1 \cdot 2} + \dfrac{1}{2 \cdot 3} + \dfrac{1}{3 \cdot 4}$$

$$\dfrac{1}{1 \cdot 2} + \dfrac{1}{2 \cdot 3} + \dfrac{1}{3 \cdot 4} + \dfrac{1}{4 \cdot 5}$$

Note the pattern in these sums, and find the sum of 50 terms, of 100 terms, and of 1000 terms.

80. In your own words, explain the procedure for adding rational expressions with different denominators.

Simplify.

81. $\dfrac{x^2 + x - 6}{x^2 + 2x - 8} \cdot \dfrac{x^2 + 5x + 4}{x^2 + 2x - 3} - \dfrac{2}{x - 1}$

82. $\dfrac{x^2 + 9x + 20}{x^2 + 4x - 5} - \dfrac{x^2 - 49}{x^2 + 6x - 7} - \dfrac{x}{x - 7}$

6.4 Complex Fractions

Objective A   *To simplify a complex fraction* ....

A **complex fraction** is a fraction whose numerator or denominator contains one or more fractions. Examples of complex fractions are shown at the right.

$$\frac{3}{2 - \dfrac{1}{2}}, \quad \frac{4 + \dfrac{1}{x}}{3 + \dfrac{2}{x}}, \quad \frac{\dfrac{1}{x-1} + x + 3}{x - 3 + \dfrac{1}{x+4}}$$

⇒ Simplify: $\dfrac{1 - \dfrac{4}{x^2}}{1 + \dfrac{2}{x}}$

The LCM of x and x^2 is x^2.

- Find the LCM of the denominators of the fractions in the numerator and denominator.

$$\frac{1 - \dfrac{4}{x^2}}{1 + \dfrac{2}{x}} = \frac{1 - \dfrac{4}{x^2}}{1 + \dfrac{2}{x}} \cdot \frac{x^2}{x^2}$$

- Multiply the numerator and denominator by the LCM.

$$= \frac{1 \cdot x^2 - \dfrac{4}{x^2} \cdot x^2}{1 \cdot x^2 + \dfrac{2}{x} \cdot x^2}$$

- Simplify.

$$= \frac{x^2 - 4}{x^2 + 2x} = \frac{(x - 2)\overset{1}{\cancel{(x + 2)}}}{x\underset{1}{\cancel{(x + 2)}}}$$

$$= \frac{x - 2}{x}$$

Example 1

Simplify: $\dfrac{\dfrac{1}{x} + \dfrac{1}{2}}{\dfrac{1}{x^2} - \dfrac{1}{4}}$

Solution

The LCM of x, 2, x^2, and 4 is $4x^2$.

$$\frac{\dfrac{1}{x} + \dfrac{1}{2}}{\dfrac{1}{x^2} - \dfrac{1}{4}} = \frac{\dfrac{1}{x} + \dfrac{1}{2}}{\dfrac{1}{x^2} - \dfrac{1}{4}} \cdot \frac{4x^2}{4x^2} = \frac{\dfrac{1}{x} \cdot 4x^2 + \dfrac{1}{2} \cdot 4x^2}{\dfrac{1}{x^2} \cdot 4x^2 - \dfrac{1}{4} \cdot 4x^2}$$

$$= \frac{4x + 2x^2}{4 - x^2} = \frac{2x\overset{1}{\cancel{(2 + x)}}}{(2 - x)\underset{1}{\cancel{(2 + x)}}} = \frac{2x}{2 - x}$$

You Try It 1

Simplify: $\dfrac{\dfrac{1}{3} - \dfrac{1}{x}}{\dfrac{1}{9} - \dfrac{1}{x^2}}$

Your solution

Solution on p. S14

Example 2

Simplify: $\dfrac{1 - \dfrac{2}{x} - \dfrac{15}{x^2}}{1 - \dfrac{11}{x} + \dfrac{30}{x^2}}$

Solution

The LCM of x and x^2 is x^2.

$$\frac{1 - \dfrac{2}{x} - \dfrac{15}{x^2}}{1 - \dfrac{11}{x} + \dfrac{30}{x^2}} = \frac{1 - \dfrac{2}{x} - \dfrac{15}{x^2}}{1 - \dfrac{11}{x} + \dfrac{30}{x^2}} \cdot \frac{x^2}{x^2}$$

$$= \frac{1 \cdot x^2 - \dfrac{2}{x} \cdot x^2 - \dfrac{15}{x^2} \cdot x^2}{1 \cdot x^2 - \dfrac{11}{x} \cdot x^2 + \dfrac{30}{x^2} \cdot x^2}$$

$$= \frac{x^2 - 2x - 15}{x^2 - 11x + 30}$$

$$= \frac{\overset{1}{\cancel{(x - 5)}}(x + 3)}{\underset{1}{\cancel{(x - 5)}}(x - 6)} = \frac{x + 3}{x - 6}$$

You Try It 2

Simplify: $\dfrac{1 + \dfrac{4}{x} + \dfrac{3}{x^2}}{1 + \dfrac{10}{x} + \dfrac{21}{x^2}}$

Your solution

Example 3

Simplify: $\dfrac{x - 8 + \dfrac{20}{x + 4}}{x - 10 + \dfrac{24}{x + 4}}$

Solution

The LCM is $x + 4$.

$$\frac{x - 8 + \dfrac{20}{x + 4}}{x - 10 + \dfrac{24}{x + 4}}$$

$$= \frac{x - 8 + \dfrac{20}{x + 4}}{x - 10 + \dfrac{24}{x + 4}} \cdot \frac{x + 4}{x + 4}$$

$$= \frac{(x - 8)(x + 4) + \dfrac{20}{x + 4} \cdot (x + 4)}{(x - 10)(x + 4) + \dfrac{24}{x + 4} \cdot (x + 4)}$$

$$= \frac{x^2 - 4x - 32 + 20}{x^2 - 6x - 40 + 24} = \frac{x^2 - 4x - 12}{x^2 - 6x - 16}$$

$$= \frac{(x - 6)\overset{1}{\cancel{(x + 2)}}}{(x - 8)\underset{1}{\cancel{(x + 2)}}} = \frac{x - 6}{x - 8}$$

You Try It 3

Simplify: $\dfrac{x + 3 - \dfrac{20}{x - 5}}{x + 8 + \dfrac{30}{x - 5}}$

Your solution

Solutions on p. S14

6.4 Exercises

· ·

Objective A

Simplify.

1. $\dfrac{1 + \dfrac{3}{x}}{1 - \dfrac{9}{x^2}}$

2. $\dfrac{1 + \dfrac{4}{x}}{1 - \dfrac{16}{x^2}}$

3. $\dfrac{2 - \dfrac{8}{x + 4}}{3 - \dfrac{12}{x + 4}}$

4. $\dfrac{5 - \dfrac{25}{x + 5}}{1 - \dfrac{3}{x + 5}}$

5. $\dfrac{1 + \dfrac{5}{y - 2}}{1 - \dfrac{2}{y - 2}}$

6. $\dfrac{2 - \dfrac{11}{2x - 1}}{3 - \dfrac{17}{2x - 1}}$

7. $\dfrac{4 - \dfrac{2}{x + 7}}{5 + \dfrac{1}{x + 7}}$

8. $\dfrac{5 + \dfrac{3}{x - 8}}{2 - \dfrac{1}{x - 8}}$

9. $\dfrac{1 - \dfrac{1}{x} - \dfrac{6}{x^2}}{1 - \dfrac{9}{x^2}}$

10. $\dfrac{1 + \dfrac{4}{x} + \dfrac{4}{x^2}}{1 - \dfrac{2}{x} - \dfrac{8}{x^2}}$

11. $\dfrac{1 - \dfrac{5}{x} - \dfrac{6}{x^2}}{1 + \dfrac{6}{x} + \dfrac{5}{x^2}}$

12. $\dfrac{1 - \dfrac{7}{a} + \dfrac{12}{a^2}}{1 + \dfrac{1}{a} - \dfrac{20}{a^2}}$

13. $\dfrac{1 - \dfrac{6}{x} + \dfrac{8}{x^2}}{\dfrac{4}{x^2} + \dfrac{3}{x} - 1}$

14. $\dfrac{1 + \dfrac{3}{x} - \dfrac{18}{x^2}}{\dfrac{21}{x^2} - \dfrac{4}{x} - 1}$

15. $\dfrac{x - \dfrac{4}{x + 3}}{1 + \dfrac{1}{x + 3}}$

16. $\dfrac{y + \dfrac{1}{y - 2}}{1 + \dfrac{1}{y - 2}}$

17. $\dfrac{1 - \dfrac{x}{2x + 1}}{x - \dfrac{1}{2x + 1}}$

18. $\dfrac{1 - \dfrac{2x - 2}{3x - 1}}{x - \dfrac{4}{3x - 1}}$

19. $\dfrac{x - 5 + \dfrac{14}{x + 4}}{x + 3 - \dfrac{2}{x + 4}}$

20. $\dfrac{a + 4 + \dfrac{5}{a - 2}}{a + 6 + \dfrac{15}{a - 2}}$

21. $\dfrac{x + 3 - \dfrac{10}{x - 6}}{x + 2 - \dfrac{20}{x - 6}}$

22. $\dfrac{x - 7 + \dfrac{5}{x - 1}}{x - 3 + \dfrac{1}{x - 1}}$

23. $\dfrac{y - 6 + \dfrac{22}{2y + 3}}{y - 5 + \dfrac{11}{2y + 3}}$

24. $\dfrac{x + 2 - \dfrac{12}{2x - 1}}{x + 1 - \dfrac{9}{2x - 1}}$

25. $\dfrac{x - \dfrac{2}{2x - 3}}{2x - 1 - \dfrac{8}{2x - 3}}$

26. $\dfrac{x + 3 - \dfrac{18}{2x + 1}}{x - \dfrac{6}{2x + 1}}$

27. $\dfrac{\dfrac{1}{x} - \dfrac{2}{x - 1}}{\dfrac{3}{x} + \dfrac{1}{x - 1}}$

28. $\dfrac{\dfrac{3}{n + 1} + \dfrac{1}{n}}{\dfrac{2}{n + 1} + \dfrac{3}{n}}$

29. $\dfrac{\dfrac{3}{2x - 1} - \dfrac{1}{x}}{\dfrac{4}{x} + \dfrac{2}{2x - 1}}$

30. $\dfrac{\dfrac{4}{3x + 1} + \dfrac{3}{x}}{\dfrac{6}{x} - \dfrac{2}{3x + 1}}$

APPLYING THE CONCEPTS

Simplify.

31. $1 + \dfrac{1}{1 + \dfrac{1}{2}}$

32. $1 + \dfrac{1}{1 + \dfrac{1}{1 + \dfrac{1}{2}}}$

33. $1 - \dfrac{1}{1 - \dfrac{1}{x}}$

34. $\dfrac{a^{-1} - b^{-1}}{a^{-2} - b^{-2}}$

35. $\left(\dfrac{y}{4} - \dfrac{4}{y}\right) \div \left(\dfrac{4}{y} - 3 + \dfrac{y}{2}\right)$

36. $\left(\dfrac{b}{8} - \dfrac{8}{b}\right) \div \left(\dfrac{8}{b} - 5 + \dfrac{b}{2}\right)$

37. $\dfrac{1 + x^{-1}}{1 - x^{-1}}$

38. $\dfrac{x + x^{-1}}{x - x^{-1}}$

39. $\dfrac{x^{-1}}{y^{-1}} + \dfrac{x}{y}$

6.5 Solving Equations Containing Fractions

Objective A   *To solve an equation containing fractions* ....

To solve an equation containing fractions, **clear denominators** by multiplying each side of the equation by the LCM of the denominators. Then solve for the variable.

➡ Solve: $\dfrac{3x-1}{4} + \dfrac{2}{3} = \dfrac{7}{6}$

$$\frac{3x-1}{4} + \frac{2}{3} = \frac{7}{6}$$

$$12\left(\frac{3x-1}{4} + \frac{2}{3}\right) = 12 \cdot \frac{7}{6}$$

- The LCM is 12. Multiply each side of the equation by the LCM.

$$12\left(\frac{3x-1}{4}\right) + 12 \cdot \frac{2}{3} = 12 \cdot \frac{7}{6}$$

- Simplify using the Distributive Property and the Properties of Fractions.

$$\frac{\overset{3}{\cancel{12}}}{1}\left(\frac{3x-1}{\underset{1}{\cancel{4}}}\right) + \frac{\overset{4}{\cancel{12}}}{1} \cdot \frac{2}{\underset{1}{\cancel{3}}} = \frac{\overset{2}{\cancel{12}}}{1} \cdot \frac{7}{\underset{1}{\cancel{6}}}$$

$$9x - 3 + 8 = 14$$

- Solve for x.

$$9x + 5 = 14$$
$$9x = 9$$
$$x = 1$$

1 checks as a solution. The solution is 1.

Occasionally, a value of the variable that appears to be a solution of an equation will make one of the denominators zero. In this case, that value is not a solution of the equation.

➡ Solve: $\dfrac{2x}{x-2} = 1 + \dfrac{4}{x-2}$

$$\frac{2x}{x-2} = 1 + \frac{4}{x-2}$$

$$(x-2)\frac{2x}{x-2} = (x-2)\left(1 + \frac{4}{x-2}\right)$$

- The LCM is $x - 2$. Multiply each side of the equation by the LCM.

$$(x-2)\frac{2x}{x-2} = (x-2) \cdot 1 + (x-2)\frac{4}{x-2}$$

- Simplify using the Distributive Property and the Properties of Fractions.

$$\frac{\overset{1}{\cancel{(x-2)}}}{1} \cdot \frac{2x}{\underset{1}{\cancel{x-2}}} = (x-2) \cdot 1 + \frac{\overset{1}{\cancel{(x-2)}}}{1} \cdot \frac{4}{\underset{1}{\cancel{x-2}}}$$

$$2x = x - 2 + 4$$

- Solve for x.

$$2x = x + 2$$
$$x = 2$$

When x is replaced by 2, the denominators of $\dfrac{2x}{x-2}$ and $\dfrac{4}{x-2}$ are zero. Therefore, the equation has no solution.

Example 1

Solve: $\dfrac{x}{x+4} = \dfrac{2}{x}$

Solution

The LCM is $x(x+4)$.

$$\frac{x}{x+4} = \frac{2}{x}$$

$$x(x+4)\left(\frac{x}{x+4}\right) = x(x+4)\left(\frac{2}{x}\right)$$

$$\frac{x\cancel{(x+4)}^{\,1}}{1} \cdot \frac{x}{\cancel{x+4}_{\,1}} = \frac{\cancel{x}^{\,1}(x+4)}{1} \cdot \frac{2}{\cancel{x}_{\,1}}$$

$$x^2 = (x+4)2$$
$$x^2 = 2x + 8$$

Solve the quadratic equation by factoring.

$$x^2 - 2x - 8 = 0$$
$$(x-4)(x+2) = 0$$
$$x - 4 = 0 \qquad x + 2 = 0$$
$$x = 4 \qquad\quad x = -2$$

Both 4 and -2 check as solutions.

The solutions are 4 and -2.

You Try It 1

Solve: $\dfrac{x}{x+6} = \dfrac{3}{x}$

Your solution

Example 2

Solve: $\dfrac{3x}{x-4} = 5 + \dfrac{12}{x-4}$

Solution

The LCM is $x - 4$.

$$\frac{3x}{x-4} = 5 + \frac{12}{x-4}$$

$$(x-4)\left(\frac{3x}{x-4}\right) = (x-4)\left(5 + \frac{12}{x-4}\right)$$

$$\frac{\cancel{(x-4)}^{\,1}}{1} \cdot \frac{3x}{\cancel{x-4}_{\,1}} = (x-4)5 + \frac{\cancel{(x-4)}^{\,1}}{1} \cdot \frac{12}{\cancel{x-4}_{\,1}}$$

$$3x = (x-4)5 + 12$$
$$3x = 5x - 20 + 12$$
$$3x = 5x - 8$$
$$-2x = -8$$
$$x = 4$$

4 does not check as a solution.

The equation has no solution.

You Try It 2

Solve: $\dfrac{5x}{x+2} = 3 - \dfrac{10}{x+2}$

Your solution

Solutions on p. S15

6.5 Exercises

. . . .

Objective A

Solve.

1. $\dfrac{2x}{3} - \dfrac{5}{2} = -\dfrac{1}{2}$

2. $\dfrac{x}{3} - \dfrac{1}{4} = \dfrac{1}{12}$

3. $\dfrac{x}{3} - \dfrac{1}{4} = \dfrac{x}{4} - \dfrac{1}{6}$

4. $\dfrac{2y}{9} - \dfrac{1}{6} = \dfrac{y}{9} + \dfrac{1}{6}$

5. $\dfrac{2x-5}{8} + \dfrac{1}{4} = \dfrac{x}{8} + \dfrac{3}{4}$

6. $\dfrac{3x+4}{12} - \dfrac{1}{3} = \dfrac{5x+2}{12} - \dfrac{1}{2}$

7. $\dfrac{6}{2a+1} = 2$

8. $\dfrac{12}{3x-2} = 3$

9. $\dfrac{9}{2x-5} = -2$

10. $\dfrac{6}{4-3x} = 3$

11. $2 + \dfrac{5}{x} = 7$

12. $3 + \dfrac{8}{n} = 5$

13. $1 - \dfrac{9}{x} = 4$

14. $3 - \dfrac{12}{x} = 7$

15. $\dfrac{2}{y} + 5 = 9$

16. $\dfrac{6}{x} + 3 = 11$

17. $\dfrac{3}{x-2} = \dfrac{4}{x}$

18. $\dfrac{5}{x+3} = \dfrac{3}{x-1}$

19. $\dfrac{2}{3x-1} = \dfrac{3}{4x+1}$

20. $\dfrac{5}{3x-4} = \dfrac{-3}{1-2x}$

21. $\dfrac{-3}{2x+5} = \dfrac{2}{x-1}$

22. $\dfrac{4}{5y-1}=\dfrac{2}{2y-1}$

23. $\dfrac{4x}{x-4}+5=\dfrac{5x}{x-4}$

24. $\dfrac{2x}{x+2}-5=\dfrac{7x}{x+2}$

25. $2+\dfrac{3}{a-3}=\dfrac{a}{a-3}$

26. $\dfrac{x}{x+4}=3-\dfrac{4}{x+4}$

27. $\dfrac{x}{x-1}=\dfrac{8}{x+2}$

28. $\dfrac{x}{x+12}=\dfrac{1}{x+5}$

29. $\dfrac{2x}{x+4}=\dfrac{3}{x-1}$

30. $\dfrac{5}{3n-8}=\dfrac{n}{n+2}$

31. $x+\dfrac{6}{x-2}=\dfrac{3x}{x-2}$

32. $x-\dfrac{6}{x-3}=\dfrac{2x}{x-3}$

33. $\dfrac{8}{y}=\dfrac{2}{y-2}+1$

APPLYING THE CONCEPTS

34. Explain the procedure for solving an equation containing fractions. Include in your discussion how the LCM is used to eliminate fractions in the equation.

Solve.

35. $\dfrac{3}{5}y-\dfrac{1}{3}(1-y)=\dfrac{2y-5}{15}$

36. $\dfrac{3}{4}a=\dfrac{1}{2}(3-a)+\dfrac{a-2}{4}$

37. $\dfrac{b+2}{5}=\dfrac{1}{4}b-\dfrac{3}{10}(b-1)$

38. $\dfrac{x}{2x^2-x-1}=\dfrac{3}{x^2-1}+\dfrac{3}{2x+1}$

39. $\dfrac{x+1}{x^2+x-2}=\dfrac{x+2}{x^2-1}+\dfrac{3}{x+2}$

40. $\dfrac{y+2}{y^2-y-2}+\dfrac{y+1}{y^2-4}=\dfrac{1}{y+1}$

6.6 Ratio and Proportion

Objective A **To solve a proportion** ....

Quantities such as 4 meters, 15 seconds, and 8 gallons are number quantities written with units. In these examples the units are meters, seconds, and gallons.

A **ratio** is the quotient of two quantities that have the same unit.

The length of a living room is 16 ft and the width is 12 ft. The ratio of the length to the width is written

$$\frac{16 \text{ ft}}{12 \text{ ft}} = \frac{16}{12} = \frac{4}{3}$$ A ratio is in simplest form when the two numbers do not have a common factor. Note that the units are not written.

A **rate** is the quotient of two quantities that have different units.

There are 2 lb of salt in 8 gal of water. The salt-to-water rate is

$$\frac{2 \text{ lb}}{8 \text{ gal}} = \frac{1 \text{ lb}}{4 \text{ gal}}$$ A rate is in simplest form when the two numbers do not have a common factor. The units are written as part of the rate.

A **proportion** is an equation that states the equality of two ratios or rates. Examples of proportions are shown at the right.

$$\frac{30 \text{ mi}}{4 \text{ h}} = \frac{15 \text{ mi}}{2 \text{ h}}$$
$$\frac{4}{6} = \frac{8}{12}$$
$$\frac{3}{4} = \frac{x}{8}$$

➡ Solve the proportion $\dfrac{4}{x} = \dfrac{2}{3}$.

$$\frac{4}{x} = \frac{2}{3}$$

$$3x\left(\frac{4}{x}\right) = 3x\left(\frac{2}{3}\right)$$ • The LCM of the denominators is 3*x*. Multiply each side of the proportion by the LCM.

$$12 = 2x$$ • Solve the equation.

$$6 = x$$

The solution is 6.

Example 1

Solve the proportion $\dfrac{8}{x + 3} = \dfrac{4}{x}$.

Solution

$$\frac{8}{x + 3} = \frac{4}{x}$$

$$x(x + 3)\frac{8}{x + 3} = x(x + 3)\frac{4}{x}$$

$$8x = 4(x + 3)$$

$$8x = 4x + 12$$

$$4x = 12$$

$$x = 3$$

The solution is 3.

You Try It 1

Solve the proportion $\dfrac{2}{x + 3} = \dfrac{6}{5x + 5}$.

Your solution

Solution on p. S15

Objective B   ***To solve application problems*** ································· (21) [CT]

Example 2
The monthly loan payment for a car is
$28.35 for each $1000 borrowed. At this
rate, find the monthly payment for a
$6000 car loan.

Strategy
To find the monthly payment, write and
solve a proportion, using P to represent the
monthly car payment.

Solution

$$\frac{28.35}{1000} = \frac{P}{6000}$$

$$6000\left(\frac{28.35}{1000}\right) = 6000\left(\frac{P}{6000}\right)$$

$$170.10 = P$$

The monthly payment is $170.10.

You Try It 2
Sixteen ceramic tiles are needed to tile a
9-square-foot area. At this rate how many
square feet can be tiled using 256 ceramic
tiles?

Your strategy

Your solution

Solution on p. S15

Objective C   ***To solve problems involving similar triangles*** ································· [CT]

Similar objects have the same shape but not necessarily the same size. A tennis
ball is similar to a basketball. A model ship is similar to an actual ship.

Similar objects have corresponding parts; for example, the rudder on the model
ship corresponds to the rudder on the actual ship. The relationship between the
sizes of each of the corresponding parts can be written as a ratio, and each ratio
will be the same. If the rudder on the model ship is $\frac{1}{100}$ the size of the rudder on
the actual ship, then the model wheelhouse is $\frac{1}{100}$ the size of the actual wheelhouse, the width of the model is $\frac{1}{100}$ the width of the actual ship, and so on.

The two triangles *ABC* and *DEF*
shown at the right are similar. Side
AB corresponds to *DE*, side *BC* corresponds to *EF*, and side *AC* corresponds to *DF*. The height *CH*
corresponds to the height *FK*. The
ratios of corresponding parts are
equal.

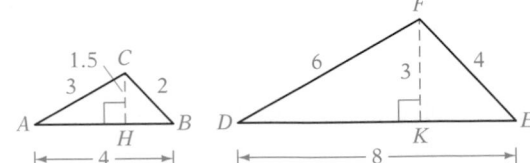

$$\frac{AB}{DE} = \frac{4}{8} = \frac{1}{2}, \qquad \frac{AC}{DF} = \frac{3}{6} = \frac{1}{2}, \qquad \frac{BC}{EF} = \frac{2}{4} = \frac{1}{2}, \qquad \text{and} \qquad \frac{CH}{FK} = \frac{1.5}{3} = \frac{1}{2}$$

Since the ratios of corresponding parts are equal, three proportions can be
formed using the sides of the triangles.

$$\frac{AB}{DE} = \frac{AC}{DF}, \qquad \frac{AB}{DE} = \frac{BC}{EF}, \qquad \text{and} \qquad \frac{AC}{DF} = \frac{BC}{EF}$$

Three proportions can also be formed by using the sides and height of the triangles.

$$\frac{AB}{DE} = \frac{CH}{FK}, \qquad \frac{AC}{DF} = \frac{CH}{FK}, \qquad \text{and} \qquad \frac{BC}{EF} = \frac{CH}{FK}$$

The corresponding angles in similar triangles are equal. Therefore,

$$\angle A = \angle D, \qquad \angle B = \angle E, \qquad \text{and} \qquad \angle C = \angle F$$

It is also true that if the three angles of one triangle are equal respectively to the three angles of another triangle, then the two triangles are similar.

TAKE NOTE

Vertical angles of intersecting lines, parallel lines, and angles of a triangle are discussed in the section "Geometry Problems" in the Solving Equations chapter.

A line *DE* is drawn parallel to the base *AB* in the triangle at the right. $\angle x = \angle m$ and $\angle y = \angle n$ because corresponding angles are equal. Angle C = angle C, thus the three angles of triangle *DEC* are equal respectively to the three angles of triangle *ABC*. The triangle *DEC* is similar to the triangle *ABC*.

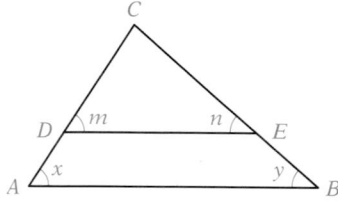

The sum of the three angles of a triangle is 180°. If two angles of one triangle are equal to two angles of another triangle, then the third angles must be equal. Thus we can say that if two angles of one triangle are equal to two angles of another triangle, then the two triangles are similar.

➡ The lines *AB* and *CD* intersect at point *O* in the figure at the right. Angles *C* and *D* are right angles. Find the length of *DO*.

First we must determine if triangle *AOC* is similar to triangle *BOD*.

Angle *C* = angle *D* because they are right angles.

Angle *x* = angle *y* because they are vertical angles.

Therefore triangle *AOC* is similar to triangle *BOD* because two angles of one triangle are equal to two angles of the other triangle.

$$\frac{AC}{DB} = \frac{CO}{DO}$$

$$\frac{4}{7} = \frac{3}{DO}$$

$$7(DO)\frac{4}{7} = 7(DO)\frac{3}{DO}$$

$$4(DO) = 7(3)$$

$$4(DO) = 21$$

$$DO = 5.25$$

• Use a proportion to find the length of the unknown side.

➡ Triangles *ABC* and *DEF* at the right are similar. Find the area of triangle *ABC*.

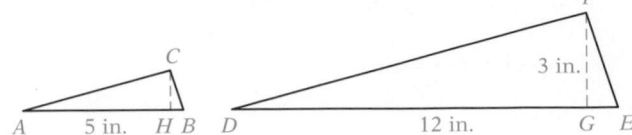

$$\frac{AB}{DE} = \frac{CH}{FG}$$

$$\frac{5}{12} = \frac{CH}{3}$$

$$12 \cdot \frac{5}{12} = 12 \cdot \frac{CH}{3}$$

$$5 = 4(CH)$$

$$1.25 = CH$$

$$A = \frac{1}{2}bh = \frac{1}{2}(5)(1.25) = 3.125$$

• Solve a proportion to find the height of triangle *ABC*.

• The height is 1.25 in. The base is 5 in.

• Use the formula for the area of a triangle.

The area of triangle *ABC* is 3.125 in^2.

Example 3

In the figure below, *AB* is parallel to *DC* and angles *B* and *D* are right angles. *AB* = 12 m, *DC* = 4 m, and *AC* = 18 m. Find the length of *CO*.

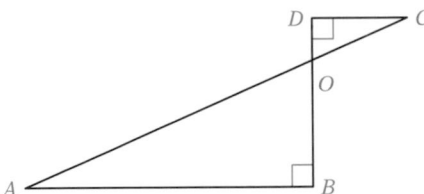

Strategy

Triangle *AOB* is similar to triangle *DOC*. Solve a proportion to find the length of *CO*. Let *x* represent the length of *CO* and 18 − *x* represent the length of *AO*.

Solution

$$\frac{DC}{AB} = \frac{CO}{AO}$$

$$\frac{4}{12} = \frac{x}{18 - x}$$

$$12(18 - x) \cdot \frac{4}{12} = 12(18 - x) \cdot \frac{x}{18 - x}$$

$$4(18 - x) = 12x$$

$$72 - 4x = 12x$$

$$72 = 16x$$

$$4.5 = x$$

The length of *CO* is 4.5 m.

You Try It 3

In the figure below, *AB* is parallel to *DC* and angles *A* and *D* are right angles. *AB* = 10 cm, *CD* = 4 cm, and *DO* = 3 cm. Find the area of triangle *AOB*.

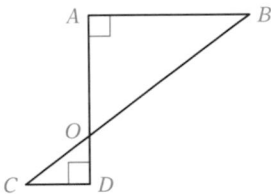

Your strategy

Your solution

Solution on p. S15

6.6 Exercises

Objective A

Solve.

1. $\dfrac{x}{12} = \dfrac{3}{4}$

2. $\dfrac{6}{x} = \dfrac{2}{3}$

3. $\dfrac{4}{9} = \dfrac{x}{27}$

4. $\dfrac{16}{9} = \dfrac{64}{x}$

5. $\dfrac{x+3}{12} = \dfrac{5}{6}$

6. $\dfrac{3}{5} = \dfrac{x-4}{10}$

7. $\dfrac{18}{x+4} = \dfrac{9}{5}$

8. $\dfrac{2}{11} = \dfrac{20}{x-3}$

9. $\dfrac{2}{x} = \dfrac{4}{x+1}$

10. $\dfrac{16}{x-2} = \dfrac{8}{x}$

11. $\dfrac{x+3}{4} = \dfrac{x}{8}$

12. $\dfrac{x-6}{3} = \dfrac{x}{5}$

13. $\dfrac{2}{x-1} = \dfrac{6}{2x+1}$

14. $\dfrac{9}{x+2} = \dfrac{3}{x-2}$

15. $\dfrac{2x}{7} = \dfrac{x-2}{14}$

Objective B   Application Problems

16. Simple syrup used in making some desserts requires 2 cups (c) of sugar for every $\dfrac{2}{3}$ c of boiling water. At this rate, how many cups of sugar are required for 2 c boiling water?

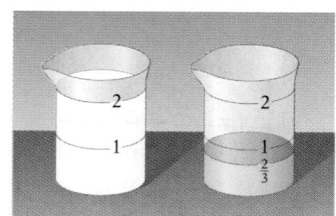

17. An exit poll survey showed that 4 out of every 7 voters cast a ballot in favor of an amendment to a city charter. At this rate, how many voters voted in favor of the amendment if 35,000 people voted?

18. In a city of 25,000 homes, a survey was taken to determine the number with cable television. Of the 300 homes surveyed, 210 had cable television. Estimate the number of homes in the city that have cable television.

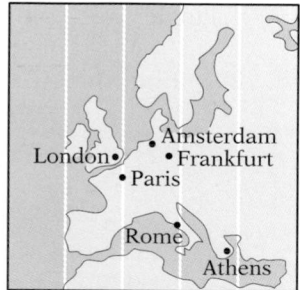

19. On a map, two cities are $2\dfrac{5}{8}$ in. apart. If $\dfrac{3}{8}$ in. on the map represents 25 mi, find the number of miles between the two cities.

20. A company decides to accept a large shipment of 10,000 computer chips if there are 2 or fewer defects in a sample of 100 randomly chosen chips. Assuming that there are 300 defective chips in the shipment and that the rate of defective chips in the sample is the same as the rate in the shipment, will the shipment be accepted?

21. The sales tax on a car that sold for $12,000 is $780. At this rate, how much higher is the sales tax on a car that sells for $13,500?

22. The lighting for some billboards is provided by using solar energy. If 3 small solar energy panels can generate 10 W of power, how many panels are necessary to provide 600 W of power?

23. To conserve energy and still allow for as much natural lighting as possible, an architect suggests that the ratio of the area of a window to the area of the total wall surface be 5 to 12. Using this ratio, determine the recommended area of a window to be installed in a wall that measures 8 ft by 12 ft.

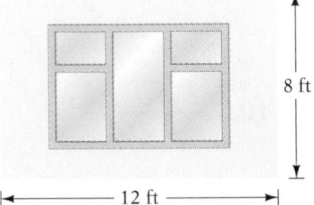

24. As part of a conservation effort for a lake, 40 fish are caught, tagged, and then released. Later 80 fish are caught. Four of the 80 fish are found to have tags. Estimate the number of fish in the lake.

25. In a wildlife preserve, 10 elk are captured, tagged, and then released. Later 15 elk are captured and 2 are found to have tags. Estimate the number of elk in the preserve.

26. The engine of a small rocket burns 170,000 lb of fuel in 1 min. At this rate, how many pounds of fuel does the rocket burn in 45 s?

Objective C

Triangles *ABC* and *DEF* in Exercises 27 to 34 are similar. Round answers to the nearest tenth.

27. Find side *AC*.

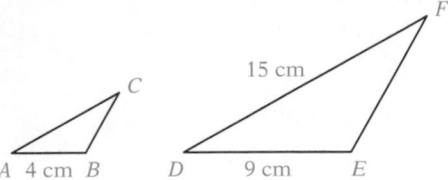

28. Find side *DE*.

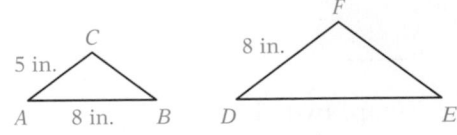

29. Find the height of triangle *ABC*.

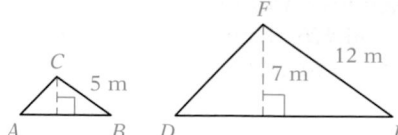

30. Find the height of triangle *DEF*.

31. Find the perimeter of triangle *DEF*.

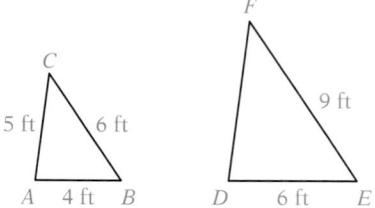

32. Find the perimeter of triangle *ABC*.

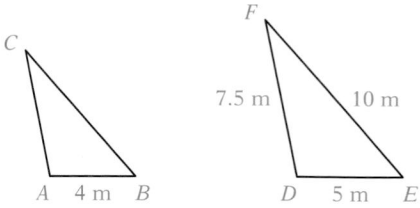

33. Find the area of triangle *ABC*.

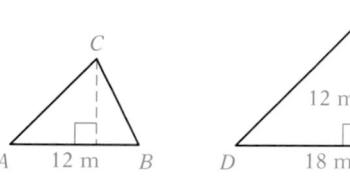

34. Find the area of triangle *ABC*.

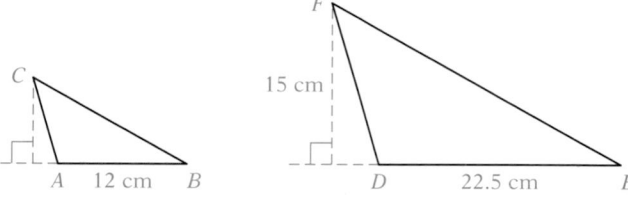

35. Given *BD* ∥ *AE*, *BD* measures 5 cm, *AE* measures 8 cm, and *AC* measures 10 cm, find the length of *BC*.

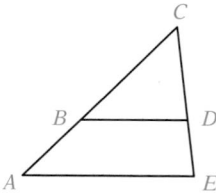

36. Given *AC* ∥ *DE*, *BD* measures 8 m, *AD* measures 12 m, and *BE* measures 6 m, find the length of *BC*.

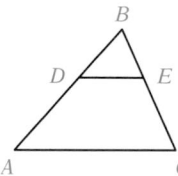

37. Given *DE* ∥ *AC*, *DE* measures 6 in., *AC* measures 10 in., and *AB* measures 15 in., find the length of *DA*.

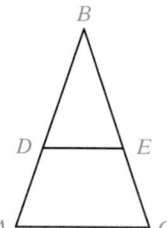

38. Given *MP* and *NQ* intersect at *O*, *NO* measures 25 ft, *MO* measures 20 ft, and *PO* measures 8 ft, find the length of *QO*.

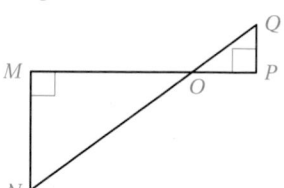

39. Given *MP* and *NQ* intersect at *O*, *NO* measures 24 cm, *MN* measures 10 cm, *MP* measures 39 cm, and *QO* measures 12 cm, find the length of *OP*.

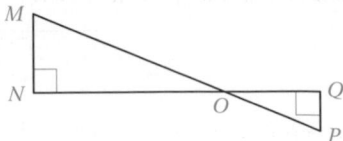

40. Given *MQ* and *NP* intersect at *O*, *NO* measures 12 m, *MN* measures 9 m, *PQ* measures 3 m, and *MQ* measures 20 m, find the perimeter of triangle *OPQ*.

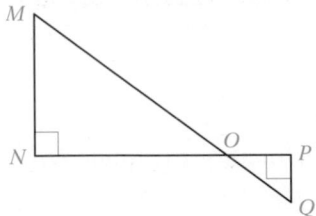

41. Similar triangles can be used as an indirect way to measure inaccessible distances. The diagram at the right represents a river of width *DC*. The triangles *AOB* and *DOC* are similar. The distances *AB*, *BO*, and *OC* can be measured. Find the width of the river.

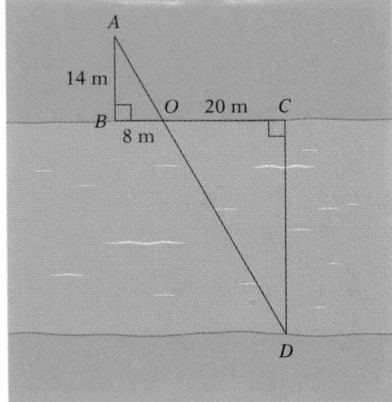

42. The sun's rays cast a shadow as shown in the diagram at the right. Find the height of the flagpole. Write the answer in terms of feet.

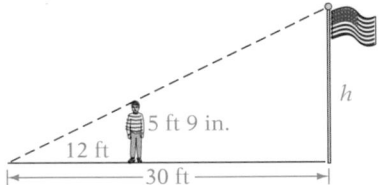

APPLYING THE CONCEPTS

43. Three people put their money together to buy lottery tickets. The first person put in $25, the second person put in $30, and the third person put in $35. One of their tickets was a winning ticket. If they won $4.5 million, what was the first person's share of the winnings?

44. No one belongs to both the Math Club and the Photography Club, but the two clubs join to hold a car wash. Ten members of the Math Club and 6 members of the Photography Club participate. The profits from the car wash are $120. If each club's profits are proportional to the number of members participating, what share of the profits does the Math Club receive?

45. A basketball player has made 5 out of every 6 foul shots attempted in one year of play. If 42 foul shots were missed that year, how many shots did the basketball player make?

6.7 Literal Equations

Objective A   To solve a literal equation for one of the variables .... CT

A **literal equation** is an equation that contains more than one variable. Examples of literal equations are shown at the right.

$$2x + 3y = 6$$
$$4w - 2x + z = 0$$

Formulas are used to express a relationship among physical quantities. A **formula** is a literal equation that states rules about measurements. Examples of formulas are shown at the right.

$$\frac{1}{R_1} + \frac{1}{R_2} = \frac{1}{R}$$ (Physics)

$$s = a + (n - 1)d$$ (Mathematics)

$$A = P + Prt$$ (Business)

The Addition and Multiplication Properties can be used to solve a literal equation for one of the variables. The goal is to rewrite the equation so that the variable being solved for is alone on one side of the equation and all the other numbers and variables are on the other side.

➡ Solve $A = P(1 + i)$ for i.

The goal is to rewrite the equation so that i is on one side of the equation and all other variables are on the other side.

$$A = P(1 + i)$$
$$A = P + Pi$$ • Use the Distributive Property to remove parentheses.
$$A - P = P - P + Pi$$ • Subtract P from each side of the equation.
$$A - P = Pi$$
$$\frac{A - P}{P} = \frac{Pi}{P}$$ • Divide each side of the equation by P.
$$\frac{A - P}{P} = i$$

Example 1
Solve $3x - 4y = 12$ for y.

Solution
$$3x - 4y = 12$$
$$3x - 3x - 4y = -3x + 12$$
$$-4y = -3x + 12$$
$$\frac{-4y}{-4} = \frac{-3x + 12}{-4}$$
$$y = \frac{3}{4}x - 3$$

You Try It 1
Solve $5x - 2y = 10$ for y.

Your solution

Solution on p. S15

Example 2

Solve $I = \dfrac{E}{R + r}$ for R.

Solution

$$I = \dfrac{E}{R + r}$$

$$(R + r)I = (R + r)\dfrac{E}{R + r}$$

$$RI + rI = E$$

$$RI + rI - rI = E - rI$$

$$RI = E - rI$$

$$\dfrac{RI}{I} = \dfrac{E - rI}{I}$$

$$R = \dfrac{E - rI}{I}$$

You Try It 2

Solve $s = \dfrac{A + L}{2}$ for L.

Your solution

Example 3

Solve $L = a(1 + ct)$ for c.

Solution

$$L = a(1 + ct)$$

$$L = a + act$$

$$L - a = a - a + act$$

$$L - a = act$$

$$\dfrac{L - a}{at} = \dfrac{act}{at}$$

$$\dfrac{L - a}{at} = c$$

You Try It 3

Solve $S = a + (n - 1)d$ for n.

Your solution

Example 4

Solve $S = C - rC$ for C.

Solution

$$S = C - rC$$

$$S = (1 - r)C$$

$$\dfrac{S}{1 - r} = \dfrac{(1 - r)C}{1 - r}$$

$$\dfrac{S}{1 - r} = C$$

You Try It 4

Solve $S = C + rC$ for C.

Your solution

Solutions on p. S16

6.7 Exercises

· ·

Objective A

Solve for y.

1. $3x + y = 10$ **2.** $2x + y = 5$ **3.** $4x - y = 3$ **4.** $5x - y = 7$

5. $3x + 2y = 6$ **6.** $2x + 3y = 9$ **7.** $2x - 5y = 10$ **8.** $5x - 2y = 4$

9. $2x + 7y = 14$ **10.** $6x - 5y = 10$ **11.** $x + 3y = 6$ **12.** $x + 2y = 8$

13. $2x - 9y - 18 = 0$ **14.** $3x - y + 7 = 0$ **15.** $2x - y + 5 = 0$

Solve for x.

16. $x + 3y = 6$ **17.** $x + 6y = 10$ **18.** $3x - y = 3$

19. $2x - y = 6$ **20.** $2x + 5y = 10$ **21.** $4x + 3y = 12$

22. $x - 2y + 1 = 0$ **23.** $x - 4y - 3 = 0$ **24.** $5x + 4y + 20 = 0$

Solve the formula for the given variable.

25. $d = rt; t$ (Physics)   **26.** $E = IR; R$ (Physics)

27. $PV = nRT; T$ (Chemistry)   **28.** $A = bh; h$ (Geometry)

29. $P = 2l + 2w; l$ (Geometry)

30. $F = \dfrac{9}{5}C + 32; C$ (Temperature conversion)

31. $A = \dfrac{1}{2}h(b_1 + b_2); b_1$ (Geometry)

32. $C = \dfrac{5}{9}(F - 32); F$ (Temperature conversion)

33. $V = \dfrac{1}{3}Ah; h$ (Geometry)

34. $P = R - C; C$ (Business)

35. $R = \dfrac{C - S}{t}; S$ (Business)

36. $P = \dfrac{R - C}{n}; R$ (Business)

37. $A = P + Prt; P$ (Business)

38. $T = fm - gm; m$ (Engineering)

39. $A = Sw + w; w$ (Physics)

40. $a = S - Sr; S$ (Mathematics)

APPLYING THE CONCEPTS

Breakeven analysis is a method used to determine the sales volume required for a company to break even, or experience neither a profit nor a loss on the sale of a product. The breakeven point represents the number of units that must be made and sold for income from sales to equal the cost of the product. The breakeven point can be calculated using the formula $B = \dfrac{F}{S - V}$, where F is the fixed costs, S is the selling price per unit, and V is the variable costs per unit.

41. a. Solve the formula $B = \dfrac{F}{S - V}$ for S.

　　b. Use your answer to part **a** to find the required selling price per unit for a company to break even. The fixed costs are $20,000, the variable costs per unit are $80, and the company plans to make and sell 200 desks.

　　c. Use your answer to part **a** to find the required selling price per unit for a company to break even. The fixed costs are $15,000, the variable costs per unit are $50, and the company plans to make and sell 600 cameras.

6.8 Application Problems

Objective A   *To solve work problems* ....

If a painter can paint a room in 4 h, then in 1 h the painter can paint $\frac{1}{4}$ of the room. The painter's rate of work is $\frac{1}{4}$ of the room each hour. The **rate of work** is the part of a task that is completed in one unit of time.

A pipe can fill a tank in 30 min. This pipe can fill $\frac{1}{30}$ of the tank in 1 min. The rate of work is $\frac{1}{30}$ of the tank each minute. If a second pipe can fill the tank in x min, the rate of work for the second pipe is $\frac{1}{x}$ of the tank each minute.

In solving a work problem, the goal is to determine the time it takes to complete a task. The basic equation that is used to solve work problems is

Rate of work × time worked = part of task completed

For example, if a faucet can fill a sink in 6 min, then in 5 min the faucet will fill $\frac{1}{6} \times 5 = \frac{5}{6}$ of the sink. In 5 min the faucet completes $\frac{5}{6}$ of the task.

➡ A painter can paint a wall in 20 min. The painter's apprentice can paint the same wall in 30 min. How long will it take to paint the wall when they work together?

> **Strategy for Solving a Work Problem**
>
> 1. For each person or machine, write a numerical or variable expression for the rate of work, the time worked, and the part of the task completed. The results can be recorded in a table.

TAKE NOTE

Use the information given in the problem to fill in the "Rate" and "Time" columns of the table. Fill in the "Part Completed" column by multiplying the two expressions you wrote in each row.

Unknown time to paint the wall working together: t

	Rate of Work	·	*Time Worked*	=	*Part of Task Completed*
Painter	$\frac{1}{20}$	·	t	=	$\frac{t}{20}$
Apprentice	$\frac{1}{30}$	·	t	=	$\frac{t}{30}$

> 2. Determine how the parts of the task completed are related. Use the fact that the sum of the parts of the task completed must equal 1, the complete task.

The sum of the part of the task completed by the painter and the part of the task completed by the apprentice is 1.

$$\frac{t}{20} + \frac{t}{30} = 1$$

$$60\left(\frac{t}{20} + \frac{t}{30}\right) = 60 \cdot 1$$

$$3t + 2t = 60$$

$$5t = 60$$

$$t = 12$$

• **Multiply by the LCM of 20 and 30.**

Working together, they will paint the wall in 12 min.

Example 1

A small water pipe takes three times longer to fill a tank than does a large water pipe. With both pipes open it takes 4 h to fill the tank. Find the time it would take the small pipe, working alone, to fill the tank.

You Try It 1

Two computer printers that work at the same rate are working together to print the payroll checks for a large corporation. After they work together for 2 h, one of the printers quits. The second requires 3 h more to complete the payroll checks. Find the time it would take one printer, working alone, to print the payroll.

Strategy

• Time for large pipe to fill the tank: t
Time for small pipe to fill the tank: $3t$

Your strategy

Fills tank in $3t$ hours   Fills tank in t hours

Fills $\frac{4}{3t}$ of the tank in 4 hours   Fills $\frac{4}{t}$ of the tank in 4 hours

	Rate	*Time*	*Part*
Small pipe	$\frac{1}{3t}$	4	$\frac{4}{3t}$
Large pipe	$\frac{1}{t}$	4	$\frac{4}{t}$

• The sum of the parts of the task completed by each pipe must equal 1.

Solution

$$\frac{4}{3t} + \frac{4}{t} = 1$$

$$3t\left(\frac{4}{3t} + \frac{4}{t}\right) = 3t \cdot 1$$

$$4 + 12 = 3t$$

$$16 = 3t$$

$$\frac{16}{3} = t$$

$$3t = 3\left(\frac{16}{3}\right) = 16$$

The small pipe working alone takes 16 h to fill the tank.

Your solution

Solution on p. S16

Objective B *To solve uniform motion problems* ....

A car that travels constantly in a straight line at 30 mph is in uniform motion. **Uniform motion** means that the speed or direction of an object does not change.

The basic equation used to solve uniform motion problems is

$$\textbf{Distance} = \textbf{rate} \times \textbf{time}$$

An alternative form of this equation can be written by solving the equation for time.

$$\frac{\textbf{Distance}}{\textbf{Rate}} = \textbf{time}$$

This form of the equation is useful when the total time of travel for two objects or the time of travel between two points is known.

⇒ The speed of a boat in still water is 20 mph. The boat traveled 75 mi down a river in the same amount of time it took to travel 45 mi up the river. Find the rate of the river's current.

> **Strategy for Solving a Uniform Motion Problem**
>
> 1. For each object, write a numerical or variable expression for the distance, rate, and time. The results can be recorded in a table.

The unknown rate of the river's current: r

TAKE NOTE

Use the information given in the problem to fill in the "Distance" and "Rate" columns of the table. Fill in the "Time" column by dividing the two expressions you wrote in each row.

	Distance	÷	*Rate*	=	*Time*
Down river	75	÷	$20 + r$	=	$\dfrac{75}{20 + r}$
Up river	45	÷	$20 - r$	=	$\dfrac{45}{20 - r}$

> 2. Determine how the times traveled by each object are related. For example, it may be known that the times are equal, or the total time may be known.

$$\frac{75}{20 + r} = \frac{45}{20 - r}$$

• The time down the river is equal to the time up the river.

$$(20 + r)(20 - r)\frac{75}{20 + r} = (20 + r)(20 - r)\frac{45}{20 - r}$$

• Multiply by the LCM.

$$(20 - r)75 = (20 + r)45$$
$$1500 - 75r = 900 + 45r$$
$$-120r = -600$$
$$r = 5$$

The rate of the river's current is 5 mph.

Example 2

A cyclist rode the first 20 mi of a trip at a constant rate. For the next 16 mi, the cyclist reduced the speed by 2 mph. The total time for the 36 mi was 4 h. Find the rate of the cyclist for each leg of the trip.

Strategy

- Rate for the first 20 mi: r
  Rate for the next 16 mi: $r - 2$

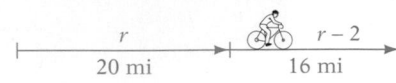

	Distance	Rate	Time
First 20 mi	20	r	$\dfrac{20}{r}$
Next 16 mi	16	$r - 2$	$\dfrac{16}{r - 2}$

- The total time for the trip was 4 h.

Solution

$$\frac{20}{r} + \frac{16}{r - 2} = 4$$

$$r(r - 2)\left[\frac{20}{r} + \frac{16}{r - 2}\right] = r(r - 2) \cdot 4$$

$$(r - 2)20 + 16r = 4r^2 - 8r$$

$$20r - 40 + 16r = 4r^2 - 8r$$

$$36r - 40 = 4r^2 - 8r$$

Solve the quadratic equation by factoring.

$$0 = 4r^2 - 44r + 40$$

$$0 = 4(r^2 - 11r + 10)$$

$$0 = 4(r - 10)(r - 1)$$

$$r - 10 = 0 \qquad r - 1 = 0$$

$$r = 10 \qquad r = 1$$

The solution $r = 1$ mph is not possible, because the rate on the last 16 mi would then be -1 mph.

10 mph was the rate for the first 20 mi.
8 mph was the rate for the next 16 mi.

You Try It 2

The total time it took for a sailboat to sail back and forth across a lake 6 km wide was 2 h. The rate sailing back was three times the rate sailing across. Find the rate sailing out across the lake.

Your strategy

Your solution

Solution on p. S16

6.8 Exercises

. . . .

Objective A   *Application Problems*

1. A park has two sprinklers that are used to fill a fountain. One sprinkler can fill the fountain in 3 h, whereas the second sprinkler can fill the fountain in 6 h. How long will it take to fill the fountain with both sprinklers operating?

2. One grocery clerk can stock a shelf in 20 min, whereas a second clerk requires 30 min to stock the same shelf. How long would it take to stock the shelf if the two clerks worked together?

3. One person with a skiploader requires 12 h to remove a large quantity of earth. A second, larger skiploader can remove the same amount of earth in 4 h. How long would it take to remove the earth with both skiploaders working together?

4. An experienced painter can paint a fence twice as fast as an inexperienced painter. Working together, the painters require 4 h to paint the fence. How long would it take the experienced painter working alone to paint the fence?

5. One computer can solve a complex prime factorization problem in 75 h. A second computer can solve the same problem in 50 h. How long would it take both computers, working together, to solve the problem?

6. A new machine can make 10,000 aluminum cans three times faster than an older machine. With both machines working, 10,000 cans can be made in 9 h. How long would it take the new machine, working alone, to make the 10,000 cans?

7. A small air conditioner can cool a room 5° in 75 min. A larger air conditioner can cool the room 5° in 50 min. How long would it take to cool the room 5° with both air conditioners working?

8. One printing press can print the first edition of a book in 55 min, whereas a second printing press requires 66 min to print the same number of copies. How long would it take to print the first edition with both presses operating?

9. Two oil pipelines can fill a small tank in 30 min. Using one of the pipelines would require 45 min to fill the tank. How long would it take the second pipeline alone to fill the tank?

10. Working together, two dock workers can load a crate in 6 min. One dock worker, working alone, can load the crate in 15 min. How long would it take the second dock worker, working alone, to load the crate?

11. A mason can construct a retaining wall in 10 h. With the mason's apprentice assisting, the task would take 6 h. How long would it take the apprentice working alone to construct the wall?

12. A mechanic requires 2 h to repair a transmission, whereas an apprentice requires 6 h to make the same repairs. The mechanic worked alone for 1 h and then stopped. How long will it take the apprentice, working alone, to complete the repairs?

13. One computer technician can wire a modem in 4 h, whereas it takes 6 h for a second technician to do the same job. After working alone for 2 h, the first technician quit. How long will it take the second technician to complete the wiring?

14. A wallpaper hanger requires 2 h to hang the wallpaper on one wall of a room. A second wallpaper hanger requires 4 h to hang the same amount of paper. The first wallpaper hanger worked alone for 1 h and then quit. How long will it take the second wallpaper hanger, working alone, to complete the wall?

15. Two welders who work at the same rate are welding the girders of a building. After they work together for 10 h, one of the welders quits. The second welder requires 20 more hours to complete the welds. Find the time it would have taken one of the welders, working alone, to complete the welds.

16. A large and a small heating unit are being used to heat the water of a pool. The larger unit, working alone, requires 8 h to heat the pool. After both units have been operating for 2 h, the larger unit is turned off. The small unit requires 9 h more to heat the pool. How long would it take the small unit, working alone, to heat the pool?

17. Two machines that fill cereal boxes work at the same rate. After they work together for 7 h, one machine breaks down. The second machine requires 14 h more to finish filling the boxes. How long would it have taken one of the machines, working alone, to fill the boxes?

18. A large and a small drain are opened to drain a pool. The large drain can empty the pool in 6 h. After both drains have been open for 1 h, the large drain becomes clogged and is closed. The smaller drain remains open and requires 9 h more to empty the pool. How long would it have taken the small drain, working alone, to empty the pool?

Objective B   *Application Problems*

19. Commuting from work to home, a lab technician traveled 10 mi at a constant rate through congested traffic. On reaching the expressway, the technician increased the speed by 20 mph. An additional 20 mi was traveled at the increased speed. The total time for the trip was 1 h. Find the rate of travel through the congested traffic.

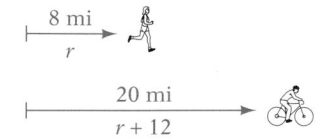

20. The president of a company traveled 1800 mi by jet and 300 mi on a prop plane. The rate of the jet was four times the rate of the prop plane. The entire trip took a total of 5 h. Find the rate of the jet plane.

21. As part of a conditioning program, a jogger ran 8 mi in the same time a cyclist rode 20 mi. The rate of the cyclist was 12 mph faster than the rate of the jogger. Find the rate of the jogger and that of the cyclist.

22. An express train travels 600 mi in the same amount of time it takes a freight train to travel 360 mi. The rate of the express train is 20 mph faster than that of the freight train. Find the rate of each train.

23. To assess the damage done by a fire, a forest ranger traveled 1080 mi by jet and then an additional 180 mi by helicopter. The rate of the jet was 4 times the rate of the helicopter. The entire trip took a total of 5 h. Find the rate of the jet.

24. A twin-engine plane can fly 800 mi in the same time that it takes a single-engine plane to fly 600 mi. The rate of the twin-engine plane is 50 mph faster than that of the single-engine plane. Find the rate of the twin-engine plane.

25. The rate of a motorcycle is 36 mph faster than the rate of a bicycle. The motorcycle travels 192 mi in the same amount of time as the bicycle travels 48 mi. Find the rate of the motorcycle.

26. A car and a bus leave a town at 1 P.M. and head for a town 300 mi away. The rate of the car is twice the rate of the bus. The car arrives 5 h ahead of the bus. Find the rate of the car.

27. A car is traveling at a rate that is 36 mph faster than the rate of a cyclist. The car travels 384 mi in the same time it takes the cyclist to travel 96 mi. Find the rate of the car.

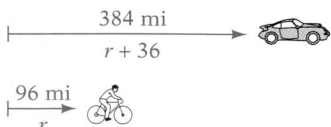

28. A backpacker hiking into a wilderness area walked 9 mi at a constant rate and then reduced this rate by 1 mph. Another 4 mi was hiked at this reduced rate. The time required to hike the 4 mi was 1 h less than the time required to walk the 9 mi. Find the rate at which the hiker walked the first 9 mi.

29. A plane can fly 180 mph in calm air. Flying with the wind, the plane can fly 600 mi in the same amount of time it takes to fly 480 mi against the wind. Find the rate of the wind.

30. A commercial jet can fly 550 mph in calm air. Traveling with the jet stream, the plane flew 2400 mi in the same amount of time it takes to fly 2000 mi against the jet stream. Find the rate of the jet stream.

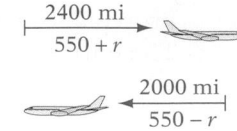

31. A cruise ship can sail at 28 mph in calm water. Sailing with the gulf current, the ship can sail 170 mi in the same amount of time that it can sail 110 mi against the gulf current. Find the rate of the gulf current.

32. Rowing with the current of a river, a rowing team can row 25 mi in the same amount of time it takes to row 15 mi against the current. The rate of the rowing team in calm water is 20 mph. Find the rate of the current.

33. On a recent trip, a trucker traveled 330 mi at a constant rate. Because of road construction, the trucker then had to reduce speed by 25 mph. An additional 30 mi was traveled at the reduced rate. The total time for the entire trip was 7 h. Find the rate of the trucker for the first 330 mi.

APPLYING THE CONCEPTS

34. One pipe can fill a tank in 2 h, a second pipe can fill the tank in 4 h, and a third pipe can fill the tank in 5 h. How long will it take to fill the tank with all three pipes working?

35. A mason can construct a retaining wall in 10 h. The mason's more-experienced apprentice can do the same job in 15 h. How long would it take the mason's less-experienced apprentice to do the job if, working together, all three can complete the job in 5 h?

36. A surveyor traveled 32 mi by canoe and then hiked 4 mi. The rate of speed by boat was four times the rate on foot. If the time spent walking was 1 h less than the time spent canoeing, find the amount of time spent traveling by canoe.

37. Because of bad weather, a bus driver reduced the usual speed along a 150-mile bus route by 10 mph. The bus arrived only 30 min later than its usual arrival time. How fast does the bus usually travel?

Focus on Problem Solving

Negations and If ... then Sentences

The sentence "George Washington was the first president of the United States" is a true sentence. The **negation** of that sentence is "George Washington was **not** the first president of the United States." That sentence is false. In general, the negation of a true sentence is a false statement.

The negation of a false sentence is a true sentence. For instance, the sentence "The moon is made of green cheese" is a false statement. The negation of that sentence, "The moon is **not** made of green cheese," is true.

The words *all, no* (or *none*), and *some* are called **quantifiers.** Writing the negation of a sentence that contains these words requires special attention. Consider the sentence "All pets are dogs." This sentence is not true because there are pets that are not dogs; cats, for example, are pets. Because the sentence is false, its negation must be true. You might be tempted to write "All pets are not dogs," but that sentence is not true because some pets are dogs. The correct negation of "All pets are dogs" is "Some pets are not dogs." Note the use of the word *some* in the negation.

Now consider the sentence "Some computers are portable." Because that sentence is true, its negation must be false. Writing "Some computers are not portable" as the negation is not correct, because that sentence is true. The negation of "Some computers are portable" is "No computers are portable."

The sentence "No flowers have red blooms" is false, because there is at least one flower (some roses, for example) that has red blooms. Because the sentence is false, its negation must be true. The negation is "Some flowers have red blooms."

Statement	*Negation*
All *A* are *B*.	Some *A* are not *B*.
No *A* are *B*.	Some *A* are *B*.
Some *A* are *B*.	No *A* are *B*.
Some *A* are not *B*.	All *A* are *B*.

Write the negation of the sentence.

1. All cats like milk.

2. All computers need people.

3. Some trees are tall.

4. No politicians are honest.

5. No houses have kitchens.

6. All police officers are tall.

7. All lakes are not polluted.

8. Some drivers are unsafe.

9. Some speeches are interesting.

10. All laws are good.

11. All businesses are not profitable.

12. All motorcycles are not large.

13. Some vegetables are good for you to eat.

14. Some banks are not open on Sunday.

A **premise** is a known or assumed fact. A premise can be stated using one of the quantifiers (*all, no, none,* or *some*) or can be stated using an *If ... then* sentence. For instance, the sentence "All triangles have three sides" can be written "*If* the figure is a triangle, *then* it has three sides."

We can write the sentence "No whole numbers are negative numbers" as an *If ... then* sentence: If a number is a whole number, then it is not a negative number.

Write the sentence as an *If ... then* sentence.

15. All students at Barlock College must take a life science course.

16. All baseballs are round.

17. All computers need people.

18. All cats like milk.

19. No odd number is evenly divisible by 2.

20. No prime number greater than 2 is an even number.

21. No rectangles have five sides.

22. All roads lead to Rome.

23. All dogs have fleas.

24. No triangle has four angles.

Projects and Group Activities

Intensity of Illumination

You are already aware that the standard unit of length in the metric system is the meter (m) and that the standard unit of mass in the metric system is the gram (g). You may not know that the standard unit of light intensity is the candela (cd).

The rate at which light falls on a 1-square-unit area of surface is called the **intensity of illumination.** Intensity of illumination is measured in **lumens** (lm). A lumen is defined in the following illustration.

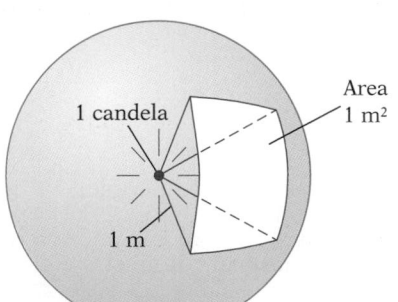
1 candela

Area 1 m²

1 m

Picture a source of light equal to 1 cd positioned at the center of a hollow sphere that has a radius of 1 m. The rate at which light falls on 1 m² of the inner surface of the sphere is equal to 1 lm. If a light source equal to 4 cd is positioned at the center of the sphere, each square meter of the inner surface receives four times as much illumination, or 4 lm.

Light rays diverge as they leave a light source. The light that falls on an area of 1 m² at a distance of 1 m from the source of light spreads out over an area of 4 m² when it is 2 m from the source. The same light spreads out over an area of 9 m² when it is 3 m from the light source and over an area of 16 m² when it is 4 m from the light source. Therefore, as a surface moves farther away from the source of light, the intensity of illumination on the surface decreases from its value at 1 m to $\left(\frac{1}{2}\right)^2$, or $\frac{1}{4}$, that value at 2 m; to $\left(\frac{1}{3}\right)^2$, or $\frac{1}{9}$, that value at 3 m; and to $\left(\frac{1}{4}\right)^2$, or $\frac{1}{16}$, that value at 4 m.

The formula for the intensity of illumination is

$$I = \frac{s}{r^2}$$

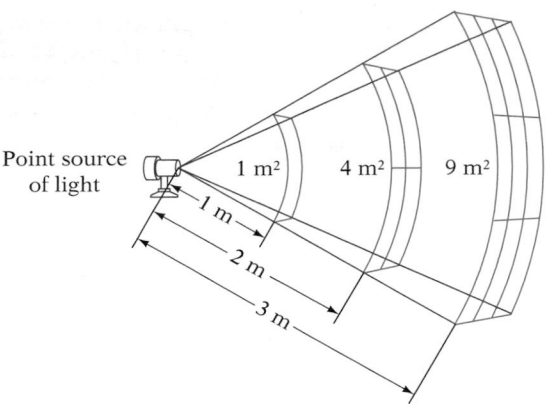

Point source of light

1 m²   4 m²   9 m²

1 m

2 m

3 m

where I is the intensity of illumination in lumens, s is the strength of the light source in candelas, and r is the distance in meters between the light source and the illuminated surface.

A 30-candela lamp is 0.5 m above a desk. Find the illumination on the desk.

$$I = \frac{s}{r^2}$$

$$I = \frac{30}{(0.5)^2} = 120$$

The illumination on the desk is 120 lm.

1. A 100-candela light is hanging 5 m above a floor. What is the intensity of the illumination on the floor beneath it?

2. A 25-candela source of light is 2 m above a desk. Find the intensity of illumination on the desk.

3. How strong a light source is needed to cast 20 lm of light on a surface 4 m from the source?

4. How strong a light source is needed to cast 80 lm of light on a surface 5 m from the source?

5. How far from the desk surface must a 40-candela light source be positioned if the desired intensity of illumination is 10 lm?

6. Find the distance between a 36-candela light source and a surface if the intensity of illumination on the surface is 0.01 lm.

7. Two lights cast the same intensity of illumination on a wall. One light is 6 m from the wall and has a rating of 36 candelas. The second light is 8 m from the wall. Find the candela rating of the second light.

8. A 40-candela light source and a 10-candela light source both throw the same intensity of illumination on a wall. The 10-candela light is 6 m from the wall. Find the distance from the 40-candela light to the wall.

Chapter Summary

Key Words   A *rational expression* is a fraction in which the numerator or denominator is a polynomial.

A *rational expression* is in *simplest form* when the numerator and denominator have no common factors.

The *reciprocal* of a fraction is a fraction with the numerator and denominator interchanged.

The *least common multiple* (LCM) of two or more numbers is the smallest number that contains the prime factorization of each number.

A *complex fraction* is a fraction whose numerator or denominator contains one or more fractions.

A *ratio* is the quotient of two quantities that have the same unit.

A *rate* is the quotient of two quantities that have different units.

A *proportion* is an equation that states the equality of two ratios or rates.

Similar triangles have the same shape but not necessarily the same size.

A *literal equation* is an equation that contains more than one variable.

A *formula* is a literal equation that states rules about measurement.

Essential Rules   To multiply rational numbers, multiply the numerators and multiply the denominators.

$$\frac{a}{b} \cdot \frac{c}{d} = \frac{ac}{bd}$$

To divide two fractions, multiply the dividend by the reciprocal of the divisor.

$$\frac{a}{b} \div \frac{c}{d} = \frac{a}{b} \cdot \frac{d}{c} = \frac{ad}{bc}$$

To add fractions, write each fraction in terms of a common denominator, then add the numerators.

$$\frac{a}{c} + \frac{b}{c} = \frac{a + b}{c}$$

To determine whether two triangles are similar, show that two angles of one triangle are equal to two angles of the other triangle.

To solve an equation containing fractions, clear denominators by multiplying each side of the equation by the LCM of the denominators.

Equation for Work Problems $$\text{Rate of Work} \times \text{time worked} = \text{part of task completed}$$

Uniform Motion Equation $$\frac{\text{Distance}}{\text{Rate}} = \text{time}$$

Chapter Review

1. Simplify: $\dfrac{6a^2b^7}{25x^3y} \div \dfrac{12a^3b^4}{5x^2y^2}$

2. Simplify: $\dfrac{x+7}{15x} + \dfrac{x-2}{20x}$

3. Simplify: $\dfrac{x - \dfrac{16}{5x-2}}{3x - 4 - \dfrac{88}{5x-2}}$

4. Simplify: $\dfrac{x^2 + x - 30}{15 + 2x - x^2}$

5. Simplify: $\dfrac{16x^5y^3}{24xy^{10}}$

6. Solve: $\dfrac{20}{x+2} = \dfrac{5}{16}$

7. Simplify: $\dfrac{10 - 23y + 12y^2}{6y^2 - y - 5} \div \dfrac{4y^2 - 13y + 10}{18y^2 + 3y - 10}$

8. Simplify: $\dfrac{8ab^2}{15x^3y} \cdot \dfrac{5xy^4}{16a^2b}$

9. Simplify: $\dfrac{1 - \dfrac{1}{x}}{1 - \dfrac{8x-7}{x^2}}$

10. Write each fraction in terms of the LCM of the denominators.

$$\dfrac{x}{12x^2 + 16x - 3} , \dfrac{4x^2}{6x^2 + 7x - 3}$$

11. Solve $T = 2(ab + bc + ca)$ for a.

12. Solve: $\dfrac{5}{7} + \dfrac{x}{2} = 2 - \dfrac{x}{7}$

13. Solve $i = \dfrac{100m}{c}$ for c.

14. Solve: $\dfrac{x+8}{x+4} = 1 + \dfrac{5}{x+4}$

15. Simplify: $\dfrac{20x^2 - 45x}{6x^3 + 4x^2} \div \dfrac{40x^3 - 90x^2}{12x^2 + 8x}$

16. Simplify: $\dfrac{2y}{5y-7} + \dfrac{3}{7-5y}$

17. Simplify: $\dfrac{5x + 3}{2x^2 + 5x - 3} - \dfrac{3x + 4}{2x^2 + 5x - 3}$

18. Find the LCM of $10x^2 - 11x + 3$ and $20x^2 - 17x + 3$.

19. Solve $4x + 9y = 18$ for y.

20. Simplify: $\dfrac{24x^2 - 94x + 15}{12x^2 - 49x + 15} \cdot \dfrac{24x^2 + 7x - 5}{4 - 27x + 18x^2}$

21. Solve: $\dfrac{20}{2x + 3} = \dfrac{17x}{2x + 3} - 5$

22. Simplify: $\dfrac{x - 1}{x + 2} + \dfrac{3x - 2}{5 - x} + \dfrac{5x^2 + 15x - 11}{x^2 - 3x - 10}$

23. Solve: $\dfrac{6}{x - 7} = \dfrac{8}{x - 6}$

24. Solve: $\dfrac{3}{20} = \dfrac{x}{80}$

25. Given MP and NQ intersect at O, NQ measures 25 cm, MO measures 6 cm, and PO measures 9 cm, find the length of QO.

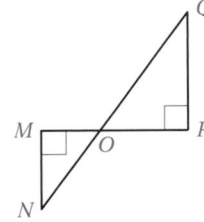

26. One hose can fill a pool in 15 h. The second hose can fill the pool in 10 h. How long would it take to fill the pool using both hoses?

27. A car travels 315 mi in the same amount of time that a bus travels 245 mi. The rate of the car is 10 mph faster than that of the bus. Find the rate of the car.

28. The rate of a jet is 400 mph in calm air. Traveling with the wind, the jet can fly 2100 mi in the same amount of time it takes to fly 1900 mi against the wind. Find the rate of the wind.

29. A pitcher's earned run average (ERA) is the average number of runs allowed in 9 innings of pitching. If a pitcher allows 15 runs in 100 innings, find the pitcher's ERA.

Chapter Test

1. Simplify: $\dfrac{x}{x+3} - \dfrac{2x-5}{x^2+x-6}$

2. Solve the proportion: $\dfrac{3}{x+4} = \dfrac{5}{x+6}$

3. Simplify: $\dfrac{x^2+2x-3}{x^2+6x+9} \cdot \dfrac{2x^2-11x+5}{2x^2+3x-5}$

4. Simplify: $\dfrac{16x^5y}{24x^2y^4}$

5. Solve $d = s + rt$ for t.

6. Solve: $\dfrac{6}{x} - 2 = 1$

7. Simplify: $\dfrac{x^2+4x-5}{1-x^2}$

8. Find the LCM of $6x - 3$ and $2x^2 + x - 1$.

9. Simplify: $\dfrac{2}{2x-1} - \dfrac{3}{3x+1}$

10. Simplify: $\dfrac{x^2+3x+2}{x^2+5x+4} \div \dfrac{x^2-x-6}{x^2+2x-15}$

11. Simplify: $\dfrac{1 + \dfrac{1}{x} - \dfrac{12}{x^2}}{1 + \dfrac{2}{x} - \dfrac{8}{x^2}}$

12. Write each fraction in terms of the LCM of the denominators.

$$\dfrac{3}{x^2-2x}, \dfrac{x}{x^2-4}$$

13. Simplify: $\dfrac{2x}{x^2 + 3x - 10} - \dfrac{4}{x^2 + 3x - 10}$

14. Solve $3x - 8y = 16$ for y.

15. Solve: $\dfrac{2x}{x + 1} - 3 = \dfrac{-2}{x + 1}$

16. Simplify: $\dfrac{x^3 y^4}{x^2 - 4x + 4} \cdot \dfrac{x^2 - x - 2}{x^6 y^4}$

17. Given $AE \parallel BD$, AB measures 5 ft, ED measures 8 ft, and BC measures 3 ft, find the length of CE.

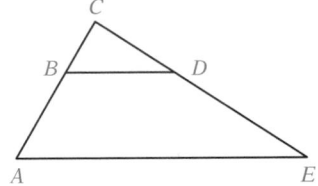

18. A saltwater solution is formed by mixing 4 lb of salt with 10 gal of water. At this rate, how many additional pounds of salt are required for 15 gal of water?

19. A pool can be filled with one pipe in 6 h, whereas a second pipe requires 12 h to fill the pool. How long would it take to fill the pool with both pipes turned on?

20. A small plane can fly at 110 mph in calm air. Flying with the wind, the plane can fly 260 mi in the same amount of time it takes to fly 180 mi against the wind. Find the rate of the wind.

21. A landscape architect uses three sprinklers for each 200 ft^2 of lawn. At this rate, how many sprinklers are needed for a 3600–square-foot lawn?

Cumulative Review

1. Simplify: $\left(\frac{2}{3}\right)^2 \div \left(\frac{3}{2} - \frac{2}{3}\right) + \frac{1}{2}$

2. Evaluate $-a^2 + (a - b)^2$ when $a = -2$ and $b = 3$.

3. Simplify: $-2x - (-3y) + 7x - 5y$

4. Simplify: $2[3x - 7(x - 3) - 8]$

5. Solve: $4 - \frac{2}{3}x = 7$

6. Solve: $3[x - 2(x - 3)] = 2(3 - 2x)$

7. Find $16\frac{2}{3}\%$ of 60.

8. Simplify: $(a^2 b^5)(ab^2)$

9. Simplify: $(a - 3b)(a + 4b)$

10. Simplify: $\frac{15b^4 - 5b^2 + 10b}{5b}$

11. Simplify: $(x^3 - 8) \div (x - 2)$

12. Factor: $12x^2 - x - 1$

13. Factor: $y^2 - 7y + 6$

14. Factor: $2a^3 + 7a^2 - 15a$

15. Factor: $4b^2 - 100$

16. Solve: $(x + 3)(2x - 5) = 0$

17. Simplify: $\frac{12x^4 y^2}{18xy^7}$

18. Simplify: $\frac{x^2 - 7x + 10}{25 - x^2}$

19. Simplify: $\dfrac{x^2 - x - 56}{x^2 + 8x + 7} \div \dfrac{x^2 - 13x + 40}{x^2 - 4x - 5}$

20. Simplify: $\dfrac{2}{2x - 1} - \dfrac{1}{x + 1}$

21. Simplify: $\dfrac{1 - \dfrac{2}{x} - \dfrac{15}{x^2}}{1 - \dfrac{25}{x^2}}$

22. Solve: $\dfrac{3x}{x - 3} - 2 = \dfrac{10}{x - 3}$

23. Solve the proportion: $\dfrac{2}{x - 2} = \dfrac{12}{x + 3}$

24. Solve $f = v + at$ for t.

25. Translate "the difference between five times a number and thirteen is the opposite of eight" into an equation and solve.

26. A silversmith mixes 60 g of an alloy that is 40% silver with 120 g of another silver alloy. The resulting alloy is 60% silver. Find the percent of silver in the 120-gram alloy.

27. The length of the base of a triangle is 2 in. less than twice the height. The area of the triangle is 30 in². Find the base and height of the triangle.

28. A life insurance policy costs $16 for every $1000 of coverage. At this rate, how much money would a policy of $5000 cost?

29. One water pipe can fill a tank in 9 min, whereas a second pipe requires 18 min to fill the tank. How long would it take both pipes, working together, to fill the tank?

30. The rower of a boat can row at a rate of 5 mph in calm water. Rowing with the current, the boat travels 14 mi in the same amount of time it takes to travel 6 mi against the current. Find the rate of the current.

CHAPTER

7

Linear Equations in Two Variables

Broadcast technicians operate the electronic equipment used to record and transmit radio and television programs, and they help prepare movie soundtracks for production studios. They work with television cameras, microphones, tape recorders, light and sound effects, transmitters, antennas, and other equipment. These technicians must be able to read and interpret graphs such as those discussed in this chapter.

Objectives

Section 7.1
To graph points in a rectangular coordinate system

To determine ordered-pair solutions of an equation in two variables

To determine whether a set of ordered pairs is a function

To evaluate a function written in functional notation

Section 7.2
To graph an equation of the form $y = mx + b$

To graph an equation of the form $Ax + By = C$

To solve application problems

Section 7.3
To find the x- and y-intercepts of a straight line

To find the slope of a straight line

To graph a line using the slope and the y-intercept

Section 7.4
To find the equation of a line given a point and the slope

To find the equation of a line given two points

To solve application problems

Magic Squares

A magic square is a square array of distinct integers so arranged that the numbers along any row, column, or main diagonal have the same sum. An example of a magic square is shown at the right.

8	3	4
1	5	9
6	7	2

The oldest known example of a magic square comes from China. Estimates are that this magic square is over 4000 years old. It is shown at the left.

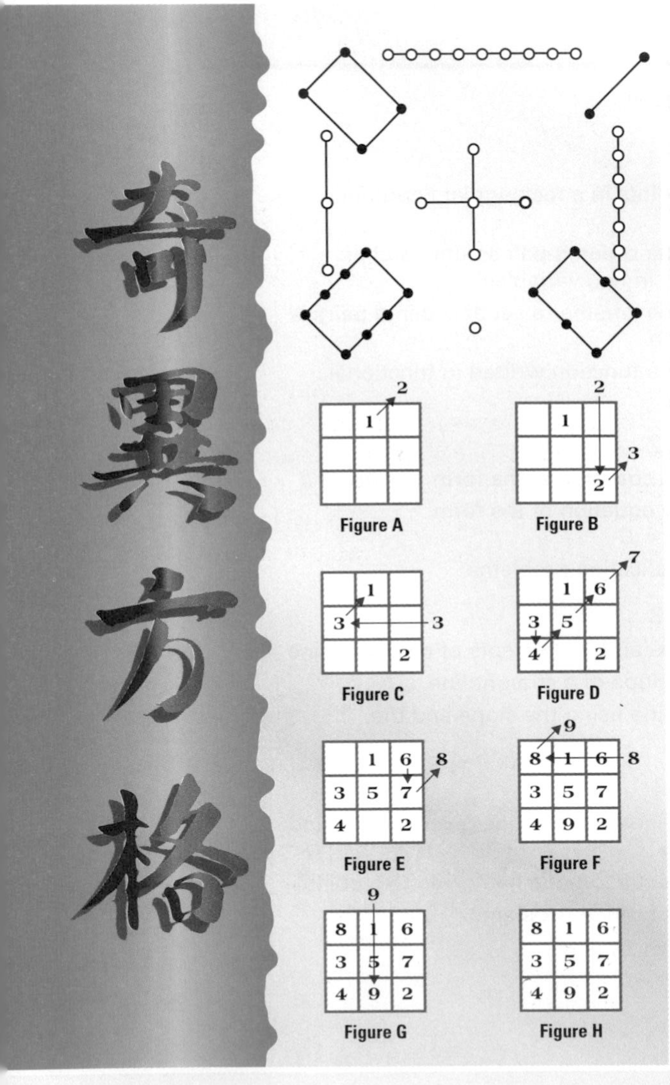

There is a simple way to produce a magic square with an odd number of cells. Start by writing a 1 in the top middle cell. The rule then is to proceed diagonally upward to the right with the successive integers.

When the rule takes you outside the square, write the number by shifting either across the square from right to left or down the square from top to bottom, as the case may be. For example, in Figure B the second number (2) is outside the square above a column. Because the 2 is above a column, it should be shifted down to the bottom cell in that column. In Figure C, the 3 is outside the square to the right of a column and should therefore be shifted all the way to the left.

If the rule takes you to a square that is already filled (as shown in Figure D), then write the number in the cell directly below the last number written. Continue until the entire square is filled.

It is possible to begin a magic square with any integer and proceed by using the above rule and consecutive integers.

For an odd magic square beginning with 1, the sum of a row, column, or diagonal is $\frac{n(n^2 + 1)}{2}$, where n is the number of rows.

Figure A

Figure B

Figure C

Figure D

Figure E

Figure F

Figure G

Figure H

7.1 The Rectangular Coordinate System

Objective A   **To graph points in a rectangular coordinate system** ....

Before the 15th century, geometry and algebra were considered separate branches of mathematics. That all changed when René Descartes, a French mathematician who lived from 1596 to 1650, founded **analytic geometry.** In this geometry, a *coordinate system* is used to study relationships between variables.

A **rectangular coordinate system** is formed by two number lines, one horizontal and one vertical, that intersect at the zero point of each line. The point of intersection is called the **origin.** The two lines are called **coordinate axes,** or simply **axes.**

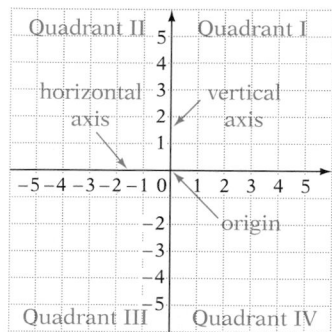

The axes determine a **plane,** which can be thought of as a large, flat sheet of paper. The two axes divide the plane into four regions called **quadrants,** which are numbered counterclockwise from I to IV.

Each point in the plane can be identified by a pair of numbers called an **ordered pair.** The first number of the pair measures a horizontal distance and is called the **abscissa.** The second number of the pair measures a vertical distance and is called the **ordinate.** The **coordinates** of the point are the numbers in the ordered pair associated with the point. The abscissa is also called the **first coordinate** of the ordered pair, and the ordinate is also called the **second coordinate** of the ordered pair.

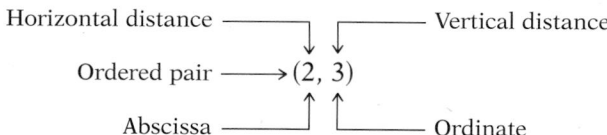

To **graph** or **plot** a point in the plane, place a dot at the location given by the ordered pair. The **graph of an ordered pair** is the dot drawn at the coordinates of the point in the plane. The points whose coordinates are (3, 4) and (−2.5, −3) are graphed in the figures below.

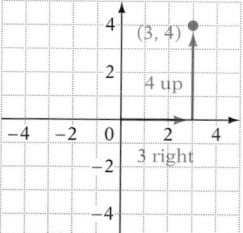

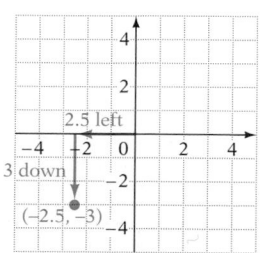

The points whose coordinates are $(3, -1)$ and $(-1, 3)$ are graphed at the right. Note that the graphed points are in different locations. *The order of the coordinates of an ordered pair is important.*

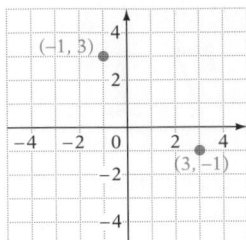

Each point in the plane is associated with an ordered pair, and each ordered pair is associated with a point in the plane. Although only the labels for integers are given on a coordinate grid, the graph of any ordered pair can be approximated. For example, the points whose coordinates are $(-2.3, 4.1)$ and $(\pi, 1)$ are shown on the graph at the right.

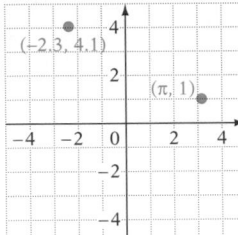

Example 1   Graph the ordered pairs $(-2, -3)$, $(3, -2)$, $(0, -2)$, and $(3, 0)$.

Solution

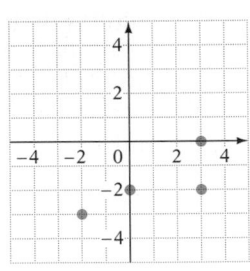

You Try It 1   Graph the ordered pairs $(-4, 1)$, $(3, -3)$, $(0, 4)$, and $(-3, 0)$.

Your solution

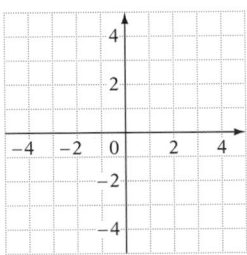

Example 2   Give the coordinates of the points labeled A and B. Give the abscissa of point C and the ordinate of point D.

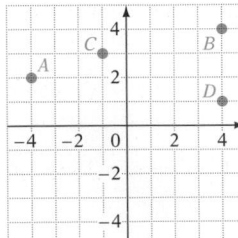

Solution   The coordinates of A are $(-4, 2)$.
The coordinates of B are $(4, 4)$.
The abscissa of C is -1.
The ordinate of D is 1.

You Try It 2   Give the coordinates of the points labeled A and B. Give the abscissa of point D and the ordinate of point C.

Your solution

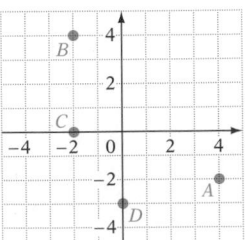

Solutions on p. S16

Objective B   *To determine ordered-pair solutions of an equation in two variables* ....

When drawing a rectangular coordinate system, we often label the horizontal axis x and the vertical axis y. In this case, the coordinate system is called an **xy-coordinate system.** The coordinates of the points are given by ordered pairs (x, y), where the abscissa is called the **x-coordinate** and the ordinate is called the **y-coordinate.**

A coordinate system is used to study the relationship between two variables. Frequently this relationship is given by an equation. Examples of equations in two variables include

$$y = 2x - 3 \qquad 3x + 2y = 6 \qquad x^2 - y = 0$$

A **solution of an equation in two variables** is an ordered pair (x, y) whose coordinates make the equation a true statement.

➡ Is $(-3, 7)$ a solution of $y = -2x + 1$?

$$y = -2x + 1$$

7	$-2(-3) + 1$
	$6 + 1$

  • Replace x by -3; replace y by 7.

$$7 = 7$$

  • The results are equal.

$(-3, 7)$ is a solution of the equation $y = -2x + 1$.

Besides $(-3, 7)$, there are many other ordered-pair solutions of $y = -2x + 1$. For example, $(0, 1)$, $\left(-\dfrac{3}{2}, 4\right)$, and $(4, -7)$ are also solutions. In general, an equation in two variables has an infinite number of solutions. By choosing any value of x and substituting that value into the equation, we can calculate a corresponding value of y.

➡ Find the ordered-pair solution of $y = \dfrac{2}{3}x - 3$ that corresponds to $x = 6$.

$$y = \dfrac{2}{3}x - 3$$

$$= \dfrac{2}{3}(6) - 3 \qquad \text{• Replace } x \text{ by 6.}$$

$$= 4 - 3 = 1 \qquad \text{• Simplify.}$$

The ordered-pair solution is $(6, 1)$.

The solutions of an equation in two variables can be graphed in an *xy*-coordinate system.

➡ Graph the ordered-pair solutions of $y = -2x + 1$ when $x = -2, -1, 0, 1,$ and 2.

Use the values of x to determine ordered-pair solutions of the equation. It is convenient to record these in a table.

x	$y = -2x + 1$	y	(x, y)
-2	$-2(-2) + 1$	5	$(-2, 5)$
-1	$-2(-1) + 1$	3	$(-1, 3)$
0	$-2(0) + 1$	1	$(0, 1)$
1	$-2(1) + 1$	-1	$(1, -1)$
2	$-2(2) + 1$	-3	$(2, -3)$

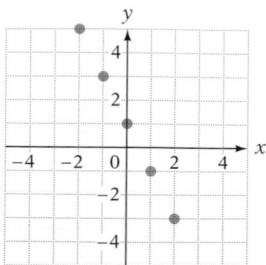

Example 3

Is $(3, -2)$ a solution of $3x - 4y = 15$?

Solution

$$3x - 4y = 15$$

$$\begin{array}{c|c} 3(3) - 4(-2) & 15 \\ 9 + 8 & \\ 17 \ne 15 & \end{array}$$ • Replace *x* by 3 and *y* by −2.

No. $(3, -2)$ is not a solution of $3x - 4y = 15$.

You Try It 3

Is $(-2, 4)$ a solution of $x - 3y = -14$?

Your solution

Example 4

Graph the ordered-pair solutions of $2x - 3y = 6$ when $x = -3, 0, 3,$ and 6.

Solution

$$2x - 3y = 6$$ • Solve $2x - 3y = 6$ for *y*.

$$-3y = -2x + 6$$

$$y = \frac{2}{3}x - 2$$

Replace x in $y = \frac{2}{3}x - 2$ by $-3, 0, 3,$ and 6. For each value of x, determine the value of y.

x	$y = \dfrac{2}{3}x - 2$	y	(x, y)
-3	$\dfrac{2}{3}(-3) - 2$	-4	$(-3, -4)$
0	$\dfrac{2}{3}(0) - 2$	-2	$(0, -2)$
3	$\dfrac{2}{3}(3) - 2$	0	$(3, 0)$
6	$\dfrac{2}{3}(6) - 2$	2	$(6, 2)$

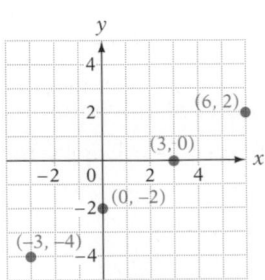

You Try It 4

Graph the ordered-pair solutions of $x + 2y = 4$ when $x = -4, -2, 0,$ and 2.

Your solution

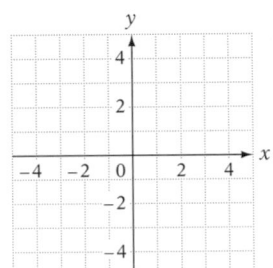

Solutions on pp. S16–S17

Objective C **To determine whether a set of ordered pairs is a function** ....

Discovering a relationship between two variables is an important task in the application of mathematics. Here are some examples.

- Botanists study the relationship between the number of bushels of wheat yielded per acre and the amount of watering per acre.
- Environmental scientists study the relationship between the incidents of skin cancer and the amount of ozone in the atmosphere.
- Business analysts study the relationship between the price of a product and the number of products that are sold at that price.

Each of these relationships can be described by a set of ordered pairs.

> **Definition of a Relation**
>
> A **relation** is any set of ordered pairs.

The following table shows the number of hours that each of 9 students spent studying for a midterm exam and the grade that each of these 9 students received.

Hours	3	3.5	2.75	2	4	4.5	3	2.5	5
Grade	78	75	70	65	85	85	80	75	90

This information can be written as the relation

{(3, 78), (3.5, 75), (2.75, 70), (2, 65), (4, 85), (4.5, 85), (3, 80), (2.5, 75), (5, 90)}

where the first coordinate of the ordered pair is the hours spent studying and the second coordinate is the score on the midterm.

The **domain** of a relation is the set of first coordinates of the ordered pairs; the **range** is the set of second coordinates. For the relation above,

Domain = {2, 2.5, 2.75, 3, 3.5, 4, 4.5, 5}   Range = {65, 70, 75, 78, 80, 85, 90}

The **graph of a relation** is the graph of the ordered pairs that belong to the relation. The graph of the relation given above is shown at the right. The horizontal axis represents the hours spent studying (the domain); the vertical axis represents the test score (the range). The axes could be labeled H for hours studied and S for test score.

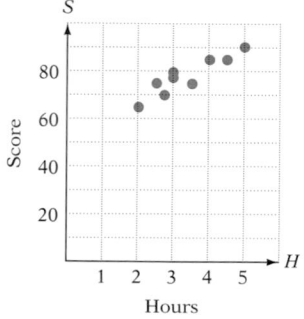

A *function* is a special type of relation for which no two ordered pairs have the same first coordinate.

> **Definition of a Function**
>
> A **function** is a relation in which no two ordered pairs that have the same first coordinate have different second coordinates.

The table at the right is the grading scale for a 100-point test. This table defines a relationship between the *score* on the test and a *letter grade*. Some of the ordered pairs of this function are (78, C), (97, A), (84, B), and (82, B).

Score	Grade
90–100	A
80–89	B
70–79	C
60–69	D
0–59	F

The grading-scale table defines a function, because no two ordered pairs can have the *same* first coordinate and *different* second coordinates. For instance, it is not possible to have the ordered pairs (72, C), and (72, B)—same first coordinate (test score) but different second coordinate (test grade). The domain of this function is {0, 1, 2,..., 99, 100}. The range is {A, B, C, D, F}.

The example of hours spent studying and test score given earlier is *not* a function, because (3, 78) and (3, 80) are ordered pairs of the relation that have the *same* first coordinate but *different* second coordinates.

Consider, again, the grading-scale example. Note that (84, B) and (82, B) are ordered pairs of the function. Ordered pairs of a function may have the same *second* coordinates but not the same first coordinates.

Although relations and functions are given by tables, they are frequently given by an equation in two variables.

The equation $y = 2x$ expresses the relationship between a number, x, and twice the number, y. For instance, if $x = 3$, then $y = 6$, which is twice 3. To indicate exactly which ordered pairs are determined by the equation, the domain (values of x) is specified. If $x \in \{-2, -1, 0, 1, 2\}$, then the ordered pairs determined by the equation are $\{(-2, -4), (-1, -2), (0, 0), (1, 2), (2, 4)\}$. This relation is a function because no two ordered pairs have the same first coordinate.

The graph of the function $y = 2x$ with domain $\{-2, -1, 0, 1, 2\}$ is shown at the right. The horizontal axis (domain) is labeled x; the vertical axis (range) is labeled y.

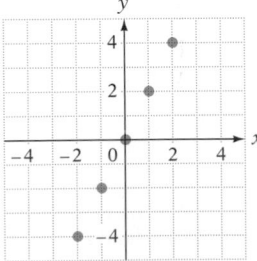

The domain $\{-2, -1, 0, 1, 2\}$ was chosen arbitrarily. Other domains could have been selected. The type of application usually influences the choice of the domain.

For the equation $y = 2x$, we say that "y is a function of x" because the set of ordered pairs is a function.

Not all equations, however, define a function. For instance, the equation $|y| = x + 2$ does not define y as a function of x. The ordered pairs (2, 4) and (2, −4) both satisfy the equation. Thus there are two ordered pairs with the same first coordinate but different second coordinates.

Example 5

The number of gold medals earned by several countries during the 1992 and 1996 Olympic Summer Games are recorded in the following table.

Country	1992	1996
United States	37	44
Canada	6	3
China	16	16
Italy	6	13
France	8	15
Germany	33	20

Write a relation where the first coordinate is the number of gold medals earned in 1992 and the second coordinate is the number earned in 1996. Is the relation a function?

Solution

{(37, 44), (6, 3), (16, 16), (6, 13), (8, 15), (33, 20)}

No. The relation is not a function. The two ordered pairs (6, 3) and (6, 13) have the same first coordinate but different second coordinates.

Example 6

Does $y = x^2 + 3$, where $x \in \{-2, -1, 1, 3\}$ define y as a function of x?

Solution

Determine the ordered pairs defined by the equation. Replace x in $y = x^2 + 3$ by the given values and solve for y.

{(−2, 7), (−1, 4), (1, 4), (3, 12)}

No two ordered pairs have the same first coordinate. Therefore, the relation is a function and the equation $y = x^2 + 3$ defines y as a function of x.

Note that (−1, 4) and (1, 4) are ordered pairs that belong to this function. Ordered pairs of a function may have the same *second* coordinates but not the same *first* coordinates.

You Try It 5

Five students decided to go on a diet and fitness program over the summer. Their weights (in pounds) at the beginning and end of the program are given in the table below.

Beginning	End
145	140
140	125
150	130
165	150
140	130
165	160

Write a relation where the first coordinate is the weight at the beginning of the summer and the second coordinate is the weight at the end of the summer. Is the relation a function?

Your solution

You Try It 6

Does $y = \frac{1}{2}x + 1$, where $x \in \{-4, 0, 2\}$,

define y as a function of x?

Your solution

Solutions on p. S17

Objective D   *To evaluate a function written in functional notation* ....

When an equation defines y as a function of x, **functional notation** is frequently used to emphasize that the relation is a function. In this case, it is common to use the notation $f(x)$, where

$f(x)$ is read "f of x" or "the value of f at x."

For instance, the equation $y = x^2 + 3$ from Example 6 defined y as a function of x. The equation can also be written in functional notation as

$$f(x) = x^2 + 3$$

where y has been replaced by $f(x)$.

The symbol $f(x)$ is called the **value of the function** at x because it is the result of evaluating a variable expression. For instance, $f(4)$ means to replace x by 4 and then simplify the resulting numerical expression.

$$f(x) = x^2 + 3$$
$$f(4) = 4^2 + 3 \qquad \bullet \text{ Replace } x \text{ by } 4.$$
$$= 16 + 3 = 19$$

This process is called **evaluating the function.**

➡ Given $f(x) = x^2 + x - 3$, find $f(-2)$.

$$f(x) = x^2 + x - 3$$
$$f(-2) = (-2)^2 + (-2) - 3 \qquad \bullet \text{ Replace } x \text{ by } -2.$$
$$= 4 - 2 - 3 = -1$$
$$f(-2) = -1$$

In this example, $f(-2)$ is the second coordinate of an ordered pair of the function; the first coordinate is -2. Therefore, an ordered pair of this function is $(-2, f(-2))$, which simplifies to $(-2, -1)$.

For the function given by $y = f(x) = x^2 + x - 3$, y is called the **dependent variable** because its value depends on the value of x. The **independent variable** is x.

Functions can be written using other letters or even combinations of letters. For instance, some calculators use $ABS(x)$ for the absolute-value function. Thus the equation $y = |x|$ would be written $ABS(x) = |x|$, where $ABS(x)$ replaces y.

Example 7

Given $G(t) = \dfrac{3t}{t + 4}$, find $G(1)$.

Solution

$$G(t) = \dfrac{3t}{t + 4}$$
$$G(1) = \dfrac{3(1)}{1 + 4} \qquad \bullet \text{ Replace } t \text{ by } 1. \text{ Then simplify.}$$
$$G(1) = \dfrac{3}{5}$$

You Try It 7

Given $H(x) = \dfrac{x}{x - 4}$, find $H(8)$.

Your solution

Solution on p. S17

7.1 Exercises

· ·

Objective A

1. Graph $(-2, 1)$, $(3, -5)$, $(-2, 4)$, and $(0, 3)$.

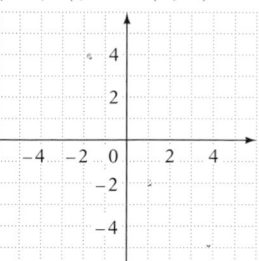

2. Graph $(5, -1)$, $(-3, -3)$, $(-1, 0)$, and $(1, -1)$.

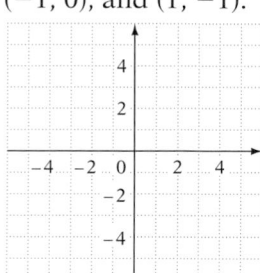

3. Graph $(0, 0)$, $(0, -5)$, $(-3, 0)$, and $(0, 2)$.

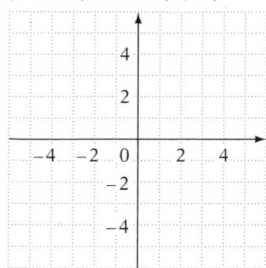

4. Graph $(-4, 5)$, $(-3, 1)$, $(3, -4)$, and $(5, 0)$.

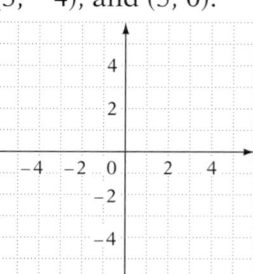

5. Graph $(-1, 4)$, $(-2, -3)$, $(0, 2)$, and $(4, 0)$.

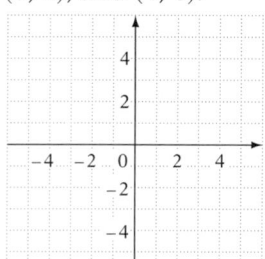

6. Graph $(5, 2)$, $(-4, -1)$, $(0, 0)$, and $(0, 3)$.

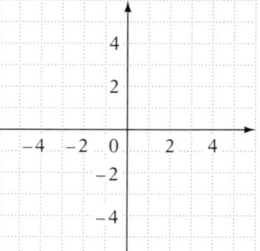

7. Find the coordinates of each of the points.

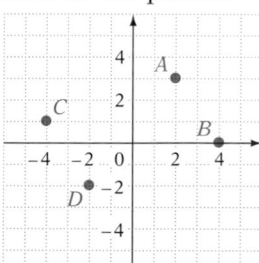

8. Find the coordinates of each of the points.

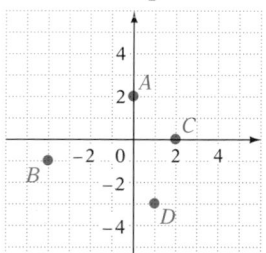

9. Find the coordinates of each of the points.

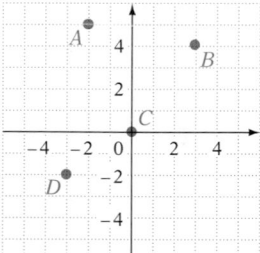

10. Find the coordinates of each of the points.

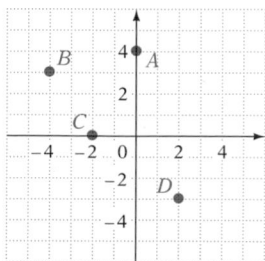

11. **a.** Name the abscissas of points A and C.
b. Name the ordinates of points B and D.

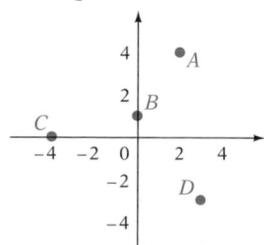

12. **a.** Name the abscissas of points A and C.
b. Name the ordinates of points B and D.

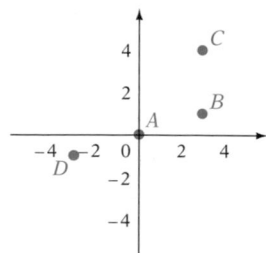

Objective B

13. Is (3, 4) a solution of $y = -x + 7$?

14. Is (2, −3) a solution of $y = x + 5$?

15. Is (−1, 2) a solution of $y = \frac{1}{2}x - 1$?

16. Is (1, −3) a solution of $y = -2x - 1$?

17. Is (4, 1) a solution of $2x - 5y = 4$?

18. Is (−5, 3) a solution of $3x - 2y = 9$?

19. Is (0, 4) a solution of $3x - 4y = -4$?

20. Is (−2, 0) a solution of $x + 2y = -1$?

Graph the ordered-pair solutions of each equation for the given values of x.

21. $y = 2x; x = -2, -1, 0, 2$

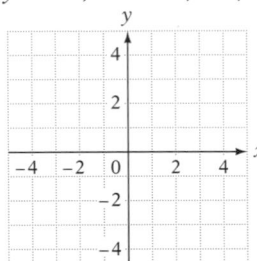

22. $y = -2x; x = -2, -1, 0, 2$

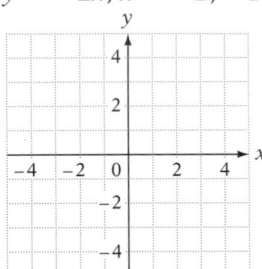

23. $y = x + 2; x = -4, -2, 0, 3$

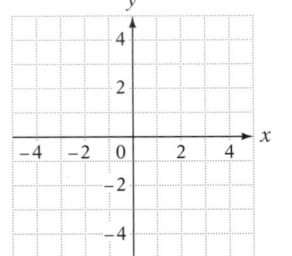

24. $y = \frac{1}{2}x - 1; x = -2, 0, 2, 4$

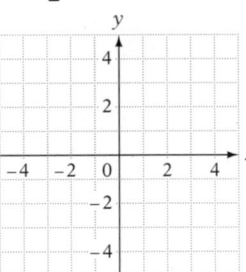

25. $y = \frac{2}{3}x + 1; x = -3, 0, 3$

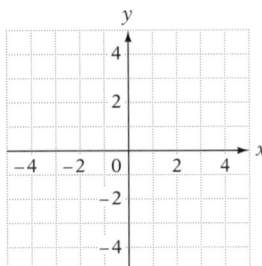

26. $y = -\frac{1}{3}x - 2; x = -3, 0, 3$

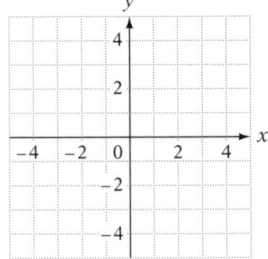

27. $2x + 3y = 6; x = -3, 0, 3$

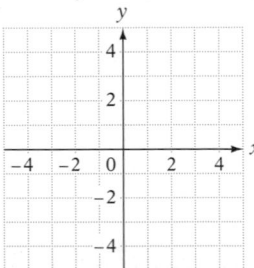

28. $x - 2y = 4; x = -2, 0, 2$

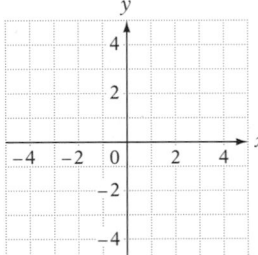

29. $2x + y = 3; x = -1, 0, 1, 2$

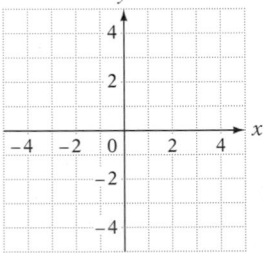

30. $3x - 4y = 8; x = -4, 0, 4$

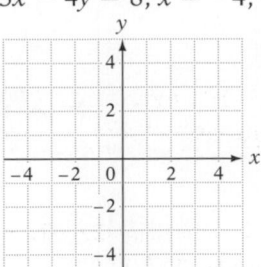

31. $5x + 2y = 0; x = -2, 0, 2$

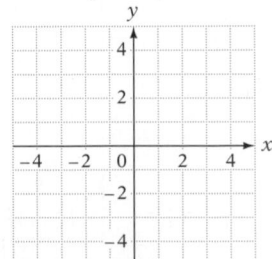

32. $-x - 2y = 0; x = -2, 0, 2$

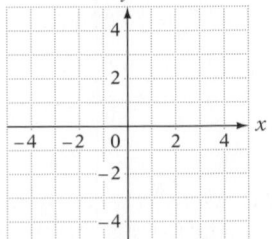

Objective C

33. The table below records the runs scored by the New York Yankees for the six games of the 1996 World Series and whether the Yankees won, *W*, or lost, *L*, the game. Write a relation where the first coordinate is the runs scored and the second coordinate is a win or a loss. Is the relation a function?

Runs scored	1	0	5	8	1	3
Won or lost	L	L	W	W	W	W

34. The table below records the goals scored by the Mighty Ducks hockey team for six games of the 1996–97 season and whether the Mighty Ducks won, *W*, tied, *T*, or lost, *L*, the game. Write a relation where the first coordinate is the goals scored and the second coordinate is a win, tie, or loss. Is the relation a function?

Goals scored	3	4	1	3	5	1
Won, lost, or tied	L	W	W	T	T	W

35. The number of sunny days in a year in five different cities and the average cost of a four bedroom house (in thousands of dollars) in those cities is given in the table to the right. Write a relation where the first coordinate is the number of sunny days annually, and the second coordinate is the cost of a house. Is the relation a function?

City	Sunny Days Annually	4-Bedroom House Cost
Nashua, NH	197	125
Portsmouth, NH	205	122
San Jose, CA	257	498
Jacksonville, FL	226	108
Manchester, NH	205	150

Source: *Money Magazine*, July, 1997

36. The budgets (in millions of dollars) for several movies and the gross ticket sales (in millions of dollars) are recorded in the table to the right. Write a relation where the first coordinate is the budget and the second coordinate is the gross sales. Is the relation a function?

Movie	Budget	Gross Sales
Seven	30	93
Apollo 13	62	172
Nixon	30	15
Toy Story	50	200
Batman Forever	100	184

37. Does $y = -2x - 3$, where $x \in \{-2, -1, 0, 3\}$, define y as a function of x?

38. Does $y = 2x + 3$, where $x \in \{-2, -1, 1, 4\}$, define y as a function of x?

39. Does $|y| = x - 1$, where $x \in \{1, 2, 3, 4\}$, define y as a function of x?

40. Does $|y| = x + 2$, where $x \in \{-2, -1, 0, 3\}$, define y as a function of x?

41. Does $y = x^2$, where $x \in \{-2, -1, 0, 1, 2\}$, define y as a function of x?

42. Does $y = x^2 - 1$, where $x \in \{-2, -1, 0, 1, 2\}$, define y as a function of x?

Objective D

43. Given $f(x) = 3x - 4$, find $f(4)$.

44. Given $f(x) = 5x + 1$, find $f(2)$.

45. Given $f(x) = x^2$, find $f(3)$.

46. Given $f(x) = x^2 - 1$, find $f(1)$.

47. Given $G(x) = x^2 + x$, find $G(-2)$.

48. Given $H(x) = x^2 - x$, find $H(-2)$.

49. Given $s(t) = \dfrac{3}{t - 1}$, find $s(-2)$.

50. Given $P(x) = \dfrac{4}{2x + 1}$, find $P(-2)$.

51. Given $h(x) = 3x^2 - 2x + 1$, find $h(3)$.

52. Given $Q(r) = 4r^2 - r - 3$, find $Q(2)$.

53. Given $f(x) = \dfrac{x}{x + 5}$, find $f(-3)$.

54. Given $v(t) = \dfrac{2t}{2t + 1}$, find $v(3)$.

55. Given $g(x) = x^3 - x^2 + 2x - 7$, find $g(0)$.

56. Given $F(z) = \dfrac{z}{z^2 + 1}$, find $F(0)$.

APPLYING THE CONCEPTS

57. Suppose you are helping a student who is having trouble graphing ordered pairs. The work of the student is at the right. What can you say to this student to correct the error that is being made?

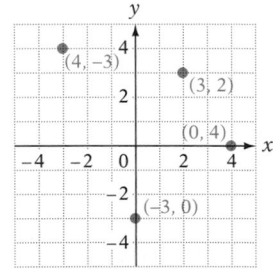

58. Write a few sentences that describe the similarities and differences between relations and functions.

59. The graph of $y^2 = x$, where $x \in \{0, 1, 4, 9\}$, is shown at the right. Is this the graph of a function? Explain your answer.

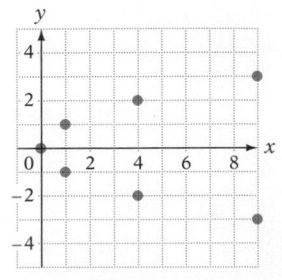

60. Is it possible to evaluate $f(x) = \dfrac{5}{x - 1}$ when $x = 1$? If so, what is $f(1)$? If not, explain why not.

7.2 Linear Equations in Two Variables

Objective A   ***To graph an equation of the form y = mx + b*** .... (23) CT

The **graph of an equation in two variables** is a graph of the ordered-pair solutions of the equation.

Consider $y = 2x + 1$. Choosing $x = -2$, -1, 0, 1, and 2 and determining the corresponding values of y produces some of the ordered pairs of the equation. These are recorded in the table at the right. See the graph of the ordered pairs in Figure 1.

x	$y = 2x + 1$	y	(x, y)
-2	$2(-2) + 1$	-3	$(-2, -3)$
-1	$2(-1) + 1$	-1	$(-1, -1)$
0	$2(0) + 1$	1	$(0, 1)$
1	$2(1) + 1$	3	$(1, 3)$
2	$2(2) + 1$	5	$(2, 5)$

Choosing values of x that are not integers produces more ordered pairs to graph, such as $\left(-\frac{5}{2}, -4\right)$ and $\left(\frac{3}{2}, 4\right)$, as shown in Figure 2. Choosing still other values of x would result in more and more ordered pairs being graphed. The result would be so many dots that the graph would appear as the straight line shown in Figure 3, which is the graph of $y = 2x + 1$.

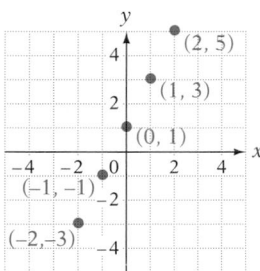

Figure 1

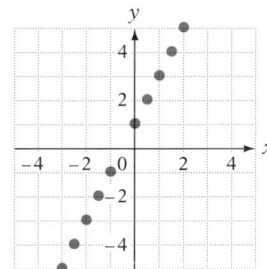

Figure 2

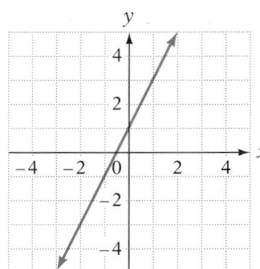

Figure 3

Equations in two variables have characteristic graphs. The equation $y = 2x + 1$ is an example of a *linear equation*, or *linear function*, because its graph is a straight line. It is also called a *first-degree equation* in two variables because the exponent on each variable is the first power.

Linear Equation in Two Variables

Any equation of the form $y = mx + b$, where m and b are constants, is a **linear equation in two variables or a first-degree equation in two variables.** The graph of a linear equation in two variables is a straight line.

Examples of linear equations are shown at the right. These equations represent linear functions because there is only one possible y for each x. Note that for $y = 3 - 2x$, m is the coefficient of x and b is the constant.

$$y = 2x + 1 \qquad (m = 2, b = 1)$$
$$y = x - 4 \qquad (m = 1, b = -4)$$
$$y = -\frac{3}{4}x \qquad \left(m = -\frac{3}{4}, b = 0\right)$$
$$y = 3 - 2x \qquad (m = -2, b = 3)$$

The equation $y = x^2 + 4x + 3$ is not a linear equation in two variables because there is a term with a variable squared. The equation $y = \frac{3}{x - 4}$ is not a linear equation because a variable occurs in the denominator of a fraction.

To graph a linear equation, choose some values of x and then find the corresponding values of y. Because a straight line is determined by two points, it is sufficient to find only two ordered-pair solutions. However, it is recommended that at least three ordered-pair solutions be used to ensure accuracy.

➡ Graph $y = -\frac{3}{2}x + 2$.

This is a linear equation with $m = -\frac{3}{2}$ and $b = 2$. Find at least three solutions.

Because m is a fraction, choose values of x that will simplify the calculations. We have chosen -2, 0, and 4 for x. (Any values of x could have been selected.)

x	$y = -\dfrac{3}{2}x + 2$	y	(x, y)
-2	$-\dfrac{3}{2}(-2) + 2$	5	$(-2, 5)$
0	$-\dfrac{3}{2}(0) + 2$	2	$(0, 2)$
4	$-\dfrac{3}{2}(4) + 2$	-4	$(4, -4)$

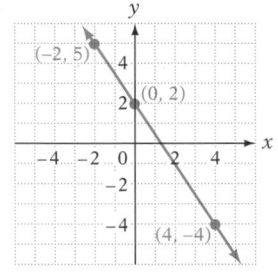

The graph of $y = -\frac{3}{2}x + 2$ is shown at the right.

Remember that a graph is a drawing of the ordered-pair solutions of the equation. Therefore, every point on the graph is a solution of the equation, and every solution of the equation is a point on the graph.

The graph at the right is the graph of $y = x + 2$. Note that $(-4, -2)$ and $(1, 3)$ are points on the graph and that these points are solutions of $y = x + 2$. The point whose coordinates are $(4, 1)$ is not a point on the graph and is not a solution of the equation.

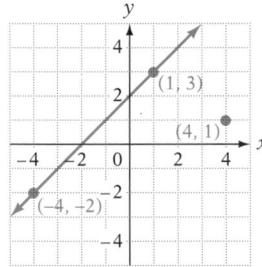

Example 1   Graph $y = 3x - 2$.

Solution

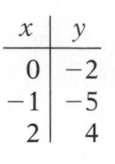

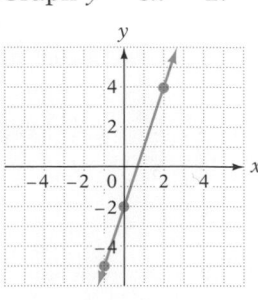

You Try It 1   Graph $y = 3x + 1$.

Your solution

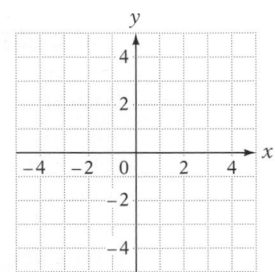

Solution on p. S17

Example 2   Graph $y = 2x$.

Solution

x	y
0	0
2	4
−2	−4

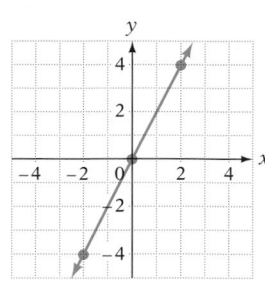

You Try It 2   Graph $y = -2x$.

Your solution

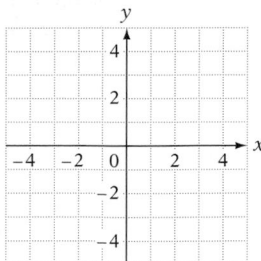

Example 3   Graph $y = \dfrac{1}{2}x - 1$.

Solution

x	y
0	−1
2	0
−2	−2

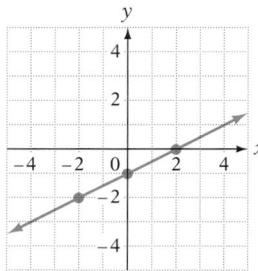

You Try It 3   Graph $y = \dfrac{1}{3}x - 3$.

Your solution

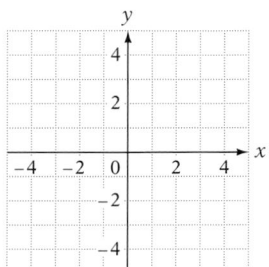

Solutions on p. S17

Objective B   ***To graph an equation of the form Ax + By = C*** ....

The equation $Ax + By = C$, where A, B, and C are constants, is also a linear equation. Examples of these equations are shown at the right.

$2x + 3y = 6$ $(A = 2, B = 3, C = 6)$
$x - 2y = -4$ $(A = 1, B = -2, C = -4)$
$2x + y = 0$ $(A = 2, B = 1, C = 0)$
$4x - 5y = 2$ $(A = 4, B = -5, C = 2)$

To graph an equation of the form $Ax + By = C$, first solve the equation for y. Then follow the same procedure used for graphing $y = mx + b$.

⇒ Graph $3x + 4y = 12$.

$3x + 4y = 12$
$\quad 4y = -3x + 12$

- Solve for *y*.
- Subtract 3*x* from each side of the equation.

$y = -\dfrac{3}{4}x + 3$

- Divide each side of the equation by 4.
- Find 3 ordered-pair solutions of the equation.

x	y
0	3
4	0
−4	6

- Graph the ordered pairs and then draw a line through the points.

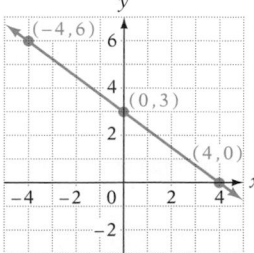

The graph of a linear equation with one of the variables missing is either a horizontal or a vertical line.

The equation $y = 2$ could be written $0 \cdot x + y = 2$. Because $0 \cdot x = 0$ for any value of x, the value of y is always 2 no matter what value of x is chosen. For instance, replace x by $-4, -1, 0,$ or 3. In each case, $y = 2$.

$$0x + y = 2$$
$$0(-4) + y = 2 \qquad (-4, 2) \text{ is a solution.}$$
$$0(-1) + y = 2 \qquad (-1, 2) \text{ is a solution.}$$
$$0(0) + y = 2 \qquad (0, 2) \text{ is a solution.}$$
$$0(3) + y = 2 \qquad (3, 2) \text{ is a solution.}$$

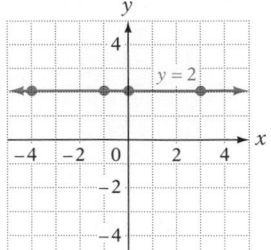

The solutions are plotted in the graph to the right, and a line is drawn through the plotted points. Note that the line is horizontal.

Graph of a Horizontal Line

The graph of $y = b$ is a horizontal line passing through $(0, b)$.

The equation $x = -2$ could be written $x + 0 \cdot y = -2$. Because $0 \cdot y = 0$ for any value of y, the value of x is always -2 no matter what value of y is chosen. For instance, replace y by $-2, 0, 2,$ or 3. In each case, $x = -2$.

$$x + 0y = -2$$
$$x + 0(-2) = -2 \qquad (-2, -2) \text{ is a solution.}$$
$$x + 0(0) = -2 \qquad (-2, 0) \text{ is a solution.}$$
$$x + 0(2) = -2 \qquad (-2, 2) \text{ is a solution.}$$
$$x + 0(3) = -2 \qquad (-2, 3) \text{ is a solution.}$$

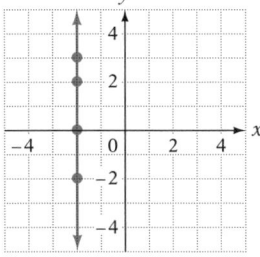

The solutions are plotted in the graph at the right, and a line is drawn through the plotted points. Note that the line is vertical.

Graph of a Vertical Line

The graph of $x = a$ is a vertical line passing through $(a, 0)$.

⇒ Graph $x = -3$ and $y = 2$ on the same coordinate grid.

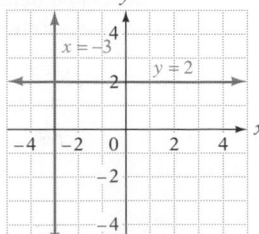

- **The graph of $x = -3$ is a vertical line passing through $(-3, 0)$.**

- **The graph of $y = 2$ is a horizontal line passing through $(0, 2)$.**

Example 4   Graph $2x - 5y = 10$.

Solution

$2x - 5y = 10$
$-5y = -2x + 10$
$y = \dfrac{2}{5}x - 2$

x	y
0	-2
5	0
-5	-4

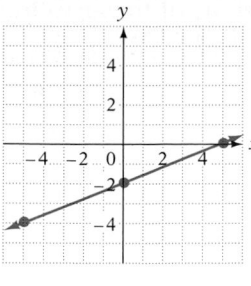

You Try It 4   Graph $5x - 2y = 10$.

Your solution

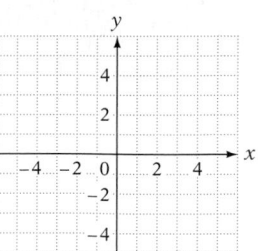

Example 5   Graph $x + 2y = 6$.

Solution

$x + 2y = 6$
$2y = -x + 6$
$y = -\dfrac{1}{2}x + 3$

x	y
0	3
-2	4
4	1

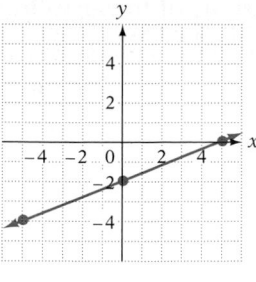

You Try It 5   Graph $x - 3y = 9$.

Your solution

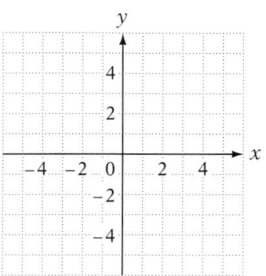

Example 6   Graph $y = -2$.

Solution

The graph of an equation of the form $y = b$ is a horizontal line passing through the point $(0, b)$.

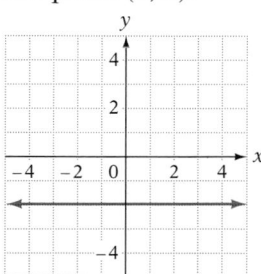

You Try It 6   Graph $y = 3$.

Your solution

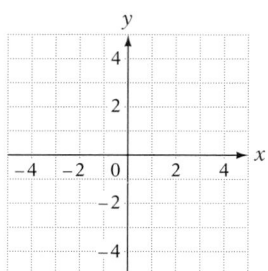

Example 7   Graph $x = 3$.

Solution

The graph of an equation of the form $x = a$ is a vertical line passing through the point $(a, 0)$.

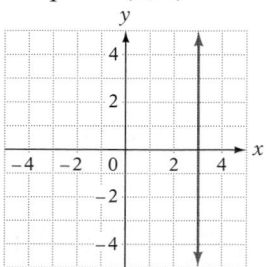

You Try It 7   Graph $x = -4$.

Your solution

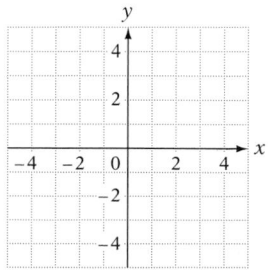

Solutions on p. S17

Objective C **To solve application problems** ....

There are a variety of applications of linear functions.

➡ Solve: An installer of marble kitchen countertops charges $250 plus $180 per foot of countertop. The equation that describes the total cost, C, to have x feet of countertop installed is $C = 180x + 250$.

a. Graph this equation for $0 \leq x \leq 25$. (*Note:* In many applications, the domain of the variable is given so that the equation makes sense. For instance, it would not be sensible to have values of x that are less than 0. This would mean negative countertop! The choice of 25 is somewhat arbitrary, but most kitchens have less than 25 ft of counter space.)

b. The point whose coordinates are (8, 1690) is on the graph. Write a sentence that describes this ordered pair.

Solution

a.

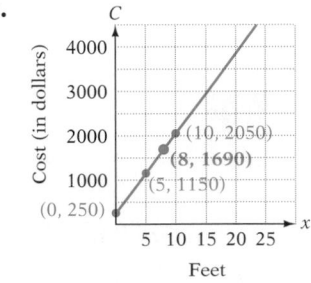

Feet

• Choosing $x = 0, 5,$ and 10, you find that the corresponding ordered pairs are (0, 250), (5, 1150), and (10, 2050). Plot these points and draw a line through them.

b. The point whose coordinates are (8, 1690) means that 8 ft of countertop costs $1690 to install.

Example 8
A local car dealer is advertising a 2-year lease for a new Honda Civic. The upfront cost is $3000 with a monthly lease payment of $150. The total cost, C, after x months of the lease is given by $C = 150x + 3000$. Graph this equation for $0 \leq x \leq 24$. The point whose coordinates are (18, 5700) is on the graph. Write a sentence that describes this ordered pair.

Solution

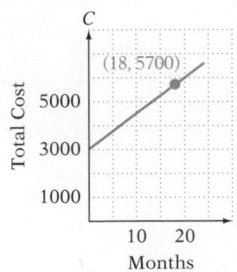

Months

The ordered pair (18, 5700) means that the total cost of the lease payments for 18 months is $5700.

You Try It 8
A car is traveling at a uniform speed of 40 mph. The distance, d, the car travels in t hours is given by $d = 40t$. Graph this equation for $0 \leq t \leq 5$. The point whose coordinates are (3, 120) is on the graph. Write a sentence that describes this ordered pair.

Your solution

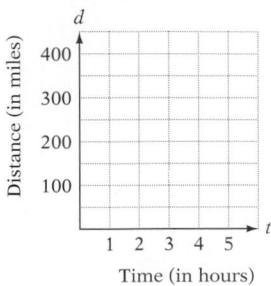

Time (in hours)

Solution on p. S17

7.2 Exercises

Objective A

Graph.

1. $y = 2x - 3$

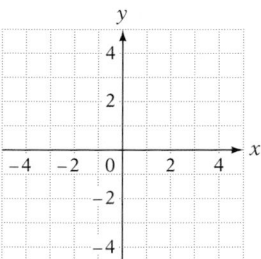

2. $y = -2x + 2$

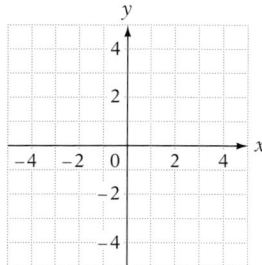

3. $y = \dfrac{1}{3}x$

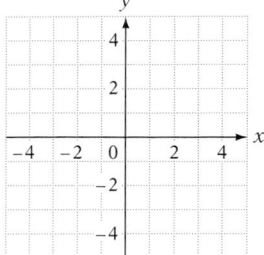

4. $y = -3x$

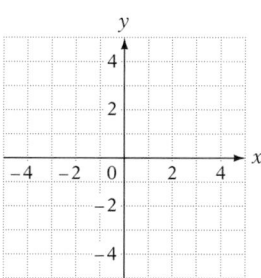

5. $y = \dfrac{2}{3}x - 1$

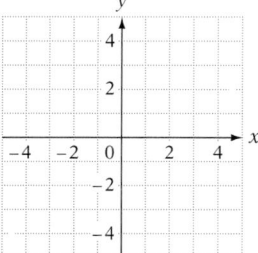

6. $y = \dfrac{3}{4}x + 2$

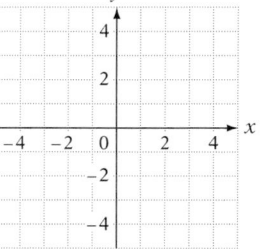

7. $y = -\dfrac{1}{4}x + 2$

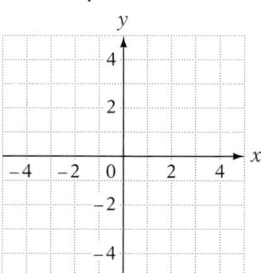

8. $y = -\dfrac{1}{3}x + 1$

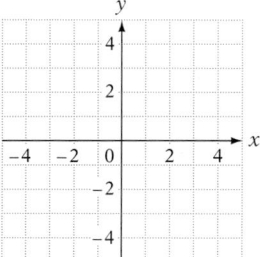

9. $y = -\dfrac{2}{5}x + 1$

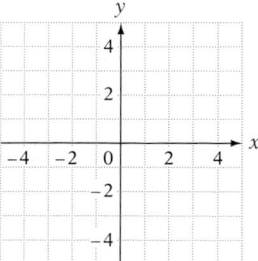

10. $y = -\dfrac{1}{2}x + 3$

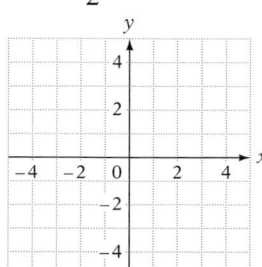

11. $y = 2x - 4$

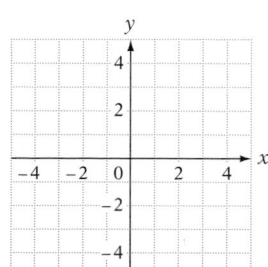

12. $y = 3x - 4$

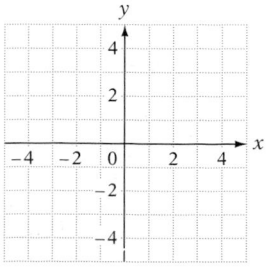

13. $y = x - 3$

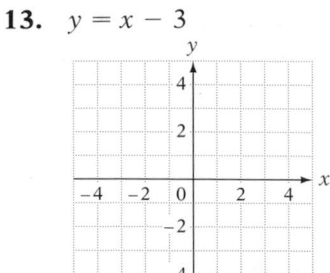

14. $y = x + 2$

15. $y = -x + 2$

16. $y = -x - 1$

17. $y = -\dfrac{2}{3}x + 1$

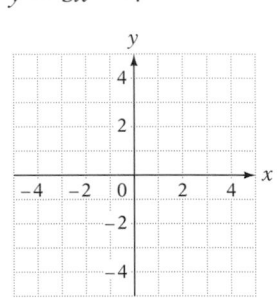

18. $y = 5x - 4$

Objective B

Graph.

19. $3x + y = 3$

20. $2x + y = 4$

21. $2x + 3y = 6$

22. $3x + 2y = 4$

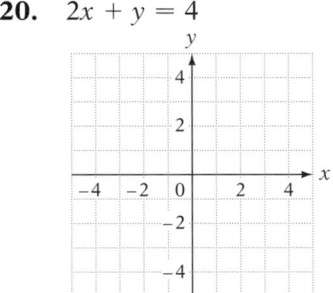

23. $x - 2y = 4$

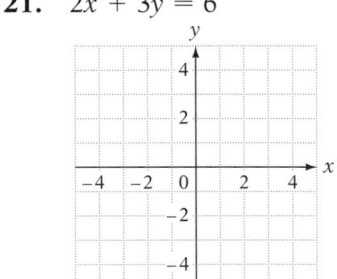

24. $x - 3y = 6$

25. $2x - 3y = 6$

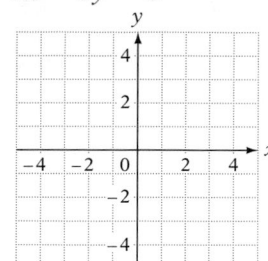

26. $3x - 2y = 8$

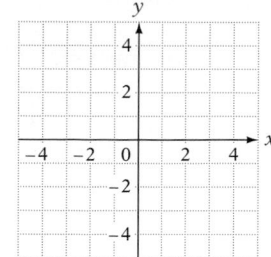

27. $2x + 5y = 10$

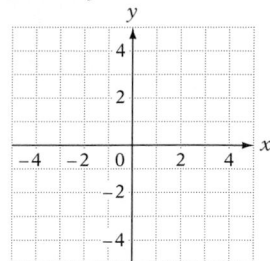

28. $3x + 4y = 12$

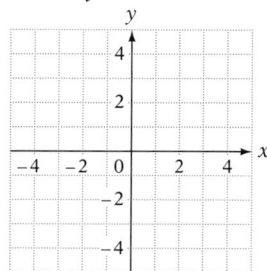

29. $x = 3$

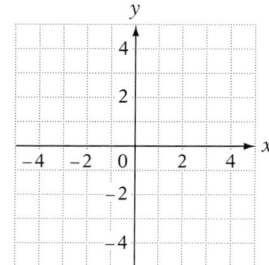

30. $y = -4$

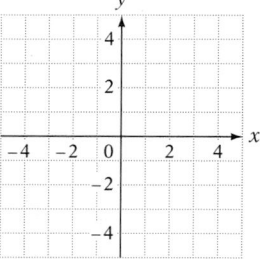

31. $x + 4y = 4$

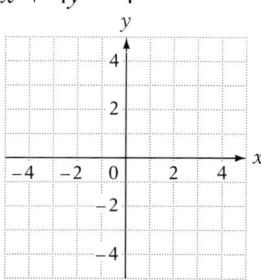

32. $4x - 3y = 12$

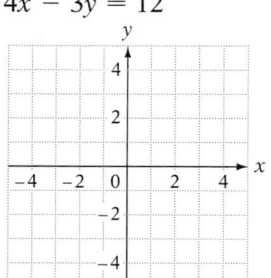

33. $y = 4$

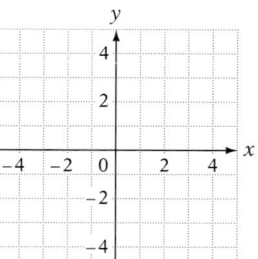

34. $x = -2$

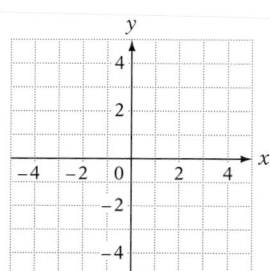

35. $\dfrac{x}{5} + \dfrac{y}{4} = 1$

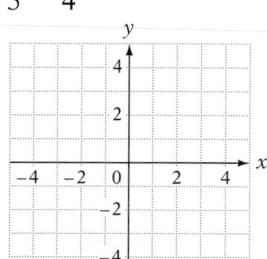

36. $\dfrac{x}{4} - \dfrac{y}{3} = 1$

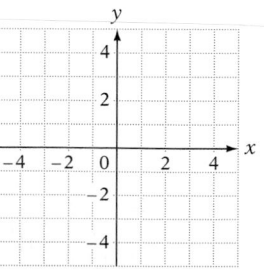

Objective C *Application Problems*

37. A rescue helicopter is rushing at a constant speed of 150 mph to reach several people stranded in the ocean 11 mi away after their boat sank. The rescuers can determine how far they are from the victims using the equation $D = 11 - 2.5t$, where D is the distance in miles and t is the time elapsed in minutes. Graph this equation for $0 \leq t \leq 4$. The point $(3, 3.5)$ is on the graph. Write a sentence that describes the meaning of this ordered pair.

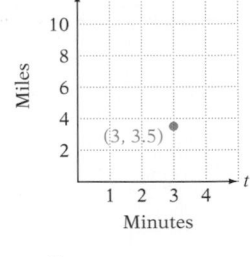

38. A custom-illustrated sign or banner can be commissioned for a cost of $25 for the material and $10.50 per square foot for the artwork. The equation that represents this cost is given by $y = 10.50x + 25$, where y is the cost and x is the number of square feet in the sign. Graph this equation for $0 \leq x \leq 20$. The point $(15, 182.5)$ is on the graph. Write a sentence that describes the meaning of this ordered pair.

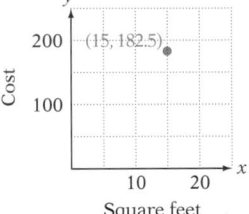

39. According to some veterinarians, the age, x, of a dog can be translated to "human years" by using the equation $H = 4x + 16$, where H is the human equivalent age for the dog. Graph this equation for $2 \leq x \leq 21$. The point whose coordinates are $(6, 40)$ is on this graph. Write a sentence that explains the meaning of this ordered pair.

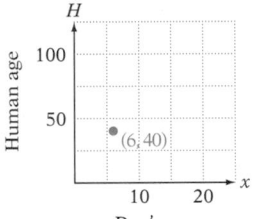

40. One projection for the total value, V, of stocks that will be bought and sold over the internet for the years 1997 through 2002 is given by the equation $V = 380x + 300$, where $0 \leq x \leq 5$ and 0 corresponds to the year 1997. Graph the equation. The point whose coordinates are $(3, 1440)$ is on the graph. Write a sentence that describes the meaning of this ordered pair.

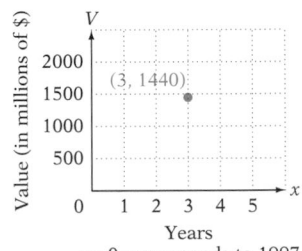

APPLYING THE CONCEPTS

41. For the equation $y = 3x + 2$, when the value of x changes from 1 to 2, does the value of y increase or decrease? What is the change in y? Suppose that the value of x changes from 13 to 14. What is the change in y?

42. For the equation $y = -2x + 1$, when the value of x changes from 1 to 2, does the value of y increase or decrease? What is the change in y? Suppose the value of x changes from 13 to 14. What is the change in y?

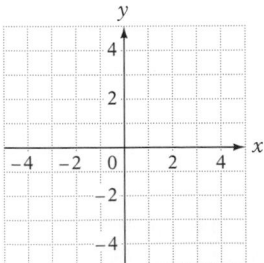

43. Graph $y = 2x - 2$, $y = 2x$, and $y = 2x + 3$ in the first coordinate system at the right. What observation can you make about the graphs?

44. Graph $y = x + 3$, $y = 2x + 3$, and $y = -\frac{1}{2}x + 3$ in the second coordinate system at the right. What observation can you make about the graphs?

7.3 Intercepts and Slopes of Straight Lines

Objective A   *To find the x- and y-intercepts of a straight line* ....

The graph of the equation $2x + 3y = 6$ is shown at the right. The graph crosses the x-axis at the point (3, 0). This point is called the **x-intercept.** The graph also crosses the y-axis at the point (0, 2). This point is called the **y-intercept.**

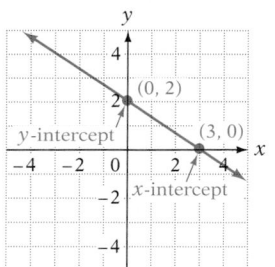

➡ Find the x-intercept and the y-intercept of the graph of the equation $2x - 3y = 12$.

To find the x-intercept, let $y = 0$. (Any point on the x-axis has y-coordinate 0.)

$$2x - 3y = 12$$
$$2x - 3(0) = 12$$
$$2x = 12$$
$$x = 6$$

The x-intercept is (6, 0).

To find the y-intercept, let $x = 0$. (Any point on the y-axis has x-coordinate 0.)

$$2x - 3y = 12$$
$$2(0) - 3y = 12$$
$$-3y = 12$$
$$y = -4$$

The y-intercept is (0, −4).

➡ Find the y-intercept of $y = 3x + 4$.

$$y = 3x + 4 = 3(0) + 4 = 4$$ • Let $x = 0$.

The y-intercept is (0, 4).

For any equation of the form $y = mx + b$, the y-intercept is (0, b).

Some linear equations can be graphed by finding the x- and y-intercepts and then drawing a line through these two points.

Example 1   Find the x- and y-intercepts for $x - 2y = 4$. Graph the line.

Solution

x-intercept:
$$x - 2y = 4$$
$$x - 2(0) = 4$$
$$x = 4$$
(4, 0)

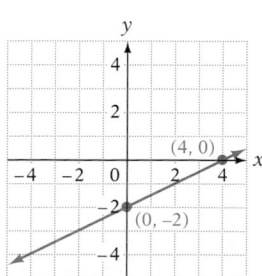

y-intercept:
$$x - 2y = 4$$
$$0 - 2y = 4$$
$$-2y = 4$$
$$y = -2$$
(0, −2)

You Try It 1   Find the x- and y-intercepts for $y = 2x - 4$. Graph the line.

Your solution

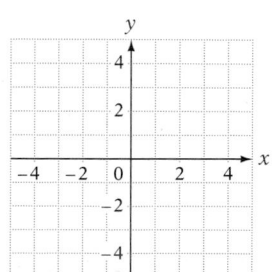

Solution on p. S18

Objective B   *To find the slope of a straight line* ....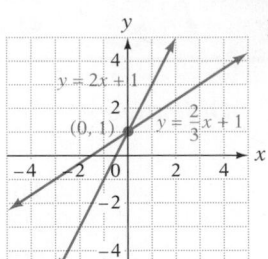

The graphs of $y = \frac{2}{3}x + 1$ and $y = 2x + 1$ are shown in Figure 1. Each graph crosses the y-axis at the point $(0, 1)$, but the graphs have different slants. The **slope** of a line is a measure of the slant of a line. The symbol for slope is m.

Figure 1

The slope of a line containing two points is the ratio of the change in the y values of the two points to the change in the x values. The line containing the points $(-2, -3)$ and $(6, 1)$ is graphed in Figure 2. The change in the y values is the difference between the two ordinates.

$$\text{Change in } y = 1 - (-3) = 4$$

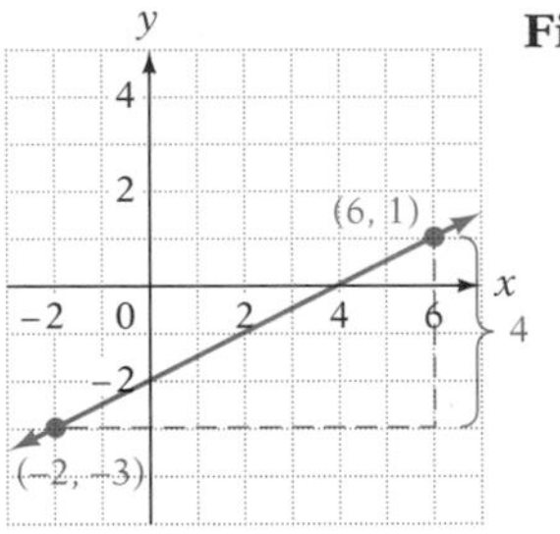

Figure 2

The change in the x values is the difference between the two abscissas (Figure 3).

$$\text{Change in } x = 6 - (-2) = 8$$

$$\text{Slope} = m = \frac{\text{change in } y}{\text{change in } x} = \frac{4}{8} = \frac{1}{2}$$

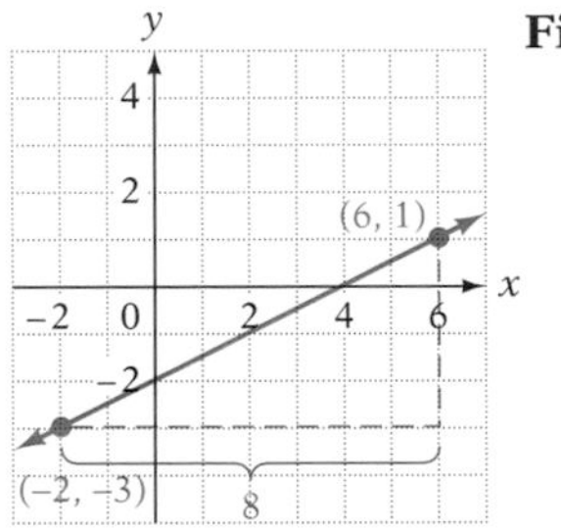

Figure 3

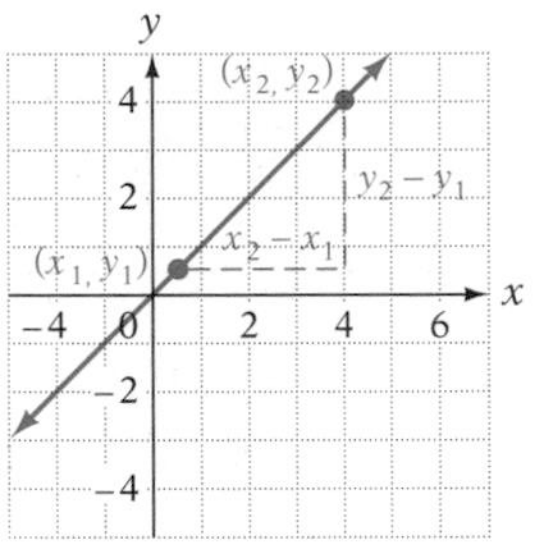

Slope Formula

If $P_1(x_1, y_1)$ and $P_2(x_2, y_2)$ are two points on a line and $x_1 \neq x_2$, then $m = \dfrac{y_2 - y_1}{x_2 - x_1}$
(Figure 4). If $x_1 = x_2$, the slope is undefined.

Figure 4

➡ Find the slope of the line containing the points $(-1, 1)$ and $(2, 3)$.

Let P_1 be $(-1, 1)$ and P_2 be $(2, 3)$. Then, $x_1 = -1$, $y_1 = 1$, $x_2 = 2$, and $y_2 = 3$.

$$m = \frac{y_2 - y_1}{x_2 - x_1} = \frac{3 - 1}{2 - (-1)} = \frac{2}{3}$$

The slope is $\frac{2}{3}$.

A line that slants upward to the right always has a **positive slope**.

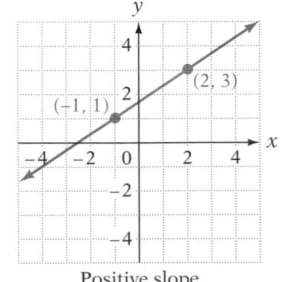

Positive slope

TAKE NOTE

Positive slope means that the value of y increases as the value of x increases.

Note that you obtain the same results if the points are named oppositely. Let P_1 be $(2, 3)$ and P_2 be $(-1, 1)$. Then $x_1 = 2$, $y_1 = 3$, $x_2 = -1$, and $y_2 = 1$.

$$m = \frac{y_2 - y_1}{x_2 - x_1} = \frac{1 - 3}{-1 - 2} = \frac{-2}{-3} = \frac{2}{3}$$

The slope is $\frac{2}{3}$.

Therefore, it does not matter which point is named P_1 and which P_2; the slope remains the same.

➡ Find the slope of the line containing the points $(-3, 4)$ and $(2, -2)$.

Let P_1 be $(-3, 4)$ and P_2 be $(2, -2)$.

$$m = \frac{y_2 - y_1}{x_2 - x_1} = \frac{-2 - 4}{2 - (-3)} = \frac{-6}{5} = -\frac{6}{5}$$

The slope is $-\frac{6}{5}$.

A line that slants downward to the right always has a **negative slope.**

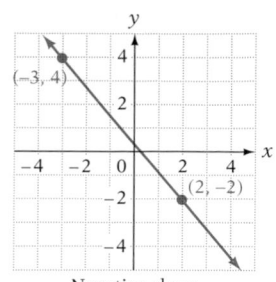

Negative slope

➡ Find the slope of the line containing the points $(-1, 3)$ and $(4, 3)$.

Let P_1 be $(-1, 3)$ and P_2 be $(4, 3)$.

$$m = \frac{y_2 - y_1}{x_2 - x_1} = \frac{3 - 3}{4 - (-1)} = \frac{0}{5} = 0$$

The slope is 0.

A horizontal line has **zero slope.**

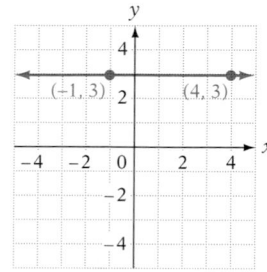

Zero slope

➡ Find the slope of the line containing the points $(2, -2)$ and $(2, 4)$.

Let P_1 be $(2, -2)$ and P_2 be $(2, 4)$.

$$m = \frac{y_2 - y_1}{x_2 - x_1} = \frac{4 - (-2)}{2 - 2} = \frac{6}{0}$$ Division by zero is not defined.

The slope of a vertical line is undefined.

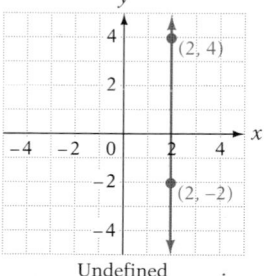

Undefined

There are many applications of the concept of slope. Here are two possibilities.

In 1988, when Florence Griffith-Joyner set the world record for the 100-meter dash, her average rate of speed was approximately 9.5 meters per second. The graph at the right shows the distance she ran during her record-setting run. From the graph, note that after 4 s she had traveled 38 m and that after 6 s she had traveled 57 m. The slope of the line between these two points is

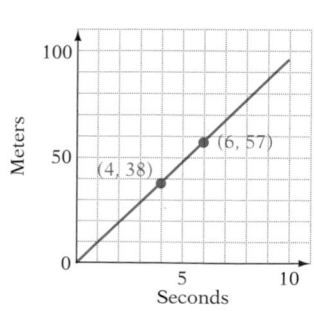

$$m = \frac{57 - 38}{6 - 4} = \frac{19}{2} = 9.5$$

Note that the slope of the line is the same as the rate she was running, 9.5 meters per second. The average speed of an object is related to slope.

Here is an example of slope taken from economics. According to the Department of Commerce, from 1987 to 1994, U.S. exports of goods to other countries increased at a rate of approximately $2.5 billion per year. The graph at the right shows the value of exports for each year. From the graph, we learn that in 1988 exports were $27 billion, and in 1992 exports were $37 billion. The slope of the line between these two points is

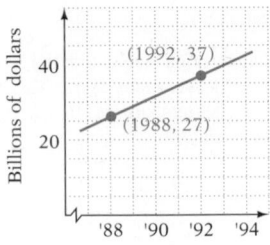

$$m = \frac{37 - 27}{1992 - 1988} = \frac{10}{4} = 2.5$$

Observe that the slope of the line is the same as the rate at which exports increased, $2.5 billion per year.

In general, any quantity that is expressed by using the word *per* is represented mathematically as slope. In the first example, slope was 9.5 meters *per* second; in the second example, slope was $2.5 billion *per* year.

Example 2
Find the slope of the line containing the points with coordinates $(-2, -3)$ and $(3, 4)$.

Solution
Let $P_1 = (-2, -3)$ and $P_2 = (3, 4)$.

$$m = \frac{y_2 - y_1}{x_2 - x_1} = \frac{4 - (-3)}{3 - (-2)} = \frac{7}{5}$$

The slope is $\frac{7}{5}$.

You Try It 2
Find the slope of the line containing the points with coordinates $(-3, 8)$ and $(1, 4)$.

Your solution

Example 3
Find the slope of the line containing the points with coordinates $(-1, 4)$ and $(-1, 0)$.

Solution
Let $P_1 = (-1, 4)$ and $P_2 = (-1, 0)$.

$$m = \frac{y_2 - y_1}{x_2 - x_1} = \frac{0 - 4}{-1 - (-1)} = \frac{-4}{0}$$

The slope is undefined.

You Try It 3
Find the slope of the line containing the points with coordinates $(-1, 2)$ and $(4, 2)$.

Your solution

Solutions on p. S18

Example 4

The graph below shows the height of a plane above an airport during its 30-minute descent from cruising altitude to landing. Find the slope of the line. Write a sentence that explains the meaning of the slope.

Solution

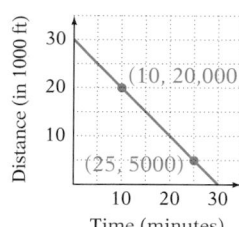

$$m = \frac{5000 - 20{,}000}{25 - 10} = \frac{-15{,}000}{15}$$

$$= -1000$$

A slope of -1000 means that the height of the plane is *decreasing* at the rate of 1000 ft/min.

You Try It 4

The graph below shows the approximate decline in the value of a used car over a five-year period. Find the slope of the line. Write a sentence that states the meaning of the slope.

Your solution

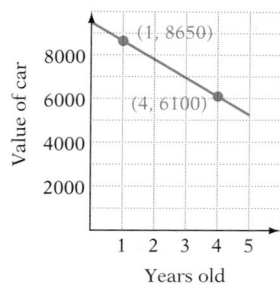

Solution on p. S18

Objective C   To graph a line using the slope and the y-intercept ....

The graph of the equation $y = \frac{2}{3}x + 1$ is shown at the right. The points $(-3, -1)$ and $(3, 3)$ are on the graph. The slope of the line between the two points is

$$m = \frac{3 - (-1)}{3 - (-3)} = \frac{4}{6} = \frac{2}{3}$$

Observe that the slope of the line is the coefficient of x in the equation $y = \frac{2}{3}x + 1$. Also recall that the y-intercept is $(0, 1)$, where 1 is the constant term of the equation.

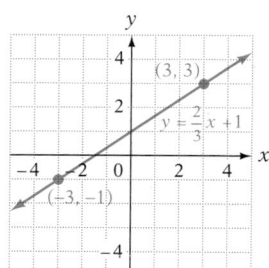

Slope-Intercept Equation of a Line

An equation of the form $y = mx + b$ is called the **slope-intercept** form of a straight line. The slope of the line is m, the coefficient of x. The y-intercept is $(0, b)$, where b is the constant term of the equation.

The following equations are written in slope-intercept form.

$y = 2x - 3$ Slope $= 2$; y-intercept $= (0, -3)$

$y = -x + 2$ Slope $= -1(-x = -1x)$; y-intercept $= (0, 2)$

$y = \dfrac{x}{2}$ Slope $= \dfrac{1}{2}\left(\dfrac{x}{2} = \dfrac{1}{2}x\right)$; y-intercept $= (0, 0)$

When an equation of a straight line is written in slope-intercept form, the graph can be drawn using the slope and the y-intercept. First locate the y-intercept. Use the slope to find a second point on the line. Then draw a line through the two points.

→ Graph $y = 2x - 3$.

y-intercept $= (0, b) = (0, -3)$

$$m = 2 = \frac{2}{1} = \frac{\text{change in } y}{\text{change in } x}$$

Beginning at the y-intercept, move right 1 unit (change in x) and then up 2 units (change in y).

$(1, -1)$ is a second point on the graph.

Draw a line through the two points $(0, -3)$ and $(1, -1)$.

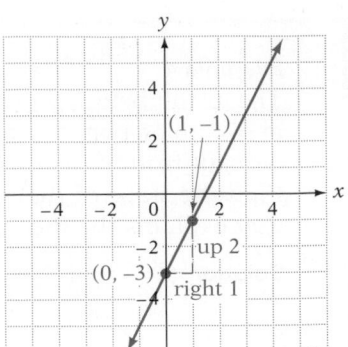

Example 5 Graph $y = -\dfrac{2}{3}x + 1$ by using the slope and y-intercept.

Solution y-intercept $= (0, b) = (0, 1)$

$$m = -\frac{2}{3} = \frac{-2}{3}$$

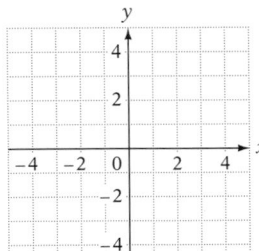

You Try It 5 Graph $y = -\dfrac{1}{4}x - 1$ by using the slope and y-intercept.

Your solution

Example 6 Graph $2x - 3y = 6$ by using the slope and y-intercept.

Solution Solve the equation for y.

$$2x - 3y = 6$$

$$-3y = -2x + 6$$

$$y = \frac{2}{3}x - 2$$

y-intercept $= (0, -2)$; $m = \dfrac{2}{3}$

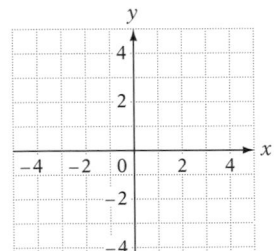

You Try It 6 Graph $x - 2y = 4$ by using the slope and y-intercept.

Your solution

Solutions on p. S18

7.3 Exercises

· ·

Objective A

Find the x- and y-intercepts.

1. $x - y = 3$

2. $3x + 4y = 12$

3. $y = 3x - 6$

4. $y = 2x + 10$

5. $x - 5y = 10$

6. $3x + 2y = 12$

7. $y = 3x + 12$

8. $y = 5x + 10$

9. $2x - 3y = 0$

10. $3x + 4y = 0$

11. $y = -\dfrac{1}{2}x + 3$

12. $y = \dfrac{2}{3}x - 4$

Find the x- and y-intercepts and then graph.

13. $5x + 2y = 10$

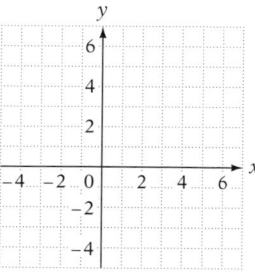

14. $x - 3y = 6$

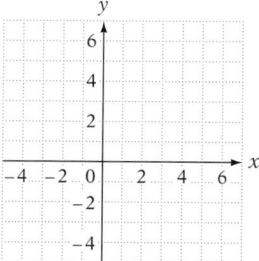

15. $y = \dfrac{3}{4}x - 3$

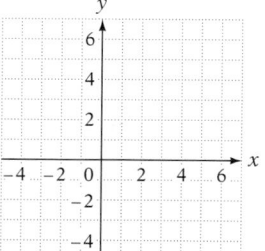

16. $y = \dfrac{2}{5}x - 2$

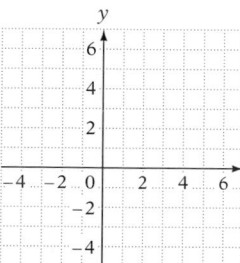

17. $5y - 3x = 15$

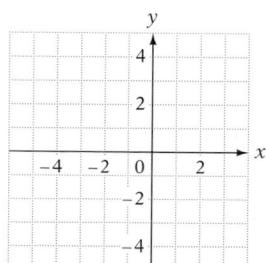

18. $9y - 4x = 18$

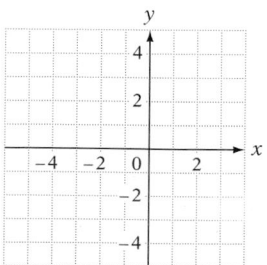

Objective B

Find the slope of the line containing the given points.

19. $P_1(4, 2)$, $P_2(3, 4)$

20. $P_1(2, 1)$, $P_2(3, 4)$

21. $P_1(-1, 3)$, $P_2(2, 4)$

22. $P_1(-2, 1)$, $P_2(2, 2)$

23. $P_1(2, 4)$, $P_2(4, -1)$

24. $P_1(1, 3)$, $P_2(5, -3)$

25. $P_1(-2, 3)$, $P_2(2, 1)$

26. $P_1(5, -2)$, $P_2(1, 0)$

27. $P_1(8, -3)$, $P_2(4, 1)$

28. $P_1(0, 3)$, $P_2(2, -1)$

29. $P_1(3, -4)$, $P_2(3, 5)$

30. $P_1(-1, 2)$, $P_2(-1, 3)$

31. $P_1(4, -2)$, $P_2(3, -2)$

32. $P_1(5, 1)$, $P_2(-2, 1)$

33. $P_1(0, -1)$, $P_2(3, -2)$

34. $P_1(3, 0)$, $P_2(2, -1)$

35. $P_1(-2, 3)$, $P_2(1, 3)$

36. $P_1(4, -1)$, $P_2(-3, -1)$

37. The graph at the right shows the cost, in dollars, to make a transatlantic telephone call. Find the slope of the line. Write a sentence that states the meaning of the slope.

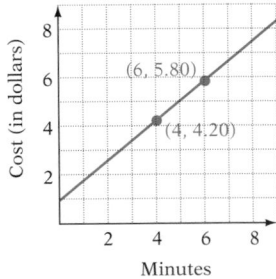

38. The pressure, in pounds per square inch, on a diver is shown in the graph on the right. Find the slope of the line. Write a sentence that explains the meaning of the slope.

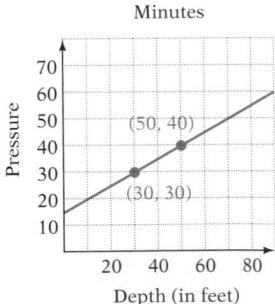

39. One measure of the affordability of a home for a given population is the percent of the population that has the necessary income to purchase a median-priced new home ($136,000 in 1996). The graph at the right shows the decrease in the percent of the population that can afford a new home. Find the slope of the line and write a sentence that states its meaning.

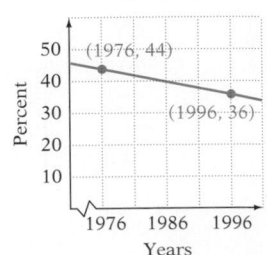

40. The stratosphere extends from approximately 11 km to 50 km above Earth. The graph at the right shows how the temperature in degrees Celsius changes in the stratosphere. Explain the meaning of the horizontal line segment from *A* to *B*. Find the slope of the line from *B* to *C* and explain its meaning.

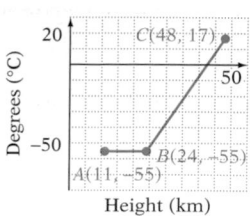

Objective C

Graph by using the slope and *y*-intercept.

41. $y = 3x + 1$

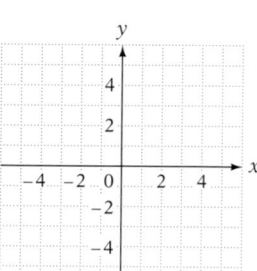

42. $y = -2x - 1$

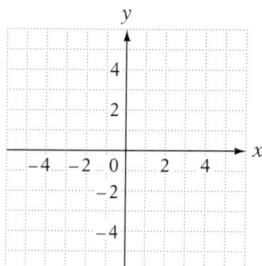

43. $y = \dfrac{2}{5}x - 2$

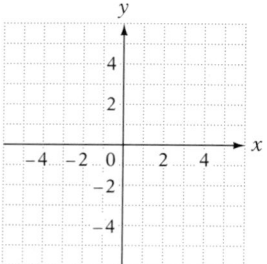

44. $y = \dfrac{3}{4}x + 1$

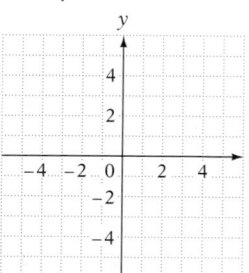

45. $2x + y = 3$

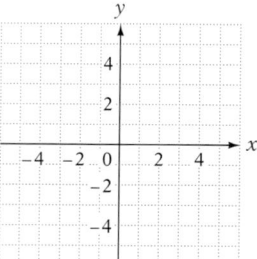

46. $3x - y = 1$

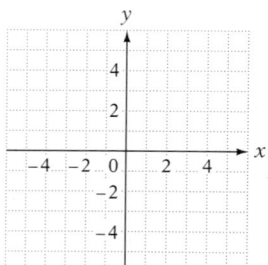

47. $x - 2y = 4$

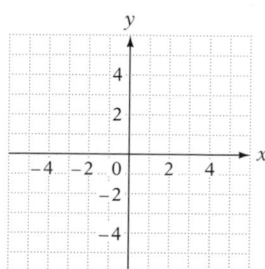

48. $x + 3y = 6$

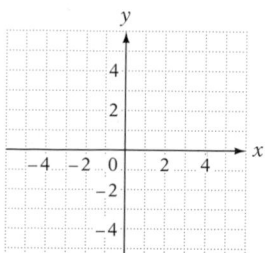

49. $y = \dfrac{2}{3}x$

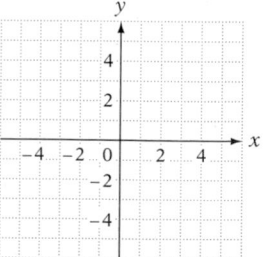

50. $y = \dfrac{1}{2}x$

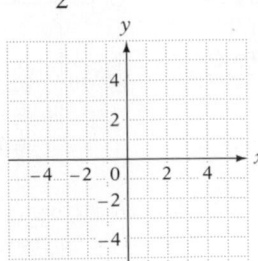

51. $y = -x + 1$

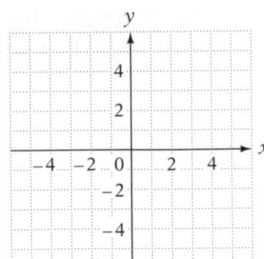

52. $y = -x - 3$

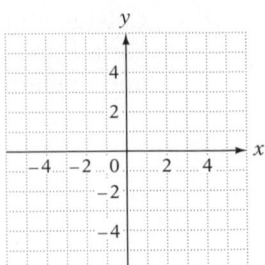

53. $3x - 4y = 12$

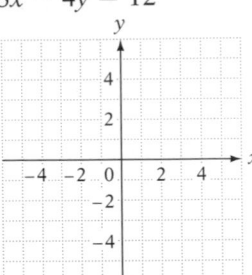

54. $5x - 2y = 10$

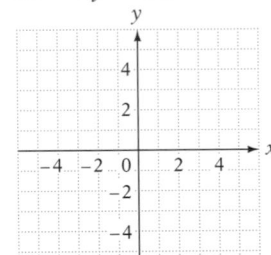

55. $y = -4x + 2$

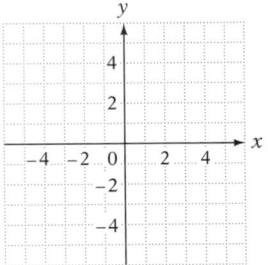

APPLYING THE CONCEPTS

56. Do all straight lines have a y-intercept? If not, give an example of one that does not.

57. If two lines have the same slope and the same y-intercept, must the graphs of the lines be the same? If not, give an example.

58. Draw the graphs of   **a.** $\dfrac{x}{3} + \dfrac{y}{4} = 1$ **b.** $\dfrac{x}{2} - \dfrac{y}{3} = 1$ **c.** $-\dfrac{x}{4} + \dfrac{y}{2} = 1$

What observations can you make about the x- and y-intercepts of these graphs and the coefficients of x and y?

d. Use this observation to draw the graph of $\dfrac{x}{4} - \dfrac{y}{3} = 1$.

a.

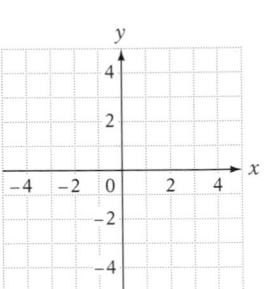

b.

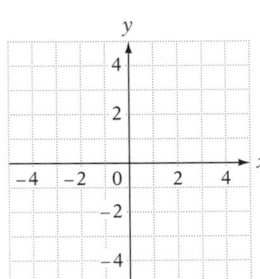

c.

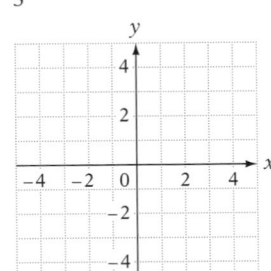

d.

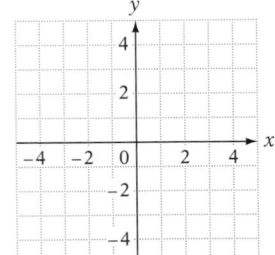

59. What does the highway sign at the right have to do with slope?

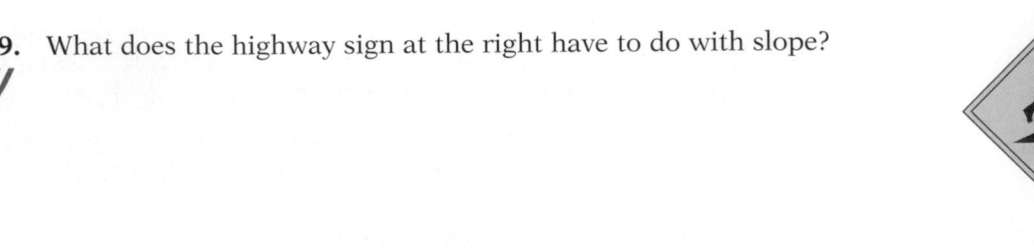

7.4 Equations of Straight Lines

Objective A   ***To find the equation of a line given a point and the slope*** ....

In earlier sections, the equation of a line was given and you were asked to determine some properties of the line, such as its intercepts and slope. Here, the process is reversed: Given properties of a line, determine its equation.

If the slope and y-intercept of the line are known, the equation of the line can be determined by using the slope-intercept form of a straight line.

➡ Find the equation of the line with slope $-\frac{1}{2}$ and y-intercept $(0, 3)$.

$$y = mx + b$$ • Use the slope-intercept formula.

$$y = -\frac{1}{2}x + 3$$ • $m = -\frac{1}{2}$; $(0, b) = (0, 3)$, so $b = 3$.

The equation of the line is $y = -\frac{1}{2}x + 3$.

When the coordinates of a point other than the y-intercept and the slope are known, the equation of the line can be found by using the formula for slope.

Suppose a line passes through the point $(3, 1)$ and has a slope of $\frac{2}{3}$. The equation of the line with these properties is determined by letting (x, y) be the coordinates of an unknown point on the line. Because the slope of the line is known, use the slope formula to write an equation. Then solve for y.

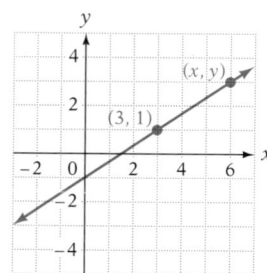

$$\frac{y - 1}{x - 3} = \frac{2}{3}$$ • $\frac{y_2 - y_1}{x_2 - x_1} = m$; $m = \frac{2}{3}$; $(x_2, y_2) = (x, y)$; $(x_1, y_1) = (3, 1)$

$$\frac{y - 1}{x - 3}(x - 3) = \frac{2}{3}(x - 3)$$ • Multiply each side by $(x - 3)$.

$$y - 1 = \frac{2}{3}x - 2$$ • Simplify.

$$y = \frac{2}{3}x - 1$$ • Solve for y.

The equation of the line is $y = \frac{2}{3}x - 1$.

The same procedure that was used above is used to derive the *point-slope formula*. We use this formula to determine the equation of a line when we are given the coordinates of a point on the line and the slope of the line.

Let (x_1, y_1) be the given coordinates of a point on a line, m the given slope of the line, and (x, y) the coordinates of an unknown point on the line. Then

$$\frac{y - y_1}{x - x_1} = m$$ • Formula for slope.

$$\frac{y - y_1}{x - x_1}(x - x_1) = m(x - x_1)$$ • Multiply each side by $x - x_1$.

$$y - y_1 = m(x - x_1)$$ • Simplify.

Point-Slope Formula

If (x_1, y_1) is a point on a line with slope m, then $y - y_1 = m(x - x_1)$.

⟶ Find the equation of the line that passes through point $(2, 3)$ and has slope -2.

$$y - y_1 = m(x - x_1)$$ • Use the point-slope formula.

$$y - 3 = -2(x - 2)$$ • $m = -2$; $(x_1, y_1) = (2, 3)$

$$y - 3 = -2x + 4$$ • Solve for y.

$$y = -2x + 7$$

The equation of the line is $y = -2x + 7$.

Example 1

Find the equation of the line whose slope is $-\frac{2}{3}$ and whose y-intercept is $(0, -1)$.

Solution

Because the slope and y-intercept are known, use the slope-intercept formula, $y = mx + b$.

$$y = -\frac{2}{3}x - 1$$ • $m = -\frac{2}{3}$; $b = -1$

Example 2

Use the point-slope formula to find the equation of the line that passes through the point $(-2, -1)$ and has slope $\frac{3}{2}$.

Solution

$$y - y_1 = m(x - x_1)$$

$$y - (-1) = \frac{3}{2}[x - (-2)]$$ • $m = \frac{3}{2}$;

$$y + 1 = \frac{3}{2}(x + 2)$$ $(x_1, y_1) = (-2, -1)$

$$y + 1 = \frac{3}{2}x + 3$$

$$y = \frac{3}{2}x + 2$$

The equation of the line is $y = \frac{3}{2}x + 2$.

You Try It 1

Find the equation of the line whose slope is $\frac{5}{3}$ and whose y-intercept is $(0, 2)$.

Your solution

You Try It 2

Use the point-slope formula to find the equation of the line that passes through the point $(4, -2)$ and has slope $\frac{3}{4}$.

Your solution

Solutions on p. S18

Objective B   To find the equation of a line given two points ....

The point-slope formula is used to find the equation of a line when a point on the line and the slope of the line are known. But this formula can also be used to find the equation of a line given two points on the line. In this case,

1. Use the slope formula to determine the slope of the line between the points.

2. Use the point-slope formula, the slope you just calculated, and one of the given points to find the equation of the line.

⇒ Find the equation of the line that passes through the points whose coordinates are $(-3, -1)$ and $(3, 3)$.

Use the slope formula to determine the slope of the line between the points.

$$m = \frac{y_2 - y_1}{x_2 - x_1} = \frac{3 - (-1)}{3 - (-3)} = \frac{4}{6} = \frac{2}{3} \qquad • (x_1, y_1) = (-3, -1); (x_2, y_2) = (3, 3)$$

Use the point-slope formula, the slope you just calculated, and one of the given points to find the equation of the line.

$$y - y_1 = m(x - x_1) \qquad\qquad • \text{ Point-slope formula}$$

$$y - (-1) = \frac{2}{3}[x - (-3)] \qquad\qquad • m = \frac{2}{3}; (x_1, y_1) = (-3, -1)$$

$$y + 1 = \frac{2}{3}(x + 3)$$

$$y + 1 = \frac{2}{3}x + 2$$

$$y = \frac{2}{3}x + 1$$

TAKE NOTE

You can verify that the equation $y = \dfrac{2}{3}x + 1$ passes through the points $(-3, -1)$ and $(3, 3)$ by substituting the coordinates of these points into the equation.

$$y = \frac{2}{3}x + 1$$

$$\begin{array}{c|c} -1 & \frac{2}{3}(-3) + 1 \\ \hline -1 & -2 + 1 \\ \end{array} \qquad • (x, y) = (-3, -1)$$

$$-1 = -1$$

$$y = \frac{2}{3}x + 1$$

$$\begin{array}{c|c} 3 & \frac{2}{3}(3) + 1 \\ \hline 3 & 2 + 1 \\ \end{array} \qquad • (x, y) = (3, 3)$$

$$3 = 3$$

The equation of the line that passes through the two points is $y = \frac{2}{3}x + 1$.

Example 3
Find the equation of the line that passes through the points $(-4, 0)$ and $(2, -3)$.

Solution
Find the slope of the line between the two points.

$$m = \frac{y_2 - y_1}{x_2 - x_1} = \frac{-3 - 0}{2 - (-4)} = \frac{-3}{6} = -\frac{1}{2}$$

Use the point-slope formula.

$$y - y_1 = m(x - x_1) \qquad • \text{ Point-slope formula}$$

$$y - 0 = -\frac{1}{2}[x - (-4)] \qquad • m = -\frac{1}{2}; (x_1, y_1) = (-4, 0)$$

$$y = -\frac{1}{2}(x + 4)$$

$$y = -\frac{1}{2}x - 2$$

The equation of the line is $y = -\frac{1}{2}x - 2$.

You Try It 3
Find the equation of the line that passes through the points $(-6, -1)$ and $(3, 1)$.

Your solution

Solution on p. S18

Objective C   **To solve application problems** ·· (26)

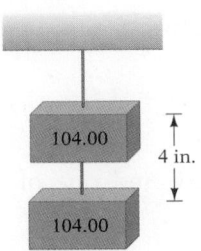

A **linear model** is a first-degree equation that is used to describe a relationship between quantities. In many cases, a linear model is used to approximate collected data. The data are graphed as points in a coordinate system, and then a line is drawn that approximates the data. The graph of the points is called a **scatter diagram;** the line is called a **line of best fit.**

Consider an experiment to determine the weight required to stretch a spring a certain distance. Data from such an experiment are shown in the table below.

Distance (in inches)	2.5	4	2	3.5	1	4.5
Weight (in pounds)	63	104	47	85	27	115

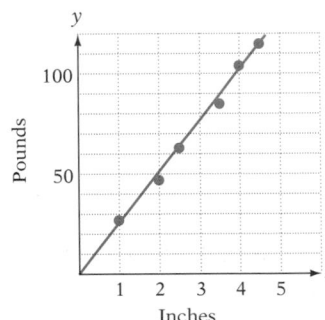

The accompanying graph shows the scatter diagram, which is the plotted points, and the line of best fit, which is the line that approximately goes through the plotted points. The equation of the line of best fit is $y = 25.7x - 1.3$, where x is the number of inches the spring is stretched and y is the weight in pounds.

The table below shows the values that the model would predict to the nearest tenth. Good linear models should predict values that are close to the actual values. A more thorough analysis of lines of best fit is undertaken in statistics courses.

Distance, x	2.5	4	2	3.5	1	4.5
Weight predicted using $y = 25.7x - 1.3$	63.0	101.5	50.1	88.7	24.4	114.4

Example 4

The data in the table below show the size of a house in square feet and the cost to build the house. The line of best fit is $y = 70.3x + 41,100$, where x is the number of square feet and y is the cost of the house.

Square feet	1250	1400	1348	2675	2900
Cost	128,000	140,000	136,100	233,450	241,500

Graph the data and the line of best fit in the coordinate system below. Write a sentence that describes the meaning of the slope of the line of best fit.

Solution

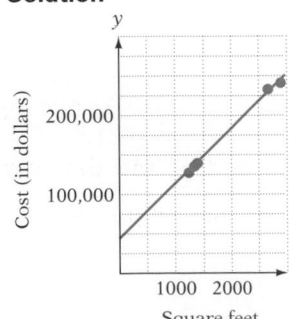

The slope of the line means that the cost to build the house increases $70.30 for each additional square foot in the size of the house.

You Try It 4

The data in the table below show a reading test grade and the final exam grade in a history class. The line of best fit is $y = 8.3x - 7.8$, where x is the reading test score and y is the history test score.

Reading	8.5	9.4	10.0	11.4	12.0
History	64	68	76	87	92

Graph the data and the line of best fit in the coordinate system below. Write a sentence that describes the meaning of the slope of the line of best fit.

Your solution

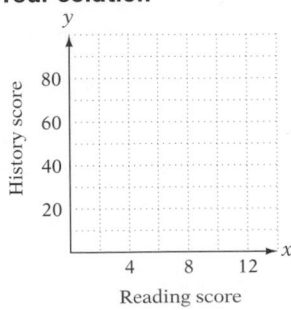

Solution on p. S18

7.4 Exercises

. . . .

Objective A

1. Find the equation of the line that contains the point $(0, 2)$ and has slope 2.

2. Find the equation of the line that contains the point $(0, -1)$ and has slope -2.

3. Find the equation of the line that contains the point $(-1, 2)$ and has slope -3.

4. Find the equation of the line that contains the point $(2, -3)$ and has slope 3.

5. Find the equation of the line that contains the point $(3, 1)$ and has slope $\frac{1}{3}$.

6. Find the equation of the line that contains the point $(-2, 3)$ and has slope $\frac{1}{2}$.

7. Find the equation of the line that contains the point $(4, -2)$ and has slope $\frac{3}{4}$.

8. Find the equation of the line that contains the point $(2, 3)$ and has slope $-\frac{1}{2}$.

9. Find the equation of the line that contains the point $(5, -3)$ and has slope $-\frac{3}{5}$.

10. Find the equation of the line that contains the point $(5, -1)$ and has slope $\frac{1}{5}$.

11. Find the equation of the line that contains the point $(2, 3)$ and has slope $\frac{1}{4}$.

12. Find the equation of the line that contains the point $(-1, 2)$ and has slope $-\frac{1}{2}$.

Objective B

13. Find the equation of the line that passes through the points $(1, -1)$ and $(-2, -7)$.

14. Find the equation of the line that passes through the points $(2, 3)$ and $(3, 2)$.

15. Find the equation of the line that passes through the points $(-2, 1)$ and $(1, -5)$.

16. Find the equation of the line that passes through the points $(-1, -3)$ and $(2, -12)$.

17. Find the equation of the line that passes through the points $(0, 0)$ and $(-3, -2)$.

18. Find the equation of the line that passes through the points $(0, 0)$ and $(-5, 1)$.

19. Find the equation of the line that passes through the points $(2, 3)$ and $(-4, 0)$.

20. Find the equation of the line that passes through the points $(3, -1)$ and $(0, -3)$.

21. Find the equation of the line that passes through the points $(-4, 1)$ and $(4, -5)$.

22. Find the equation of the line that passes through the points $(-5, 0)$ and $(10, -3)$.

23. Find the equation of the line that passes through the points $(-2, 1)$ and $(2, 4)$.

24. Find the equation of the line that passes through the points $(3, -2)$ and $(-3, -3)$.

_____

Objective C   *Application Problems*

25. The data in the table below are estimates that a study projected for the number of hours, on average, a person will spend watching "basic cable" television channels each year. The line of best fit is $y = 12.9x + 332$, where x is the year (with $x = 0$ corresponding to 1990) and y is the number of hours per person.

Year, x	5	6	7	8	9
Hours per Person, y	398	408	420	435	449

Graph the data and the line of best fit in the coordinate system at the right. Write a sentence that describes the meaning of the slope of the line of best fit.

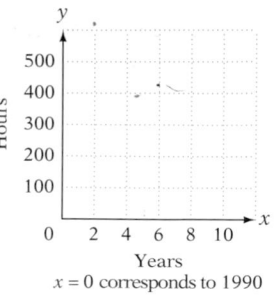

26. The data in the table below show the projected median annual income for a four-person family during different years. The line of best fit is $y = 1460x + 47{,}016$, where x is the year (with $x = 0$ corresponding to 1994) and y is the annual income.

Year, x	0	1	2	3	4
Annual Income, y	47,012	48,452	49,987	51,406	52,843

Graph the data and the line of best fit in the coordinate system at the right. Write a sentence that describes the meaning of the slope of the line of best fit.

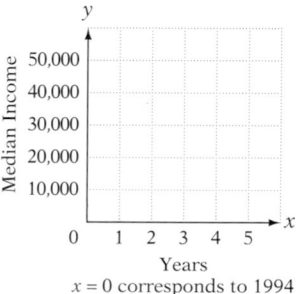

27. The data in the table below show the number of visitors (in millions) to U.S. national parks during different years. The line of best fit is $y = -2.1x + 275$, where x is the year (with $x = 0$ corresponding to 1992) and y is the number of visitors in millions.

Year, x	0	1	2	3	4
Visitors (in millions), y	274.7	273.1	268.6	269.6	265.8

Graph the data and the line of best fit in the coordinate system at the right. Write a sentence that describes the meaning of the slope of the line of best fit.

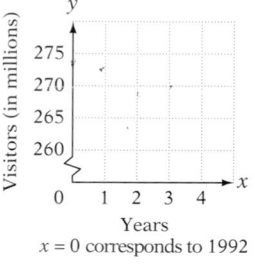

28. The data in the table below show the average lifetime for women in the United States during different years. The line of best fit is $y = 0.2x + 73$, where x is the year (with $x = 0$ corresponding to 1960) and y is the length of the lifetime in years.

Year, x	0	10	20	30	40
Life Expectancy (in years), y	73.1	74.7	77.4	78.8	81.2

Graph the data and the line of best fit in the coordinate system at the right. Write a sentence that describes the meaning of the slope of the line of best fit.

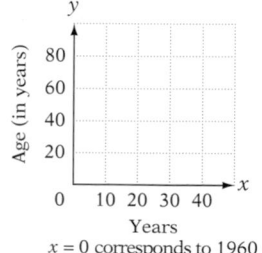

APPLYING THE CONCEPTS

In Exercises 29 to 32, the first two given points are on a line. Determine whether the third point is on the line.

29. $(-3, 2)$, $(4, 1)$; $(-1, 0)$

30. $(2, -2)$, $(3, 4)$; $(-1, 5)$

31. $(-3, -5)$, $(1, 3)$; $(4, 9)$

32. $(-3, 7)$, $(0, -2)$; $(1, -5)$

33. If $(-2, 4)$ are the coordinates of a point on the line whose equation is $y = mx + 1$, what is the slope of the line?

34. If $(3, 1)$ are the coordinates of a point on the line whose equation is $y = mx - 3$, what is the slope of the line?

35. If $(0, -3)$, $(6, -7)$, and $(3, n)$ are coordinates of points on the same line, determine n.

36. If $(-4, 11)$, $(2, -4)$, and $(6, n)$ are coordinates of points on the same line, determine n.

The formula $y - y_1 = \frac{y_2 - y_1}{x_2 - x_1}(x - x_1)$, where $x_1 \neq x_2$, is called the **two-point formula** for a straight line. This formula can be used to find the equation of a line given two points. Use this formula for Exercises 37 and 38.

37. Find the equation of the line passing through $(-2, 3)$ and $(4, -1)$.

38. Find the equation of the line passing through $(3, -1)$ and $(4, -3)$.

39. Explain why the condition $x_1 \neq x_2$ is placed on the two-point formula given above.

40. Explain how the two-point formula given above can be derived from the point-slope formula.

Focus on Problem Solving

Counterexamples Some of the exercises in this text ask you to determine whether a statement is true or false. For instance, the statement "every real number has a reciprocal" is false because 0 is a real number and 0 does not have a reciprocal.

Finding an example, such as 0 has no reciprocal, to show that a statement is not always true is called "finding a counterexample." A counterexample is an example that shows that a statement is not always true.

Consider the statement "the product of two numbers is greater than either factor." A counterexample to this statement is the factors $\frac{2}{3}$ and $\frac{3}{4}$. The product of these numbers is $\frac{1}{2}$, and $\frac{1}{2}$ is smaller than $\frac{2}{3}$ or $\frac{3}{4}$. There are many other counterexamples to the given statement.

Here are some counterexamples to the statement "the square of a number is always larger than the number."

$$\left(\frac{1}{2}\right)^2 = \frac{1}{4} \quad \text{but} \quad \frac{1}{4} < \frac{1}{2} \qquad 1^2 = 1 \quad \text{but} \quad 1 = 1$$

For each of the next five statements, find at least one counterexample to show that the statement, or conjecture, is false.

1. The product of two integers is always a positive number.
2. The sum of two prime numbers is never a prime number.
3. For all real numbers, $|x + y| = |x| + |y|$.
4. If x and y are nonzero real numbers and $x > y$, then $x^2 > y^2$.
5. The quotient of any two nonzero real numbers is less than either one of the numbers.

When a problem is posed, it may not be known whether the statement is true or false. For instance, Christian Goldbach (1690–1764) stated that every even integer greater than 2 can be written as the sum of two prime numbers. No one has been able to find a counterexample to this statement, but neither has anyone been able to prove that it is always true.

In the next five exercises, answer true if the statement is always true. If there is an instance when the statement is false, give a counterexample.

6. The reciprocal of a positive number is always smaller than the number.
7. If $x < 0$, then $|x| = -x$.
8. For any two real numbers x and y, $x + y > x - y$.
9. For any positive integer n, $n^2 + n + 17$ is a prime number.
10. The list of numbers 1, 11, 111, 1111, 11111, ... contains infinitely many composite numbers. (*Hint:* A number is divisible by 3 if the sum of the digits of the number is divisible by 3.)

Projects and Group Activities

Graphing Linear Equations with a Graphing Utility

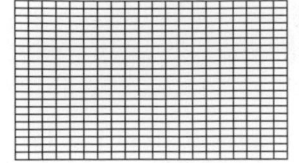

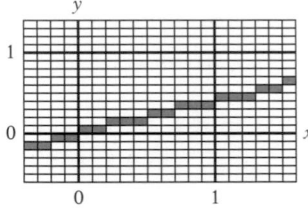

A computer or graphing calculator screen is divided into *pixels*. There are approximately 6000 to 790,000 pixels available on the screen (depending on the computer or calculator). The greater the number of pixels, the smoother a graph will appear. A portion of a screen is shown at the left. Each little rectangle represents one pixel.

The graphing utilities that are used by computers or calculators to graph an equation do basically what we have shown in the text: They choose values of x and, for each, calculate the corresponding value of y. The pixel corresponding to the ordered pair is then turned on. The graph is jagged because pixels are much larger than the dots we draw on paper.

The graph of $y = 0.45x$ is shown at the left as the calculator drew it (jagged). The x- and y-axes have been chosen so that each pixel represents $\frac{1}{10}$ of a unit. Consider the region of the graph where $x = 1$, 1.1, and 1.2.

The corresponding values of y are 0.45, 0.495, and 0.54. Because the y-axis is in tenths, the numbers 0.45, 0.495, and 0.54 are rounded to the nearest tenth before plotting. Rounding 0.45, 0.495, and 0.54 to the nearest tenth results in 0.5 for each number. Thus the ordered pairs (1, 0.45), (1.1, 0.495), and (1.2, 0.54) are graphed as (1, 0.5), (1.1, 0.5), and (1.2, 0.5). These points appear as three illuminated horizontal pixels. The graph of the line appears horizontal. However, if you use the **TRACE** feature of the calculator (see the appendix), the actual y-coordinate for each value of x is displayed.

TAKE NOTE

Xmin and Xmax are the smallest and largest values of x that will be shown on the screen. Ymin and Ymax are the smallest and largest values of y that will be shown on the screen.

Here are the keystrokes to graph $y = \frac{2}{3}x + 1$. First the equation is entered. Then the domain (Xmin to Xmax) and the range (Ymin to Ymax) are entered. This is called the **viewing window.** By changing the keystrokes 2 [X,T,θ,n] [÷] 3 [+] 1 (use [X/θ/T/n] for the Sharp EL-9600 or use [X,θ,T] for the Casio CFX-9850), you can graph different equations.

TI-83	*SHARP EL-9600*	*CASIO CFX-9850*
[Y=] [CLEAR] 2 [X,T,θ,n] [÷] 3	[Y=] [CL] 2 [X/θ/T/n] [÷] 3 [+] 1	[MENU] 5 [F2] [F1] 2 [X,θ,T]
[+] 1 [WINDOW] [(−)] 10	[WINDOW] [(−)] 10 [ENTER] 10	[÷] 3 [+] 1 [EXE] [SHIFT] F3
[ENTER] 10 [ENTER] 1 [ENTER]	[ENTER] 1 [ENTER] [(−)] 10	[(−)] 10 [EXE] 10 [EXE] 1 [EXE]
[(−)] 10 [ENTER] 10 [ENTER] 1	[ENTER] 10 [ENTER] 1 [ENTER]	[(−)] 10 [EXE] 10 [EXE] 1 [EXE]
[ENTER] [GRAPH]	[GRAPH]	[EXIT] [F6]

1. $y = 2x + 1$ — For $2x$, you may enter $2 \times x$ or just $2x$. The times sign $\times$ is not necessary on many graphing calculators.

2. $y = -\frac{1}{2}x - 2$ — Use the [(−)] key to enter a negative sign.

3. $3x + 2y = 6$ — Solve for y. Then enter the equation.

4. $4x + 3y = 75$ — You must adjust the viewing window.

Suggestion: Xmin = −25, Xmax = 25, Xscl = 5, Ymin = −35, Ymax = 35, Yscl = 5. See the appendix for assistance.

Graphs of Motion

A graph can be useful in analyzing the motion of a body. For example, consider an airplane in uniform motion traveling at 100 m/s. The table at the right shows the distance, in meters, traveled by the plane at the end of each of five one-second intervals.

Time (in seconds)	Distance (in meters)
0	0
1	100
2	200
3	300
4	400
5	500

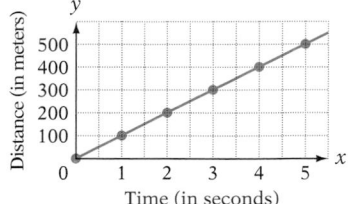

These data can be graphed on a rectangular coordinate system and a straight line drawn through the points plotted. The travel time is shown along the horizontal axis, and the distance traveled by the plane is shown along the vertical axis. (Note that the units along the two axes are not the same length.)

To write the equation for the line just graphed, use the coordinates of any two points on the line to find the slope. The y-intercept is $(0, 0)$.

Let $(x_1, y_1) = (1, 100)$ and $(x_2, y_2) = (2, 200)$.

$$m = \frac{y_2 - y_1}{x_2 - x_1} = \frac{200 - 100}{2 - 1} = 100$$

$$y = mx + b$$
$$y = 100x + 0$$
$$y = 100x$$

Note that the slope of the line, 100, is equal to the speed, 100 m/s. *The slope of a distance-time graph represents the speed of the object.*

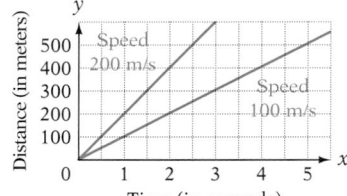

The distance-time graphs for two planes are shown at the left. One plane is traveling at 100 m/s, and the other is traveling at 200 m/s. The slope of the line representing the faster plane is greater than the slope of the line representing the slower plane.

In the speed-time graph at the left, the time a plane has been flying at 100 m/s is shown along the horizontal axis and its speed is shown along the vertical axis. Because the speed is constant, the graph is a horizontal line.

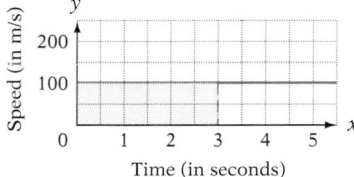

The area between the horizontal line graphed and the horizontal axis is equal to the distance traveled by the plane up to that time. For example, the area of the shaded region on the graph is

$$\text{Length} \cdot \text{width} = (3 \text{ s})(100 \text{ m/s}) = 300 \text{ m}$$

The distance traveled by the plane in 3 s is equal to 300 m.

1. A car in uniform motion is traveling at 20 m/s.
   a. Prepare a distance-time graph for the car for 0 s to 5 s.
   b. Find the slope of the line.
   c. Find the equation of the line.
   d. Prepare a speed-time graph for the car for 0 s to 5 s.
   e. Find the distance traveled by the car after 3 s.

2. One car in uniform motion is traveling at 10 m/s. A second car in uniform motion is traveling at 15 m/s.
   a. Prepare one distance-time graph for both cars for 0 s to 5 s.
   b. Find the slope of each line.
   c. Find the equation of each line graphed.
   d. Assuming that the cars started at the same point at 0 s, find the distance between the cars at the end of 5 s.

3. a. In a distance-time graph, is it possible for the graph to be a horizontal line?
   b. What does a horizontal line reveal about the motion of the object during that time period?

Chapter Summary

Key Words
A *rectangular coordinate system* is formed by two number lines, one horizontal and one vertical, that intersect at the zero point of each line.

The number lines that make up a rectangular coordinate system are called the *coordinate axes* or simply *axes*.

The *origin* is the point of intersection of the two coordinate axes.

A rectangular coordinate system divides the plane into four regions called *quadrants*.

An *ordered pair* (x, y) is used to locate a point in a plane.

The first number in an ordered pair is called the *abscissa* or x-coordinate.

The second number in an ordered pair is called the *ordinate* or y-coordinate.

The *coordinates* of a point are the numbers in the ordered pair that is associated with the point.

A *relation* is any set of ordered pairs.

A *function* is a relation in which no two ordered pairs with the same first coordinates have different second coordinates.

A function designated by $f(x)$ is written in *functional notation*. The *value of the function* at x is $f(x)$.

An equation of the form $y = mx + b$, where m and b are constants, is a *linear equation in two variables* or a *linear function*.

The point at which a graph crosses the x-axis is called the *x-intercept*.

The point at which a graph crosses the y-axis is called the *y-intercept*.

The *slope* of a line is the measure of the slant of a line. The symbol for slope is m.

A line that slants upward to the right has a *positive slope*.

A line that slants downward to the right has a *negative slope*.

A horizontal line has *zero slope*.

The slope of a vertical line is *undefined*.

Essential Rules
Slope of a straight line

$$\text{Slope} = m = \frac{y_2 - y_1}{x_2 - x_1}$$

Slope-intercept form of a straight line

$$y = mx + b$$

Point-slope formula

$$y - y_1 = m(x - x_1)$$

Chapter Review

1. **a.** Graph the ordered pairs $(-2, 4)$ and $(3, -2)$.
   b. Name the abscissa of point A.
   c. Name the ordinate of point B.

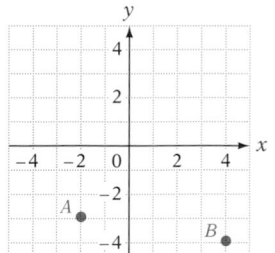

2. Graph the ordered-pair solutions of
   $y = -\frac{1}{2}x - 2$ when $x \in \{-4, -2, 0, 2\}$.

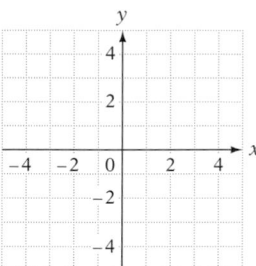

3. Determine the equation of the line that passes through the points $(-1, 3)$ and $(2, -5)$.

4. Determine the equation of the line that passes through the point $(6, 1)$ and has slope $-\frac{5}{2}$.

5. Graph $y = \frac{1}{4}x + 3$.

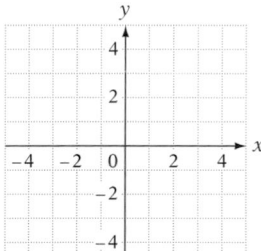

6. Graph $5x + 3y = 15$.

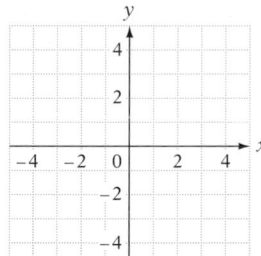

7. Determine the equation of the line that passes through the point $(-3, 4)$ and has slope $\frac{2}{3}$.

8. Given $f(x) = x^2 - 2$, find $f(-1)$.

9. Determine the equation of the line that passes through the points $(-2, 5)$ and $(4, 1)$.

10. Does $y = -x + 3$, where $x \in \{-2, 0, 3, 5\}$, define y as a function of x?

11. Find the slope of the line containing the points $(9, 8)$ and $(-2, 1)$.

12. Find the x- and y-intercepts of $3x - 2y = 24$.

13. Find the slope of the line containing the points $(-2, -3)$ and $(4, -3)$.

14. Graph the line that has slope $\frac{1}{2}$ and y-intercept $(0, -1)$.

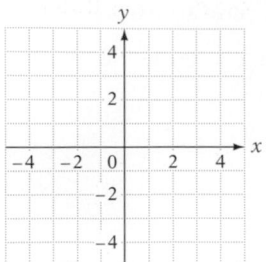

15. Graph $x = -3$.

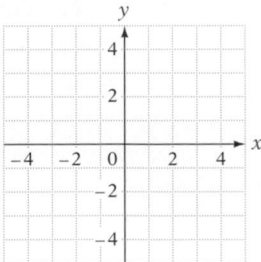

16. Graph the line that has slope $-\frac{2}{3}$ and y-intercept $(0, 2)$.

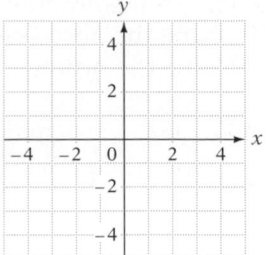

17. Graph $y = -2x - 1$.

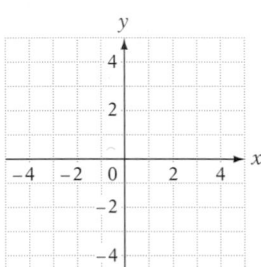

18. Graph the line that has slope 2 and y-intercept $(0, -4)$.

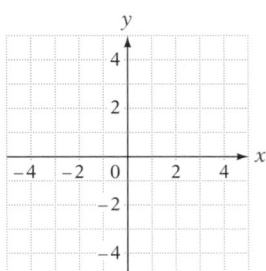

19. Graph $3x - 2y = -6$.

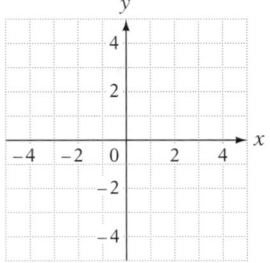

20. The height and weight of 8 seventh-grade students are shown in the following table. Write a relation where the first coordinate is height, in inches, and the second coordinate is weight, in pounds. Is the relation a function?

Height	55	57	53	57	60	61	58	54
Weight	95	101	94	98	100	105	97	95

21. An on-line research service charges a monthly access fee of $75 plus $.45 per minute to use the service. An equation that represents the monthly cost to use this service is $C = 0.45x + 75$, where C is the monthly cost and x is the number of minutes. Graph this equation for $0 \le x \le 100$. The point $(50, 97.5)$ is on the graph. Write a sentence that describes the meaning of this ordered pair.

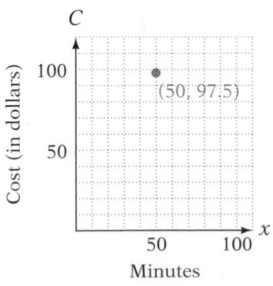

22. The data in the table below show the amount spent on health care in the United States. The line of best fit for this data is $y = 3.85x + 15.78$, where $x = 0$ corresponds to the year 1990. Graph the data and the line of best fit in the coordinate system at the right. How much is the amount spent on health care increasing each year?

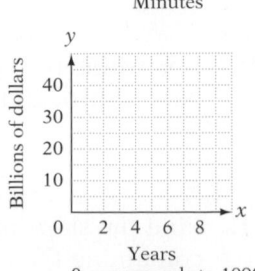

Year	1990	1992	1994	1996	1998
Amount spent (billions)	14.9	22.7	30.9	36.0	42.1*

*Projected

Chapter Test

1. Find the ordered-pair solution of $2x - 3y = 15$ corresponding to $x = 3$.

2. Graph the ordered-pair solutions of $y = -\frac{3}{2}x + 1$ for $x \in \{-2, 0, 4\}$.

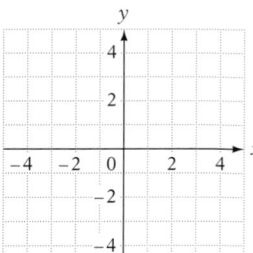

3. Does $y = \frac{1}{2}x - 3$ define y as a function of x for $x \in \{-2, 0, 4\}$?

4. Given $f(t) = t^2 + t$, find $f(2)$.

5. Given $f(x) = x^2 - 2x$, find $f(-1)$.

6. The distance a house is from a fire station and the amount of damage that the house sustained in a fire are given in the following table. Write a relation where the first coordinate of the ordered pair is the distance in miles from the fire station and the second coordinate is the amount of damage in thousands of dollars. Is the relation a function?

Distance	3.5	4.0	5.2	5.0	4.0	6.3	5.4
Damage	25	30	45	38	42	12	34

7. Graph $y = 3x + 1$.

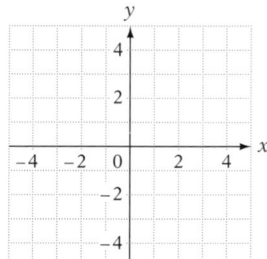

8. Graph $y = -\frac{3}{4}x + 3$.

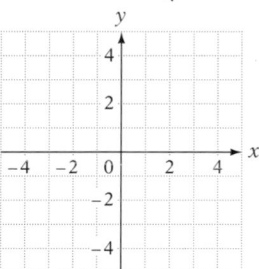

9. Graph $3x - 2y = 6$.

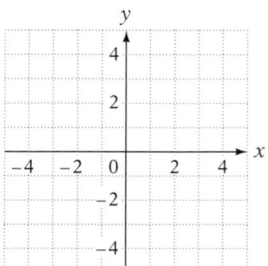

10. Graph $x + 3 = 0$.

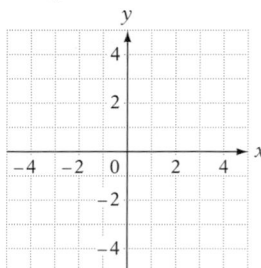

11. Graph the line that has slope $-\frac{2}{3}$ and y-intercept $(0, 4)$.

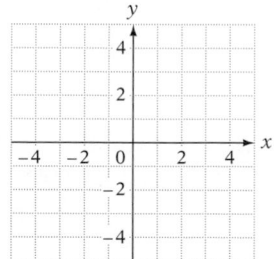

12. Graph the line that has slope 2 and y-intercept -2.

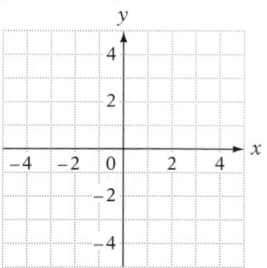

13. The equation for the speed of a ball that is thrown straight up with an initial speed of 128 ft/s is $v = 128 - 32t$, where v is the speed of the ball after t seconds. Graph this equation for $0 \le t \le 4$. The point whose coordinates are (1, 96) is on the graph in Figure 1. Write a sentence that describes this ordered pair.

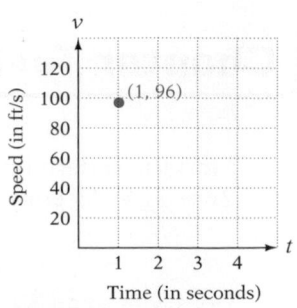

Figure 1

14. The graph in Figure 2 shows the increase in the cost of tuition for a college for the years 1989 through 1994 (with 1989 as 0). Find the slope of the line. Write a sentence that states the meaning of the slope.

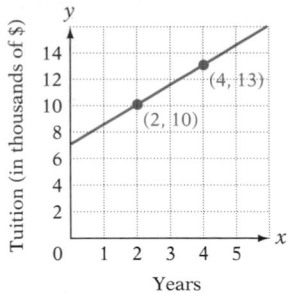

Figure 2

15. The data in the following table show the number of mutual fund companies for selected years between 1983 and 1993. The line of best fit is $y = 330x + 1016$, where x is the year (with 1983 as 0) and y is the number of mutual fund companies.

Year, x	0 (1983)	3 (1986)	5 (1988)	8 (1991)	10 (1993)
No. of companies, y	1020	2000	2670	3660	4320

Graph the data and the line of best fit in the coordinate system in Figure 3. Write a sentence that describes the meaning of the slope of the line of best fit.

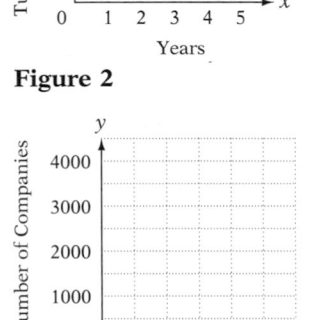

Figure 3

16. Find the x- and y-intercepts for $6x - 4y = 12$.

17. Find the x- and y-intercepts for $y = \frac{1}{2}x + 1$.

18. Find the slope of the line containing the points $(2, -3)$ and $(4, 1)$.

19. Find the slope of the line containing the points $(3, -4)$ and $(1, -4)$.

20. Find the slope of the line containing the points $(-5, 2)$ and $(-5, 7)$.

21. Find the slope of the line whose equation is $2x + 3y = 6$.

22. Find the equation of the line that contains the point $(0, -1)$ and has slope 3.

23. Find the equation of the line that contains the point $(-3, 1)$ and has slope $\frac{2}{3}$.

24. Find the equation of the line that passes through the points $(5, -4)$ and $(-3, 1)$.

25. Find the equation of the line that passes through the points $(-2, 0)$ and $(5, -2)$.

Cumulative Review

1. Simplify: $12 - 18 \div 3 \cdot (-2)^2$

2. Evaluate $\dfrac{a-b}{a^2-c}$ when $a = -2$, $b = 3$, and $c = -4$.

3. Given $f(x) = \dfrac{2}{x-1}$, find $f(-2)$.

4. Solve: $2x - \dfrac{2}{3} = \dfrac{7}{3}$

5. Solve: $3x - 2[x - 3(2 - 3x)] = x - 7$

6. Write $6\dfrac{2}{3}\%$ as a fraction.

7. Simplify: $(-2x^2y)^3(2xy^2)^2$

8. Simplify: $\dfrac{-15x^7}{5x^5}$

9. Divide: $(x^2 - 4x - 21) \div (x - 7)$

10. Factor: $5x^2 + 15x + 10$

11. Factor: $x(a + 2) + y(a + 2)$

12. Solve: $x(x - 2) = 8$

13. Simplify: $\dfrac{x^5y^3}{x^2 - x - 6} \cdot \dfrac{x^2 - 9}{x^2y^4}$

14. Simplify: $\dfrac{3x}{x^2 + 5x - 24} - \dfrac{9}{x^2 + 5x - 24}$

15. Solve: $3 - \dfrac{1}{x} = \dfrac{5}{x}$

16. Solve $4x - 5y = 15$ for y.

17. Find the ordered-pair solution of $y = 2x - 1$ corresponding to $x = -2$.

18. Find the slope of the line that contains the points $(2, 3)$ and $(-2, 3)$.

19. Find the equation of the line that contains the point $(2, -1)$ and has slope $\frac{1}{2}$.

20. Find the equation of the line that contains the point $(0, 2)$ and has slope -3.

21. Find the equation of the line that contains the point $(-1, 0)$ and has slope 2.

22. Find the equation of the line that contains the point $(6, 1)$ and has slope $\frac{2}{3}$.

23. A suit that regularly sells for $89 is on sale for 30% off the regular price. Find the sale price.

24. The first angle of a triangle is 3° more than the measure of the second angle. The third angle is 5° more than twice the measure of the second angle. Find the measure of each angle.

25. The real estate tax for a home that costs $50,000 is $625. At this rate, what is the value of a home for which the real estate tax is $1375?

26. An electrician requires 6 h to wire a garage. An apprentice can do the same job in 10 h. How long would it take to wire the garage if both the electrician and the apprentice were working?

27. Graph $y = \frac{1}{2}x - 1$.

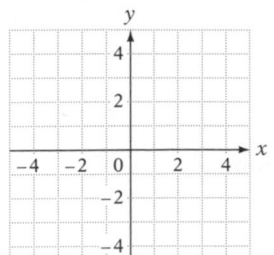

28. Graph the line that has slope $-\frac{2}{3}$ and y-intercept 2.

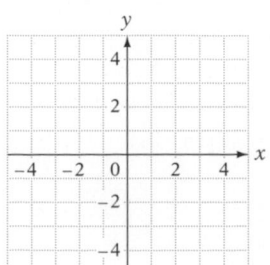

8

Systems of Linear Equations

Objectives

Section 8.1
To solve a system of linear equations by graphing

Section 8.2
To solve a system of linear equations by the substitution method
To solve investment problems

Section 8.3
To solve a system of linear equations by the addition method

Section 8.4
To solve rate-of-wind or -current problems
To solve application problems using two variables

A mechanical engineer designs engines and motors. It is part of the mechanical engineer's job to determine the size and the layout of pipes that are needed to transport water or air or any other material from one place to another within a motor. In these designs, the temperatures and pressures of the materials being transported must be taken into consideration. Therefore, calculations performed by a mechanical engineer normally require equations that have more than one variable.

Input-Output Analysis

The economies of the industrial nations are very complex; they comprise hundreds of different industries, and each industry supplies other industries with goods and services needed in the production process. For example, the steel industry requires coal to produce steel, and the coal industry requires steel (in the form of machinery) to mine and transport coal.

Wassily Leontief, a Russian-born economist, developed a method of describing mathematically the interactions of an economic system. His technique was to examine various sectors of an economy (steel industry, oil, farms, autos, and so on) and determine how each sector interacted with the others. More than five hundred sectors of the economy were studied.

The interaction of each sector with the others was written as a series of equations. This series of equations is called a *system of equations.* Using a computer, economists searched for a solution to the system of equations that would determine the output levels various sectors would have to meet to satisfy the requests from other sectors. The method is called input-output analysis.

Input-output analysis has many applications. For example, it is used today to predict the production needs of large corporations and to determine the effect of price changes on the economy. In recognition of the importance of his ideas, Leontief was awarded the Nobel Prize in Economics in 1973.

This chapter begins the study of systems of equations.

8.1 Solving Systems of Linear Equations by Graphing

Objective A   *To solve a system of linear equations by graphing* ....

Equations considered together are called a **system of equations.** A system of equations is shown at the right.

$$2x + 3y = 2$$
$$3x - 5y = 22$$

A **solution of a system of equations in two variables** is an ordered pair that is a solution of each equation of the system.

➡ Is $(4, -2)$ a solution of the following system of equations?

$$2x + 3y = 2$$
$$3x - 5y = 22$$

$2x + 3y = 2$	
$2(4) + 3(-2)$	2
$8 + (-6)$	2
	$2 = 2$

$3x - 5y = 22$	
$3(4) - 5(-2)$	22
$12 - (-10)$	22
	$22 = 22$

Yes, because $(4, -2)$ is a solution of each equation, it is the solution of the system. However, $(7, -4)$ is not a solution, because

$2x + 3y = 2$	
$2(7) + 3(-4)$	2
$14 + (-12)$	2
	$2 = 2$

• **(7, −4) is a solution.**

$3x - 5y = 22$	
$3(7) - 5(-4)$	22
$21 - (-20)$	22
	$41 \neq 22$

• **(7, −4) is not a solution.**

➡ Is $(3, -3)$ a solution of the following system of equations?

$$2x + y = 3$$
$$x + y = 1$$

$2x + y = 3$	
$2(3) + (-3)$	3
$6 + (-3)$	3
	$3 = 3$

$x + y = 1$	
$3 + (-3)$	1
	$0 \neq 1$

Because $(3, -3)$ is not a solution of each equation, $(3, -3)$ is not a solution of the system of equations.

Graphing the equations in a system of linear equations is one method of finding a solution of the system of equations. The lines can intersect at one point, the lines can intersect at infinitely many points (the graphs are the same line), or the lines can be parallel and not intersect at all.

Such systems are called **independent, dependent, and inconsistent,** respectively.

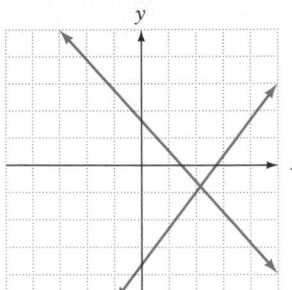

Independent:
one solution

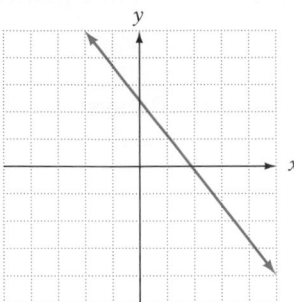

Dependent:
infinitely many solutions

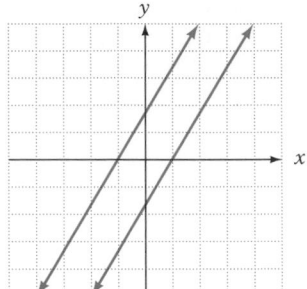

Inconsistent:
no solutions

POINT OF INTEREST

The "Projects and Group Activities" at the end of this chapter discusses using a calculator to approximate the solution of a system of equations.

➡ Solve by graphing: $2x + 3y = 6$
$\qquad\qquad\qquad\quad 2x + y = -2$

Graph each line.

Find the point of intersection.

$(-3, 4)$ is a solution of each equation. The system of equations is *independent*.

The solution is $(-3, 4)$.

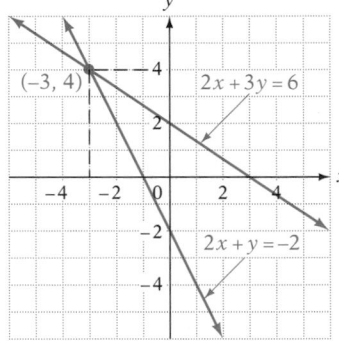

➡ Solve by graphing: $2x - y = 1$
$\qquad\qquad\qquad\quad 6x - 3y = 12$

Graph each line.

The lines are parallel and therefore do not intersect. The system of equations is *inconsistent* and has no solution.

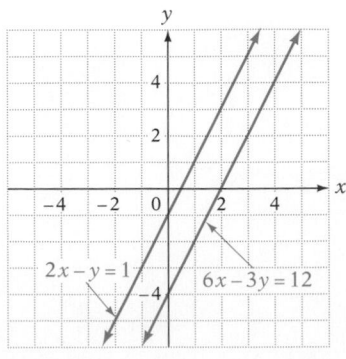

When a system of equations is *dependent*, the graphs of the two equations are the same line. Therefore, the lines intersect at infinitely many points. The solutions of the system of equations are the ordered pairs that satisfy either one (and hence both) of the two equations of the system of equations.

➡ Solve by graphing: $2x + 3y = 6$
$6x + 9y = 18$

Graph each line.

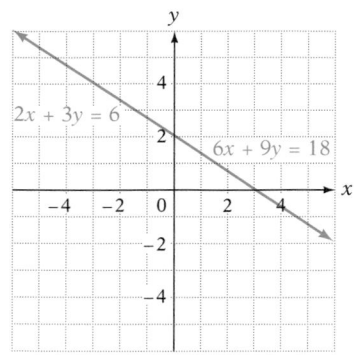

The two equations represent the same line. The system of equations is dependent, so there are an infinite number of solutions. The solutions are the ordered pairs that satisfy both equations. The solutions are stated by using the ordered pairs of one of the equations. Therefore, the solutions are the ordered pairs that satisfy the equation $2x + 3y = 6$.

By choosing values of x, we can find some specific ordered-pair solutions. For example, when $x = -3$, 0, and 6, three of the infinite solutions of the system of equations are $(-3, 4)$, $(0, 2)$, and $(6, -2)$.

Example 1

Is $(1, -3)$ a solution of the following system?

$3x + 2y = -3$
$x - 3y = 6$

Solution

$$
\begin{array}{c|c}
3x + 2y = -3 & x - 3y = 6 \\
\hline
3 \cdot 1 + 2(-3) \;\big|\; -3 & 1 - 3(-3) \;\big|\; 6 \\
3 + (-6) \;\big|\; -3 & 1 - (-9) \;\big|\; 6 \\
-3 = -3 & 10 \neq 6
\end{array}
$$

No, $(1, -3)$ is not a solution of the system of equations.

You Try It 1

Is $(-1, -2)$ a solution of the following system?

$2x - 5y = 8$
$-x + 3y = -5$

Your solution

Solution on p. S19

Example 2
Solve by graphing:
$$x - 2y = 2$$
$$x + y = 5$$

Solution

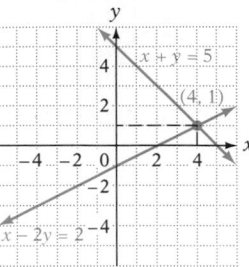

The solution is (4, 1).

You Try It 2
Solve by graphing:
$$x + 3y = 3$$
$$-x + y = 5$$

Your solution

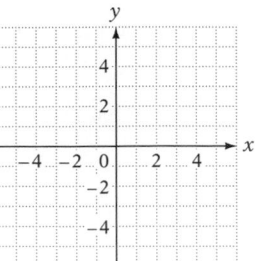

Example 3
Solve by graphing:
$$4x - 2y = 6$$
$$y = 2x - 3$$

Solution

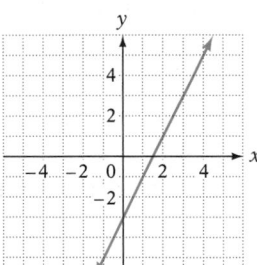

The solutions are the ordered pairs that satisfy the equation $y = 2x - 3$.

You Try It 3
Solve by graphing:
$$y = 3x - 1$$
$$6x - 2y = -6$$

Your solution

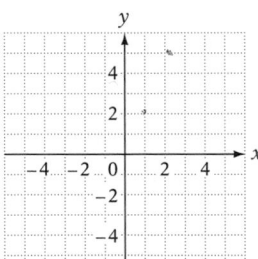

Solutions on p. S19

8.1 Exercises

Objective A

1. Is (2, 3) a solution of this system?
$$3x + 4y = 18$$
$$2x - y = 1$$

2. Is (2, −1) a solution of this system?
$$x - 2y = 4$$
$$2x + y = 3$$

3. Is (1, −2) a solution of this system?
$$3x - y = 5$$
$$2x + 5y = -8$$

4. Is (−1, −1) a solution of this system?
$$x - 4y = 3$$
$$3x + y = 2$$

5. Is (4, 3) a solution of this system?
$$5x - 2y = 14$$
$$x + y = 8$$

6. Is (2, 5) a solution of this system?
$$3x + 2y = 16$$
$$2x - 3y = 4$$

7. Is (−1, 3) a solution of this system?
$$4x - y = -5$$
$$2x + 5y = 13$$

8. Is (4, −1) a solution of this system?
$$x - 4y = 9$$
$$2x - 3y = 11$$

9. Is (0, 0) a solution of this system?
$$4x + 3y = 0$$
$$2x - y = 1$$

10. Is (2, 0) a solution of this system?
$$3x - y = 6$$
$$x + 3y = 2$$

11. Is (2, −3) a solution of this system?
$$y = 2x - 7$$
$$3x - y = 9$$

12. Is (−1, −2) a solution of this system?
$$3x - 4y = 5$$
$$y = x - 1$$

13. Is (5, 2) a solution of this system?
$$y = 2x - 8$$
$$y = 3x - 13$$

14. Is (−4, 3) a solution of this system?
$$y = 2x + 11$$
$$y = 5x - 19$$

15. Is (−2, −3) a solution of this system?
$$3x - 4y = 6$$
$$2x - 7y = 17$$

16. Is (0, 0) a solution of this system?
$$y = 2x$$
$$3x + 5y = 0$$

17. Is (0, −3) a solution of this system?
$$4x - 3y = 9$$
$$2x + 5y = 15$$

18. Is (4, 0) a solution of this system?
$$2x + 3y = 8$$
$$x - 5y = 4$$

Solve by graphing.

19. $x - y = 3$
$x + y = 5$

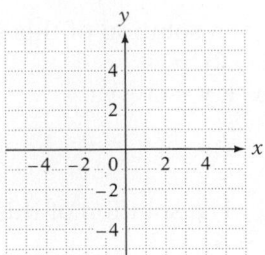

20. $2x - y = 4$
$x + y = 5$

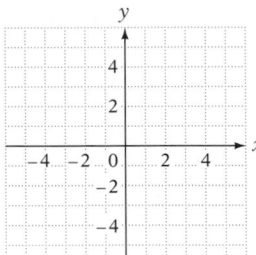

21. $x + 2y = 6$
$x - y = 3$

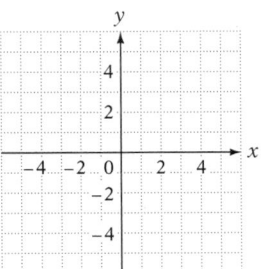

22. $3x - y = 3$
$2x + y = 2$

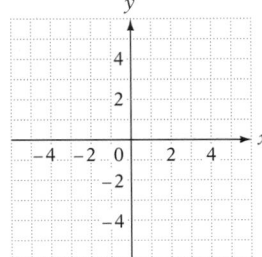

23. $3x - 2y = 6$
$y = 3$

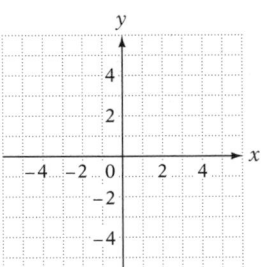

24. $x = 2$
$3x + 2y = 4$

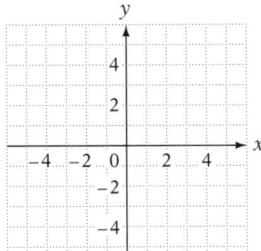

25. $x = 3$
$y = -2$

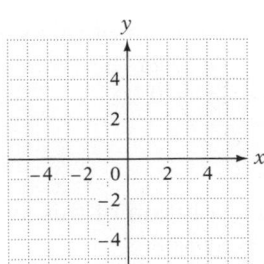

26. $x + 1 = 0$
$y - 3 = 0$

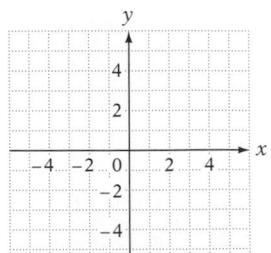

27. $y = 2x - 6$
$x + y = 0$

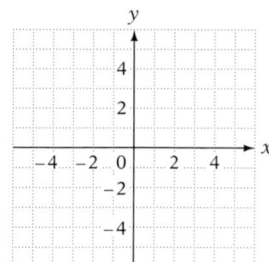

28. $5x - 2y = 11$
$y = 2x - 5$

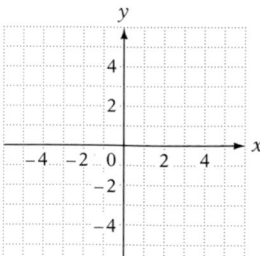

29. $2x + y = -2$
$6x + 3y = 6$

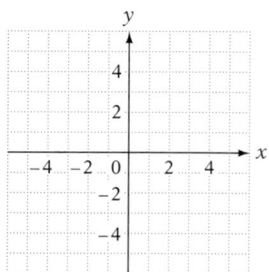

30. $x + y = 5$
$3x + 3y = 6$

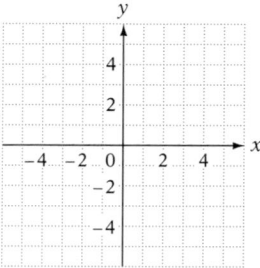

31. $y = 2x - 2$
$4x - 2y = 4$

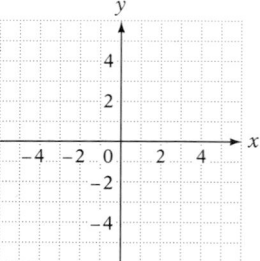

32. $y = -\dfrac{1}{3}x + 1$
$2x + 6y = 6$

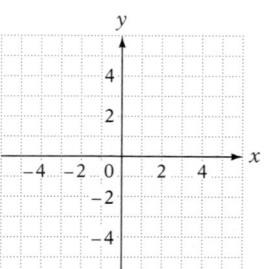

33. $x - y = 5$
$2x - y = 6$

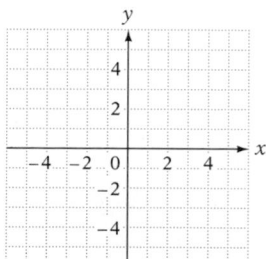

34. $5x - 2y = 10$
$3x + 2y = 6$

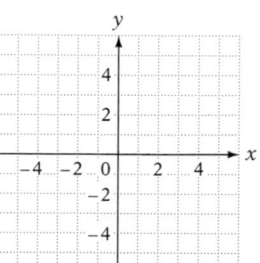

35. $3x + 4y = 0$
$2x - 5y = 0$

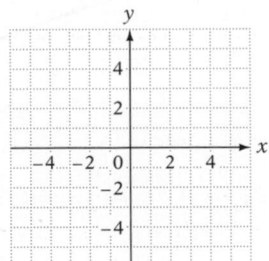

36. $2x - 3y = 0$
$y = -\dfrac{1}{3}x$

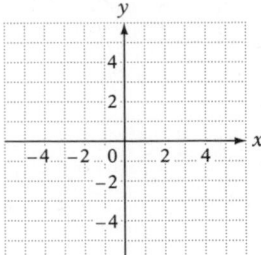

37. $x - 3y = 3$
$2x - 6y = 12$

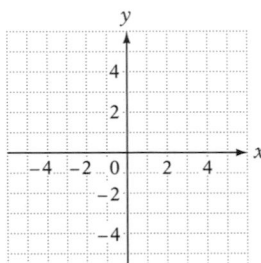

38. $4x + 6y = 12$
$6x + 9y = 18$

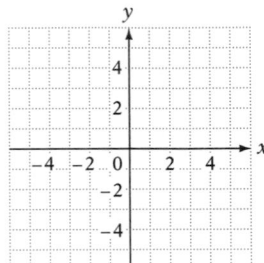

APPLYING THE CONCEPTS

39. Determine whether the statement is always true, sometimes true, or never true.
  a. A solution of a system of two equations with two variables is a point in the plane.
  b. Two parallel lines have the same slope.
  c. Two different lines with the same y-intercept are parallel.
  d. Two different lines with the same slope are parallel.

40. Explain how you can determine from the graph of a system of two equations in two variables whether it is an independent system of equations.

41. Explain how you can determine from the graph of a system of two equations in two variables whether it is an inconsistent system of equations.

42. Write a system of equations that has $(-2, 4)$ as its only solution.

43. Write a system of equations for which there is no solution.

44. Write a system of equations that is a dependent system of equations.

8.2 Solving Systems of Linear Equations by the Substitution Method

Objective A   *To solve a system of linear equations by the substitution method* ....

A graphical solution of a system of equations is based on approximating the coordinates of a point of intersection. An algebraic method called the **substitution method** can be used to find an exact solution of a system of equations.

➡ Solve by the substitution method: (1) $2x + 5y = -11$
$\qquad\qquad\qquad\qquad\qquad\qquad$ (2) $y = 3x - 9$

Equation (2) states that $y = 3x - 9$. Substitute $3x - 9$ for y in Equation (1). Then solve for x.

$$2x + 5y = -11 \qquad \bullet \text{ This is Equation (1).}$$
$$2x + 5(3x - 9) = -11 \qquad \bullet \text{ From Equation (2), substitute } 3x - 9 \text{ for } y.$$
$$2x + 15x - 45 = -11 \qquad \bullet \text{ Solve for } x.$$
$$17x - 45 = -11$$
$$17x = 34$$
$$x = 2$$

Now substitute the value of x into Equation (2) and solve for y.

$$y = 3x - 9 \qquad \bullet \text{ This is Equation (2).}$$
$$y = 3(2) - 9 \qquad \bullet \text{ Substitute 2 for } x.$$
$$y = 6 - 9 = -3$$

The solution is the ordered pair $(2, -3)$.

The graph of the equations in this system of equations is shown at the right. Note that the lines intersect at the point whose coordinates are $(2, -3)$, which is the algebraic solution we determined by the substitution method.

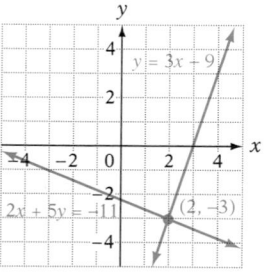

To solve a system of equations by the substitution method, we may need to solve one of the equations in the system of equations for one of its variables. For instance, the first step in solving the system of equations

$$\text{(1)} \qquad x + 2y = -3$$
$$\text{(2)} \qquad 2x - 3y = 5$$

is to solve an equation of the system for one of its variables. Either equation can be used.

Solving Equation (1) for x:

$$x + 2y = -3$$
$$x = -2y - 3$$

Solving Equation (2) for x:

$$2x - 3y = 5$$
$$2x = 3y + 5$$
$$x = \frac{3y + 5}{2}$$

Because solving Equation (1) for x does not result in fractions, it is the easier of the two equations to use.

Here is the solution of the system of equations given on the previous page.

➡ Solve by the substitution method: (1) $x + 2y = -3$
                                                    (2) $2x - 3y = 5$

To use the substitution method, we must solve an equation for one of its variables. Equation (1) is used here because solving it for x does not result in fractions.

$$x + 2y = -3$$

(3) $x = -2y - 3$ • Solve for x. This is Equation (3).

Now substitute $-2y - 3$ for x in Equation (2) and solve for y.

$$2x - 3y = 5$$ • This is Equation (2).
$$2(-2y - 3) - 3y = 5$$ • From Equation (3), substitute $-2y - 3$ for x.
$$-4y - 6 - 3y = 5$$ • Solve for y.
$$-7y - 6 = 5$$
$$-7y = 11$$
$$y = -\frac{11}{7}$$

Substitute the value of y into Equation (3) and solve for x.

$$x = -2y - 3$$ • This is Equation (3).
$$= -2\left(-\frac{11}{7}\right) - 3$$ • Substitute $-\frac{11}{7}$ for y.
$$= \frac{22}{7} - 3 = \frac{22}{7} - \frac{21}{7} = \frac{1}{7}$$

The solution is $\left(\frac{1}{7}, -\frac{11}{7}\right)$.

The graph of the system of equations given above is shown at the right. It would be difficult to determine the exact solution of this system of equations from the graphs of the equations.

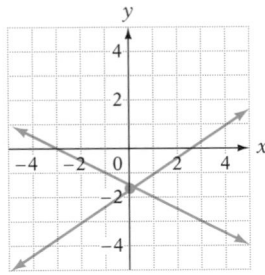

➡ Solve by the substitution method: (1) $y = 3x - 1$
                                                    (2) $y = -2x - 6$

$$y = -2x - 6$$
$$3x - 1 = -2x - 6$$ • Substitute $3x - 1$ for y in Equation (2).
$$5x = -5$$ • Solve for x.
$$x = -1$$

Substitute this value of x into Equation (1) or Equation (2) and solve for y. Equation (1) is used here.

$$y = 3x - 1$$
$$y = 3(-1) - 1 = -4$$

The solution is $(-1, -4)$.

The substitution method can be used to analyze inconsistent and dependent systems of equations.

➡ Solve by the substitution method: (1) $2x + 3y = 3$

(2) $y = -\dfrac{2}{3}x + 3$

$$2x + 3y = 3$$ • This is Equation (1).

$$2x + 3\left(-\dfrac{2}{3}x + 3\right) = 3$$ • From Equation (2), replace y with $-\dfrac{2}{3}x + 3$.

$$2x - 2x + 9 = 3$$ • Solve for x.

$$9 = 3$$ • This is not a true equation.

Because $9 = 3$ is not a true equation, the system of equations has no solution.

Solving Equation (1) above for y, we have $y = -\dfrac{2}{3}x + 1$. Comparing this with Equation (2) reveals that the slopes are equal and the y-intercepts are different. The graphs of the equations that make up this system of equations are parallel and thus never intersect. Because the graphs do not intersect, there are no solutions of the system of equations. The system of equations is inconsistent.

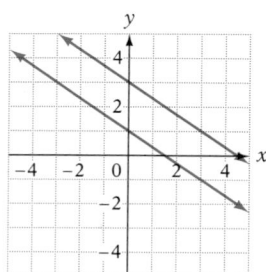

➡ Solve by the substitution method: (1) $x = 2y + 3$
(2) $4x - 8y = 12$

$$4x - 8y = 12$$ • This is Equation (2).

$$4(2y + 3) - 8y = 12$$ • From Equation (1), replace x by $2y + 3$.

$$8y + 12 - 8y = 12$$ • Solve for y.

$$12 = 12$$ • This is a true equation.

The true equation $12 = 12$ indicates that any ordered pair (x, y) that satisfies one equation of the system satisfies the other equation. Therefore, the system of equations has an infinite number of solutions. The solutions are the ordered pairs (x, y) that are solutions of $x = 2y + 3$.

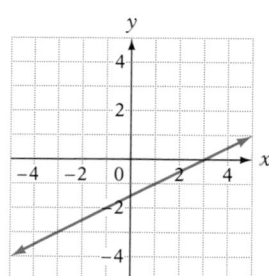

If we write Equation (1) and Equation (2) in slope-intercept form, we have

$$x = 2y + 3 \qquad\qquad 4x - 8y = 12$$
$$-2y = -x + 3 \qquad\qquad -8y = -4x + 12$$
$$y = \dfrac{1}{2}x - \dfrac{3}{2} \qquad\qquad y = \dfrac{1}{2}x - \dfrac{3}{2}$$

The slope-intercept forms of the equations are the same, and therefore the graphs are the same. If we graph these two equations, we essentially graph one over the other. Accordingly, the graphs intersect at an infinite number of points.

Example 1   Solve by substitution:
(1) $3x + 4y = -2$
(2) $-x + 2y = 4$

You Try It 1   Solve by substitution:
(1) $7x - y = 4$
(2) $3x + 2y = 9$

Solution   Solve Equation (2) for x.
$$-x + 2y = 4$$
$$-x = -2y + 4$$
$$x = 2y - 4$$

Substitute in Equation (1).
(1) $3x + 4y = -2$
$$3(2y - 4) + 4y = -2$$
$$6y - 12 + 4y = -2$$
$$10y - 12 = -2$$
$$10y = 10$$
$$y = 1$$

Substitute in Equation (2).
(2) $-x + 2y = 4$
$$-x + 2(1) = 4$$
$$-x + 2 = 4$$
$$-x = 2$$
$$x = -2$$

The solution is $(-2, 1)$.

Your solution

Example 2   Solve by substitution:
$$4x + 2y = 5$$
$$y = -2x + 1$$

You Try It 2   Solve by substitution:
$$3x - y = 4$$
$$y = 3x + 2$$

Solution
$$4x + 2y = 5$$
$$4x + 2(-2x + 1) = 5$$
$$4x - 4x + 2 = 5$$
$$2 = 5$$

This is not a true equation. The system of equations is inconsistent and therefore does not have a solution.

Your solution

Example 3   Solve by substitution:
$$y = 3x - 2$$
$$6x - 2y = 4$$

You Try It 3   Solve by substitution:
$$y = -2x + 1$$
$$6x + 3y = 3$$

Solution
$$6x - 2y = 4$$
$$6x - 2(3x - 2) = 4$$
$$6x - 6x + 4 = 4$$
$$4 = 4$$

This is a true equation. The system of equations is dependent. The solutions are the ordered pairs that satisfy the equation $y = 3x - 2$.

Your solution

Solutions on p. S19

Objective B   *To solve investment problems* .... CT

The annual simple interest that an investment earns is given by the equation $Pr = I$, where P is the principal, or the amount invested, r is the simple interest rate, and I is the simple interest.

For instance, if you invest $750 at a simple interest rate of 6%, then the interest earned after one year is calculated as follows.

$$Pr = I$$
$$750(0.06) = I \qquad \bullet \text{ Replace } P \text{ by 750 and } r \text{ by 0.06 (6\%).}$$
$$45 = I \qquad \bullet \text{ Simplify.}$$

The amount of interest earned is $45.

➡ A medical lab technician decided to open an Individual Retirement Account (IRA) by placing $2000 in two simple-interest accounts. On one account, a corporate bond fund, the annual simple interest rate is 7.5%. On the second account, a real estate investment trust, the annual simple interest rate is 9%. If the technician's annual earnings were $168 per year from these two investments, how much was invested in each account?

> **Strategy for Solving Simple-Interest Investment Problems**
>
> 1. For each amount invested, use the equation $Pr = I$. Write a numerical or variable expression for the principal, the interest rate, and the interest earned.

Amount invested at 7.5%: x
Amount invested at 9%: y

	Principal, P	·	Interest rate, r	=	Interest earned, I
Amount at 7.5%	x	·	0.075	=	$0.075x$
Amount at 9%	y	·	0.09	=	$0.09y$

> 2. Write a system of equations. One equation will express the relationship among the amounts invested. The second equation will express the relationship among the interest earned by each investment.

The total amount invested is $2000: $x + y = 2000$
The total annual interest earned is $168: $0.075x + 0.09y = 168$

Solve the system of equations.

(1) $x + y = 2000$
(2) $0.075x + 0.09y = 168$

Solve Equation (1) for y and substitute into Equation (2).

(3) $y = -x + 2000$

$$0.075x + 0.09(-x + 2000) = 168$$
$$0.075x - 0.09x + 180 = 168$$
$$-0.015x = -12$$
$$x = 800$$

Substitute the value of x into Equation (3) and solve for y.

$$y = -x + 2000$$
$$y = -800 + 2000 = 1200$$

The amount invested at 7.5% is $800. The amount invested at 9% is $1200.

Example 4

A hair stylist invested $2000 at an annual simple interest rate of 5.2%. How much additional money must be invested at an annual simple interest rate of 7.2% so that the total interest earned is 6.4% of the total investment?

Strategy

- Amount invested at 5.2%: 2000
  Amount invested at 7.2%: x
  Total amount invested: y

	Principal	Rate	Interest
Amount at 5.2%	2000	0.052	0.052(2000)
Amount at 7.2%	x	0.072	0.072x
Amount at 6.4%	y	0.064	0.064y

- The total amount invested (y) is $2000 more than the amount invested at 7.2% (x):

$y = x + 2000$

The sum of the interest earned at 5.2% and the interest earned at 7.2% equals the interest earned at 6.4%:

$0.052(2000) + 0.072x = 0.064y$

Solution

(1) $\qquad\qquad\qquad y = x + 2000$

(2) $\quad 0.052(2000) + 0.072x = 0.064y$

Replace y in Equation (2) by $x + 2000$ from Equation (1). Then solve for x.

$0.052(2000) + 0.072x = 0.064(x + 2000)$

$104 + 0.072x = 0.064x + 128$

$0.008x = 24$

$x = 3000$

$3000 must be invested at an annual simple interest rate of 7.2%.

You Try It 4

The manager of a city's investment income wished to place $330,000 in two simple-interest accounts. The first account earns 6.5% annual interest and the second account earns 4.5%. How much should be invested in each account so that both accounts earn the same annual interest?

Your strategy

Your solution

Solution on p. S19

8.2 Exercises

. . . .

Objective A

Solve by substitution.

1. $2x + 3y = 7$
 $x = 2$

2. $y = 3$
 $3x - 2y = 6$

3. $y = x - 3$
 $x + y = 5$

4. $y = x + 2$
 $x + y = 6$

5. $x = y - 2$
 $x + 3y = 2$

6. $x = y + 1$
 $x + 2y = 7$

7. $y = 4 - 3x$
 $3x + y = 5$

8. $y = 2 - 3x$
 $6x + 2y = 7$

9. $x = 3y + 3$
 $2x - 6y = 12$

10. $x = 2 - y$
 $3x + 3y = 6$

11. $3x + 5y = -6$
 $x = 5y + 3$

12. $y = 2x + 3$
 $4x - 3y = 1$

13. $3x + y = 4$
 $4x - 3y = 1$

14. $x - 4y = 9$
 $2x - 3y = 11$

15. $3x - y = 6$
 $x + 3y = 2$

16. $4x - y = -5$
 $2x + 5y = 13$

17. $3x - y = 5$
 $2x + 5y = -8$

18. $3x + 4y = 18$
 $2x - y = 1$

19. $4x + 3y = 0$
 $2x - y = 0$

20. $5x + 2y = 0$
 $x - 3y = 0$

21. $2x - y = 2$
 $6x - 3y = 6$

22. $3x + y = 4$
$9x + 3y = 12$

23. $x = 3y + 2$
$y = 2x + 6$

24. $x = 4 - 2y$
$y = 2x - 13$

25. $y = 2x + 11$
$y = 5x - 19$

26. $y = 2x - 8$
$y = 3x - 13$

27. $y = -4x + 2$
$y = -3x - 1$

28. $x = 3y + 7$
$x = 2y - 1$

29. $x = 4y - 2$
$x = 6y + 8$

30. $x = 3 - 2y$
$x = 5y - 10$

Objective B   *Application Problems*

31. An investment of $3500 is divided between two simple-interest accounts. On one account, the annual simple interest rate is 5%, and on the second account the annual simple interest rate is 7.5%. How much should be invested in each account so that the total interest from the two accounts is $215?

32. A mortgage broker purchased two trust deeds for a total of $250,000. One trust deed earns 7% simple annual interest whereas the second one earns 8% simple annual interest. If the total annual interest from the two trust deeds is $18,500, what was the purchase price of each trust deed?

33. When Sara Whitehorse changed jobs, she rolled over the $6000 in her retirement account into two simple-interest accounts. On one account, the annual simple interest rate is 9%; on the second account, the annual simple interest rate is 6%. How much must be invested in each account if the accounts earn the same amount of annual interest?

34. An animal trainer decided to take the $15,000 won on a game show and deposit it in two simple-interest accounts. Part of the winnings were placed in a 7% annual simple-interest account and the remainder was used to purchase a government bond that earns 6.5% annual simple interest. The amount of interest earned for one year was $1020. How much was invested in each account?

35. A police officer has chosen a high-yield stock fund that earns 8% annual simple interest for part of a $6000 investment. The remaining portion is used to purchase a preferred stock that earns 11% annual simple interest. How much should be invested in each account so that the amount earned on the 8% account is twice the amount earned on the 11% account?

36. To plan for the purchase of a new car, a deposit was made into an account that earns 7% annual simple interest. Another deposit, $1500 less than the first deposit, was placed in a 9% annual simple-interest certificate of deposit. The total interest earned on both accounts for one year was $505. How much money was deposited in the certificate of deposit?

37. The Pacific Investment Group invested some money in a certificate of deposit (CD) that earns 6.5% annual simple interest. Twice the amount invested at 6.5% was invested in a second CD that earns 8.5% annual simple interest. If the total annual interest earned from the two investments was $4935, how much was invested at 6.5%?

38. A corporation gave a university $300,000 to support product safety research. The university deposited some of the money in a 10% simple-interest account and the remainder in an 8.5% simple-interest account. How much should be deposited in each account so that the annual interest earned is $28,500?

39. Ten coworkers formed an investment club, and each deposited $2000 in the club's account. They decided to take the total amount and invest some of it in preferred stock that pays 8% annual simple interest and the remainder in a municipal bond that pays 7% annual simple interest. The amount of interest earned each year from the investments was $1520. How much was invested in each?

40. A financial consultant advises a client to invest part of $30,000 in municipal bonds that earn 6.5% annual simple interest and the remainder of the money in 8.5% corporate bonds. How much should be invested in each so that the total annual interest earned each year is $2190?

41. Alisa Rhodes placed some money in a real estate investment trust that earns 7.5% annual simple interest. A second investment, which was one-half the amount placed in the real estate investment trust, was used to purchase a trust deed that earns 9% annual simple interest. If the total annual interest earned from the two investments was $900, how much was invested in the trust deed?

APPLYING THE CONCEPTS

For what value of k does the system of equations have no solution?

42. $2x - 3y = 7$
$kx - 3y = 4$

43. $8x - 4y = 1$
$2x - ky = 3$

44. $x = 4y + 4$
$kx - 8y = 4$

45. Describe in your own words the process of solving a system of equations by the substitution method.

46. When you solve a system of equations by the substitution method, how do you determine whether the system of equations is dependent?

47. The following was offered as a solution to the system of equations

(1) $\qquad y = \dfrac{1}{2}x + 2$

(2) $\quad 2x + 5y = 10$

$\qquad\qquad 2x + 5y = 10 \qquad$ • Equation (2)

$\qquad 2x + 5\left(\dfrac{1}{2}x + 2\right) = 10 \qquad$ • Substitute $\dfrac{1}{2}x + 2$ for y.

$\qquad\qquad 2x + \dfrac{5}{2}x + 10 = 10 \qquad$ • Solve for x.

$\qquad\qquad\qquad \dfrac{9}{2}x = 0$

$\qquad\qquad\qquad\qquad x = 0$

At this point the student stated that because $x = 0$, the system of equations has no solution. If this assertion is correct, is the system of equations independent, dependent, or inconsistent? If the assertion is not correct, what is the correct solution?

48. When you solve a system of equations by the substitution method, how do you determine whether the system of equations is inconsistent?

49. A sales representative invests in a stock paying 9% dividends. A research consultant invests $5000 more than the sales representative in bonds paying 8% annual simple interest. The research consultant's income from the investment is equal to the sales representative's. Find the amount of the research consultant's investment.

50. A plant manager invested $3000 more in stocks than in bonds. The stocks paid 8% annual simple interest, and the bonds paid 9.5% annual simple interest. Both investments yielded the same income. Find the total annual interest received on both investments.

51. The exercises in this objective were based on annual *simple* interest, r, which means that the amount of interest earned after one year is given by $I = Pr$. For *compound* interest, the interest earned for a certain period of time (usually daily or monthly) is added to the principal before the interest for the next period is calculated. The compound interest earned in one year is given by the formula

$I = P\left[\left(1 + \dfrac{r}{n}\right)^{n} - 1\right]$, where n is the number of times per year that

interest is compounded. For instance, if interest is compounded daily, then $n = 365$; if interest is compounded monthly, then $n = 12$. Suppose an investment of $5000 is made into three different accounts. The first account earns 8% annual simple interest, the second earns 8% compounded monthly ($n = 12$), and the third earns 8% compounded daily ($n = 365$). Find the amount of interest earned from each account.

8.3 Solving Systems of Equations by the Addition Method

Objective A   *To solve a system of linear equations by the addition method* ....

Another method of solving a system of equations is called the **addition method.** This method is based on the Addition Property of Equations.

Note, for the system of equations at the right, the effect of adding Equation (2) to Equation (1). Because $2y$ and $-2y$ are opposites, adding the equations results in an equation with only one variable.

(1) $5x + 2y = 11$
(2) $3x - 2y = 13$
$\overline{8x + 0y = 24}$
$8x = 24$

Solving $8x = 24$ for x gives the first coordinate of the ordered-pair solution of the system of equations.

$\dfrac{8x}{8} = \dfrac{24}{8}$
$x = 3$

The second coordinate is found by substituting the value of x into Equation (1) or Equation (2) and then solving for y. Equation (1) is used here.

(1) $5x + 2y = 11$
$5(3) + 2y = 11$
$15 + 2y = 11$
$2y = -4$
$y = -2$

The solution is $(3, -2)$.

Sometimes adding the two equations does not eliminate one of the variables. In this case, use the Multiplication Property of Equations to rewrite one or both of the equations such that the coefficients of one of the variables are opposites.

➡ Solve by the addition method: (1) $4x + 3y = -1$
(2) $2x - 5y = 19$

Multiply Equation (2) by -2. The coefficients of x will then be opposites.

$-2(2x - 5y) = -2 \cdot 19$ • Multiply Equation (2) by -2.
(3) $-4x + 10y = -38$ • Simplify. This is Equation (3).

Add Equation (1) to Equation (3). Then solve for y.

(1) $4x + 3y = -1$
(3) $\underline{-4x + 10y = -38}$ • Note that the coefficients of x are opposites.
$13y = -39$ • Add the two equations.
$y = -3$ • Solve for y.

Substitute the value of y into Equation (1) or Equation (2) and solve for x. Equation (1) will be used here.

(1) $4x + 3y = -1$
$4x + 3(-3) = -1$ • Substitute -3 for y.
$4x - 9 = -1$ • Solve for x.
$4x = 8$
$x = 2$

The solution is $(2, -3)$.

Sometimes each equation of the system of equations must be multiplied by a constant so that the coefficients of one of the variable terms are opposites.

➡ Solve by the addition method: (1) $3x + 7y = 2$
    (2) $5x - 3y = -26$

To eliminate x, multiply Equation (1) by 5 and Equation (2) by -3. Note at the right how the constants are chosen.

$5(3x + 7y) = 5 \cdot 2$

$-3(5x - 3y) = -3(-26)$

└ • **The negative is used so that the coefficients will be opposites.**

$15x + 35y = 10$ • **5 times Equation (1).**
$\underline{-15x + 9y = 78}$ • **-3 times Equation (2).**
$44y = 88$ • **Add the equations.**
$y = 2$ • **Solve for y.**

Substitute the value of y into Equation (1) or Equation (2) and solve for x. Equation (1) will be used here.

(1) $3x + 7y = 2$
    $3x + 7(2) = 2$ • **Substitute 2 for y.**
    $3x + 14 = 2$ • **Solve for x.**
    $3x = -12$
    $x = -4$

The solution is $(-4, 2)$.

For the previous system of equations, the value of x was determined by substitution. This value can also be determined by eliminating y from the system.

$9x + 21y = 6$ • **3 times Equation (1).**
$\underline{35x - 21y = -182}$ • **7 times Equation (2).**
$44x = -176$ • **Add the equations.**
$x = -4$ • **Solve for x.**

Note that this is the same value of x as was determined by using substitution.

➡ Solve by the addition method: (1) $5x - 2y = -4$
    (2) $3y = 7x + 5$

Rewrite Equation (2) in the form $Ax + By = C$.

(2) $3y = 7x + 5$ • **Subtract $7x$ from each side of the**
(3) $-7x + 3y = 5$ **equation. This is Equation (3).**

Eliminate x or y. We will eliminate x by using Equations (1) and (3).

$35x - 14y = -28$ • **7 times Equation (1).**
$\underline{-35x + 15y = 25}$ • **5 times Equation (3).**
$y = -3$ • **Add the equations.**

Substitute the value of y into Equation (1) or Equation (2) and solve for x. Equation (1) will be used here.

(1) $5x - 2y = -4$
    $5x - 2(-3) = -4$ • **Substitute -3 for y.**
    $5x + 6 = -4$ • **Solve for x.**
    $5x = -10$
    $x = -2$

The solution is $(-2, -3)$.

➡ Solve by the addition method: (1) $2x + y = 2$
                                   (2) $4x + 2y = -5$

Eliminate y. Multiply Equation (1) by -2.

(1) $-2(2x + y) = -2 \cdot 2$ • -2 times Equation (1).
(3) $-4x - 2y = -4$ • This is Equation (3).

Add Equation (2) to Equation (3) and solve for x.

(3) $-4x - 2y = -4$
(2) $\underline{4x + 2y = -5}$

       $0x + 0y = -9$ • Add Equation (2) to Equation (3).
              $0 = -9$ • This is not a true equation.

The system of equations is inconsistent and therefore does not have a solution.

The graphs of the two equations in the system of equations above are shown at the right. Note that the graphs are parallel and therefore do not intersect. Thus the system of equations has no solutions.

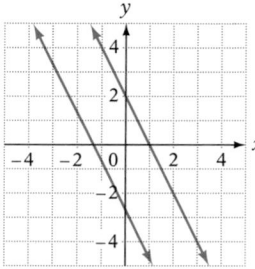

Example 1
Solve by the addition method:
(1) $2x + 4y = 7$
(2) $5x - 3y = -2$

Solution
Eliminate x.
  $5(2x + 4y) = 5 \cdot 7$ • 5 times Equation (1).
$-2(5x - 3y) = -2(-2)$ • -2 times Equation (2).

  $10x + 20y = 35$
$\underline{-10x + 6y = 4}$
          $26y = 39$ • Add the equations.

          $y = \dfrac{39}{26} = \dfrac{3}{2}$ • Solve for y.

Substitute $\dfrac{3}{2}$ for y in Equation (1).

(1) $2x + 4y = 7$

   $2x + 4\left(\dfrac{3}{2}\right) = 7$ • Replace y by $\dfrac{3}{2}$.

        $2x + 6 = 7$ • Solve for x.
          $2x = 1$

            $x = \dfrac{1}{2}$

The solution is $\left(\dfrac{1}{2}, \dfrac{3}{2}\right)$.

You Try It 1
Solve by the addition method:
(1) $x - 2y = 1$
(2) $2x + 4y = 0$

Your solution

Solution on p. S20

Example 2

Solve by the addition method:

(1) $6x + 9y = 15$
(2) $4x + 6y = 10$

Solution

Eliminate x.

$4(6x + 9y) = 4 \cdot 15$ • 4 times Equation (1).
$-6(4x + 6y) = -6 \cdot 10$ • −6 times Equation (2).

$\begin{array}{r} 24x + 36y = 60 \\ -24x - 36y = -60 \\ \hline 0x + 0y = 0 \\ 0 = 0 \end{array}$ • Add the equations.

The system of equations is dependent.
The solutions are the ordered pairs that
satisfy the equation $6x + 9y = 15$.

You Try It 2

Solve by the addition method:

$2x - 3y = 4$
$-4x + 6y = -8$

Your solution

Example 3

Solve by the addition method:

(1) $2x = y + 8$
(2) $3x + 2y = 5$

Solution

Write Equation (1) in the form
$Ax + By = C$.

$2x = y + 8$
(3) $2x - y = 8$ • This is Equation (3).

Eliminate y.

$2(2x - y) = 2 \cdot 8$ • 2 times Equation (3).
$3x + 2y = 5$ • This is Equation (2).

$\begin{array}{r} 4x - 2y = 16 \\ 3x + 2y = 5 \\ \hline 7x = 21 \\ x = 3 \end{array}$ • Add the equations.

Replace x in Equation (1).

(1) $2x = y + 8$
$2 \cdot 3 = y + 8$ • Replace x by 3.
$6 = y + 8$
$-2 = y$

The solution is $(3, -2)$.

You Try It 3

Solve by the addition method:

$4x + 5y = 11$
$3y = x + 10$

Your solution

Solutions on p. S20

8.3 Exercises

· ·

Objective A

Solve by the addition method.

1. $x + y = 4$
   $x - y = 6$

2. $2x + y = 3$
   $x - y = 3$

3. $x + y = 4$
   $2x + y = 5$

4. $x - 3y = 2$
   $x + 2y = -3$

5. $2x - y = 1$
   $x + 3y = 4$

6. $x - 2y = 4$
   $3x + 4y = 2$

7. $4x - 5y = 22$
   $x + 2y = -1$

8. $3x - y = 11$
   $2x + 5y = 13$

9. $2x - y = 1$
   $4x - 2y = 2$

10. $x + 3y = 2$
    $3x + 9y = 6$

11. $4x + 3y = 15$
    $2x - 5y = 1$

12. $3x - 7y = 13$
    $6x + 5y = 7$

13. $2x - 3y = 1$
    $4x - 6y = 2$

14. $2x + 4y = 6$
    $3x + 6y = 9$

15. $5x - 2y = -1$
    $x + 3y = -5$

16. $4x - 3y = 1$
    $8x + 5y = 13$

17. $5x + 7y = 10$
    $3x - 14y = 6$

18. $7x + 10y = 13$
    $4x + 5y = 6$

19. $3x - 2y = 0$
    $6x + 5y = 0$

20. $5x + 2y = 0$
    $3x + 5y = 0$

21. $2x - 3y = 16$
    $3x + 4y = 7$

22. $3x + 4y = 10$
$4x + 3y = 11$

23. $5x + 3y = 7$
$2x + 5y = 1$

24. $-2x + 7y = 9$
$3x + 2y = -1$

25. $7x - 2y = 13$
$5x + 3y = 27$

26. $12x + 5y = 23$
$2x - 7y = 39$

27. $8x - 3y = 11$
$6x - 5y = 11$

28. $4x - 8y = 36$
$3x - 6y = 27$

29. $5x + 15y = 20$
$2x + 6y = 8$

30. $\quad\quad y = 2x - 3$
$3x + 4y = -1$

31. $\quad\quad 3x = 2y + 7$
$5x - 2y = 13$

32. $\quad\quad 2y = 4 - 9x$
$9x - y = 25$

33. $2x + 9y = 16$
$\quad\quad 5x = 1 - 3y$

34. $\quad 3x - 4 = y + 18$
$4x + 5y = -21$

35. $2x + 3y = 7 - 2x$
$7x + 2y = 9$

36. $5x - 3y = 3y + 4$
$4x + 3y = 11$

APPLYING THE CONCEPTS

37. Describe in your own words the process of solving a system of equations by the addition method.

38. The point of intersection of the graphs of the equations $Ax + 2y = 2$ and $2x + By = 10$ is $(2, -2)$. Find A and B.

39. The point of intersection of the graphs of the equations $Ax - 4y = 9$ and $4x + By = -1$ is $(-1, -3)$. Find A and B.

40. For what value of k is the system of equations dependent?

   a. $2x + 3y = 7$ **b.** $y = \dfrac{2}{3}x - 3$ **c.** $x = ky - 1$

      $4x + 6y = k$ $y = kx - 3$ $y = 2x + 2$

41. For what value of k is the system of equations independent?

   a. $x + y = 7$ **b.** $x + 2y = 4$ **c.** $2x + ky = 1$

      $kx + y = 3$ $kx + 3y = 2$ $x + 2y = 2$

8.4 Application Problems in Two Variables

Objective A   *To solve rate-of-wind or -current problems* ....

Motion problems that involve an object moving with or against a wind or current normally require two variables to solve.

➡ Flying with the wind, a small plane can fly 600 mi in 3 h. Against the wind, the plane can fly the same distance in 4 h. Find the rate of the plane in calm air and the rate of the wind.

> **Strategy for Solving Rate-of-Wind or -Current Problems**
>
> Choose one variable to represent the rate of the object in calm conditions and a second variable to represent the rate of the wind or current. Using these variables, express the rate of the object with and against the wind or current. Use the equation $d = rt$ to write expressions for the distance traveled by the object. The results can be recorded in a table.

Rate of plane in calm air: p
Rate of wind: w

	Rate	·	Time	=	Distance
With the wind	$p + w$	·	3	=	$3(p + w)$
Against the wind	$p - w$	·	4	=	$4(p - w)$

> Determine how the expressions for distance are related.

The distance traveled with the wind is 600 mi. $3(p + w) = 600$
The distance traveled against the wind is 600 mi. $4(p - w) = 600$

Solve the system of equations.

$$3(p + w) = 600 \quad\rightarrow\quad \frac{1}{3} \cdot 3(p + w) = \frac{1}{3} \cdot 600 \quad\rightarrow\quad p + w = 200$$

$$4(p - w) = 600 \qquad\qquad \frac{1}{4} \cdot 4(p - w) = \frac{1}{4} \cdot 600 \qquad\qquad p - w = 150$$

$$2p = 350$$
$$p = 175$$

$$p + w = 200$$
$$175 + w = 200$$
$$w = 25$$

The rate of the plane in calm air is 175 mph.
The rate of the wind is 25 mph.

Example 1

A 450-mile trip from one city to another takes 3 h when a plane is flying with the wind. The return trip, against the wind, takes 5 h. Find the rate of the plane in still air and the rate of the wind.

Strategy

- Rate of the plane in still air: p
  Rate of the wind: w

	Rate	Time	Distance
With wind	$p + w$	3	$3(p + w)$
Against wind	$p - w$	5	$5(p - w)$

- The distance traveled with the wind is 450 mi. The distance traveled against the wind is 450 mi.

Solution

$$3(p + w) = 450 \qquad \frac{1}{3} \cdot 3(p + w) = \frac{1}{3} \cdot 450$$

$$5(p - w) = 450 \qquad \frac{1}{5} \cdot 5(p - w) = \frac{1}{5} \cdot 450$$

$$p + w = 150$$
$$p - w = 90$$

$$2p = 240$$
$$p = 120$$

$$p + w = 150$$
$$120 + w = 150$$
$$w = 30$$

The rate of the plane in still air is 120 mph.
The rate of the wind is 30 mph.

You Try It 1

A canoeist paddling with the current can travel 15 mi in 3 h. Against the current, it takes 5 h to travel the same distance. Find the rate of the current and the rate of the canoeist in calm water.

Your strategy

Your solution

Solution on p. S20

Objective B   To solve application problems using two variables .... (29) CT

The application problems in this section are varieties of those problems solved earlier in the text. Each of the strategies for the problems in this section will result in a system of equations.

POINT OF INTEREST

The Babylonians had a method for solving a system of equations. Here is an adaptation of a problem from an ancient (around 1500 B.C.) Babylonian text. "There are two silver blocks. The sum of $\frac{1}{7}$ of the first block and $\frac{1}{11}$ of the second block is one sheqel (a weight). The first block diminished by $\frac{1}{7}$ of its weight equals the second diminished by $\frac{1}{11}$ of its weight. What are the weights of the two blocks?"

➡ A jeweler purchased 5 oz of a gold alloy and 20 oz of a silver alloy for a total cost of $540. The next day, at the same prices per ounce, the jeweler purchased 4 oz of the gold alloy and 25 oz of the silver alloy for a total cost of $450. Find the cost per ounce of the gold and silver alloys.

> **Strategy for Solving an Application Problem in Two Variables**
>
> Choose one variable to represent one of the unknown quantities and a second variable to represent the other unknown quantity. Write numerical or variable expressions for all the remaining quantities. These results can be recorded in two tables, one for each of the conditions.

Cost per ounce of gold: g
Cost per ounce of silver: s

First day:

	Amount	·	Unit Cost	=	Value
Gold	5	·	g	=	$5g$
Silver	20	·	s	=	$20s$

Second day:

	Amount	·	Unit Cost	=	Value
Gold	4	·	g	=	$4g$
Silver	25	·	s	=	$25s$

> Determine a system of equations. Each table will give one equation of the system.

The total value of the purchase on the first day was $540. $5g + 20s = 540$

The total value of the purchase on the second day was $450. $4g + 25s = 450$

Solve the system of equations.

$$5g + 20s = 540 \qquad 4(5g + 20s) = 4 \cdot 540 \qquad 20g + 80s = 2160$$
$$4g + 25s = 450 \qquad -5(4g + 25s) = -5 \cdot 450 \qquad \underline{-20g - 125s = -2250}$$
$$-45s = -90$$
$$s = 2$$

$$5g + 20s = 540$$
$$5g + 20(2) = 540 \qquad \bullet\ s = 2$$
$$5g + 40 = 540$$
$$5g = 500$$
$$g = 100$$

The cost per ounce of the gold alloy was $100.
The cost per ounce of the silver alloy was $2.

Example 2

A store owner purchased 20 incandescent light bulbs and 30 fluorescent bulbs for a total cost of $40. A second purchase, at the same prices, included 30 incandescent bulbs and 10 fluorescent bulbs for a total cost of $25. Find the cost of an incandescent bulb and of a fluorescent bulb.

Strategy

Cost of an incandescent bulb: b
Cost of a fluorescent bulb: f

First purchase:

	Amount	Unit Cost	Value
Incandescent	20	b	$20b$
Fluorescent	30	f	$30f$

Second purchase:

	Amount	Unit Cost	Value
Incandescent	30	b	$30b$
Fluorescent	10	f	$10f$

The total of the first purchase was $40.
The total of the second purchase was $25.

Solution

$$20b + 30f = 40 \qquad 3(20b + 30f) = 3 \cdot 40$$
$$30b + 10f = 25 \qquad -2(30b + 10f) = -2 \cdot 25$$

$$\begin{aligned} 60b + 90f &= 120 \\ -60b - 20f &= -50 \\ \hline 70f &= 70 \\ f &= 1 \end{aligned}$$

$$20b + 30f = 40$$
$$20b + 30(1) = 40$$
$$20b = 10$$
$$b = \frac{1}{2}$$

The cost of an incandescent bulb was $.50.
The cost of a fluorescent bulb was $1.00.

You Try It 2

A citrus grower purchased 25 orange trees and 20 grapefruit trees for $290. The next week, at the same prices, the grower bought 20 orange trees and 30 grapefruit trees for $330. Find the cost of an orange tree and the cost of a grapefruit tree.

Your strategy

Your solution

Solution on p. S21

8.4 Exercises

Objective A   *Application Problems*

1. A whale swimming against an ocean current traveled 60 mi in 2 h. Swimming in the opposite direction, with the current, the whale was able to travel the same distance in 1.5 h. Find the speed of the whale in calm water and the rate of the ocean current.

2. A plane flying with the jet stream flew from Los Angeles to Chicago, a distance of 2250 mi, in 5 h. Flying against the jet stream, the plane could fly only 1750 mi in the same amount of time. Find the rate of the plane in calm air and the rate of the wind.

3. A rowing team rowing with the current traveled 40 km in 2 h. Rowing against the current, the team could travel only 16 km in 2 h. Find the rate of rowing in calm water and the rate of the current.

4. The bird capable of the fastest flying speed is the swift. A swift flying with the wind to a favorite feeding spot traveled 26 mi in 0.2 h. On returning, now against the wind, the swift was able to travel only 16 mi in the same amount of time. What is the rate of the swift in calm air and what was the rate of the wind?

5. A private Learjet 31A transporting passengers was flying with a tailwind and traveled 1120 mi in 2 h. Flying against the wind on the return trip the jet was able to travel only 980 mi in 2 h. Find the speed of the jet in calm air and the rate of the wind.

6. A plane flying with a tailwind flew 300 mi in 2 h. Against the wind, it took 3 h to travel the same distance. Find the rate of the plane in calm air and the rate of the wind.

7. A Boeing Apache Longbow military helicopter traveling directly into a strong headwind was able to travel 450 mi in 2.5 h. The return trip, now with a tailwind, took 1 h 40 min. Find the speed of the helicopter in calm air and the rate of the wind.

8. A seaplane pilot flying with the wind flew from an ocean port to a lake, a distance of 240 mi, in 2 h. Flying against the wind, the trip from the lake to the ocean port took 2 h 40 min. Find the rate of the plane in calm air and the rate of the wind.

9. Rowing with the current, a canoeist paddled 14 mi in 2 h. Against the current, the canoeist could paddle only 10 mi in the same amount of time. Find the rate of the canoeist in calm water and the rate of the current.

Objective B   *Application Problems*

10. A computer on-line service charges one hourly price for regular use but a higher hourly rate for designated "premium" areas. One customer was charged $28 after spending 2 h in premium areas and 9 regular hours; another spent 3 h in the premium areas and 6 regular hours and was charged $27. What does the service charge per hour for regular and premium services?

11. A baker purchased 12 lb of wheat flour and 15 lb of rye flour for a total cost of $18.30. A second purchase, at the same prices, included 15 lb of wheat flour and 10 lb of rye flour. The cost of the second purchase was $16.75. Find the cost per pound of the wheat flour and of the rye flour.

12. An investor owned 300 shares of an oil company and 200 shares of a movie company. The quarterly dividend from the two stocks was $165. After the investor sold 100 shares of the oil company and bought an additional 100 shares of the movie company, the quarterly dividend became $185. Find the dividend per share for each stock.

13. The charge for 25 min of prime time and 35 min of nonprime time to a customer for using a computerized financial news network was $10.75. A second customer used the system for 30 min of prime time and 45 min of nonprime time for a cost of $13.35. Find the cost per minute for using the financial news network during prime time and during nonprime time.

14. A stocker at a grocery store gets paid a standard hourly rate for her day hours but a higher hourly rate for any hours she works during the night shift. One week she worked 17 daytime hours and 8 nighttime hours and earned $191. The next week she earned $219 for a total of 12 daytime and 15 nighttime hours. What is the rate she is being paid for day hours and what is the rate for nighttime hours?

15. The employees of a hardware store ordered lunch from a local delicatessen. The lunch consisted of 4 submarine sandwiches and 7 orders of french fries for a total cost of $23.30. The next day, the employees ordered 5 submarine sandwiches and 5 orders of french fries totaling $25.75. What does the delicatessen charge for a submarine sandwich and for an order of french fries?

APPLYING THE CONCEPTS

16. Two angles are supplementary. The larger angle is 15° more than twice the measure of the smaller angle. Find the measure of the two angles. (Supplementary angles are two angles whose sum is 180°.)

17. The value of the nickels and dimes in a coin bank is $.25. If the number of nickels and the number of dimes were doubled, the value of the coins would be $.50. How many nickels and how many dimes are in the bank?

18. An investor has $5000 to invest in two accounts. The first account earns 8% annual simple interest and the second account earns 10% annual simple interest. How much money should be invested in each account so that the annual simple interest earned is $600?

19. Solve the following problem, which dates from a Chinese manuscript called the Jinzhang that is approximately 2100 years old. "The price of 1 acre of good land is 300 pieces of gold; the price of 7 acres of bad land is 500 pieces of gold. One has purchased altogether 100 acres. The price was 10,000 pieces of gold. How much good land and how much bad land was bought?" Adapted from *A History of Mathematics, An Introduction*, Victor J. Katz (New York: HarperCollins, 1993, p. 15).

20. A coin bank contains only nickels or dimes, but there are no more than 27 coins. The value of the coins is $2.10. How many different combinations of nickels and dimes could be in the coin bank?

Focus on Problem Solving

Using a Table and Searching for a Pattern

Consider the numbers 10, 12, and 28 and the sum of the proper factors (the natural number factors less than the number) of those numbers.

$$10: 1 + 2 + 5 = 8 \qquad 12: 1 + 2 + 3 + 4 + 6 = 16 \qquad 28: 1 + 2 + 4 + 7 + 14 = 28$$

10 is called a *deficient number* because the sum of its proper factors is less than the number ($8 < 10$). 12 is called an *abundant number* because the sum of its proper factors is greater than the number ($16 > 12$), and 28 is called a *perfect number* because the sum of its proper divisors equals the number ($28 = 28$).

Our goal for this "Focus on Problem Solving" is to try to find a method that will determine whether a number is deficient, abundant, or perfect without having to first find all the factors and then add them up. We will use a table and search for a pattern.

Before we begin, recall that a prime number is a number greater than 1 whose only factors are itself and 1, and each natural number greater than 1 has a unique prime factorization. For instance, the prime factorization of 36 is given by $36 = 2^2 \cdot 3^2$. Note that the proper factors of 36 (1, 2, 3, 4, 6, 9, 12, 18) can be represented in terms of the same prime numbers.

$$1 = 2^0, \quad 2 = 2^1, \quad 3 = 3^1, \quad 4 = 2^2, \quad 6 = 2 \cdot 3, \quad 9 = 3^2, \quad 12 = 2^2 \cdot 3, \quad 18 = 2 \cdot 3^2$$

Now let us consider a trial problem of determining whether 432 is deficient, abundant, or perfect.

TAKE NOTE

This table contains the factor $432 = 2^4 \cdot 3^3$, which is not a proper factor.

We write the prime factorization of 432 as $2^4 \cdot 3^3$ and place the factors of 432 in a table as shown at the right. This table contains *all* the factors of 432 represented in terms of the prime number factors. The sum of each column is shown at the bottom.

	1	$1 \cdot 3$	$1 \cdot 3^2$	$1 \cdot 3^3$
	2	$2 \cdot 3$	$2 \cdot 3^2$	$2 \cdot 3^3$
	2^2	$2^2 \cdot 3$	$2^2 \cdot 3^2$	$2^2 \cdot 3^3$
	2^3	$2^3 \cdot 3$	$2^3 \cdot 3^2$	$2^3 \cdot 3^3$
	2^4	$2^4 \cdot 3$	$2^4 \cdot 3^2$	$2^4 \cdot 3^3$
Sum	31	$31 \cdot 3$	$31 \cdot 3^2$	$31 \cdot 3^3$

Here is the calculation of the sum for the column headed by $1 \cdot 3$.

$$1 \cdot 3 + 2 \cdot 3 + 2^2 \cdot 3 + 2^3 \cdot 3 + 2^4 \cdot 3 = (1 + 2 + 2^2 + 2^3 + 2^4)3 = 31(3)$$

For the column headed by $1 \cdot 3^2$ there is a similar situation.

$$1 \cdot 3^2 + 2 \cdot 3^2 + 2^2 \cdot 3^2 + 2^3 \cdot 3^2 + 2^4 \cdot 3^2 = (1 + 2 + 2^2 + 2^3 + 2^4)3^2 = 31(3^2)$$

The sum of *all* the factors (including 432) is the sum of the last row.

$$\text{Sum of all factors} = 31 + 31 \cdot 3 + 31 \cdot 3^2 + 31 \cdot 3^3 = 31(1 + 3 + 3^2 + 3^3) = 31(40) = 1240$$

To find the sum of the *proper* factors, we must subtract 432 from 1240; we get 808 (see "Take Note"). Thus, 432 is abundant.

We now look for some pattern for the sum of all the factors. Note that

Sum of left column $\quad 1 + 2 + 2^2 + 2^3 + 2^4 = \qquad \qquad = 1 + 3 + 3^2 + 3^3 \quad$ Sum of top row

$$31(40) = 1240$$

This suggests that the sum of the proper factors can be found by finding the sum of all the prime power factors for each prime, multiplying those numbers, and then subtracting the original number. Although we have not proved this for all cases, it is a true statement.

For instance, to find the sum of the proper factors of 3240, first find the prime factorization.

$$3240 = 2^3 \cdot 3^4 \cdot 5$$

Now find the following sums:

$$1 + 2 + 2^2 + 2^3 = 15 \qquad 1 + 3 + 3^2 + 3^3 + 3^4 = 121 \qquad 1 + 5 = 6$$

The sum of the proper factors $= (15)(121)6 - 3240 = 7650$.

Determine whether the number is deficient, abundant, or perfect.

1. 200   **2.** 3125   **3.** 8128   **4.** 10,000

5. Is a prime number deficient, abundant, or perfect?

Projects and Group Activities

Find a Pattern   The "Focus on Problem Solving" involved finding the sum of $1 + 3 + 3^2$ and $1 + 2 + 2^2 + 2^3$. For sums that contain a larger number of terms, it may be difficult or time consuming to try to evaluate the sum. Perhaps there is a pattern for these sums that can be used to calculate them without having to evaluate each exponential expression and then add the results.

Look at the following from the calculation of the sum of the factors of 3240.

$$1 + 2 + 2^2 + 2^3 = 1 + 2 + 4 + 8 = 15$$

$$\frac{2^{3+1} - 1}{2 - 1} = \frac{2^4 - 1}{1} = 16 - 1 = 15$$

$$1 + 3 + 3^2 + 3^3 + 3^4 = 1 + 3 + 9 + 27 + 81 = 121$$

$$\frac{3^{4+1} - 1}{3 - 1} = \frac{3^5 - 1}{2} = \frac{243 - 1}{2} = \frac{242}{2} = 121$$

Consider another sum of this type.

$$1 + 7 + 7^2 + 7^3 + 7^4 + 7^5 = 1 + 7 + 49 + 343 + 2401 + 16{,}807 = 19{,}608$$

$$\frac{7^{5+1} - 1}{7 - 1} = \frac{7^6 - 1}{6} = \frac{117{,}649 - 1}{6} = \frac{117{,}648}{6} = 19{,}608$$

On the basis of these examples shown above, make a conjecture as to the value of $1 + n + n^2 + n^3 + n^4 + \cdots + n^k$, where n and k are natural numbers greater than 1.

Solving a System of Equations with a Scientific Calculator   By using the addition method, it is possible to solve the system of equations.

$$\begin{aligned} ax + by &= c \\ dx + ey &= f \end{aligned}$$

 The solution is

$$x = \frac{ce - bf}{ae - bd} \qquad \text{and} \qquad y = \frac{af - cd}{ae - bd} \qquad \text{where } ae - bd \neq 0$$

Using this solution, a system of two equations in two variables can be solved with a calculator. It is helpful to observe that the denominators for both expressions are identical. The calculation for the denominator is done first and then stored in the calculator's memory. If the value of the denominator is zero, the system of equations is dependent or inconsistent, and this calculator method cannot be used.

Solve: $2x - 5y = 9$
 $4x + 3y = 2$

Make a list of the values of $a, b, c, d, e,$ and f.

$$a = 2 \qquad b = -5 \qquad c = 9$$
$$d = 4 \qquad e = 3 \qquad f = 2$$

Calculate the denominator
$D = ae - bd$.

2 $\boxed{\times}$ 3 $\boxed{-}$ 5 $\boxed{+/-}$ $\boxed{\times}$ 4 $\boxed{=}$ $\boxed{M+}$[1]

Find x. Replace the
variables in $x = \dfrac{ce - bf}{ae - bd}$
by their values.

$\boxed{(}$ 9 $\boxed{\times}$ 3 $\boxed{-}$ 5 $\boxed{+/-}$ $\boxed{\times}$ 2 $\boxed{)}$ $\boxed{\div}$ $\boxed{MR}$ $\boxed{=}$
The result should be approximately 1.423077.

Find y. Replace the
variables in $y = \dfrac{af - cd}{ae - bd}$
by their values.

$\boxed{(}$ 2 $\boxed{\times}$ 2 $\boxed{-}$ 9 $\boxed{\times}$ 4 $\boxed{)}$ $\boxed{\div}$ $\boxed{MR}$ $\boxed{=}$
The result should be approximately -1.230769.

The approximate solution is the ordered pair $(1.423077, -1.230769)$. The result is an approximation because the calculator display is an approximation to the exact result.

Solve by using a scientific calculator.

1. $3.29x + 4.17y = -2.34$
 $0.34x - 0.17y = 0.1$

2. $27x + 17y = 50$
 $4.5x - 9.2y = 18.3$

3. $y = \dfrac{2}{3}x - 4$

 $2x + y = 5$

4. $y = \dfrac{7}{4}x + 2$

 $y = \dfrac{2}{3}x - 3$

5.   Use the addition method to show that the solution of the system of equations
$\begin{aligned} ax + by &= c \\ dx + ey &= f \end{aligned}$ is given by $x = \dfrac{ce - bf}{ae - bd}$ and $y = \dfrac{af - cd}{ae - bd}$, where $ae - bd \neq 0$.

**Solving a System of
Equations with a
Graphing Calculator**

A graphing calculator can also be used to approximate the solution of a system of equations in two variables. Graph each equation of the system of equations, and then approximate the coordinates of the point of intersection. The process by which you approximate the solution depends on the model of calculator you have. In all cases, however, you must first solve each equation in the system of equations for y.

Solve: $2x - 5y = 9$
 $4x + 3y = 2$

Solve each equation for y.

$\begin{aligned} 2x - 5y &= 9 \\ -5y &= -2x + 9 \\ y &= \frac{2}{5}x - \frac{9}{5} \end{aligned}$
$\qquad\qquad$
$\begin{aligned} 4x + 3y &= 2 \\ 3y &= -4x + 2 \\ y &= -\frac{4}{3}x + \frac{2}{3} \end{aligned}$

[1]Some calculators use STO to store a result and use RCL to recall the result.

TI-83   Press $\boxed{Y=}$. Enter one equation as Y1 and the other equation as Y2. Press $\boxed{GRAPH}$. The intersection point must be shown in the viewing window. If it is not shown, adjust the viewing window. Press $\boxed{2nd}$ CALC 5 $\boxed{ENTER}$ $\boxed{ENTER}$ $\boxed{ENTER}$.

The point of intersection will show on the bottom of the screen as X = 1.4230769 Y = −1.230769.

Sharp EL-9600   Press $\boxed{Y=}$. Enter one equation as Y1 and the other equation as Y2. Press $\boxed{GRAPH}$. The point of intersection must be shown on the display. If it is not shown, adjust the viewing window. Press $\boxed{2ndF}$ CALC 2.

The point of intersection will show on the bottom of the screen as X = 1.4230769 Y = −1.230769.

Casio CFX 9850   Press $\boxed{MENU}$ 5. Enter one equation as Y1 and the other equation as Y2. Press $\boxed{F6}$. The intersection point must be shown in the viewing window. If it is not shown, adjust the viewing window. Press $\boxed{SHIFT}$ G-SOLV $\boxed{F5}$.

The point of intersection will show on the bottom of the screen as X = 1.4230769 Y = −1.230769.

Each of these calculators has a built-in method of solving a system of equations. For calculators without those methods, use the ZOOM and TRACE features of the calculator. Graph the two equations and then use the arrow keys to place the cursor near the intersection point. Then ZOOM in on the point of intersection, and use TRACE to determine the approximate coordinates. Each time you ZOOM in on the point of intersection, the solution of the system of equations becomes more accurate (up to the limits of the calculator).

Solve by using a graphing calculator.

1. $4x - 5y = 8$
$5x + 7y = 7$

2. $3x + 2y = 11$
$7x - 6y = 13$

3. $x = 3y + 2$
$y = 4x - 2$

4. $x = 2y - 5$
$x = 3y + 2$

Chapter Summary

Key Words   Equations considered together are called a *system of equations*.

A *solution of a system of equations in two variables* is an ordered pair that is a solution of each equation of the system.

An *independent system of equations* has one solution.

A *dependent system of equations* has an infinite number of solutions.

An *inconsistent system of equations* has no solution.

Essential Rules   A system of equations can be solved by the *graphing* method, the *substitution* method, or the *addition* method.

Annual Simple-Interest Equation

$I = Pr$, where I is the annual simple interest, P is the principal, and r is the annual interest rate as a decimal.

Chapter Review

1. Is $(-1, -3)$ a solution of this system of equations?
$5x + 4y = -17$
$2x - y = 1$

2. Is $(-2, 0)$ a solution of this system of equations?
$-x + 9y = 2$
$6x - 4y = 12$

3. Solve by graphing:
$3x - y = 6$
$y = -3$

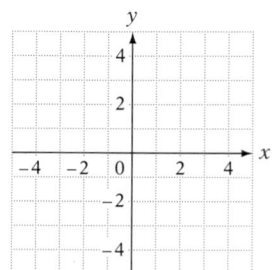

4. Solve by graphing:
$4x - 2y = 8$
$y = 2x - 4$

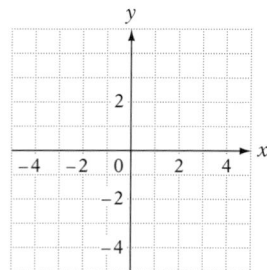

5. Solve by graphing:
$x + 2y = 3$
$y = -\dfrac{1}{2}x + 1$

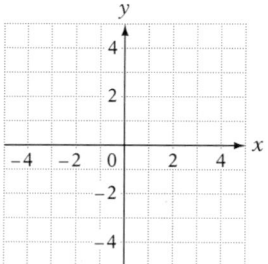

6. Solve by substitution:
$4x + 7y = 3$
$x = y - 2$

7. Solve by substitution:
$6x - y = 0$
$7x - y = 1$

8. Solve by the addition method:
$3x + 8y = -1$
$x - 2y = -5$

9. Solve by the addition method:
$6x + 4y = -3$
$12x - 10y = -15$

10. Solve by substitution:
$12x - 9y = 18$
$y = \dfrac{4}{3}x - 3$

11. Solve by substitution:
$8x - y = 2$
$y = 5x + 1$

12. Solve by the addition method:
$4x - y = 9$
$2x + 3y = -13$

13. Solve by the addition method:
$5x + 7y = 21$
$20x + 28y = 63$

14. Solve by substitution:
$4x + 3y = 12$
$y = -\dfrac{4}{3}x + 4$

15. Solve by substitution:
$$7x + 3y = -16$$
$$x - 2y = 5$$

16. Solve by the addition method:
$$3x + y = -2$$
$$-9x - 3y = 6$$

17. Solve by the addition method:
$$6x - 18y = 7$$
$$9x + 24y = 2$$

18. A sculling team rowing with the current went 24 mi in 2 h. Rowing against the current, the sculling team went 18 mi in 3 h. Find the rate of the sculling team in calm water and the rate of the current.

19. An investor bought 1500 shares of stock, some at $6 per share and the rest at $25 per share. If $12,800 worth of stock was purchased, how many shares of each kind did the investor buy?

20. A flight crew flew 420 km in 3 h with a tailwind. Flying against the wind, the flight crew flew 440 km in 4 h. Find the rate of the flight crew in calm air and the rate of the wind.

21. A small plane flying with the wind flew 360 mi in 3 h. Against a headwind, the plane took 4 h to fly the same distance. Find the rate of the plane in calm air and the rate of the wind.

22. A small wood carving company mailed 190 advertisements, some requiring $.25 postage and others $.45. The total cost for mailing was $59.50. Find the number of advertisements mailed at each rate.

23. A Terra Cotta Art Center receives an annual income of $915 from two simple-interest investments. One investment, in a corporate bond fund, earns 8.5% annual simple interest. The second investment, in a real estate investment trust, earns 7% annual simple interest. If the total amount invested in the two accounts is $12,000, how much is invested in each account?

24. A silo contains a mixture of lentils and corn. If 50 bushels of lentils were added, there would be twice as many bushels of lentils as of corn; if 150 bushels of corn were added instead, there would be the same amount of corn as of lentils. How many bushels of each were originally in the silo?

25. Mosher Children's Hospital received a $300,000 donation that it invested in two simple-interest accounts, one earning 5.4% and the other earning 6.6%. If each account earned the same amount of annual interest, how much was invested in each account?

Chapter Test

1. Is $(-2, 3)$ a solution of this system?
$$2x + 5y = 11$$
$$x + 3y = 7$$

2. Is $(1, -3)$ a solution of this system?
$$3x - 2y = 9$$
$$4x + y = 1$$

3. Solve by graphing: $3x + 2y = 6$
$$5x + 2y = 2$$

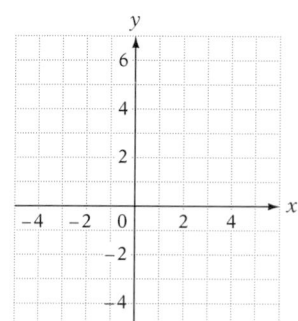

4. Solve by substitution:
$$4x - y = 11$$
$$y = 2x - 5$$

5. Solve by substitution:
$$x = 2y + 3$$
$$3x - 2y = 5$$

6. Solve by substitution:
$$3x + 5y = 1$$
$$2x - y = 5$$

7. Solve by substitution:
$$3x - 5y = 13$$
$$x + 3y = 1$$

8. Solve by substitution:
$$2x - 4y = 1$$
$$y = \frac{1}{2}x + 3$$

9. Solve by the addition method:
$$4x + 3y = 11$$
$$5x - 3y = 7$$

10. Solve by the addition method:
$$2x - 5y = 6$$
$$4x + 3y = -1$$

11. Solve by the addition method:

$x + 2y = 8$
$3x + 6y = 24$

12. Solve by the addition method:

$7x + 3y = 11$
$2x - 5y = 9$

13. Solve by the addition method:

$5x + 6y = -7$
$3x + 4y = -5$

14. With the wind, a plane flies 240 mi in 2 h. Against the wind, the plane requires 3 h to fly the same distance. Find the rate of the plane in calm air and the rate of the wind.

15. For the first performance of a play in a community theater, 50 reserved-seat tickets and 80 general-admission tickets were sold. The total receipts were $980. For the second performance, 60 reserved-seat tickets and 90 general-admission tickets were sold. The total receipts were $1140. Find the price of a reserved-seat ticket and the price of a general-admission ticket.

16. Bernardo Community Library received a $28,000 donation that it invested in two simple-interest accounts, one earning 7.6% and the other earning 6.4%. If each account earned the same amount of annual interest, how much was invested in each account?

Cumulative Review

1. Evaluate $\dfrac{a^2 - b^2}{2a}$ when $a = 4$ and $b = -2$.

2. Solve: $-\dfrac{3}{4}x = \dfrac{9}{8}$

3. Given $f(x) = x^2 + 2x - 1$, find $f(2)$.

4. Simplify: $(2a^2 - 3a + 1)(2 - 3a)$

5. Simplify: $\dfrac{(-2x^2y)^4}{-8x^3y^2}$

6. Simplify: $(4b^2 - 8b + 4) \div (2b - 3)$

7. Simplify: $\dfrac{8x^{-2}y^5}{-2xy^4}$

8. Factor: $4x^2y^4 - 64y^2$

9. Solve: $(x - 5)(x + 2) = -6$

10. Simplify: $\dfrac{x^2 - 6x + 8}{2x^3 + 6x^2} \div \dfrac{2x - 8}{4x^3 + 12x^2}$

11. Simplify: $\dfrac{x - 1}{x + 2} + \dfrac{2x + 1}{x^2 + x - 2}$

12. Simplify: $\dfrac{x + 4 - \dfrac{7}{x - 2}}{x + 8 + \dfrac{21}{x - 2}}$

13. Solve: $\dfrac{x}{2x - 3} + 2 = \dfrac{-7}{2x - 3}$

14. Solve $A = P + Prt$ for r.

15. Find the x- and y-intercepts for $2x - 3y = 12$.

16. Find the slope of the line that passes through the points $(2, -3)$ and $(-3, 4)$.

17. Find the equation of the line that passes through the point $(-2, 3)$ and has slope $-\dfrac{3}{2}$.

18. Is $(2, 0)$ a solution of this system?
$$5x - 3y = 10$$
$$4x + 7y = 8$$

19. Solve by substitution:
$3x - 5y = -23$
$x + 2y = -4$

20. Solve by the addition method:
$5x - 3y = 29$
$4x + 7y = -5$

21. A total of $8750 is invested in two simple-interest accounts. On one account, the annual simple interest rate is 9.6%; on the second account, the annual simple interest rate is 7.2%. How much should be invested in each account so that both accounts earn the same interest?

22. A passenger train leaves a train depot $\frac{1}{2}$ h after a freight train leaves the same depot. The freight train is traveling 8 mph slower than the passenger train. Find the rate of each train if the passenger train overtakes the freight train in 3 h.

23. The length of each side of a square is extended 4 in. The area of the resulting square is 144 in². Find the length of a side of the original square.

24. A plane can travel 160 mph in calm air. Flying with the wind, the plane can fly 570 mi in the same amount of time as it takes to fly 390 mi against the wind. Find the rate of the wind.

25. Graph $2x - 3y = 6$.

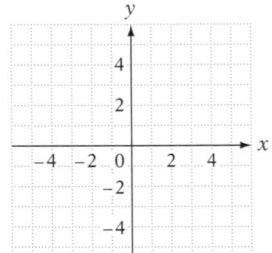

26. Solve by graphing: $3x + 2y = 6$
$3x - 2y = 6$

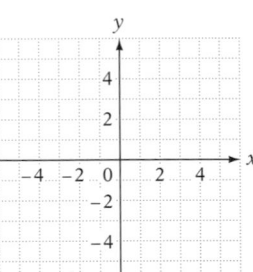

27. With the current, a motorboat can travel 48 mi in 3 h. Against the current, the boat requires 4 h to travel the same distance. Find the rate of the boat in calm water.

28. A child adds 8 g of sugar to a 50-gram serving of a breakfast cereal that is 25% sugar. What is now the percent concentration of sugar in the mixture? Round to the nearest tenth of a percent.

9

Inequalities

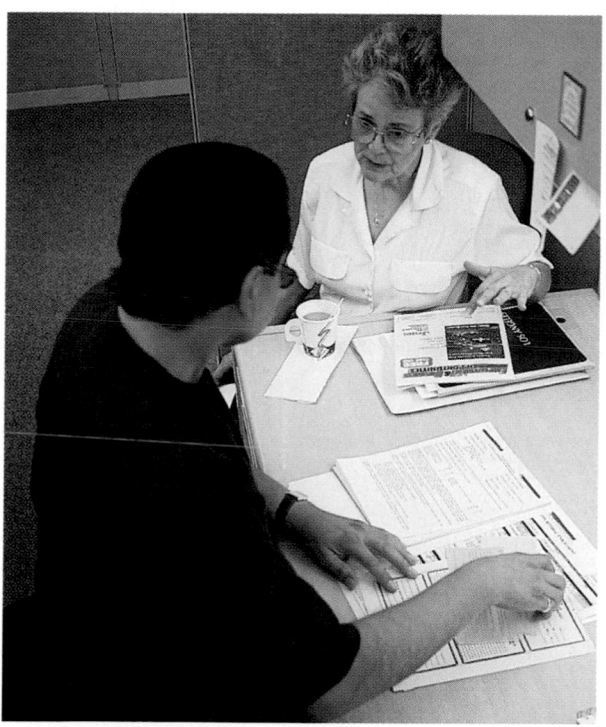

Objectives

Section 9.1
To write a set using the roster method
To write a set using set-builder notation
To graph an inequality on the number line

Section 9.2
To solve an inequality using the Addition Property of Inequalities
To solve an inequality using the Multiplication Property of Inequalities
To solve application problems

Section 9.3
To solve general inequalities
To solve application problems

Section 9.4
To graph an inequality in two variables

The human resources department of a company is involved in all areas of a company's dealings and relationships with its employees. One member of this department is the employee benefits manager, who is responsible for the selection and administration of such company programs as retirement packages, profit-sharing plans, and group medical insurance. Because a benefits officer must compare benefits packages, an understanding of inequalities is important.

Calculations of Pi

There are many early references to estimated values for pi. One of the earliest is from the Rhind Papyrus, which was found in Egypt in the 1800s. Scientists have estimated that these tablets were written around 1600 B.C. The Rhind Papyrus contains the estimate 3.1604 for pi.

One of the most famous calculations of pi occurred around 240 B.C. and was performed by Archimedes. The calculation was based on finding the perimeter of inscribed and circumscribed six-sided polygons (hexagons). Once the perimeter for a hexagonal figure was calculated, known formulas could be used to calculate the perimeter of polygons with twice that number of sides. Continuing in this way, Archimedes calculated the perimeters for polygons with 12, 24, 48, and 96 sides.

His calculations resulted in a value of pi between $3\frac{10}{71}$ and $3\frac{1}{7}$. You might recognize $3\frac{1}{7}$ or $\frac{22}{7}$, as an approximation for pi still used today.

Calculations to improve the accuracy of pi continued. One French mathematician, relying on Archimedes's method, estimated pi by using a polygon of 393,216 sides. A mathematician from the Netherlands estimated pi by using a polygon with over one million sides.

Around the 1650s, new mathematical methods were developed to estimate the value of pi. These methods started yielding estimates of pi that were accurate to over 70 places. By the 1850s, an estimate for pi was accurate to 200 places.

Today, thanks to more refined mathematical methods and computers, estimates of the value of pi now exceed one million places.

In 1914 an issue of *Scientific American* contained the following short note:

> "See, I have a rhyme assisting my feeble brain,
> its tasks oftimes resisting."

Can you see what this note has to do with the estimates for the value of pi?

(Each word length represents a digit in the approximation 3.141592653579.)

9.1 Sets

Objective A   *To write a set using the roster method* ....

Recall that a *set* is a collection of objects, which are called the *elements* of the set.

The **roster method** of writing a set encloses a list of the elements in braces.

The set of the last three letters of the alphabet is written {x, y, z}.

The set of the positive integers less than 5 is written {1, 2, 3, 4}.

➡ Use the roster method to write the set of integers between 0 and 10.

$A = \{1, 2, 3, 4, 5, 6, 7, 8, 9\}$ • **A set can be designated by a capital letter. Note that 0 and 10 are not elements of the set.**

➡ Use the roster method to write the set of natural numbers.

$A = \{1, 2, 3, 4, \ldots\}$ • **The three dots mean that the pattern of numbers continues without end.**

The **empty set,** or **null set,** is the set that contains no elements. The symbol ∅ or { } is used to represent the empty set.

The set of people who have run a 2-minute mile is the empty set.

The **union** of two sets, written $A \cup B$, is the set that contains the elements of A and the elements of B.

➡ Find $A \cup B$, given $A = \{1, 2, 3, 4\}$ and $B = \{3, 4, 5, 6\}$.

$A \cup B = \{1, 2, 3, 4, 5, 6\}$ • **The union of *A* and *B* contains all the elements of *A* and all the elements of *B*. Any elements that are in both *A* and *B* are listed only once.**

The **intersection** of two sets, written $A \cap B$, is the set that contains the elements that are common to both A and B.

➡ Find $A \cap B$, given $A = \{1, 2, 3, 4\}$ and $B = \{3, 4, 5, 6\}$.

$A \cap B = \{3, 4\}$ • **The intersection of *A* and *B* contains the elements common to *A* and *B*.**

Example 1

Use the roster method to write the set of the odd positive integers less than 12.

Solution

$A = \{1, 3, 5, 7, 9, 11\}$

You Try It 1

Use the roster method to write the set of the odd negative integers greater than −10.

Your solution

Solution on p. S21

Example 2
Use the roster method to write the set of the even positive integers.

Solution
$A = \{2, 4, 6, \ldots\}$

You Try It 2
Use the roster method to write the set of the odd positive integers.

Your solution

Example 3
Find $D \cup E$, given
$D = \{6, 8, 10, 12\}$ and
$E = \{-8, -6, 10, 12\}$.

Solution
$D \cup E = \{-8, -6, 6, 8, 10, 12\}$

You Try It 3
Find $A \cup B$, given
$A = \{-2, -1, 0, 1, 2\}$ and
$B = \{0, 1, 2, 3, 4\}$.

Your solution

Example 4
Find $A \cap B$, given
$A = \{5, 6, 9, 11\}$ and
$B = \{5, 9, 13, 15\}$.

Solution
$A \cap B = \{5, 9\}$

You Try It 4
Find $C \cap D$, given
$C = \{10, 12, 14, 16\}$ and
$D = \{10, 16, 20, 26\}$.

Your solution

Example 5
Find $A \cap B$, given
$A = \{1, 2, 3, 4\}$ and
$B = \{8, 9, 10, 11\}$.

Solution
$A \cap B = \varnothing$

You Try It 5
Find $A \cap B$, given
$A = \{-5, -4, -3, -2\}$ and
$B = \{2, 3, 4, 5\}$.

Your solution

Solutions on p. S21

Objective B **To write a set using set-builder notation** ....

POINT OF INTEREST

The symbol $\in$ was first used in the book *Arithmeticae Principia*, published in 1889. It was the first letter of the Greek word $\varepsilon\sigma\tau\iota$ which means "is." The symbols for union and intersection were also introduced at that time.

Another method of representing sets is called **set-builder notation.** Using set-builder notation, the set of all positive integers less than 10 is represented as

$\{x \,|\, x < 10, x \in \text{positive integers}\}$, which is read "the set of all x such that x is less than 10 and x is an element of the positive integers."

➡ Use set-builder notation to write the set of real numbers greater than 4.

$\{x \,|\, x > 4, x \in \text{real numbers}\}$

- "$x \in$ real numbers" is read "x is an element of the real numbers."

Example 6

Use set-builder notation to write the set of negative integers greater than -100.

Solution

$\{x | x > -100, x \in \text{negative integers}\}$

You Try It 6

Use set-builder notation to write the set of positive even integers less than 59.

Your solution

Example 7

Use set-builder notation to write the set of real numbers less than 60.

Solution

$\{x | x < 60, x \in \text{real numbers}\}$

You Try It 7

Use set-builder notation to write the set of real numbers greater than -3.

Your solution

Solutions on p. S21

Objective C   **To graph an inequality on the number line** ....

An expression that contains the symbol $>$, $<$, $\geq$ (is greater than or equal to), or $\leq$ (is less than or equal to) is called an **inequality.** An inequality expresses the relative order of two mathematical expressions. The expressions can be either numerical or variable.

$$\left.\begin{array}{l} 4 > 2 \\ 3x \leq 7 \\ x^2 - 2x > y + 4 \end{array}\right\} \text{Inequalities}$$

An **inequality** can be graphed on the number line.

➡ Graph: $x > 1$

The graph is the real numbers greater than 1. The circle at 1 indicates that 1 is not included in the graph.

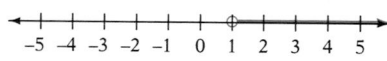

➡ Graph: $x \geq 1$

The dot at 1 indicates that 1 is included in the solution set.

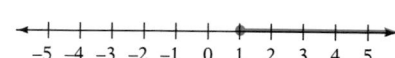

➡ Graph: $-1 > x$

$-1 > x$ is equivalent to $x < -1$. The numbers less than -1 are to the left of -1 on the number line.

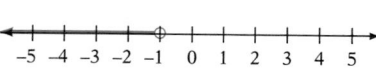

The union of two sets is the set that contains all the elements of each set.

➡ Graph: $\{x | x > 4\} \cup \{x | x < 1\}$

The graph is the numbers greater than 4 and the numbers less than 1.

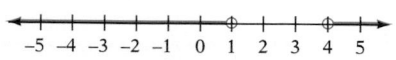

TAKE NOTE

For the remainder of this section, all variables will represent real numbers. Using this convention, the expression $\{x | x > 4, x \in \text{real numbers}\}$ will be written as $\{x | x > 4\}$, as shown in the example at the right.

The intersection of two sets is the set that contains the elements common to both sets.

➡ Graph: $\{x|x > -1\} \cap \{x|x < 2\}$

The graphs of $\{x|x > -1\}$ and $\{x|x < 2\}$ are shown at the right.

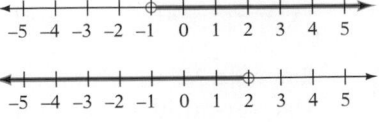

The graph of $\{x|x > -1\} \cap \{x|x < 2\}$ is the numbers between -1 and 2.

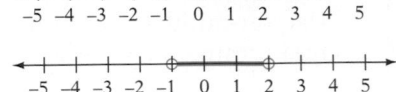

Example 8
Graph: $x < 5$

Solution
The graph is the numbers less than 5.

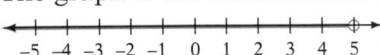

You Try It 8
Graph: $-2 < x$

Your solution

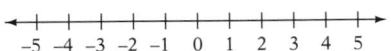

Example 9
Graph: $\{x|x > -2\} \cap \{x|x < 1\}$

Solution
The graph is the numbers between -2 and 1.

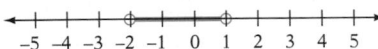

You Try It 9
Graph: $\{x|x > -1\} \cup \{x|x < -3\}$

Your solution

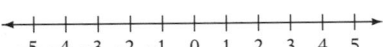

Example 10
Graph: $\{x|x \le 5\} \cup \{x|x \ge -3\}$

Solution
The graph is the real numbers.

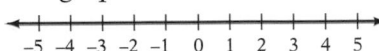

You Try It 10
Graph: $\{x|x < 2\} \cup \{x|\ge -2\}$

Your solution

Example 11
Graph: $\{x|x > 3\} \cup \{x|x < 1\}$

Solution
The graph is the numbers greater than 3 or the numbers less than 1.

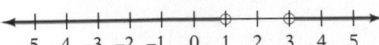

You Try It 11
Graph: $\{x|x \le 4\} \cap \{x|x \ge -4\}$

Your solution

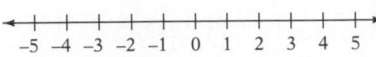

Solutions on p. S21

9.1 Exercises

· ·

Objective A

Use the roster method to write the set.

1. the integers between 15 and 22

2. the integers between −10 and −4

3. the odd integers between 8 and 18

4. the even integers between −11 and −1

5. the letters of the alphabet between a and d

6. the letters of the alphabet between p and v

Find $A \cup B$.

7. $A = \{3, 4, 5\}$ $B = \{4, 5, 6\}$

8. $A = \{-3, -2, -1\}$ $B = \{-2, -1, 0\}$

9. $A = \{-10, -9, -8\}$ $B = \{8, 9, 10\}$

10. $A = \{a, b, c\}$ $B = \{x, y, z\}$

11. $A = \{a, b, d, e\}$ $B = \{c, d, e, f\}$

12. $A = \{m, n, p, q\}$ $B = \{m, n, o\}$

13. $A = \{1, 3, 7, 9\}$ $B = \{7, 9, 11, 13\}$

14. $A = \{-3, -2, -1\}$ $B = \{-1, 1, 2\}$

Find $A \cap B$.

15. $A = \{3, 4, 5\}$ $B = \{4, 5, 6\}$

16. $A = \{-4, -3, -2\}$ $B = \{-6, -5, -4\}$

17. $A = \{-4, -3, -2\}$ $B = \{2, 3, 4\}$

18. $A = \{1, 2, 3, 4\}$ $B = \{1, 2, 3, 4\}$

19. $A = \{a, b, c, d, e\}$ $B = \{c, d, e, f, g\}$

20. $A = \{m, n, o, p\}$ $B = \{k, l, m, n\}$

Objective B

Use set-builder notation to write the set.

21. the negative integers greater than −5

22. the positive integers less than 5

23. the integers greater than 30

24. the integers less than −70

25. the even integers greater than 5

26. the odd integers less than −2

27. the real numbers greater than 8

28. the real numbers less than 57

Objective C

Graph.

29. $x > 2$

```
<——+——+——+——+——+——+——+——+——+——+——+——>
   −5  −4  −3  −2  −1   0   1   2   3   4   5
```

30. $x \geq -1$

```
<——+——+——+——+——+——+——+——+——+——+——+——>
   −5  −4  −3  −2  −1   0   1   2   3   4   5
```

31. $0 \geq x$

```
<——+——+——+——+——+——+——+——+——+——+——+——>
   −5  −4  −3  −2  −1   0   1   2   3   4   5
```

32. $4 > x$

```
<——+——+——+——+——+——+——+——+——+——+——+——>
   −5  −4  −3  −2  −1   0   1   2   3   4   5
```

33. $\{x \,|\, x > -2\} \cup \{x \,|\, x < -4\}$

```
<——+——+——+——+——+——+——+——+——+——+——+——>
   −5  −4  −3  −2  −1   0   1   2   3   4   5
```

34. $\{x \,|\, x > 4\} \cup \{x \,|\, x < -2\}$

```
<——+——+——+——+——+——+——+——+——+——+——+——>
   −5  −4  −3  −2  −1   0   1   2   3   4   5
```

35. $\{x \,|\, x > -2\} \cap \{x < 4\}$

```
<——+——+——+——+——+——+——+——+——+——+——+——>
   −5  −4  −3  −2  −1   0   1   2   3   4   5
```

36. $\{x \,|\, x > -3\} \cap \{x \,|\, x < 3\}$

```
<——+——+——+——+——+——+——+——+——+——+——+——>
   −5  −4  −3  −2  −1   0   1   2   3   4   5
```

37. $\{x \,|\, x \geq -2\} \cup \{x \,|\, x < 4\}$

```
<——+——+——+——+——+——+——+——+——+——+——+——>
   −5  −4  −3  −2  −1   0   1   2   3   4   5
```

38. $\{x \,|\, x > 0\} \cup \{x \,|\, x \leq 4\}$

```
<——+——+——+——+——+——+——+——+——+——+——+——>
   −5  −4  −3  −2  −1   0   1   2   3   4   5
```

APPLYING THE CONCEPTS

39. Explain how to find the union of two sets.

40. Explain how to find the intersection of two sets.

41. Determine whether the statement is always true, sometimes true, or never true.
   a. Given that $a > 0$ and $b < 0$, then $ab > 0$.
   b. Given that $a < 0$, then $a^2 > 0$.
   c. Given that $a > 0$ and $b < 0$, then $a^2 > b$.

42. By trying various sets, make a conjecture as to whether the union of two sets is
   a. a commutative operation
   b. an associative operation

43. By trying various sets, make a conjecture as to whether the intersection of two sets is
   a. a commutative operation
   b. an associative operation

9.2 The Addition and Multiplication Properties of Inequalities

Objective A   *To solve an inequality using the Addition Property of Inequalities* ....

The **solution set of an inequality** is a set of numbers, each element of which, when substituted for the variable, results in a true inequality.

The inequality at the right is true if the variable is replaced by 7, 9.3, or $\frac{15}{2}$.

$$x + 5 > 8$$

$$\left.\begin{array}{c} 7 + 5 > 8 \\ 9.3 + 5 > 8 \\ \frac{15}{2} + 5 > 8 \end{array}\right\} \text{True inequalities}$$

The inequality $x + 5 > 8$ is false if the variable is replaced by 2, 1.5, or $-\frac{1}{2}$.

$$\left.\begin{array}{c} 2 + 5 > 8 \\ 1.5 + 5 > 8 \\ -\frac{1}{2} + 5 > 8 \end{array}\right\} \text{False inequalities}$$

There are many values of the variable x that will make the inequality $x + 5 > 8$ true. The solution set of $x + 5 > 8$ is any number greater than 3.

At the right is the graph of the solution set of $x + 5 > 8$.

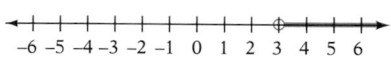

In solving an inequality, the goal is to rewrite the given inequality in the form *variable > constant* or *variable < constant*. The Addition Property of Inequalities is used to rewrite an inequality in this form.

Addition Property of Inequalities

The same term can be added to each side of an inequality without changing the solution set of the inequality.

If $a > b$, then $a + c > b + c$.
If $a < b$, then $a + c < b + c$.

The Addition Property of Inequalities also holds true for an inequality containing the symbol $\geq$ or $\leq$.

The Addition Property of Inequalities is used when, in order to rewrite an inequality in the form *variable > constant* or *variable < constant*, we must remove a term from one side of the inequality. Add the opposite of that term to each side of the inequality.

➡ Solve: $x - 4 < -3$

$$x - 4 < -3$$
$$x - 4 + 4 < -3 + 4 \qquad \bullet \text{ Add 4 to each side of the inequality.}$$
$$x < 1 \qquad\qquad \bullet \text{ Simplify.}$$

At the right is the graph of the solution set of $x - 4 < -3$.

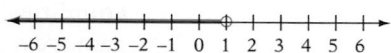

Because subtraction is defined in terms of addition, the Addition Property of Inequalities allows the same term to be subtracted from each side of an inequality.

➡ Solve: $5x - 6 \leq 4x - 4$

$$5x - 6 \leq 4x - 4$$

$$5x - 4x - 6 \leq 4x - 4x - 4$$ • Subtract 4*x* from each side of the inequality.

$$x - 6 \leq -4$$ • Simplify.

$$x - 6 + 6 \leq -4 + 6$$ • Add 6 to each side of the inequality.

$$x \leq 2$$ • Simplify.

Example 1

Solve and graph the solution set of $3 < x + 5$.

Solution

$$3 < x + 5$$
$$3 - 5 < x + 5 - 5$$
$$-2 < x$$

Example 2

Solve: $7x - 14 \leq 6x - 16$

Solution

$$7x - 14 \leq 6x - 16$$
$$7x - 6x - 14 \leq 6x - 6x - 16$$
$$x - 14 \leq -16$$
$$x - 14 + 14 \leq -16 + 14$$
$$x \leq -2$$

You Try It 1

Solve and graph the solution set of $x + 2 < -2$.

Your solution

You Try It 2

Solve: $5x + 3 > 4x + 5$

Your solution

Solutions on pp. S21–S22

Objective B **To solve an inequality using the Multiplication Property of Inequalities** ....

In solving an inequality, the goal is to rewrite the given inequality in the form *variable > constant* or *variable < constant*. The Multiplication Property of Inequalities is used when, in order to rewrite an inequality in this form, we must remove a coefficient from one side of the inequality.

> **Multiplication Property of Inequalities**
>
> Each side of an inequality can be multiplied by the same positive number without changing the solution set of the inequality.
>
> If $a > b$ and $c > 0$, then $ac > bc$.
> If $a < b$ and $c > 0$, then $ac < bc$.
>
> If each side of an inequality is multiplied by the same negative number and the inequality symbol is reversed, then the solution set of the inequality is not changed.
>
> If $a > b$ and $c < 0$, then $ac < bc$.
> If $a < b$ and $c < 0$, then $ac > bc$.

TAKE NOTE

Any time an inequality is multiplied or divided by a negative number, the inequality symbol must be reversed. Compare the next two examples.

$2x < -4$ Divide each side
$\dfrac{2x}{2} < \dfrac{-4}{2}$ by *positive* 2.
  Inequality *is not*
$x < -2$ reversed.

$-2x < 4$ Divide each side
$\dfrac{-2x}{-2} > \dfrac{4}{-2}$ by *negative* 2.
  Inequality *is*
$x > -2$ reversed.

$$5 > 4$$
$$5(2) > 4(2) \qquad \text{• Multiply by \emph{positive} 2.}$$
$$10 > 8 \qquad \text{• Still a true inequality}$$

$$6 < 9$$
$$6(-3) > 9(-3) \qquad \text{• Multiply by \emph{negative} 3 and \emph{reverse} the inequality.}$$
$$-18 > -27 \qquad \text{• Still a true inequality}$$

The Multiplication Property of Inequalities also holds true for an inequality containing the symbol $\geq$ or $\leq$.

➡ Solve $-\dfrac{3}{2}x \leq 6$ and graph the solution set.

$$-\frac{3}{2}x \leq 6$$

• Multiply each side of the inequality by $-\dfrac{2}{3}$.

$$-\frac{2}{3}\left(-\frac{3}{2}x\right) \geq -\frac{2}{3}(6)$$

Because $-\dfrac{2}{3}$ is a negative number, the inequality symbol must be reversed.

$$x \geq -4$$

• Graph $x \geq -4$.

Because division is defined in terms of multiplication, the Multiplication Property of Inequalities allows each side of an inequality to be divided by a nonzero constant.

➡ Solve: $-4 < 6x$

$$-4 < 6x$$
$$\frac{-4}{6} < \frac{6x}{6} \qquad \text{• Divide each side of the inequality by 6.}$$
$$-\frac{2}{3} < x \qquad \text{• Simplify: } \frac{-4}{6} = -\frac{2}{3}$$

Example 3 Solve and graph the solution set of $-7x > 14$.

Solution $-7x > 14$

$$\frac{-7x}{-7} < \frac{14}{-7}$$

$$x < -2$$

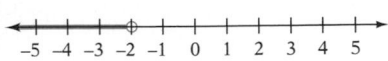

You Try It 3 Solve and graph the solution set of $-3x > -9$.

Your solution

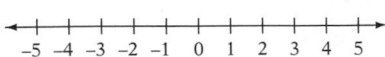

Example 4 Solve: $-\dfrac{5}{8}x \le \dfrac{5}{12}$

Solution $-\dfrac{5}{8}x \le \dfrac{5}{12}$

$$-\frac{8}{5}\left(-\frac{5}{8}x\right) \ge -\frac{8}{5}\left(\frac{5}{12}\right)$$

$$x \ge -\frac{2}{3}$$

You Try It 4 Solve: $-\dfrac{3}{4}x \ge 18$

Your solution

Solutions on p. S22

Objective C *To solve application problems* ....

Example 5
A student must have at least 450 points out of 500 points on five tests to receive an A in a course. One student's results on the first four tests were 94, 87, 77, and 95. What scores on the last test will enable this student to receive an A in the course?

Strategy
To find the scores, write and solve an inequality using N to represent the possible scores on the last test.

Solution

Total number of points on the 5 tests	is greater than or equal to	450

$$94 + 87 + 77 + 95 + N \ge 450$$
$$353 + N \ge 450$$
$$353 - 353 + N \ge 450 - 353$$
$$N \ge 97$$

The student's score on the last test must be equal to or greater than 97.

You Try It 5
An appliance dealer will make a profit on the sale of a television set if the cost of the new set is less than 70% of the selling price. What selling prices will enable the dealer to make a profit on a television set that costs the dealer $314?

Your strategy

Your solution

Solution on p. S22

9.2 Exercises

· ·

Objective A

Solve and graph the solution set.

1. $x + 1 < 3$

2. $y + 2 < 2$

3. $x - 5 > -2$

4. $x - 3 > -2$

5. $7 \leq n + 4$

6. $3 \leq 5 + x$

7. $x - 6 \leq -10$

8. $y - 8 \leq -11$

Solve.

9. $y - 3 \geq -12$

10. $x + 8 \geq -14$

11. $3x - 5 < 2x + 7$

12. $5x + 4 < 4x - 10$

13. $8x - 7 \geq 7x - 2$

14. $3n - 9 \geq 2n - 8$

15. $2x + 4 < x - 7$

16. $9x + 7 < 8x - 7$

17. $4x - 8 \leq 2 + 3x$

18. $5b - 9 < 3 + 4b$

19. $6x + 4 \geq 5x - 2$

20. $7x - 3 \geq 6x - 2$

21. $2x - 12 > x - 10$

22. $3x + 9 > 2x + 7$

23. $d + \dfrac{1}{2} < \dfrac{1}{3}$

24. $x - \dfrac{3}{8} < \dfrac{5}{6}$

25. $x + \dfrac{5}{8} \geq -\dfrac{2}{3}$

26. $y + \dfrac{5}{12} \geq -\dfrac{3}{4}$

27. $x - \dfrac{3}{8} < \dfrac{1}{4}$

28. $y + \dfrac{5}{9} \leq \dfrac{5}{6}$

29. $2x - \dfrac{1}{2} < x + \dfrac{3}{4}$

30. $6x - \dfrac{1}{3} \leq 5x - \dfrac{1}{2}$

31. $3x + \dfrac{5}{8} > 2x + \dfrac{5}{6}$

32. $4b - \dfrac{7}{12} \geq 3b - \dfrac{9}{16}$

33. $3.8x < 2.8x - 3.8$

34. $1.2x < 0.2x - 7.3$

35. $x + 5.8 \leq 4.6$

36. $n - 3.82 \leq 3.95$

37. $x - 3.5 < 2.1$

38. $x - 0.23 \leq 0.47$

Objective B

Solve and graph the solution set.

39. $3x < 12$

40. $8x \leq -24$

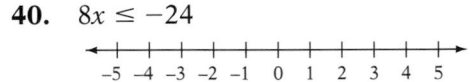

41. $15 \leq 5y$

42. $-48 < 24x$

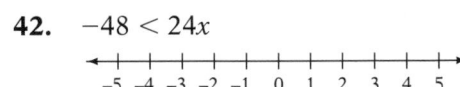

43. $16x \leq 16$

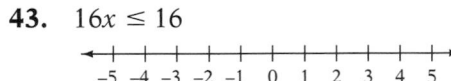

44. $3x > 0$

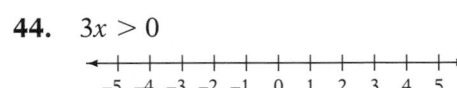

45. $-8x > 8$

46. $-2n \leq -8$

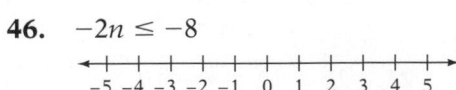

47. $-6b > 24$

48. $-4x < 8$

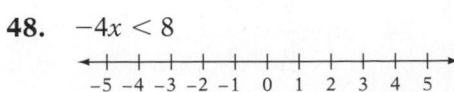

49. $-5y \geq 0$ **50.** $-3z < 0$ **51.** $7x > 2$ **52.** $6x \leq -1$

53. $2x \leq -5$ **54.** $\frac{5}{6}n < 15$ **55.** $\frac{3}{4}x < 12$ **56.** $\frac{2}{3}y \geq 4$

57. $10 \leq \frac{5}{8}x$ **58.** $4 \geq \frac{2}{3}x$ **59.** $-\frac{3}{7}x \leq 6$ **60.** $-\frac{2}{11}b \geq -6$

61. $-\frac{4}{7}x \geq -12$ **62.** $\frac{2}{3}n < \frac{1}{2}$ **63.** $-\frac{3}{5}x < 0$ **64.** $-\frac{2}{3}x \geq 0$

65. $-\frac{3}{8}x \geq \frac{9}{14}$ **66.** $-\frac{3}{5}x < -\frac{6}{7}$ **67.** $-\frac{4}{5}x < -\frac{8}{15}$ **68.** $-\frac{3}{4}y \geq -\frac{5}{8}$

69. $-\frac{8}{9}x \geq -\frac{16}{27}$ **70.** $1.5x \leq 6.30$ **71.** $2.3x \leq 5.29$ **72.** $-3.5d > 7.35$

73. $-0.24x > 0.768$ **74.** $4.25m > -34$ **75.** $-3.9x \geq -19.5$

Objective C *Application Problems*

76. Three-fifths of a number is greater than two-thirds. Find the smallest integer that satisfies this inequality.

77. To be eligible for a basketball tournament, a basketball team must win at least 60% of its remaining games. If the team has 17 games remaining, how many games must the team win to qualify for the tournament?

78. To avoid a tax penalty, at least 90% of a self-employed person's total annual income tax liability must be paid by April 15. What amount of income tax must a person with an annual income tax liability of $3500 pay?

79. A service organization will receive a bonus of $200 for collecting more than 1850 lb of aluminum cans during its four collection drives. On the first three drives, the organization collected 505 lb, 493 lb, and 412 lb. How many pounds of cans must the organization collect on the fourth drive to receive the bonus?

80. Computer software engineers are fond of saying that software takes at least twice as long to develop as they think it will. Applying that saying, how many hours will it take to develop a software product that an engineer thinks can be finished in 50 h?

81. A government agency recommends a minimum daily allowance of vitamin C of 60 mg. How many additional milligrams of vitamin C does a person who drank a glass of orange juice with 10 mg of vitamin C need in order to satisfy the recommended daily allowance?

82. To pass a course with a B grade, a student must have an average of 80 points on five tests. The student's grades on the first four tests were 75, 83, 86, and 78. What scores can the student receive on the fifth test to earn a B grade?

83. A professor scores all tests with a maximum of 100 points. To earn an A grade in this course, a student must have an average of 92 on four tests. A student's grades on the first three tests were 89, 86, and 90. Can this student earn an A grade?

84. A health official recommends a maximum cholesterol level of 200 units. How many units must a patient with a cholesterol level of 275 units reduce her cholesterol level to satisfy the recommended maximum level?

APPLYING THE CONCEPTS

Given that $a > b$ and that a and b are real numbers, determine for which real numbers c the statement is true. Use set-builder notation to write the answer.

85. $ac > bc$

86. $ac < bc$

87. $a + c > b + c$

88. $a + c < b + c$

89. $\dfrac{a}{c} > \dfrac{b}{c}$

90. $\dfrac{a}{c} < \dfrac{b}{c}$

91. In your own words, state the Addition Property of Inequalities.

92. In your own words, state the Multiplication Property of Inequalities.

9.3 General Inequalities

Objective A   *To solve general inequalities* ....

Solving an inequality frequently requires application of both the Addition and the Multiplication Properties of Inequalities.

⇒ Solve: $4y - 3 \geq 6y + 5$

$$4y - 3 \geq 6y + 5$$

$$4y - 6y - 3 \geq 6y - 6y + 5$$ • Subtract 6y from each side of the inequality.

$$-2y - 3 \geq 5$$ • Simplify.

$$-2y - 3 + 3 \geq 5 + 3$$ • Add 3 to each side of the inequality.

$$-2y \geq 8$$ • Simplify.

$$\frac{-2y}{-2} \leq \frac{8}{-2}$$ • Divide each side of the inequality by −2.

$$y \leq -4$$ Because −2 is a negative number, the inequality symbol must be reversed.

When an inequality contains parentheses, one of the steps in solving the inequality requires the use of the Distributive Property.

⇒ Solve: $-2(x - 7) > 3 - 4(2x - 3)$

$$-2(x - 7) > 3 - 4(2x - 3)$$

$$-2x + 14 > 3 - 8x + 12$$ • Use the Distributive Property to remove parentheses.

$$-2x + 14 > -8x + 15$$ • Simplify.

$$-2x + 8x + 14 > -8x + 8x + 15$$ • Add 8x to each side of the inequality.

$$6x + 14 > 15$$ • Simplify.

$$6x + 14 - 14 > 15 - 14$$ • Subtract 14 from each side of the inequality.

$$6x > 1$$ • Simplify.

$$\frac{6x}{6} > \frac{1}{6}$$ • Divide each side of the inequality by 6.

$$x > \frac{1}{6}$$

Example 1   Solve: $7x - 3 \leq 3x + 17$

Solution
$$7x - 3 \leq 3x + 17$$
$$7x - 3x - 3 \leq 3x - 3x + 17$$
$$4x - 3 \leq 17$$
$$4x - 3 + 3 \leq 17 + 3$$
$$4x \leq 20$$
$$\frac{4x}{4} \leq \frac{20}{4}$$
$$x \leq 5$$

You Try It 1   Solve: $5 - 4x > 9 - 8x$

Your solution

Solution on p. S22

Example 2

Solve:

$3(3 - 2x) \geq -5x - 2(3 - x)$

Solution

$$3(3 - 2x) \geq -5x - 2(3 - x)$$
$$9 - 6x \geq -5x - 6 + 2x$$
$$9 - 6x \geq -3x - 6$$
$$9 - 6x + 3x \geq -3x + 3x - 6$$
$$9 - 3x \geq -6$$
$$9 - 9 - 3x \geq -6 - 9$$
$$-3x \geq -15$$
$$\frac{-3x}{-3} \leq \frac{-15}{-3}$$
$$x \leq 5$$

You Try It 2

Solve:

$8 - 4(3x + 5) \leq 6(x - 8)$

Your solution

Solution on p. S22

Objective B   To solve application problems ....

Example 3

A rectangle is 10 ft wide and $(2x + 4)$ ft long. Express as an integer the maximum length of the rectangle when the area is less than 200 ft². (The area of a rectangle is equal to its length times its width.)

Strategy

To find the maximum length:

• Replace the variables in the area formula by the given values and solve for x.

• Replace the variable in the expression $2x + 4$ with the value found for x.

Solution

Length times width	is less than	200 ft²

$$10(2x + 4) < 200$$
$$20x + 40 < 200$$
$$20x + 40 - 40 < 200 - 40$$
$$20x < 160$$
$$\frac{20x}{20} < \frac{160}{20}$$
$$x < 8$$

The length is $(2x + 4)$ ft. Because $x < 8$, $2x + 4 < 2(8) + 4 = 20$. Therefore, the length is less than 20 ft. The maximum length is 19 ft.

You Try It 3

Company A rents cars for $8 a day and $.10 for every mile driven. Company B rents cars for $10 a day and $.08 per mile driven. You want to rent a car for one week. What is the maximum number of miles you can drive a Company A car if it is to cost you less than a Company B car?

Your strategy

Your solution

Solution on p. S22

9.3 Exercises

Objective A

Solve.

1. $4x - 8 < 2x$

2. $7x - 4 < 3x$

3. $2x - 8 > 4x$

4. $3y + 2 > 7y$

5. $8 - 3x \le 5x$

6. $10 - 3x \le 7x$

7. $3x + 2 > 5x - 8$

8. $2n - 9 \ge 5n + 4$

9. $5x - 2 < 3x - 2$

10. $8x - 9 > 3x - 9$

11. $0.1(180 + x) > x$

12. $x > 0.2(50 + x)$

13. $2(2y - 5) \le 3(5 - 2y)$

14. $2(5x - 8) \le 7(x - 3)$

15. $5(2 - x) > 3(2x - 5)$

16. $4(3d - 1) > 3(2 - 5d)$

17. $4 - 3(3 - n) \le 3(2 - 5n)$

18. $15 - 5(3 - 2x) \le 4(x - 3)$

19. $2x - 3(x - 4) \ge 4 - 2(x - 7)$

20. $4 + 2(3 - 2y) \le 4(3y - 5) - 6y$

Objective B   *Application Problems*

21. The sales agent for a jewelry company is offered a flat monthly salary of $3200 or a salary of $1000 plus an 11% commission on the selling price of each item sold by the agent. If the agent chooses the $3200, what dollar amount does the agent expect to sell in one month?

22. A baseball player is offered an annual salary of $200,000 or a base salary of $100,000 plus a bonus of $1000 for each hit over 100 hits. How many hits must the baseball player make to earn more than $200,000?

23. A computer bulletin board service charges a flat fee of $10 per month or a fee of $4 per month plus $.10 for each minute the service is used. How many minutes must a person use this service to exceed $10?

24. A site licensing fee for a computer program is $1500. Paying this fee allows the company to use the program at any computer terminal within the company. Alternatively, the company can choose to pay $200 for each individual computer it has. How many individual computers must a company have for the site license to be more economical for the company?

25. For a product to be labeled orange juice, a state agency requires that at least 80% of the drink be real orange juice. How many ounces of artificial flavors can be added to 32 oz of real orange juice and have it still be legal to label the drink orange juice?

26. Grade A hamburger cannot contain more than 20% fat. How much fat can a butcher mix with 300 lb of lean meat to meet the 20% requirement?

27. A shuttle service taking skiers to a ski area charges $8 per person each way. Four skiers are debating whether to take the shuttle bus or rent a car for $45 plus $.25 per mile. Assuming that the skiers will share the cost of the car and that they want the least expensive method of transportation, find how far away the ski area is if they choose the shuttle service.

APPLYING THE CONCEPTS

28. Determine whether the statement is always true, sometimes true, or never true, given that a, b, and c are real numbers.
    a. If $a > b$, then $-a > -b$.
    b. If $a < b$, then $ac < bc$.
    c. If $a > b$, then $a + c > b + c$.
    d. If $a \neq 0$, $b \neq 0$, and $a > b$, then $\frac{1}{a} > \frac{1}{b}$.

Use the roster method to list the set of positive integers that are solutions of the inequality.

29. $7 - 2b \leq 15 - 5b$

30. $-6(2 - d) \geq 4d - 9$

Use the roster method to list the set of integers that are common to the solution sets of the two inequalities.

31. $5x - 12 \leq x + 8$
    $3x - 4 \geq 2 + x$

32. $3(x + 2) > 9x - 2$
    $4(x + 5) > 3(x + 6)$

33. Determine the solution set of $2 - 3(x + 4) < 5 - 3x$.

34. Determine the solution set of $3x + 2(x - 1) > 5(x + 1)$.

9.4 Graphing Linear Inequalities

Objective A   *To graph an inequality in two variables* ....

The graph of the linear equation $y = x - 2$ separates a plane into three sets:

the set of points on the line
the set of points above the line
the set of points below the line

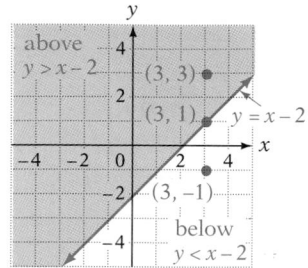

The point $(3, 1)$ is a solution of $y = x - 2$.

$$y = x - 2$$
$$\frac{1 \mid 3 - 2}{}$$
$$1 = 1$$

The point $(3, 3)$ is a solution of $y > x - 2$.

$$y > x - 2$$
$$\frac{3 \mid 3 - 2}{}$$
$$3 > 1$$

Any point above the line is a solution of $y > x - 2$.

The point $(3, -1)$ is a solution of $y < x - 2$.

$$y < x - 2$$
$$\frac{-1 \mid 3 - 2}{}$$
$$-1 < 1$$

Any point below the line is a solution of $y < x - 2$.

The solution set of $y = x - 2$ is all points on the line. The solution set of $y > x - 2$ is all points above the line. The solution set of $y < x - 2$ is all points below the line. The solution set of an inequality in two variables is a **half-plane.**

The following illustrates the procedure for graphing a linear inequality.

⇒ Graph the solution set of $2x + 3y \leq 6$.

Solve the inequality for y.

$$2x + 3y \leq 6$$
$$2x - 2x + 3y \leq -2x + 6$$ • Subtract 2x from each side.
$$3y \leq -2x + 6$$ • Simplify.
$$\frac{3y}{3} \leq \frac{-2x + 6}{3}$$ • Divide each side by 3.
$$y \leq -\frac{2}{3}x + 2$$ • Simplify.

Change the inequality to an equality and graph $y = -\frac{2}{3}x + 2$. If the inequality is ≥ or ≤, the line is in the solution set and is shown by a **solid line.** If the inequality is > or <, the line is not a part of the solution set and is shown by a **dotted line.**

If the inequality is > or ≥, shade the **upper half-plane.** If the inequality is < or ≤, shade the **lower half-plane.**

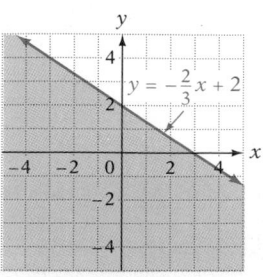

Example 1
Graph the solution set of $3x + y > -2$.

Solution
$$3x + y > -2$$
$$3x - 3x + y > -3x - 2$$
$$y > -3x - 2$$

Graph $y = -3x - 2$ as a dotted line.
Shade the upper half-plane.

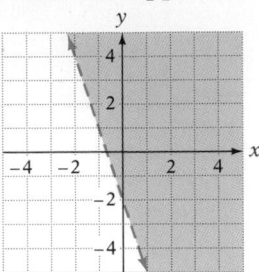

Example 2
Graph the solution set of $2x - y \geq 2$.

Solution
$$2x - y \geq 2$$
$$2x - 2x - y \geq -2x + 2$$
$$-y \geq -2x + 2$$
$$-1(-y) \leq -1(-2x + 2)$$
$$y \leq 2x - 2$$

Graph $y = 2x - 2$ as a solid line. Shade
the lower half-plane.

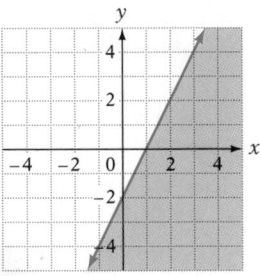

Example 3
Graph the solution set of $y > 3$.

Solution
Graph $y = 3$ as a dotted line.
Shade the upper half-plane.

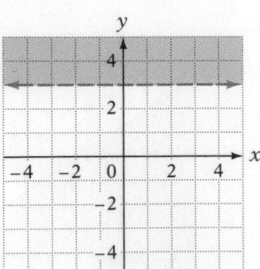

You Try It 1
Graph the solution set of $x - 3y < 2$.

Your solution

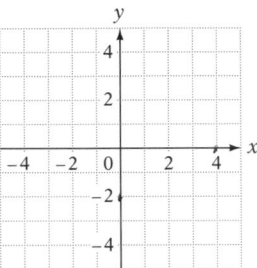

You Try It 2
Graph the solution set of $2x - 4y \leq 8$.

Your solution

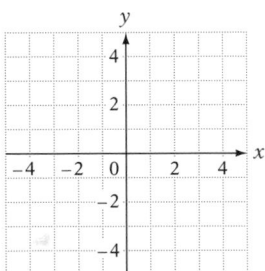

You Try It 3
Graph the solution set of $x < 3$.

Your solution

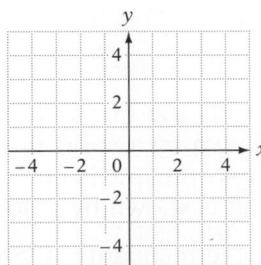

Solutions on pp. S22–S23

9.4 Exercises

Objective A

Graph the solution set.

1. $x + y > 4$

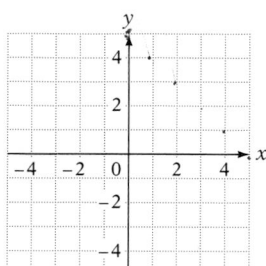

2. $x - y > -3$

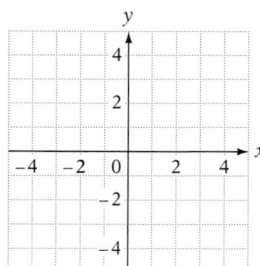

3. $2x - y < -3$

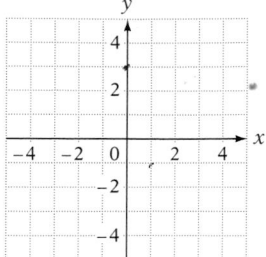

4. $3x - y < 9$

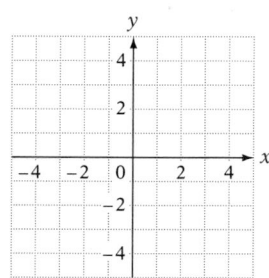

5. $2x + y \geq 4$

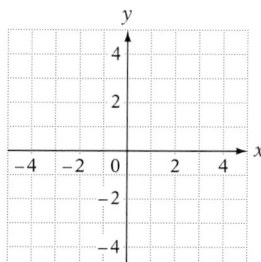

6. $3x + y \geq 6$

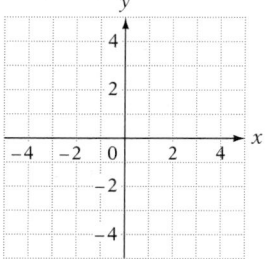

7. $y \leq -2$

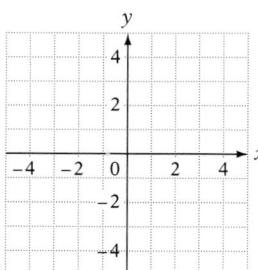

8. $y > 3$

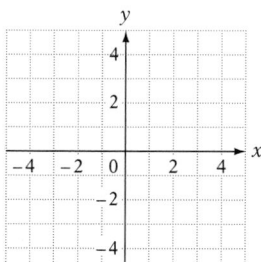

9. $3x - 2y < 8$

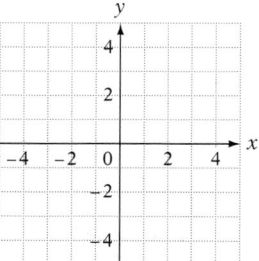

10. $5x + 4y > 4$

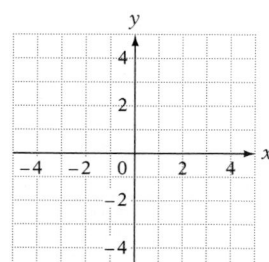

11. $-3x - 4y \geq 4$

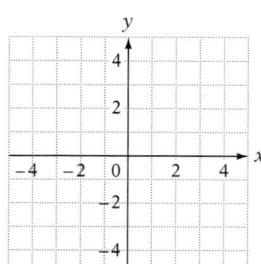

12. $-5x - 2y \geq 8$

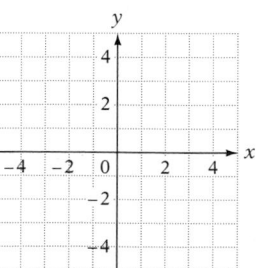

13. $6x + 5y \le -10$

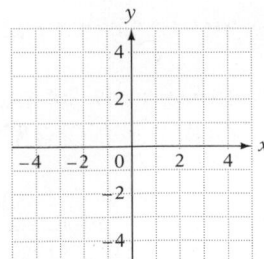

14. $2x + 2y \le -4$

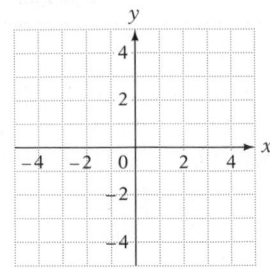

15. $-4x + 3y < -12$

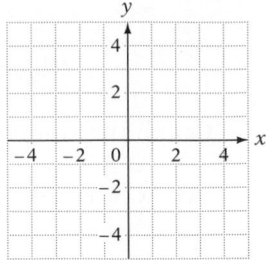

16. $-4x + 5y < 15$

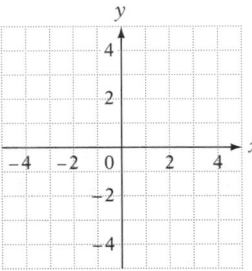

17. $-2x + 3y \le 6$

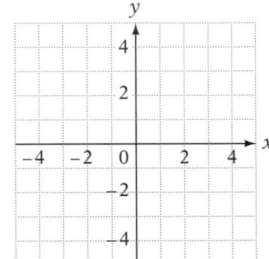

18. $3x - 4y > 12$

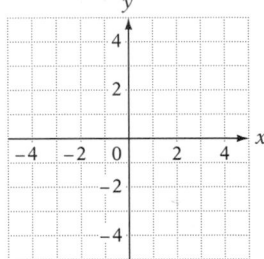

APPLYING THE CONCEPTS

Graph the solution set.

19. $\dfrac{x}{4} + \dfrac{y}{2} > 1$

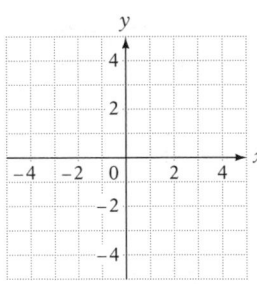

20. $2x - 3(y + 1) > y - (4 - x)$

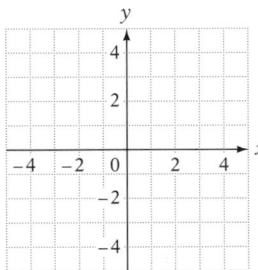

21. $4y - 2(x + 1) \ge 3(y - 1) + 3$

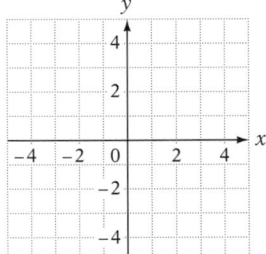

Write the inequality given its graph.

22.

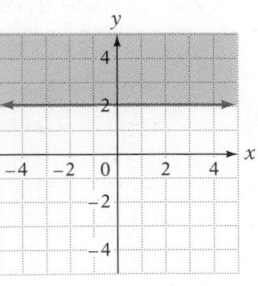

23.

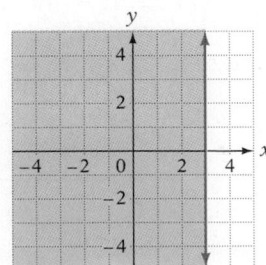

24.

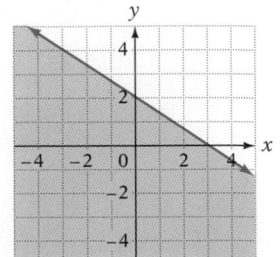

Focus on Problem Solving

Graphing Data   Graphs are very useful in displaying data. Highs and lows can be shown and trends observed from the graph. By showing the trends, predictions can be made for a future time by assuming that these trends will continue.

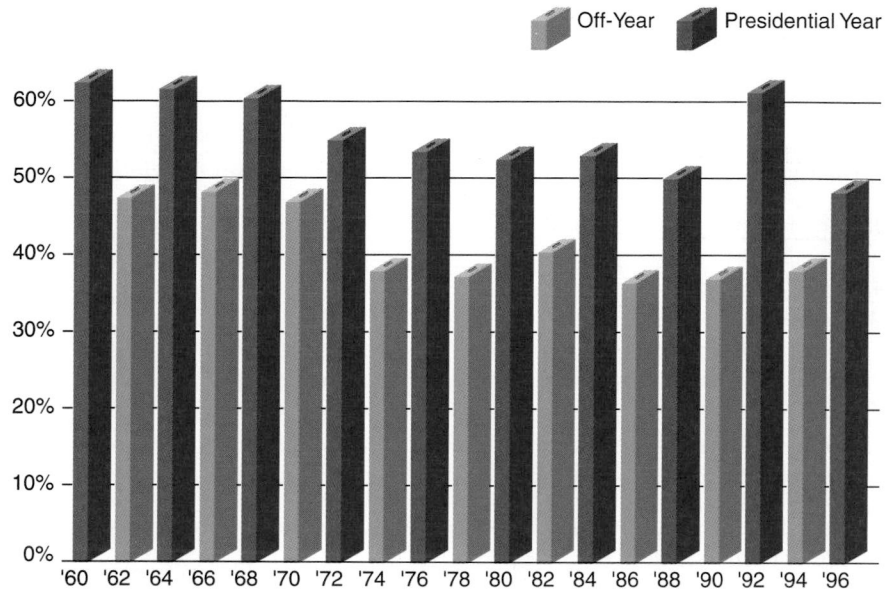

Off-Year   Presidential Year

The bar graph at the left depicts U.S. voter turnout during presidential election years and during off-year elections.

The heights of the bars indicate the percents of eligible voters who cast ballots.

1. During which presidential election years was voter turnout greater than 60%?

2. During which off-year elections was voter turnout less than 40%?

3. During which presidential election years was voter turnout less than 50%?

4. Write a paragraph describing any pattern you see in the graph.

5. Using any patterns that you may have observed, make a prediction about voter turnout in 1998 and 2000.

The table at the right shows the number of mobile phone users (in millions) for the years 1988 to 1996.

Year	Number	Year	Number
'88	2.1	'93	16.0
'89	3.5	'94	24.1
'90	5.3	'95	33.8
'91	7.6	'96	44.0
'92	11.0		

6. Make a bar graph of the number of mobile phone users.

7. Note the trend that this bar graph indicates. Do you expect the number of mobile phone users to be closer to 48 million, 55 million, or 80 million in 1997?

The federal budget deficit (in billions) since 1980 is shown below. The deficits for the years 1997, 1998, and 1999 are estimates made by the Office of Management and Budget.

Year	Deficit	Year	Deficit	Year	Deficit	Year	Deficit	Year	Deficit
'80	73.8	'84	185.3	'88	155.2	'92	290.4	'96	107.3
'81	78.9	'85	212.3	'89	152.5	'93	255.0	'97	67.0
'82	127.9	'86	221.2	'90	221.2	'94	203.1	'98	90.0
'83	207.8	'87	149.8	'91	269.4	'95	163.9	'99	90.0

8. Make a bar graph showing the federal budget deficits.

9. During which consecutive three-year period was the deficit the greatest?

10. Write a paragraph describing any pattern you see in the graph.

Projects and Group Activities

Mean and Standard Deviation

An automotive engineer tests the miles-per-gallon ratings of 15 cars and records the results as follows:

$$25 \quad 22 \quad 21 \quad 27 \quad 25 \quad 35 \quad 29 \quad 31 \quad 25 \quad 26 \quad 21 \quad 39 \quad 34 \quad 32 \quad 28$$

The **mean** of the data is the sum of the measurements divided by the number of measurements. The symbol for the mean is $\bar{x}$.

$$\text{Mean} = \bar{x} = \frac{\text{sum of all data values}}{\text{number of data values}}$$

To find the mean for the data above, add the numbers and then divide by 15.

$$\bar{x} = \frac{25 + 22 + 21 + 27 + 25 + 35 + 29 + 31 + 25 + 26 + 21 + 39 + 34 + 32 + 28}{15}$$

$$= \frac{420}{15} = 28$$

The mean number of miles per gallon for the 15 cars tested was 28 mi/gal.

The mean is one of the most frequently computed averages. It is the one that is commonly used to calculate a student's performance in a class.

The scores for a history student on 5 tests were 78, 82, 91, 87, and 93. What was the mean score for this student?

To find the mean, add the numbers. Then divide by 5.

$$\bar{x} = \frac{78 + 82 + 91 + 87 + 93}{5}$$

$$= \frac{431}{5} = 86.2$$

The mean score for the history student was 86.2.

Consider two students, each of whom has taken 5 exams.

Scores for Student A

84	86	83	85	87

Scores for Student B

90	75	94	68	98

$$\bar{x} = \frac{84 + 86 + 83 + 85 + 87}{5} = \frac{425}{5} = 85$$

$$\bar{x} = \frac{90 + 75 + 94 + 68 + 98}{5} = \frac{425}{5} = 85$$

The mean for Student A is 85.

The mean for Student B is 85.

For each of these students, the mean (average) for the 5 exams is 85. However, Student A has a more consistent record of scores than Student B. One way to measure the consistency, or "clustering" near the mean, of data is to use the **standard deviation.**

To calculate the standard deviation:

Step 1. Sum the squares of the differences between each value of the data and the mean.

Step 2. Divide the result in step 1 by the number of items in the set of data.

Step 3. Take the square root of the result in step 2.

The calculation for Student A is shown at the right.

Step 1:

x	$x - \bar{x}$	$(x - \bar{x})^2$
84	$84 - 85$	$(-1)^2 = 1$
86	$86 - 85$	$1^2 = 1$
83	$83 - 85$	$(-2)^2 = 4$
85	$85 - 85$	$0^2 = 0$
87	$87 - 85$	$2^2 = 4$
		Total $= 10$

The symbol for standard deviation is the lower case Greek letter *sigma*, σ.

Step 2: $\frac{10}{5} = 2$

Step 3: $\sigma = \sqrt{2} \approx 1.414$

The standard deviation for Student A's scores is approximately 1.414.

Following a similar procedure for Student B shows that the standard deviation for Student B's scores is approximately 11.524. Because the standard deviation of Student B's scores is greater than that of Student A's ($11.524 > 1.414$), Student B's scores are not as consistent as those of Student A.

1. The weights in ounces of 6 newborn infants were recorded by a hospital. The weights were 96, 105, 84, 90, 102, and 99. Find the standard deviation of the weights.

2. The numbers of rooms occupied in a hotel on 6 consecutive days were 234, 321, 222, 246, 312, and 396. Find the standard deviation for the number of rooms occupied.

3. Seven coins were tossed 100 times. The numbers of heads recorded for each coin were 56, 63, 49, 50, 48, 53, and 52. Find the standard deviation of the number of heads.

4. The temperatures for 11 consecutive days at a desert resort were 95°, 98°, 98°, 104°, 97°, 100°, 96°, 97°, 108°, 93°, and 104°. For the same days, temperatures in Antarctica were 27°, 28°, 28°, 30°, 28°, 27°, 30°, 25°, 24°, 26°, and 21°. Which location has the greater standard deviation of temperatures?

5. The scores for 5 college basketball games were 56, 68, 60, 72, and 64. The scores for 5 professional basketball games were 106, 118, 110, 122, and 114. Which scores have the greater standard deviation?

6. The weights in pounds of the 5-man front line of a college football team are 210, 245, 220, 230, and 225. Find the standard deviation of the weights.

7. One student received test scores of 85, 92, 86, and 89. A second student received scores of 90, 97, 91, and 94 (exactly 5 points more on each test). Are the means of the two students the same? If not, what is the relationship between the means of the two students? Are the standard deviations of the scores of the two students the same? If not, what is the relationship between the standard deviations of the scores of the two students?

8. Grade-point average (GPA) is a *weighted* mean. It is called a weighted mean because a grade in a 5-unit course has more influence on your GPA than a grade in a 2-unit course. GPA is calculated by multiplying the numerical equivalent of each grade by the number of units, adding those products, and then dividing by the total number of units. Calculate your GPA for the last quarter or semester.

9. If you average 40 mph for 1 h and then 50 mph for 1 h, is your average speed $\frac{40 + 50}{2} = 45$ mph? Why or why not?

10. A company is negotiating with its employees the terms of a raise in salary. One proposal would add $500 a year to each employee's salary. The second proposal would give each employee a 4% raise. Explain how each of these proposals would affect the current mean and standard deviation of salaries for the company.

Chapter Summary

Key Words

A *set* is a collection of objects. The objects of a set are called the *elements* of the set.

The *roster method* of writing a set encloses a list of the elements in braces.

The *empty set,* or *null set,* written $\varnothing$ or { }, is the set that contains no elements.

The *union* of two sets, written $A \cup B$, is the set that contains all the elements of A and all the elements of B (any elements that are in both sets A and B are listed only once).

The *intersection* of two sets, written $A \cap B$, is the set that contains the elements that are common to both A and B.

An *inequality* is an expression that contains the symbol $<$, $>$, $\leq$, or $\geq$.

The *solution set of an inequality* is a set of numbers, each element of which, when substituted for the variable, results in a true inequality. The solution set of an inequality can be graphed on the number line.

The solution set of an inequality in two variables is a *half-plane*.

Essential Rules

Addition Property of Inequalities

The same term can be added to each side of an inequality without changing the solution set of the inequality.

$$\text{If } a > b, \text{ then } a + c > b + c.$$
$$\text{If } a < b, \text{ then } a + c < b + c.$$

The Addition Property of Inequalities also holds true for an inequality containing the symbol $\geq$ or $\leq$.

Multiplication Property of Inequalities

Each side of an inequality can be multiplied by the same **positive number** without changing the solution set of the inequality.

$$\text{If } a > b \text{ and } c > 0, \text{ then } ac > bc.$$
$$\text{If } a < b \text{ and } c > 0, \text{ then } ac < bc.$$

If each side of an inequality is multiplied by the same **negative number** and the inequality symbol is reversed, then the solution set of the inequality is not changed.

$$\text{If } a > b \text{ and } c < 0, \text{ then } ac < bc.$$
$$\text{If } a < b \text{ and } c < 0, \text{ then } ac > bc.$$

The Multiplication Property of Inequalities also holds true for an inequality containing the symbol $\geq$ or $\leq$.

Chapter Review

1. Solve: $2x - 3 > x + 15$

2. Find $A \cap B$, given $A = \{0, 2, 4, 6, 8\}$ and $B = \{-2, -4\}$.

3. Use set-builder notation to write the set of odd integers greater than -8.

4. Find $A \cup B$, given $A = \{6, 8, 10\}$ and $B = \{2, 4, 6\}$.

5. Use the roster method to write the set of odd positive integers less than 8.

6. Solve: $12 - 4(x - 1) \le 5(x - 4)$

7. Graph: $x > 3$

   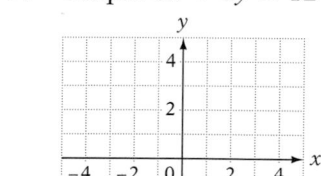

8. Solve: $3x + 4 \ge -8$

9. Graph: $3x + 2y \le 12$

   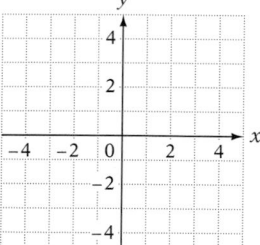

10. Graph: $5x + 2y < 6$

    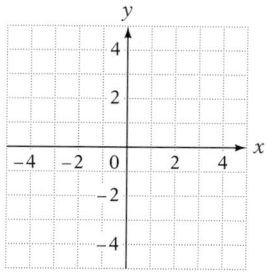

11. Use set-builder notation to write the set of real numbers greater than 3.

12. Solve and graph the solution set of $x - 3 > -1$.

13. Find $A \cap B$, given $A = \{1, 5, 9, 13\}$ and $B = \{1, 3, 5, 7, 9\}$.

14. Graph: $\{x | x < 2\} \cup \{x | x > 5\}$

    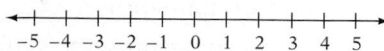

15. Graph: $\{x|x > -1\} \cap \{x|x \leq 2\}$

<-+--+--+--+--+--+--+--+--+--+--+->
-5 -4 -3 -2 -1 0 1 2 3 4 5

16. Solve: $-15x \leq 45$

17. Solve: $6x - 9 < 4x + 3(x + 3)$

18. Solve: $5 - 4(x + 9) > 11(12x - 9)$

19. Solve: $-\frac{3}{4}x > \frac{2}{3}$

20. Graph: $2x - 3y < 9$

21. Solve: $7x - 2(x + 3) \geq x + 10$

22. Florist A charges a $3 delivery fee plus $21 per bouquet delivered. Florist B charges a $15 delivery fee plus $18 per bouquet delivered. A church wants to supply each resident of a small nursing home with a bouquet for Grandparent's Day. Find the number of residents of the nursing home if Florist B is more economical than Florist A.

23. The width of a rectangular garden is 12 ft. The length of the garden is $(3x + 5)$ ft. Express as an integer the minimum length of the garden when the area is greater than 276 ft². (The area of a rectangle is equal to its length times its width.)

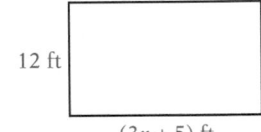

12 ft

$(3x + 5)$ ft

24. Six less than a number is greater than twenty-five. Find the smallest integer that will satisfy the inequality.

25. A student's grades on five sociology tests were 68, 82, 90, 73, 95. What is the lowest score the student can receive on the next test and still be able to attain a minimum of 480 points?

Chapter Test

1. Graph: $\{x | x < 5\} \cap \{x | x > 0\}$

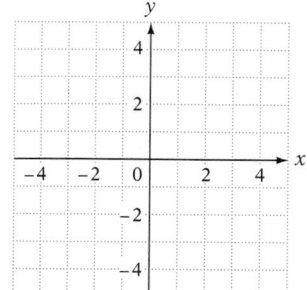

2. Use set-builder notation to write the set of the positive integers less than 50.

3. Use the roster method to write the set of the even positive integers between 3 and 9.

4. Solve: $3(2x - 5) \geq 8x - 9$

5. Solve: $x + \dfrac{1}{2} > \dfrac{5}{8}$

6. Graph: $x > -2$

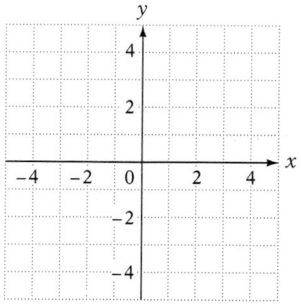

7. Solve: $5 - 3x > 8$

8. Use set-builder notation to write the set of the real numbers greater than -23.

9. Graph the solution set of $3x + y > 4$.

10. Graph the solution set of $4x - 5y \geq 15$.

11. Find $A \cap B$, given $A = \{6, 8, 10, 12\}$ and $B = \{12, 14, 16\}$.

12. Solve and graph the solution set of $4 + x < 1$.

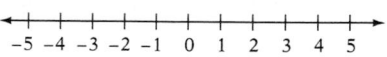

13. Solve: $-\dfrac{3}{8}x \leq 5$

14. Solve: $6x - 3(2 - 3x) < 4(2x - 7)$

15. Solve and graph the solution set of $\frac{2}{3}x \geq 2$.

```
  <—+—+—+—+—+—+—+—+—+—+—+—>
   -5 -4 -3 -2 -1  0  1  2  3  4  5
```

16. Solve: $2x - 7 \leq 6x + 9$

17. To ride a certain roller coaster at an amusement park, a person must be at least 48 in. tall. How many inches must a child who is 43 in. tall grow to be eligible to ride the roller coaster?

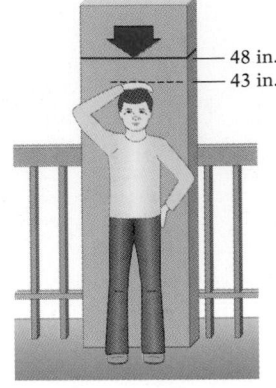

48 in.
43 in.

18. A rectangle is 15 ft long and $(2x - 4)$ ft wide. Express an integer as the maximum width of the rectangle if the area is less than 180 ft². (The area of a rectangle is equal to its length times its width.)

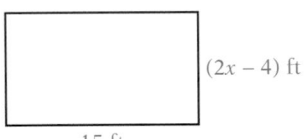

$(2x - 4)$ ft

15 ft

19. A ball bearing for a rotary engine must have a circumference between 0.1220 in. and 0.1240 in. What are the allowable diameters for the bearings to the nearest ten-thousandth of an inch? Recall that $C = \pi d$.

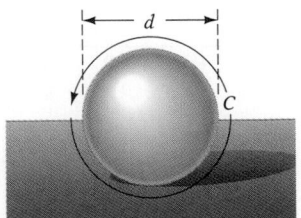

d

C

20. A stockbroker receives a monthly salary that is the greater of $2500 or $1000 plus 2% of the total value of all stock transactions the broker processes during the month. What dollar amounts of transactions did the broker process in a month for which the broker's salary was $2500?

Cumulative Review

1. Simplify: $2[5a - 3(2 - 5a) - 8]$

2. Solve: $\frac{5}{8} - 4x = \frac{1}{8}$

3. Solve: $2x - 3[x - 2(x - 3)] = 2$

4. Simplify: $(-3a)(-2a^3b^2)^2$

5. Simplify: $\frac{27a^3b^2}{(-3ab^2)^3}$

6. Simplify: $(16x^2 - 12x - 2) \div (4x - 1)$

7. Given $f(x) = x^2 - 4x - 5$, find $f(-1)$.

8. Factor: $27a^2x^2 - 3a^2$

9. Simplify: $\frac{x^2 - 2x}{x^2 - 2x - 8} \div \frac{x^3 - 5x^2 + 6x}{x^2 - 7x + 12}$

10. Simplify: $\frac{4a}{2a - 3} - \frac{2a}{a + 3}$

11. Solve: $\frac{5y}{6} - \frac{5}{9} = \frac{y}{3} - \frac{5}{6}$

12. Solve $R = \frac{C - S}{t}$ for C.

13. Find the slope of the line that passes through the points $(2, -3)$ and $(-1, 4)$.

14. Find the equation of the line that passes through the point $(1, -3)$ and has slope $-\frac{3}{2}$.

15. Solve by substitution.
$$x = 3y + 1$$
$$2x + 5y = 13$$

16. Solve by the addition method.
$$9x - 2y = 17$$
$$5x + 3y = -7$$

17. Find $A \cup B$, given $A = \{0, 1, 2\}$ and $B = \{-10, -2\}$.

18. Use set-builder notation to write the set of the real numbers less than 48.

19. Graph: $\{x \,|\, x > 1\} \cup \{x \,|\, x < -1\}$

$$\xleftarrow{\quad\begin{array}{ccccccccccc} + & + & + & + & + & + & + & + & + & + & + \\ -5 & -4 & -3 & -2 & -1 & 0 & 1 & 2 & 3 & 4 & 5 \end{array}}\rightarrow$$

20. Graph the solution set of $\frac{3}{8}x > -\frac{3}{4}$.

$$\xleftarrow{\quad\begin{array}{ccccccccccc} + & + & + & + & + & + & + & + & + & + & + \\ -5 & -4 & -3 & -2 & -1 & 0 & 1 & 2 & 3 & 4 & 5 \end{array}}\rightarrow$$

21. Solve: $-\frac{4}{5}x > 12$

22. Solve: $15 - 3(5x - 7) < 2(7 - 2x)$

23. Three-fifths of a number is less than negative fifteen. What integers satisfy this inequality? Write the answer in set builder notation.

24. Company A rents cars for $6 a day and $.25 for every mile driven. Company B rents cars for $15 a day and $.10 per mile. You want to rent a car for 6 days. What is the maximum number of miles you can drive a Company A car if it is to cost you less than a Company B car?

25. In a lake, 100 fish are caught, tagged, and then released. Later, 150 fish are caught. Three of the 150 fish are found to have tags. Estimate the number of fish in the lake.

26. The first angle of a triangle is 30 degrees more than the second angle. The third angle is 10 degrees more than twice the second angle. Find the measure of each angle.

27. Graph: $y = 2x - 1$

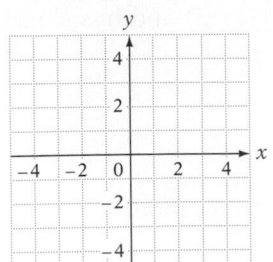

28. Graph the solution set of $6x - 3y \geq 6$.

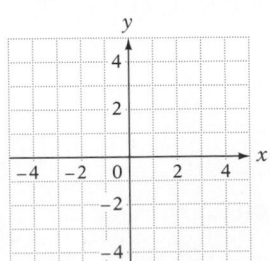

CHAPTER

10

Radical Expressions

Objectives

Section 10.1
To simplify numerical radical expressions
To simplify variable radical expressions

Section 10.2
To add and subtract radical expressions

Section 10.3
To multiply radical expressions
To divide radical expressions

Section 10.4
To solve an equation containing a radical expression
To solve application problems

Drafters prepare detailed drawings from sketches and specifications made by architects, designers, engineers, and scientists. Usually drafters specialize in a particular field, such as architectural, civil, mechanical, electrical, or aeronautical drafting. The study of radical expressions is important for drafters as working with right triangles requires radicals. See Section 4 of this chapter.

A Table of Square Roots

The practice of finding the square root of a number has existed for at least two thousand years. Because the process of finding a square root before the invention of the calculator was tedious and time-consuming, it was convenient to have tables of square roots.

The table shown at the left is part of an old Babylonian clay tablet that was written around 350 B.C. It is an incomplete table of square roots written in a style called *cuneiform*.

The number base of the Babylonians was 60 instead of 10, as we use today. The symbol ∀ was used for 1, and 10 was written as ⊿. Some examples of numbers written in this system are given below.

Translations of the first two lines of the table are given below. The number given in parentheses is the equivalent base-10 number that would be used today. You might try to translate the third line. The answer is given at the bottom of this page.

40 × 60 + 1 (= 2401), which is the square of 49

41 × 60 + 40 (= 2500), which is the square of 50

Answer: 43 × 60 + 21 (= 2601), which is the square of 51

10.1 Introduction to Radical Expressions

Objective A   *To simplify numerical radical expressions* ....

A **square root** of a positive number x is a number whose square is x.

A square root of 16 is 4 because $4^2 = 16$.
A square root of 16 is -4 because $(-4)^2 = 16$.

Every positive number has two square roots, one a positive and one a negative number. The symbol $\sqrt{}$, called a **radical sign,** is used to indicate the positive or **principal square root** of a number. For example, $\sqrt{16} = 4$ and $\sqrt{25} = 5$. The number under the radical sign is called the **radicand.**

When the negative square root of a number is to be found, a negative sign is placed in front of the radical. For example, $-\sqrt{16} = -4$ and $-\sqrt{25} = -5$.

The square of an integer is a **perfect square.** 49, 81, and 144 are examples of perfect squares.

$$7^2 = 49$$
$$9^2 = 81$$
$$12^2 = 144$$

An integer that is a perfect square can be written as the product of prime factors, each of which has an even exponent when expressed in exponential form.

$$49 = 7 \cdot 7 = 7^2$$
$$81 = 3 \cdot 3 \cdot 3 \cdot 3 = 3^4$$
$$144 = 2 \cdot 2 \cdot 2 \cdot 2 \cdot 3 \cdot 3 = 2^4 3^2$$

➡ Simplify $\sqrt{625}$.

$$\sqrt{625} = \sqrt{5^4}$$

$$= 5^2$$

$$= 25$$

- Write the prime factorization of the radicand in exponential form.

- Remove the radical sign and multiply the exponent by $\frac{1}{2}$.

- Simplify.

If a number is not a perfect square, its square root can only be approximated. For example, 2 and 7 are not perfect squares. The square roots of these numbers are **irrational numbers.** Their decimal representations never terminate or repeat.

$$\sqrt{2} \approx 1.4142135\cdots \qquad \sqrt{7} \approx 2.6457513\cdots$$

A radical expression is in simplest form when the radicand contains no factor greater than 1 that is a perfect square. The Product Property of Square Roots is used to simplify radical expressions.

> **The Product Property of Square Roots**
> If a and b are positive real numbers, then $\sqrt{ab} = \sqrt{a} \cdot \sqrt{b}$.

➡ Simplify: $\sqrt{96}$

$\sqrt{96} = \sqrt{2^5 \cdot 3}$

- Write the prime factorization of the radicand in exponential form.

$\quad = \sqrt{2^4(2 \cdot 3)}$

- Write the radicand as a product of a perfect square and factors that do not contain a perfect square.

$\quad = \sqrt{2^4}\sqrt{2 \cdot 3}$

- Use the Product Property of Square Roots.

$\quad = 2^2\sqrt{6}$

- Simplify.

$\quad = 4\sqrt{6}$

➡ Simplify: $\sqrt{360}$

$\sqrt{360} = \sqrt{2^3 \cdot 3^2 \cdot 5}$

- Write the prime factorization of the radicand in exponential form.

$\quad = \sqrt{(2^2 \cdot 3^2)(2 \cdot 5)}$

- Write the radicand as a product of perfect squares and factors that do not contain a perfect square.

$\quad = \sqrt{2^2 \cdot 3^2}\sqrt{2 \cdot 5}$

- Use the Product Property of Square Roots.

$\quad = (2 \cdot 3)\sqrt{10}$

- Simplify.

$\quad = 6\sqrt{10}$

From the last example, note that $\sqrt{360} = 6\sqrt{10}$. The two expressions are different representations of the same number. Using a calculator, we find that $\sqrt{360} \approx 18.973666$ and $6\sqrt{10} \approx 6(3.1622777) = 18.9736662$.

➡ Simplify: $\sqrt{-16}$

Because the square of any real number is positive, there is no real number whose square is -16. $\sqrt{-16}$ is not a real number.

Example 1   Simplify: $3\sqrt{90}$

Solution $3\sqrt{90} = 3\sqrt{2 \cdot 3^2 \cdot 5}$
$= 3\sqrt{3^2(2 \cdot 5)}$
$= 3\sqrt{3^2}\sqrt{2 \cdot 5}$
$= 3 \cdot 3\sqrt{10} = 9\sqrt{10}$

You Try It 1   Simplify: $-5\sqrt{32}$

Your solution

Example 2   Simplify: $\sqrt{252}$

Solution $\sqrt{252} = \sqrt{2^2 \cdot 3^2 \cdot 7}$
$= \sqrt{2^2 \cdot 3^2}\sqrt{7}$
$= 2 \cdot 3\sqrt{7}$
$= 6\sqrt{7}$

You Try It 2   Simplify: $\sqrt{216}$

Your solution

Solutions on p. S23

Objective B ***To simplify variable radical expressions*** ....

Variable expressions that contain radicals do not always represent real numbers. For example, if $a = -4$, then

$$\sqrt{a^3} = \sqrt{(-4)^3} = \sqrt{-64}$$

and $\sqrt{-64}$ is not a real number.

Now consider the expression $\sqrt{x^2}$. Evaluate this expression for $x = -2$ and $x = 2$.

$$\sqrt{x^2} \qquad\qquad\qquad\qquad\qquad \sqrt{x^2}$$
$$\sqrt{(-2)^2} = \sqrt{4} = 2 = |-2| \qquad\qquad \sqrt{2^2} = \sqrt{4} = 2 = |2|$$

This suggests the following:

For any real number a, $\sqrt{a^2} = |a|$. If $a \geq 0$, then $\sqrt{a^2} = a$.

In order to avoid variable expressions that do not represent real numbers, and so that absolute-value signs are not needed for certain expressions, the variables in this chapter will represent *positive* numbers unless otherwise stated.

A variable or a product of variables written in exponential form is a perfect square when each exponent is an even number.

To find the square root of a perfect square, remove the radical sign and multiply each exponent by $\frac{1}{2}$.

➡ Simplify: $\sqrt{a^6}$

$$\sqrt{a^6} = a^3 \qquad\qquad \bullet \text{ Remove the radical sign and multiply the exponent by } \frac{1}{2}.$$

A variable radical expression is in simplest form when the radicand contains no factor greater than 1 that is a perfect square.

➡ Simplify: $\sqrt{x^7}$

$$\sqrt{x^7} = \sqrt{x^6 \cdot x} \qquad\qquad \bullet \text{ Write } x^7 \text{ as the product of a perfect square and } x.$$
$$= \sqrt{x^6}\sqrt{x} \qquad\qquad \bullet \text{ Use the Product Property of Square Roots.}$$
$$= x^3\sqrt{x} \qquad\qquad\quad \bullet \text{ Simplify the perfect square.}$$

➡ Simplify: $3x\sqrt{8x^3y^{13}}$

$$3x\sqrt{8x^3y^{13}} = 3x\sqrt{2^3x^3y^{13}} \qquad\qquad \bullet \text{ Write the prime factorization of the coefficient}$$
$$\text{of the radicand in exponential form.}$$
$$= 3x\sqrt{2^2x^2y^{12}(2xy)} \qquad\qquad \bullet \text{ Write the radicand as a product of perfect}$$
$$\text{squares and factors that do not contain a}$$
$$\text{perfect square.}$$
$$= 3x\sqrt{2^2x^2y^{12}}\sqrt{2xy} \qquad\qquad \bullet \text{ Use the Product Property of Square Roots.}$$
$$= 3x \cdot 2xy^6\sqrt{2xy} \qquad\qquad\quad \bullet \text{ Simplify.}$$
$$= 6x^2y^6\sqrt{2xy}$$

⇒ Simplify: $\sqrt{25(x + 2)^2}$

$\sqrt{25(x + 2)^2} = \sqrt{5^2(x + 2)^2}$

$= 5(x + 2)$

$= 5x + 10$

• Write the prime factorization of 25 in exponential form.

Example 3
Simplify: $\sqrt{b^{15}}$

Solution
$\sqrt{b^{15}} = \sqrt{b^{14} \cdot b} = \sqrt{b^{14}} \cdot \sqrt{b} = b^7\sqrt{b}$

You Try It 3
Simplify: $\sqrt{y^{19}}$

Your solution

Example 4
Simplify: $\sqrt{24x^5}$

Solution
$\sqrt{24x^5} = \sqrt{2^3 \cdot 3 \cdot x^5} = \sqrt{2^2x^4(2 \cdot 3x)}$

$= \sqrt{2^2 \cdot x^4}\sqrt{2 \cdot 3x}$

$= 2x^2\sqrt{6x}$

You Try It 4
Simplify: $\sqrt{45b^7}$

Your solution

Example 5
Simplify: $2a\sqrt{18a^3b^{10}}$

Solution
$2a\sqrt{18a^3b^{10}} = 2a\sqrt{2 \cdot 3^2 \cdot a^3b^{10}}$

$= 2a\sqrt{3^2a^2b^{10}(2a)}$

$= 2a\sqrt{3^2a^2b^{10}}\sqrt{2a}$

$= 2a \cdot 3ab^5\sqrt{2a}$

$= 6a^2b^5\sqrt{2a}$

You Try It 5
Simplify: $3a\sqrt{28a^9b^{18}}$

Your solution

Example 6
Simplify: $\sqrt{16(x + 5)^2}$

Solution
$\sqrt{16(x + 5)^2} = \sqrt{2^4(x + 5)^2} = 2^2(x + 5)$

$= 4(x + 5) = 4x + 20$

You Try It 6
Simplify: $\sqrt{25(a + 3)^2}$

Your solution

Example 7
Simplify: $\sqrt{x^2 + 10x + 25}$

Solution
$\sqrt{x^2 + 10x + 25} = \sqrt{(x + 5)^2} = x + 5$

You Try It 7
Simplify: $\sqrt{x^2 + 14x + 49}$

Your solution

Solutions on p. S23

10.1 Exercises

· ·

___

Objective A

Simplify.

1. $\sqrt{16}$ **2.** $\sqrt{64}$ **3.** $\sqrt{49}$ **4.** $\sqrt{144}$ **5.** $\sqrt{32}$ **6.** $\sqrt{50}$

7. $\sqrt{8}$ **8.** $\sqrt{12}$ **9.** $6\sqrt{18}$ **10.** $-3\sqrt{48}$ **11.** $5\sqrt{40}$ **12.** $2\sqrt{28}$

13. $\sqrt{15}$ **14.** $\sqrt{21}$ **15.** $\sqrt{29}$ **16.** $\sqrt{13}$ **17.** $-9\sqrt{72}$ **18.** $11\sqrt{80}$

19. $\sqrt{45}$ **20.** $\sqrt{225}$ **21.** $\sqrt{0}$ **22.** $\sqrt{210}$ **23.** $6\sqrt{128}$ **24.** $9\sqrt{288}$

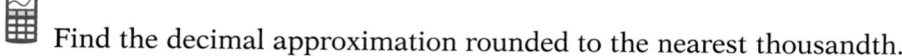 Find the decimal approximation rounded to the nearest thousandth.

25. $\sqrt{240}$ **26.** $\sqrt{300}$ **27.** $\sqrt{288}$ **28.** $\sqrt{600}$ **29.** $\sqrt{256}$ **30.** $\sqrt{324}$

___

Objective B

Simplify.

31. $\sqrt{x^6}$ **32.** $\sqrt{x^{12}}$ **33.** $\sqrt{y^{15}}$ **34.** $\sqrt{y^{11}}$

35. $\sqrt{a^{20}}$ **36.** $\sqrt{a^{16}}$ **37.** $\sqrt{x^4y^4}$ **38.** $\sqrt{x^{12}y^8}$

39. $\sqrt{4x^4}$ **40.** $\sqrt{25y^8}$ **41.** $\sqrt{24x^2}$ **42.** $\sqrt{x^3y^{15}}$

43. $\sqrt{60x^5}$ **44.** $\sqrt{72y^7}$ **45.** $\sqrt{49a^4b^8}$ **46.** $\sqrt{144x^2y^8}$

47. $\sqrt{18x^5y^7}$ **48.** $\sqrt{32a^5b^{15}}$ **49.** $\sqrt{40x^{11}y^7}$ **50.** $\sqrt{72x^9y^3}$

51. $\sqrt{80a^9b^{10}}$ **52.** $\sqrt{96a^5b^7}$ **53.** $2\sqrt{16a^2b^3}$ **54.** $5\sqrt{25a^4b^7}$

55. $x\sqrt{x^4y^2}$

56. $y\sqrt{x^3y^6}$

57. $4\sqrt{20a^4b^7}$

58. $5\sqrt{12a^3b^4}$

59. $3x\sqrt{12x^2y^7}$

60. $4y\sqrt{18x^5y^4}$

61. $2x^2\sqrt{8x^2y^3}$

62. $3y^2\sqrt{27x^4y^3}$

63. $\sqrt{25(a+4)^2}$

64. $\sqrt{81(x+y)^4}$

65. $\sqrt{4(x+2)^4}$

66. $\sqrt{9(x+2)^8}$

67. $\sqrt{x^2+4x+4}$

68. $\sqrt{b^2+8b+16}$

69. $\sqrt{y^2+2y+1}$

70. $\sqrt{a^2+6a+9}$

APPLYING THE CONCEPTS

71. If a and b are positive real numbers, does $\sqrt{a+b} = \sqrt{a} + \sqrt{b}$? If not, give an example in which the expressions are not equal.

72. **a.** Find the two-digit perfect square that has exactly nine factors.
b. Find two whole numbers such that their difference is 10, the smaller number is a perfect square, and the larger number is two less than a perfect square.

73. Describe in your own words how to simplify a radical expression.

74. Explain why $2\sqrt{2}$ is in simplest form and $\sqrt{8}$ is not in simplest form.

75. Use the roster method to list the whole numbers between $\sqrt{8}$ and $\sqrt{90}$.

76. Simplify. Assume that no radicand is negative.
a. $\sqrt{x^2y^3 + x^3y^2}$ **b.** $\sqrt{4a^5b^4 - 4a^4b^5}$ **c.** $\sqrt{(x^2-y^2)(x-y)}$

77. You are to grade the solution to the problem "Write $\sqrt{72}$ in simplest form." Is the solution correct? If not, what error was made? What is the correct solution?

$\sqrt{72} = \sqrt{4}\sqrt{18}$
$= 2\sqrt{18}$

78. Simplify.
a. $\sqrt{\sqrt{16}}$ **b.** $\sqrt{\sqrt{81}}$

79. Approximate to the nearest ten-thousandth.
 a. $\sqrt{\sqrt{77}}$ **b.** $\sqrt{\sqrt{17}}$

80. Given $f(x) = \sqrt{2x-1}$, find each of the following. Write your answer in simplest form.
a. $f(1)$ **b.** $f(5)$ **c.** $f(14)$

10.2 Addition and Subtraction of Radical Expressions

Objective A   *To add and subtract radical expressions* ....

The Distributive Property is used to simplify the sum or difference of radical expressions with like radicands.

$$5\sqrt{2} + 3\sqrt{2} = (5 + 3)\sqrt{2} = 8\sqrt{2}$$

$$6\sqrt{2x} - 4\sqrt{2x} = (6 - 4)\sqrt{2x} = 2\sqrt{2x}$$

Radical expressions that are in simplest form and have unlike radicands cannot be simplified by the Distributive Property.

$2\sqrt{3} + 4\sqrt{2}$ cannot be simplified by the Distributive Property.

➡ Simplify: $4\sqrt{8} - 10\sqrt{2}$

$$4\sqrt{8} - 10\sqrt{2} = 4\sqrt{2^3} - 10\sqrt{2}$$

- **Write the prime factorization of the radicands.**

$$= 4\sqrt{2^2 \cdot 2} - 10\sqrt{2}$$
$$= 4\sqrt{2^2}\sqrt{2} - 10\sqrt{2}$$

- **Use the Product Property of Radicals.**

$$= 4 \cdot 2\sqrt{2} - 10\sqrt{2}$$
$$= 8\sqrt{2} - 10\sqrt{2}$$
$$= (8 - 10)\sqrt{2}$$

- **Simplify the expression by using the Distributive Property.**

$$= -2\sqrt{2}$$

➡ Simplify: $8\sqrt{18x} - 2\sqrt{32x}$

$$8\sqrt{18x} - 2\sqrt{32x} = 8\sqrt{2 \cdot 3^2 x} - 2\sqrt{2^5 x}$$

- **Write the prime factorization of the coefficients of the radicands.**

$$= 8\sqrt{3^2 \cdot 2x} - 2\sqrt{2^4 \cdot 2x}$$
$$= 8\sqrt{3^2}\sqrt{2x} - 2\sqrt{2^4}\sqrt{2x}$$

- **Use the Product Property of Radicals.**

$$= 8 \cdot 3\sqrt{2x} - 2 \cdot 2^2\sqrt{2x}$$
$$= 24\sqrt{2x} - 8\sqrt{2x}$$
$$= (24 - 8)\sqrt{2x}$$

- **Simplify the expression by using the Distributive Property.**

$$= 16\sqrt{2x}$$

Example 1

Simplify: $5\sqrt{2} - 3\sqrt{2} + 12\sqrt{2}$

Solution

$5\sqrt{2} - 3\sqrt{2} + 12\sqrt{2} = 14\sqrt{2}$

You Try It 1

Simplify: $9\sqrt{3} + 3\sqrt{3} - 18\sqrt{3}$

Your solution

Example 2

Simplify: $3\sqrt{12} - 5\sqrt{27}$

Solution

$$
\begin{aligned}
3\sqrt{12} - 5\sqrt{27} &= 3\sqrt{2^2 \cdot 3} - 5\sqrt{3^3} \\
&= 3\sqrt{2^2}\sqrt{3} - 5\sqrt{3^2}\sqrt{3} \\
&= 3 \cdot 2\sqrt{3} - 5 \cdot 3\sqrt{3} \\
&= 6\sqrt{3} - 15\sqrt{3} \\
&= -9\sqrt{3}
\end{aligned}
$$

You Try It 2

Simplify: $2\sqrt{50} - 5\sqrt{32}$

Your solution

Example 3

Simplify: $3\sqrt{12x^3} - 2x\sqrt{3x}$

Solution

$$
\begin{aligned}
3&\sqrt{12x^3} - 2x\sqrt{3x} \\
&= 3\sqrt{2^2 \cdot 3 \cdot x^3} - 2x\sqrt{3x} \\
&= 3\sqrt{2^2 \cdot x^2}\sqrt{3x} - 2x\sqrt{3x} \\
&= 3 \cdot 2 \cdot x\sqrt{3x} - 2x\sqrt{3x} \\
&= 6x\sqrt{3x} - 2x\sqrt{3x} \\
&= 4x\sqrt{3x}
\end{aligned}
$$

You Try It 3

Simplify: $y\sqrt{28y} + 7\sqrt{63y^3}$

Your solution

Example 4

Simplify: $2x\sqrt{8y} - 3\sqrt{2x^2y} + 2\sqrt{32x^2y}$

Solution

$$
\begin{aligned}
2x&\sqrt{8y} - 3\sqrt{2x^2y} + 2\sqrt{32x^2y} \\
&= 2x\sqrt{2^3y} - 3\sqrt{2x^2y} + 2\sqrt{2^5x^2y} \\
&= 2x\sqrt{2^2}\sqrt{2y} - 3\sqrt{x^2}\sqrt{2y} + 2\sqrt{2^4x^2}\sqrt{2y} \\
&= 2x \cdot 2\sqrt{2y} - 3 \cdot x\sqrt{2y} + 2 \cdot 2^2 \cdot x\sqrt{2y} \\
&= 4x\sqrt{2y} - 3x\sqrt{2y} + 8x\sqrt{2y} \\
&= 9x\sqrt{2y}
\end{aligned}
$$

You Try It 4

Simplify: $2\sqrt{27a^5} - 4a\sqrt{12a^3} + a^2\sqrt{75a}$

Your solution

Solutions on p. S23

10.2 Exercises

Objective A

Simplify.

1. $2\sqrt{2} + \sqrt{2}$

2. $3\sqrt{5} + 8\sqrt{5}$

3. $-3\sqrt{7} + 2\sqrt{7}$

4. $4\sqrt{5} - 10\sqrt{5}$

5. $-3\sqrt{11} - 8\sqrt{11}$

6. $-3\sqrt{3} - 5\sqrt{3}$

7. $2\sqrt{x} + 8\sqrt{x}$

8. $3\sqrt{y} + 2\sqrt{y}$

9. $8\sqrt{y} - 10\sqrt{y}$

10. $-5\sqrt{2a} + 2\sqrt{2a}$

11. $-2\sqrt{3b} - 9\sqrt{3b}$

12. $-7\sqrt{5a} - 5\sqrt{5a}$

13. $3x\sqrt{2} - x\sqrt{2}$

14. $2y\sqrt{3} - 9y\sqrt{3}$

15. $2a\sqrt{3a} - 5a\sqrt{3a}$

16. $-5b\sqrt{3x} - 2b\sqrt{3x}$

17. $3\sqrt{xy} - 8\sqrt{xy}$

18. $-4\sqrt{xy} + 6\sqrt{xy}$

19. $\sqrt{45} + \sqrt{125}$

20. $\sqrt{32} - \sqrt{98}$

21. $2\sqrt{2} + 3\sqrt{8}$

22. $4\sqrt{128} - 3\sqrt{32}$

23. $5\sqrt{18} - 2\sqrt{75}$

24. $5\sqrt{75} - 2\sqrt{18}$

25. $5\sqrt{4x} - 3\sqrt{9x}$

26. $-3\sqrt{25y} + 8\sqrt{49y}$

27. $3\sqrt{3x^2} - 5\sqrt{27x^2}$

28. $-2\sqrt{8y^2} + 5\sqrt{32y^2}$

29. $2x\sqrt{xy^2} - 3y\sqrt{x^2y}$

30. $4a\sqrt{b^2a} - 3b\sqrt{a^2b}$

31. $3x\sqrt{12x} - 5\sqrt{27x^3}$

32. $2a\sqrt{50a} + 7\sqrt{32a^3}$

33. $4y\sqrt{8y^3} - 7\sqrt{18y^5}$

34. $2a\sqrt{8ab^2} - 2b\sqrt{2a^3}$

35. $b^2\sqrt{a^5b} + 3a^2\sqrt{ab^5}$

36. $y^2\sqrt{x^5y} + x\sqrt{x^3y^5}$

37. $4\sqrt{2} - 5\sqrt{2} + 8\sqrt{2}$

38. $3\sqrt{3} + 8\sqrt{3} - 16\sqrt{3}$

39. $5\sqrt{x} - 8\sqrt{x} + 9\sqrt{x}$

40. $\sqrt{x} - 7\sqrt{x} + 6\sqrt{x}$

41. $8\sqrt{2} - 3\sqrt{y} - 8\sqrt{2}$

42. $8\sqrt{3} - 5\sqrt{2} - 5\sqrt{3}$

43. $8\sqrt{8} - 4\sqrt{32} - 9\sqrt{50}$

44. $2\sqrt{12} - 4\sqrt{27} + \sqrt{75}$

45. $-2\sqrt{3} + 5\sqrt{27} - 4\sqrt{45}$

46. $-2\sqrt{8} - 3\sqrt{27} + 3\sqrt{50}$

47. $4\sqrt{75} + 3\sqrt{48} - \sqrt{99}$

48. $2\sqrt{75} - 5\sqrt{20} + 2\sqrt{45}$

49. $\sqrt{25x} - \sqrt{9x} + \sqrt{16x}$

50. $\sqrt{4x} - \sqrt{100x} - \sqrt{49x}$

51. $3\sqrt{3x} + \sqrt{27x} - 8\sqrt{75x}$

52. $5\sqrt{5x} + 2\sqrt{45x} - 3\sqrt{80x}$

53. $2a\sqrt{75b} - a\sqrt{20b} + 4a\sqrt{45b}$

54. $2b\sqrt{75a} - 5b\sqrt{27a} + 2b\sqrt{20a}$

55. $x\sqrt{3y^2} - 2y\sqrt{12x^2} + xy\sqrt{3}$

56. $a\sqrt{27b^2} + 3b\sqrt{147a^2} - ab\sqrt{3}$

APPLYING THE CONCEPTS

57. Given $G(x) = \sqrt{x + 5} + \sqrt{5x + 3}$, write $G(3)$ in simplest form.

58. Is the equation $\sqrt{a^2 + b^2} = \sqrt{a} + \sqrt{b}$ true for all real numbers a and b?

59. Use complete sentences to explain the steps in simplifying $4\sqrt{2a^3b} + 5\sqrt{5a^3b}$.

60. For each problem, write "ok" if the answer is correct. If the answer is incorrect, write the correct answer.
a. $3\sqrt{ab} + 5\sqrt{ab} = 8\sqrt{2ab}$
b. $7\sqrt{x^3} - 3x\sqrt{x} - x\sqrt{16x} = 0$
c. $5 - 2\sqrt{y} = 3\sqrt{y}$

Simplify.

61. $2\sqrt{8x + 4y} - 5\sqrt{18x + 9y}$

62. $6\sqrt{16x - 16} + \sqrt{25x - 25}$

63. $3\sqrt{a^3 + a^2} + 5\sqrt{4a^3 + 4a^2}$

64. $3\sqrt{x^3y^2 + x^2y^3} + xy\sqrt{4x + 4y}$

10.3 Multiplication and Division of Radical Expressions

Objective A   *To multiply radical expressions* ....

The Product Property of Square Roots is used to multiply variable radical expressions.

$$\sqrt{2x}\,\sqrt{3y} = \sqrt{2x \cdot 3y} = \sqrt{6xy}$$

➡ Simplify: $\sqrt{2x^2}\sqrt{32x^5}$

$$\begin{aligned}
\sqrt{2x^2}\,\sqrt{32x^5} &= \sqrt{2x^2 \cdot 32x^5} \\
&= \sqrt{64x^7} \\
&= \sqrt{2^6 x^7} \\
&= \sqrt{2^6 x^6}\,\sqrt{x} \\
&= 2^3 x^3\sqrt{x} \\
&= 8x^3\sqrt{x}
\end{aligned}$$

- Use the Product Property of Square Roots.
- Multiply the radicands.
- Simplify.

➡ Simplify: $\sqrt{2x}(x + \sqrt{2x})$

$$\begin{aligned}
\sqrt{2x}(x + \sqrt{2x}) &= \sqrt{2x}(x) + \sqrt{2x}\sqrt{2x} \\
&= x\sqrt{2x} + \sqrt{4x^2} \\
&= x\sqrt{2x} + \sqrt{2^2 x^2} \\
&= x\sqrt{2x} + 2x
\end{aligned}$$

- Use the Distributive Property to remove parentheses.
- Simplify.

➡ Simplify: $(\sqrt{2} - 3x)(\sqrt{2} + x)$

$$\begin{aligned}
(\sqrt{2} - 3x)(\sqrt{2} + x) &= \sqrt{2 \cdot 2} + x\sqrt{2} - 3x\sqrt{2} - 3x^2 \\
&= \sqrt{2^2} + (x - 3x)\sqrt{2} - 3x^2 \\
&= 2 - 2x\sqrt{2} - 3x^2
\end{aligned}$$

- Use the FOIL method to remove parentheses.

The expressions $a + b$ and $a - b$, which are the sum and difference of two terms, are called **conjugates** of each other. You will recall that $(a + b)(a - b) = a^2 - b^2$.

➡ Simplify: $(2 + \sqrt{7})(2 - \sqrt{7})$

$$\begin{aligned}
(2 + \sqrt{7})(2 - \sqrt{7}) &= 2^2 - (\sqrt{7})^2 \\
&= 4 - 7 \\
&= -3
\end{aligned}$$

- $(2 + \sqrt{7})(2 - \sqrt{7})$ is the product of conjugates.

TAKE NOTE

For $x > 0$, $(\sqrt{x})^2 = x$.

➡ Simplify: $(3 + \sqrt{y})(3 - \sqrt{y})$

$$\begin{aligned}
(3 + \sqrt{y})(3 - \sqrt{y}) &= 3^2 - (\sqrt{y})^2 \\
&= 9 - y
\end{aligned}$$

- $(3 + \sqrt{y})(3 - \sqrt{y})$ is the product of conjugates.

Example 1
Simplify: $\sqrt{3x^4}\sqrt{2x^2y}\sqrt{6xy^2}$

Solution

$$\sqrt{3x^4}\sqrt{2x^2y}\sqrt{6xy^2} = \sqrt{36x^7y^3}$$
$$= \sqrt{2^2 3^2 x^7 y^3}$$
$$= \sqrt{2^2 3^2 x^6 y^2}\sqrt{xy}$$
$$= 2 \cdot 3x^3 y\sqrt{xy}$$
$$= 6x^3 y\sqrt{xy}$$

You Try It 1
Simplify: $\sqrt{5a}\sqrt{15a^3b^4}\sqrt{3b^5}$

Your solution

Example 2
Simplify: $\sqrt{3ab}(\sqrt{3a} + \sqrt{9b})$

Solution

$$\sqrt{3ab}(\sqrt{3a} + \sqrt{9b})$$
$$= \sqrt{3^2 a^2 b} + \sqrt{3^3 ab^2}$$
$$= \sqrt{3^2 a^2}\sqrt{b} + \sqrt{3^2 b^2}\sqrt{3a}$$
$$= 3a\sqrt{b} + 3b\sqrt{3a}$$

You Try It 2
Simplify: $\sqrt{5x}(\sqrt{5x} - \sqrt{25y})$

Your solution

Example 3
Simplify: $(\sqrt{a} - \sqrt{b})(\sqrt{a} + \sqrt{b})$

Solution

$$(\sqrt{a} - \sqrt{b})(\sqrt{a} + \sqrt{b}) = (\sqrt{a})^2 - (\sqrt{b})^2$$
$$= a - b$$

You Try It 3
Simplify: $(2\sqrt{x} + 7)(2\sqrt{x} - 7)$

Your solution

Example 4
Simplify: $(2\sqrt{x} - \sqrt{y})(5\sqrt{x} - 2\sqrt{y})$

Solution

$$(2\sqrt{x} - \sqrt{y})(5\sqrt{x} - 2\sqrt{y})$$
$$= 10(\sqrt{x})^2 - 4\sqrt{xy} - 5\sqrt{xy} + 2(\sqrt{y})^2$$
$$= 10x - 9\sqrt{xy} + 2y$$

You Try It 4
Simplify: $(3\sqrt{x} - \sqrt{y})(5\sqrt{x} - 2\sqrt{y})$

Your solution

Solutions on p. S23

Objective B　***To divide radical expressions*** ....

The Quotient Property of Square Roots

If a and b are positive real numbers, then

$$\sqrt{\frac{a}{b}} = \frac{\sqrt{a}}{\sqrt{b}} \quad \text{and} \quad \frac{\sqrt{a}}{\sqrt{b}} = \sqrt{\frac{a}{b}}$$

The square root of a quotient is equal to the quotient of the square roots.

POINT OF INTEREST

A radical expression that occurs in Einstein's Theory of Relativity is

$$\frac{1}{\sqrt{1 - \dfrac{v^2}{c^2}}}$$

where v is the velocity of an object and c is the speed of light.

➡️ Simplify: $\sqrt{\dfrac{4x^2}{z^6}}$

$$\sqrt{\frac{4x^2}{z^6}} = \frac{\sqrt{4x^2}}{\sqrt{z^6}}$$

$$= \frac{\sqrt{2^2 x^2}}{\sqrt{z^6}} = \frac{2x}{z^3}$$

- Rewrite the radical expression as the quotient of the square roots.

- Simplify.

➡️ Simplify: $\sqrt{\dfrac{24x^3 y^7}{3x^7 y^2}}$

$$\sqrt{\frac{24x^3 y^7}{3x^7 y^2}} = \sqrt{\frac{8y^5}{x^4}}$$

$$= \frac{\sqrt{8y^5}}{\sqrt{x^4}}$$

$$= \frac{\sqrt{2^3 y^5}}{\sqrt{x^4}}$$

$$= \frac{\sqrt{2^2 y^4}\sqrt{2y}}{\sqrt{x^4}}$$

$$= \frac{2y^2 \sqrt{2y}}{x^2}$$

- Simplify the radicand.

- Rewrite the radical expression as the quotient of the square roots.

- Simplify.

➡️ Simplify: $\dfrac{\sqrt{4x^2 y}}{\sqrt{xy}}$

$$\frac{\sqrt{4x^2 y}}{\sqrt{xy}} = \sqrt{\frac{4x^2 y}{xy}}$$

$$= \sqrt{4x}$$

$$= \sqrt{2^2}\sqrt{x}$$

$$= 2\sqrt{x}$$

- Use the Quotient Property of Square Roots.

- Simplify the radicand.

- Simplify the radical expression.

A radical expression is not considered to be in simplest form if a radical remains in the denominator. The procedure used to remove a radical from the denominator is called **rationalizing the denominator.**

➡️ Simplify: $\dfrac{2}{\sqrt{3}}$

$$\frac{2}{\sqrt{3}} = \frac{2}{\sqrt{3}} \cdot \boxed{\frac{\sqrt{3}}{\sqrt{3}}}$$

$$= \frac{2\sqrt{3}}{(\sqrt{3})^2}$$

$$= \frac{2\sqrt{3}}{3}$$

- Multiply the expression by $\dfrac{\sqrt{3}}{\sqrt{3}}$, which equals 1.

- The radicand in the denominator is a perfect square.

- Simplify.

The radical expression is in simplest form, because no radical remains in the denominator and the radical in the numerator contains no perfect-square factors other than 1.

When the denominator contains a binomial radical expression, simplify the radical expression by multiplying the numerator and denominator by the conjugate of the denominator.

➡ Simplify: $\dfrac{\sqrt{2y}}{\sqrt{y}+3}$

$\dfrac{\sqrt{2y}}{\sqrt{y}+3} = \dfrac{\sqrt{2y}}{\sqrt{y}+3} \cdot \dfrac{\sqrt{y}-3}{\sqrt{y}-3}$

• Multiply the numerator and denominator by $\sqrt{y}-3$, the conjugate of $\sqrt{y}+3$.

$= \dfrac{\sqrt{2y^2}-3\sqrt{2y}}{(\sqrt{y})^2-3^2}$

• Simplify.

$= \dfrac{y\sqrt{2}-3\sqrt{2y}}{y-9}$

Example 5

Simplify: $\dfrac{\sqrt{4x^2y^5}}{\sqrt{3x^4y}}$

Solution

$\dfrac{\sqrt{4x^2y^5}}{\sqrt{3x^4y}} = \sqrt{\dfrac{2^2x^2y^5}{3x^4y}} = \sqrt{\dfrac{2^2y^4}{3x^2}} = \dfrac{\sqrt{2^2y^4}}{\sqrt{3x^2}} = \dfrac{2y^2}{x\sqrt{3}}$

$= \dfrac{2y^2}{x\sqrt{3}} \cdot \dfrac{\sqrt{3}}{\sqrt{3}} = \dfrac{2y^2\sqrt{3}}{3x}$

You Try It 5

Simplify: $\dfrac{\sqrt{15x^6y^7}}{\sqrt{3x^7y^9}}$

Your solution

Example 6

Simplify: $\dfrac{\sqrt{2}}{\sqrt{2}+\sqrt{6}}$

Solution

The denominator contains a binomial expression. Multiply the numerator and denominator by the conjugate of the denominator.

$\dfrac{\sqrt{2}}{\sqrt{2}+\sqrt{6}} = \dfrac{\sqrt{2}}{\sqrt{2}+\sqrt{6}} \cdot \dfrac{\sqrt{2}-\sqrt{6}}{\sqrt{2}-\sqrt{6}}$

$= \dfrac{\sqrt{4}-\sqrt{12}}{2-6} = \dfrac{2-2\sqrt{3}}{-4} = \dfrac{2(1-\sqrt{3})}{-4}$

$= \dfrac{1-\sqrt{3}}{-2} = -\dfrac{1-\sqrt{3}}{2}$

You Try It 6

Simplify: $\dfrac{\sqrt{3}}{\sqrt{3}-\sqrt{6}}$

Your solution

Example 7

Simplify: $\dfrac{3-\sqrt{5}}{2+3\sqrt{5}}$

Solution

$\dfrac{3-\sqrt{5}}{2+3\sqrt{5}} = \dfrac{3-\sqrt{5}}{2+3\sqrt{5}} \cdot \dfrac{2-3\sqrt{5}}{2-3\sqrt{5}}$

$= \dfrac{6-9\sqrt{5}-2\sqrt{5}+3(\sqrt{5})^2}{4-9\cdot5}$

$= \dfrac{6-11\sqrt{5}+15}{4-45}$

$= \dfrac{21-11\sqrt{5}}{-41} = -\dfrac{21-11\sqrt{5}}{41}$

You Try It 7

Simplify: $\dfrac{5+\sqrt{y}}{1-2\sqrt{y}}$

Your solution

Solutions on p. S24

10.3 Exercises

· ·

Objective A

Simplify.

1. $\sqrt{5} \cdot \sqrt{5}$

2. $\sqrt{11} \cdot \sqrt{11}$

3. $\sqrt{3} \cdot \sqrt{12}$

4. $\sqrt{2} \cdot \sqrt{8}$

5. $\sqrt{x} \cdot \sqrt{x}$

6. $\sqrt{y} \cdot \sqrt{y}$

7. $\sqrt{xy^3} \cdot \sqrt{x^5y}$

8. $\sqrt{a^3b^5} \cdot \sqrt{ab^5}$

9. $\sqrt{3a^2b^5} \cdot \sqrt{6ab^7}$

10. $\sqrt{5x^3y} \cdot \sqrt{10x^2y}$

11. $\sqrt{6a^3b^2} \cdot \sqrt{24a^5b}$

12. $\sqrt{8ab^5} \cdot \sqrt{12a^7b}$

13. $\sqrt{2}(\sqrt{2} - \sqrt{3})$

14. $3(\sqrt{12} - \sqrt{3})$

15. $\sqrt{x}(\sqrt{x} - \sqrt{y})$

16. $\sqrt{b}(\sqrt{a} - \sqrt{b})$

17. $\sqrt{5}(\sqrt{10} - \sqrt{x})$

18. $\sqrt{6}(\sqrt{y} - \sqrt{18})$

19. $\sqrt{8}(\sqrt{2} - \sqrt{5})$

20. $\sqrt{10}(\sqrt{20} - \sqrt{a})$

21. $(\sqrt{x} - 3)^2$

22. $(2\sqrt{a} - y)^2$

23. $\sqrt{3a}(\sqrt{3a} - \sqrt{3b})$

24. $\sqrt{5x}(\sqrt{10x} - \sqrt{x})$

25. $\sqrt{2ac} \cdot \sqrt{5ab} \cdot \sqrt{10cb}$

26. $\sqrt{3xy} \cdot \sqrt{6x^3y} \cdot \sqrt{2y^2}$

27. $(\sqrt{5} + 3)(2\sqrt{5} - 4)$

28. $(2 - 3\sqrt{7})(5 + 2\sqrt{7})$

29. $(4 + \sqrt{8})(3 + \sqrt{2})$

30. $(6 - \sqrt{27})(2 + \sqrt{3})$

31. $(2\sqrt{x} + 4)(3\sqrt{x} - 1)$

32. $(5 + \sqrt{y})(6 - 3\sqrt{y})$

33. $(3\sqrt{x} - 2y)(5\sqrt{x} - 4y)$

34. $(5\sqrt{x} + 2\sqrt{y})(3\sqrt{x} - \sqrt{y})$

35. $(\sqrt{x} - \sqrt{y})(\sqrt{x} + \sqrt{y})$

Objective B

Simplify.

36. $\dfrac{\sqrt{32}}{\sqrt{2}}$

37. $\dfrac{\sqrt{45}}{\sqrt{5}}$

38. $\dfrac{\sqrt{98}}{\sqrt{2}}$

39. $\dfrac{\sqrt{48}}{\sqrt{3}}$

40. $\dfrac{\sqrt{27a}}{\sqrt{3a}}$

41. $\dfrac{\sqrt{72x^5}}{\sqrt{2x}}$

42. $\dfrac{\sqrt{15x^3y}}{\sqrt{3xy}}$

43. $\dfrac{\sqrt{40x^5y^2}}{\sqrt{5xy}}$

44. $\dfrac{\sqrt{2a^5b^4}}{\sqrt{98ab^4}}$

45. $\dfrac{\sqrt{48x^5y^2}}{\sqrt{3x^3y}}$

46. $\dfrac{\sqrt{9xy^2}}{\sqrt{27x}}$

47. $\dfrac{\sqrt{4x^2y}}{\sqrt{3xy^3}}$

48. $\dfrac{\sqrt{16x^3y^2}}{\sqrt{8x^3y}}$

49. $\dfrac{\sqrt{2}}{\sqrt{8}+4}$

50. $\dfrac{1}{\sqrt{2}-3}$

51. $\dfrac{5}{\sqrt{7}-3}$

52. $\dfrac{3}{5+\sqrt{5}}$

53. $\dfrac{\sqrt{3}}{5-\sqrt{27}}$

54. $\dfrac{7}{\sqrt{2}-7}$

55. $\dfrac{3-\sqrt{6}}{5-2\sqrt{6}}$

56. $\dfrac{6-2\sqrt{3}}{4+3\sqrt{3}}$

57. $\dfrac{-6}{4+\sqrt{2}}$

58. $\dfrac{\sqrt{2}+2\sqrt{6}}{2\sqrt{2}-3\sqrt{6}}$

59. $\dfrac{2\sqrt{3}-\sqrt{6}}{5\sqrt{3}+2\sqrt{6}}$

60. $\dfrac{3+\sqrt{x}}{2-\sqrt{x}}$

61. $\dfrac{-\sqrt{15}}{3-\sqrt{12}}$

62. $\dfrac{\sqrt{a}-4}{2\sqrt{a}+2}$

63. $\dfrac{\sqrt{xy}}{\sqrt{x}-\sqrt{y}}$

64. $\dfrac{\sqrt{x}}{\sqrt{x}-\sqrt{y}}$

65. $\dfrac{-12}{\sqrt{6}-3}$

APPLYING THE CONCEPTS

66. In your own words, describe the process of rationalizing the denominator.

67. Show that $(1+\sqrt{6})$ and $(1-\sqrt{6})$ are solutions of the equation $x^2 - 2x - 5 = 0$.

68. Answer true or false. If the answer is false, write the correct answer.

a. $(\sqrt{y})^4 = y^2$ **b.** $(2\sqrt{x})^3 = 8x\sqrt{x}$ **c.** $(\sqrt{x}+1)^2 = x+1$ **d.** $\dfrac{1}{2-\sqrt{3}} = 2+\sqrt{3}$

10.4 Solving Equations Containing Radical Expressions

Objective A *To solve an equation containing a radical expression* ....   CT

An equation that contains a variable expression in a radicand is a **radical equation.**

$$\sqrt{x} = 4$$
$$\sqrt{x + 2} = \sqrt{x - 7}$$
Radical equations

The following property of equality states that if two numbers are equal, the squares of the numbers are equal. This property is used to solve radical equations.

Property of Squaring Both Sides of an Equation

If a and b are real numbers and $a = b$, then $a^2 = b^2$.

The first step when solving a radical equation is to isolate a radical in the equation.

➡ Solve: $\sqrt{x - 2} - 7 = 0$

$\sqrt{x - 2} - 7 = 0$ • Rewrite the equation with the radical on one side
$\sqrt{x - 2} = 7$ of the equation and the constant on the other side.
$(\sqrt{x - 2})^2 = 7^2$ • Square both sides of the equation.
$x - 2 = 49$ • Solve the resulting equation.
$x = 51$

Check: $\sqrt{x - 2} - 7 = 0$

$$
\begin{array}{c|c}
\sqrt{51 - 2} - 7 & 0 \\
\sqrt{49} - 7 & 0 \\
\sqrt{7^2} - 7 & 0 \\
7 - 7 & 0 \\
0 = 0 & \text{A true equation}
\end{array}
$$

The solution is 51.

When both sides of an equation are squared, the resulting equation may have a solution that is not a solution of the original equation. Checking a proposed solution of a radical equation, as we did in the previous example, is a necessary step.

➡ Solve: $\sqrt{2x - 5} + 3 = 0$

$\sqrt{2x - 5} + 3 = 0$ • Rewrite the equation with the radical on one side
$\sqrt{2x - 5} = -3$ of the equation and the constant on the other side.
$(\sqrt{2x - 5})^2 = (-3)^2$ • Square each side of the equation.
$2x - 5 = 9$ • Solve for x.
$2x = 14$
$x = 7$

TAKE NOTE

Any time each side of an equation is squared, you must check the proposed solution of the equation.

Here is the check for the equation on the previous page.

Check:

$$\begin{array}{r|l} \sqrt{2x-5}+3 & 0 \\ \hline \sqrt{2\cdot 7-5}+3 & 0 \\ \sqrt{14-5}+3 & 0 \\ \sqrt{9}+3 & 0 \\ 3+3 & 0 \\ 6 \neq 0 & \end{array}$$

7 does not check as a solution. The equation has no solution.

Example 1
Solve: $\sqrt{3x}+2=5$

Solution

$$\begin{aligned} \sqrt{3x}+2&=5 \\ \sqrt{3x}&=3 \\ (\sqrt{3x})^2&=3^2 \\ 3x&=9 \\ x&=3 \end{aligned}$$

Check:

$$\begin{array}{r|l} \sqrt{3x}+2 & 5 \\ \hline \sqrt{3\cdot 3}+2 & 5 \\ \sqrt{3^2}+2 & 5 \\ 3+2 & 5 \\ 5 = 5 & \end{array}$$

The solution is 3.

You Try It 1
Solve: $\sqrt{4x}+3=7$

Your solution

Example 2
Solve: $\sqrt{x}-\sqrt{x-5}=1$

Solution

$$\begin{aligned} \sqrt{x}-\sqrt{x-5}&=1 \\ \sqrt{x}&=1+\sqrt{x-5} \\ (\sqrt{x})^2&=(1+\sqrt{x-5})^2 \\ x&=1+2\sqrt{x-5}+(x-5) \\ 4&=2\sqrt{x-5} \\ 2&=\sqrt{x-5} \\ 2^2&=(\sqrt{x-5})^2 \\ 4&=x-5 \\ 9&=x \end{aligned}$$

Check:

$$\begin{array}{r|l} \sqrt{x}-\sqrt{x-5} & 1 \\ \hline \sqrt{9}-\sqrt{9-5} & 1 \\ \sqrt{9}-\sqrt{4} & 1 \\ 3-2 & 1 \\ 1 = 1 & \end{array}$$

The solution is 9.

You Try It 2
Solve: $\sqrt{x}+\sqrt{x+9}=9$

Your solution

Solutions on p. S24

Objective B **To solve application problems** ....

A right triangle contains one 90° angle. The side opposite the 90° angle is called the **hypotenuse.** The other two sides are called **legs.**

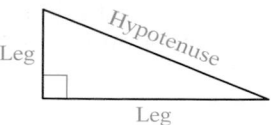

Pythagoras, a Greek mathematician who lived around 550 B.C., is given credit for the Pythagorean Theorem. It states that the square of the hypotenuse of a right triangle is equal to the sum of the squares of the two legs. Actually, this theorem was known to the Babylonians around 1200 B.C.

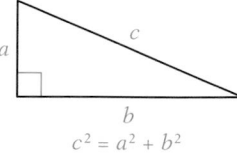

POINT OF INTEREST

The first known proof of this theorem occurs in a Chinese text, *Arithmetic Classic*, which was first written around 600 B.C. (but there are no existing copies) and revised over a period of 500 years. The earliest known copy of this text dates from approximately 100 B.C.

> **Pythagorean Theorem**
>
> If a and b are the lengths of the legs of a right triangle and c is the length of the hypotenuse, then $c^2 = a^2 + b^2$.

Using this theorem, we can find the hypotenuse of a right triangle when we know the two legs. Use the formula

$$\text{Hypotenuse} = \sqrt{(\text{leg})^2 + (\text{leg})^2}$$
$$c = \sqrt{a^2 + b^2}$$
$$= \sqrt{(5)^2 + (12)^2}$$
$$= \sqrt{25 + 144}$$
$$= \sqrt{169}$$
$$= 13$$

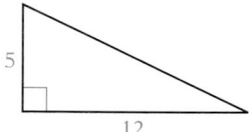

The leg of a right triangle can be found when one leg and the hypotenuse are known. Use the formula

$$\text{Leg} = \sqrt{(\text{hypotenuse})^2 - (\text{leg})^2}$$
$$a = \sqrt{c^2 - b^2}$$
$$= \sqrt{(25)^2 - (20)^2}$$
$$= \sqrt{625 - 400}$$
$$= \sqrt{225}$$
$$= 15$$

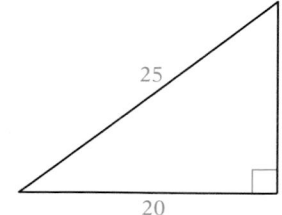

Example 3 and You Try It 3 on the following page illustrate the use of the Pythagorean Theorem. Example 4 and You Try It 4 illustrate other applications of radical equations.

Example 3

A guy wire is attached to a point 20 m above the ground on a telephone pole. The wire is anchored to the ground at a point 8 m from the base of the pole. Find the length of the guy wire. Round to the nearest tenth.

Strategy

To find the length of the guy wire, use the Pythagorean Theorem. One leg is 20 m. The other leg is 8 m. The guy wire is the hypotenuse. Solve the Pythagorean Theorem for the hypotenuse.

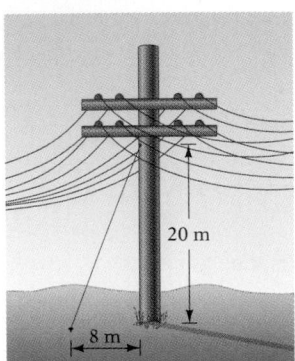

20 m

8 m

Solution

$$c = \sqrt{a^2 + b^2}$$
$$= \sqrt{(20)^2 + (8)^2}$$
$$= \sqrt{400 + 64} = \sqrt{464} \approx 21.5$$

The guy wire has a length of 21.5 m.

Example 4

How far would a submarine periscope have to be above the water to locate a ship 4 mi away? The equation for the distance in miles that the lookout can see is $d = \sqrt{1.5h}$, where h is the height in feet above the surface of the water. Round to the nearest hundredth.

Strategy

To find the height above the water, replace d in the equation with the given value and solve for h.

Solution

$$\sqrt{1.5h} = d$$
$$\sqrt{1.5h} = 4$$
$$(\sqrt{1.5h})^2 = 4^2$$
$$1.5h = 16$$
$$h = \frac{16}{1.5} \approx 10.67$$

The periscope must be 10.67 ft above the water.

You Try It 3

A ladder 8 ft long is resting against a building. How high on the building will the ladder reach when the bottom of the ladder is 3 ft from the building? Round to the nearest hundredth.

Your strategy

Your solution

You Try It 4

Find the length of a pendulum that makes one swing in 2.5 s. The equation for the time for one swing is $T = 2\pi\sqrt{\dfrac{L}{32}}$, where T is the time in seconds and L is the length in feet. Use 3.14 for π. Round to the nearest hundredth.

Your strategy

Your solution

Solutions on p. S24

10.4 Exercises

. . . .

Objective A

Solve and check.

1. $\sqrt{x} = 5$ **2.** $\sqrt{y} = 7$ **3.** $\sqrt{a} = 12$ **4.** $\sqrt{a} = 9$ **5.** $\sqrt{5x} = 5$

6. $\sqrt{4x} + 5 = 2$ **7.** $\sqrt{3x} + 9 = 4$ **8.** $\sqrt{3x - 2} = 4$ **9.** $\sqrt{5x + 6} = 1$

10. $\sqrt{2x + 1} = 7$ **11.** $\sqrt{5x + 4} = 3$ **12.** $0 = 2 - \sqrt{3 - x}$ **13.** $0 = 5 - \sqrt{10 + x}$

14. $\sqrt{5x + 2} = 0$ **15.** $\sqrt{3x - 7} = 0$ **16.** $\sqrt{3x} - 6 = -4$ **17.** $\sqrt{5x} + 8 = 23$

18. $0 = 3 - \sqrt{3x - 9}$ **19.** $\sqrt{x + 2} = \sqrt{x + 1}$ **20.** $\sqrt{3x - 2} = \sqrt{5 - 2x}$

Objective B   *Application Problems*

21. The infield of a baseball diamond is a square. The distance between successive bases is 90 ft. The pitcher's mound is on the diagonal between home plate and second base at a distance of 60.5 ft from home plate. (See the figure to the right.) Is the pitcher's mound more or less than halfway between home plate and second base?

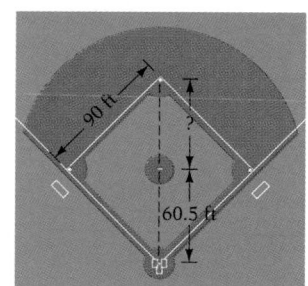

22. The infield of a softball diamond is a square. The distance between successive bases is 60 ft. The pitcher's mound is on the diagonal between home plate and second base at a distance of 46 ft from home plate. Is the pitcher's mound more or less than halfway between home plate and second base?

23. How far would a submarine periscope have to be above the water to locate a ship 5 mi away? The equation for the distance in miles that the lookout can see is $d = \sqrt{1.5h}$, where h is the height in feet above the surface of the water. Round to the nearest hundredth.

24. A 16-foot ladder is leaning against a building. How high on the building will the ladder reach when the bottom of the ladder is 5 ft from the building? (See the figure to the right.) Round to the nearest tenth.

25. The measure of a big-screen television is given by the length of a diagonal across the screen. A 36-inch television has a width of 28.8 in. Find the height of the screen to the nearest tenth of an inch.

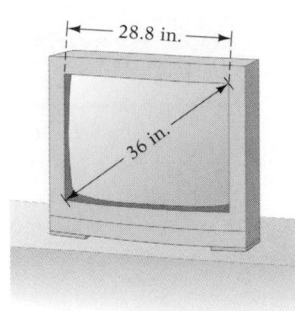

26. The measure of a television screen is given by the length of a diagonal across the screen. A 33-inch big-screen television has a width of 26.4 in. Find the height of the screen to the nearest tenth of an inch.

27. The speed of a child riding a merry-go-round at a carnival is given by the equation $v = \sqrt{12r}$, where v is the speed in feet per second and r is the distance in feet from the center of the merry-go-round to the rider. If a child is moving at 15 ft/s, how far is the child from the center of the merry-go-round?

28. Find the length of a pendulum that makes one swing in 1.5 s. The equation for the time of one swing of a pendulum is $T = 2\pi\sqrt{\dfrac{L}{32}}$, where T is the time in seconds and L is the length in feet. Round to the nearest hundredth.

APPLYING THE CONCEPTS

29. In the coordinate plane, a triangle is formed by drawing lines between the points (0, 0) and (5, 0), (5, 0) and (5, 12), and (5, 12) and (0, 0). Find the perimeter of the triangle.

30. The hypotenuse of a right triangle is $5\sqrt{2}$ cm, and one leg is $4\sqrt{2}$ cm.
  a. Find the perimeter of the triangle.
  b. Find the area of the triangle.

31. If a and b are real numbers and $a^2 = b^2$, does $a = b$? Explain your answer.

32. Can the Pythagorean Theorem be used to find the length of side c of the triangle at the right? If so, determine c. If not, explain why the theorem cannot be used.

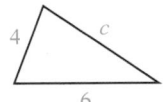

33. A circular fountain is being designed for a triangular plaza in a cultural center. The fountain is placed so that each side of the triangle touches the fountain as shown in the diagram at the right. Find the area of the fountain. The formula for the radius of the circle is given by

$$r = \sqrt{\dfrac{(s - a)(s - b)(s - c)}{s}}$$

where $s = \dfrac{1}{2}(a + b + c)$ and a, b, and c are the lengths of the sides of the triangle. Round to the nearest hundredth.

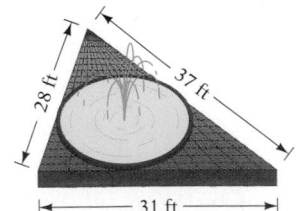

34. A farmer owns a triangular piece of land that measures 100 ft by 120 ft by 150 ft, as shown at the right. Find the maximum area that can be irrigated with a circular irrigation system in which the irrigation does not go outside the triangular shape. Use the formulas in Exercise 33. Round to the nearest hundredth.

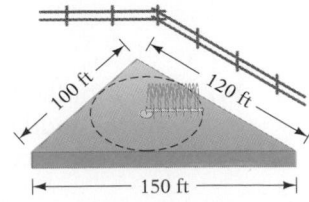

Focus on Problem Solving

Deductive Reasoning

Deductive reasoning uses a rule or statement of fact to reach a conclusion. We established the rule in the section "Ratio and Proportion," Objective C, in the Rational Expressions chapter, that if two angles of one triangle are equal to two angles of another triangle, then the two triangles are similar. Thus any time we establish this fact about two triangles, we know that the triangles are similar. Below are two examples of deductive reasoning.

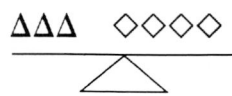

Given that ΔΔΔ = ◇◇◇◇ and ◇◇◇◇ = ÓÓ, then ΔΔΔΔΔΔ is equivalent to how many Ós?

Because 3 Δs = 4 ◇s and 4 ◇s = 2 Ós, 3 Δs = 2 Ós.

6 Δs is twice 3 Δs. We need to find twice 2 Ós, which is 4 Ós.

Therefore, ΔΔΔΔΔΔ = ÓÓÓÓ.

Lomax, Parish, Thorpe, and Wong are neighbors. Each drives a different type of vehicle: a compact car, a sedan, a sports car, or a station wagon. From the following statements, determine which type of vehicle each of the neighbors drives.

1. Although the vehicle owned by Lomax has more mileage on it than does either the sedan or the sports car, it does not have the highest mileage of all four cars. (Use X1 in the chart below to eliminate possibilities due to this statement.)

2. Wong and the owner of the sports car live on one side of the street, and Thorpe and the owner of the compact car live on the other side of the street. (Use X2 to eliminate possibilities due to this statement.)

3. Thorpe owns the vehicle with the most mileage on it. (Use X3 to eliminate possibilities due to this statement.)

	Compact	*Sedan*	*Sports Car*	*Wagon*
Lomax	√	X1	X1	X2
Parish	X2	X2	√	X2
Thorpe	X2	X3	X2	√
Wong	X2		X2	

Lomax drives the compact car, Parish drives the sports car, Thorpe drives the station wagon, and Wong drives the sedan.

4. Given that ‡‡ = ●●●●● and ●●●●● = ΛΛ, then ‡‡‡‡‡ = how many Λs?

5. Given that □□□□□□ = ÓÓÓÓ and ÓÓÓÓ = ÎÎ, then □□□ = how many Îs?

6. Given that ¤¤¤¤ = ΩΩΩ and ΩΩΩ = ΔΔ, then ΔΔΔΔ = how many ¤s?

7. Given that ¥¥¥¥¥ = §§ and §§ = ÂÂÂ, then ÂÂÂÂÂÂ = how many ¥s?

8. Anna, Kay, Megan, and Nicole decide to travel together during spring break, but they need to find a destination where each of them will be able to participate in her favorite sport (golf, horseback riding, sailing, or tennis). From the following statements, determine the favorite sport of each student.

   a. Anna and the student whose favorite sport is sailing both like to swim, whereas Nicole and the student whose favorite sport is tennis would prefer to scuba dive.

   b. Megan and the student whose favorite sport is sailing are roommates. Nicole and the student whose favorite sport is golf each live in a single.

9. Chang, Nick, Pablo, and Saul each take a different form of transportation (bus, car, subway, or taxi) from the office to the airport. From the following statements, determine which form of transportation each takes.

   a. Chang spent more on transportation than the fellow who took the bus but less than the fellow who took the taxi.

   b. Pablo, who did not travel by bus and who spent the least on transportation, arrived at the airport after Nick but before the fellow who took the subway.

   c. Saul spent less on transportation than either Chang or Nick.

Projects and Group Activities

Measurements as Approximations

From arithmetic, you know the rules for rounding decimals.

If the digit to the right of the given place value is less than 5, drop that digit and all digits to the right.

> 6.31 rounded to the nearest tenth is 6.3.

If the digit to the right of the given place value is greater than or equal to 5, increase the given place value by 1 and drop all digits to its right.

> 6.28 rounded to the nearest tenth is 6.3.

Given the rules for rounding numbers, what range of values can the number 6.3 represent? The smallest possible value of 6.3 is 6.25; any number smaller than that would not have been rounded up to 6.3. What about the largest possible value of 6.3? The number 6.34 would be rounded down to 6.3. So would the numbers 6.349, 6.3499, 6.34999, and so on. Therefore, we cannot name the largest possible value of 6.3. We can say that the number must be less than 6.35. Any number less than 6.35 would be rounded down to 6.3. The exact value of 6.3 is greater than or equal to 6.25 and less than 6.35.

The dimensions of a rectangle are given as 4.3 cm by 3.2 cm. Using the smallest and the largest possible values of the length and of the width, we can represent the possible values of the area, A, of the rectangle as follows:

$$4.25(3.15) \leq A < 4.35(3.25)$$

$$13.3875 \leq A < 14.1375$$

The area is greater than or equal to 13.3875 cm² and less than 14.1375 cm².

1. The measurements of the three sides of a triangle are given as 8.37 m, 5.42 m, and 9.61 m. Find the possible lengths of the perimeter of the triangle.

2. The length of a side of a square is given as 4.7 cm. Find the possible values for the area of the square.

3. What are the possible values for the area of a rectangle whose dimensions are 6.5 cm by 7.8 cm?

4. The length of a box is 40 cm, the width is 25 cm, and the height is 8 cm. What are the possible values of the volume of the box?

Distance to the Horizon

In Section 4 of this chapter, we used the formula $d = \sqrt{1.5h}$ to calculate the approximate distance d (in miles) that a person could see who uses a periscope h feet above the water. That formula is derived by using the Pythagorean Theorem.

Consider the diagram (not to scale) at the right, which shows the earth as a sphere and the periscope extending h feet above the surface. From geometry, because AB is tangent to the circle and OA is a radius, triangle AOB is a right triangle. Therefore,

$$(OA)^2 + (AB)^2 = (OB)^2$$

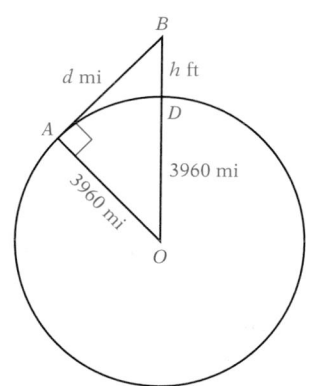

Substituting into this formula, we have

$$3960^2 + d^2 = \left(3960 + \frac{h}{5280}\right)^2$$

$$3960^2 + d^2 = 3960^2 + \frac{2 \cdot 3960}{5280}h + \left(\frac{h}{5280}\right)^2$$

$$d^2 = \frac{3}{2}h + \left(\frac{h}{5280}\right)^2$$

$$d = \sqrt{\frac{3}{2}h + \left(\frac{h}{5280}\right)^2}$$

• Because h is in feet, $\dfrac{h}{5280}$ is in miles.

At this point, an assumption is made that $\sqrt{\frac{3}{2}h + \left(\frac{h}{5280}\right)^2} \approx \sqrt{1.5h}$, where we have written $\frac{3}{2}$ as 1.5. Thus $d \approx \sqrt{1.5h}$ is used to approximate the distance that can be seen using a periscope h feet above the water.

1. Write a paragraph that justifies the assumption that

$$\sqrt{\frac{3}{2}h + \left(\frac{h}{5280}\right)^2} \approx \sqrt{1.5h}$$

(*Suggestion:* Evaluate each expression for various values of h. Because h is the height of a periscope above water, it is unlikely that $h > 25$ ft.)

2. The distance d is the distance from the top of the periscope to A. The distance along the surface of the water is given by arc AD. This distance, D, can be approximated by the equation

$$D \approx \sqrt{1.5h} + 0.306186\left(\sqrt{\frac{h}{5280}}\right)^3$$

Using this formula, calculate D when $h = 10$.

Chapter Summary

Key Words   A *square root* of a positive number x is a number whose square is x.

The *principal square root* of a number is the positive square root.

The symbol $\sqrt{}$ is called a *radical sign* and is used to indicate the principal square root of a number. The *radicand* is the number under the radical sign.

The square of an integer is a *perfect square*.

If a whole number is not a perfect square, its square root can only be approximated. Such numbers are *irrational numbers*. Their decimal representations never terminate or repeat.

Conjugates are binomial expressions that differ only in the sign of a term. (The expressions $a + b$ and $a - b$ are conjugates.)

Rationalizing the denominator is the procedure used to remove a radical from the denominator of a fraction.

A *radical equation* is an equation that contains a variable expression in a radicand.

Essential Rules   *The Product Property of Square Roots*

If a and b are positive real numbers, then $\sqrt{ab} = \sqrt{a}\sqrt{b}$.

The Quotient Property of Square Roots

If a and b are positive real numbers, then $\sqrt{\dfrac{a}{b}} = \dfrac{\sqrt{a}}{\sqrt{b}}$ and $\dfrac{\sqrt{a}}{\sqrt{b}} = \sqrt{\dfrac{a}{b}}$.

Property of Squaring Both Sides of an Equation

If a and b are real numbers and $a = b$, then $a^2 = b^2$.

Pythagorean Theorem

If a and b are legs of a right triangle and c is the hypotenuse, then $c^2 = a^2 + b^2$.

Chapter Review

1. Simplify: $\sqrt{3}(\sqrt{12} - \sqrt{3})$

2. Simplify: $3\sqrt{18a^5b}$

3. Simplify: $2\sqrt{36}$

4. Simplify: $\sqrt{6a}(\sqrt{3a} + \sqrt{2a})$

5. Simplify: $\dfrac{2x}{\sqrt{3} - \sqrt{5}}$

6. Simplify: $-3\sqrt{120}$

7. Solve: $\sqrt{5x} = 10$

8. Simplify: $5\sqrt{48}$

9. Simplify: $\dfrac{\sqrt{98x^7y^9}}{\sqrt{2x^3y}}$

10. Solve: $3 - \sqrt{7x} = 5$

11. Simplify: $6a\sqrt{80b} - \sqrt{180a^2b} + 5a\sqrt{b}$

12. Simplify: $4\sqrt{250}$

13. Simplify: $2x\sqrt{60x^3y^3} + 3x^2y\sqrt{15xy}$

14. Simplify: $(4\sqrt{y} - \sqrt{5})(2\sqrt{y} + 3\sqrt{5})$

15. Simplify: $3\sqrt{12x} + 5\sqrt{48x}$

16. Solve: $\sqrt{2x - 3} + 4 = 0$

17. Simplify: $\dfrac{8}{\sqrt{x} - 3}$

18. Simplify: $4y\sqrt{243x^{17}y^9}$

19. Simplify: $y\sqrt{24y^6}$

20. Solve: $\sqrt{5x + 1} = \sqrt{20x - 8}$

21. Simplify:
$2x^2\sqrt{18x^2y^5} + 6y\sqrt{2x^6y^3} - 9xy^2\sqrt{8x^4y}$

22. Simplify: $\dfrac{16}{\sqrt{a}}$

23. The weight of an object is related to the distance the object is above the surface of the earth. An equation for this relationship is $d = 4000\sqrt{\dfrac{W_0}{W_d}} - 4000$, where W_0 is an object's weight on the surface of the earth and W_d is the object's weight at a distance of d miles above the earth's surface. If a space explorer weighs 36 lb at a distance of 4000 mi above the surface of the earth, how much does the explorer weigh on the surface of the earth?

24. A tsunami is a great sea wave produced by underwater earthquakes or volcanic eruption. The velocity of a tsunami as it approaches land depends on the depth of the water and can be approximated by the equation $v = 3\sqrt{d}$, where d is the depth of the water in feet and v is the velocity of the tsunami in feet per second. Find the depth of the water if the velocity is 30 ft/s.

25. A bicycle will overturn if it rounds a corner too sharply or too fast. An equation for the maximum velocity at which a cyclist can turn a corner without tipping over is $v = 4\sqrt{r}$, where v is the velocity of the bicycle in miles per hour and r is the radius of the corner in feet. What is the radius of the sharpest corner that a cyclist can safely turn if riding at 20 mph?

Chapter Test

1. Simplify: $\sqrt{121x^8y^2}$

2. Simplify: $\sqrt{3x^2y}\sqrt{6xy^2}\sqrt{2x}$

3. Simplify: $5\sqrt{8} - 3\sqrt{50}$

4. Simplify: $\sqrt{45}$

5. Simplify: $\dfrac{\sqrt{162}}{\sqrt{2}}$

6. Solve: $\sqrt{9x} + 3 = 18$

7. Simplify: $\sqrt{32a^5b^{11}}$

8. Simplify: $\dfrac{\sqrt{98a^6b^4}}{\sqrt{2a^3b^2}}$

9. Simplify: $\dfrac{2}{\sqrt{3} - 1}$

10. Simplify: $\sqrt{8x^3y}\sqrt{10xy^4}$

11. Solve: $\sqrt{2x - 4} = \sqrt{3x - 5}$

12. Simplify: $3\sqrt{8y} - 2\sqrt{72x} + 5\sqrt{18y}$

13. Simplify: $\sqrt{72x^7y^2}$

14. Simplify: $(\sqrt{y} - 3)(\sqrt{y} + 5)$

15. Simplify: $2x\sqrt{3xy^3} - 2y\sqrt{12x^3y} - 3xy\sqrt{xy}$

16. Simplify: $\dfrac{2 - \sqrt{5}}{6 + \sqrt{5}}$

17. Simplify: $\sqrt{a}(\sqrt{a} - \sqrt{b})$

18. Simplify: $\sqrt{75}$

19. Find the length of a pendulum that makes one swing in 3 s. The equation for the time of one swing of a pendulum is $T = 2\pi\sqrt{\dfrac{L}{32}}$, where T is the time in seconds and L is the length in feet. Round to the nearest hundredth.

20. The square root of the sum of two consecutive odd integers is equal to 10. Find the larger integer.

Cumulative Review

1. Simplify:

   $\left(\frac{2}{3}\right)^2 \cdot \left(\frac{3}{4} - \frac{3}{2}\right) + \left(\frac{1}{2}\right)^2$

2. Simplify:

   $-3[x - 2(3 - 2x) - 5x] + 2x$

3. Solve:
   $2x - 4[3x - 2(1 - 3x)] = 2(3 - 4x)$

4. Simplify: $(-3x^2y)(-2x^3y^4)$

5. Simplify: $\dfrac{12b^4 - 6b^2 + 2}{-6b^2}$

6. Given $f(x) = \dfrac{2x}{x - 3}$, find $f(-3)$.

7. Factor: $2a^3 - 16a^2 + 30a$

8. Simplify: $\dfrac{3x^3 - 6x^2}{4x^2 + 4x} \cdot \dfrac{3x - 9}{9x^3 - 45x^2 + 54x}$

9. Simplify: $\dfrac{x + 2}{x - 4} - \dfrac{6}{(x - 4)(x - 3)}$

10. Solve: $\dfrac{x}{2x - 5} - 2 = \dfrac{3x}{2x - 5}$

11. Find the equation of the line that contains the point $(-2, -3)$ and has slope $\frac{1}{2}$.

12. Solve by substitution:
    $4x - 3y = 1$
    $2x + y = 3$

13. Solve by the addition method:
    $5x + 4y = 7$
    $3x - 2y = 13$

14. Solve: $3(x - 7) \geq 5x - 12$

15. Simplify: $\sqrt{108}$

16. Simplify: $3\sqrt{32} - 2\sqrt{128}$

17. Simplify: $2a\sqrt{2ab^3} + b\sqrt{8a^3b} - 5ab\sqrt{ab}$

18. Simplify: $\sqrt{2a^9b}\sqrt{98ab^3}\sqrt{2a}$

19. Simplify: $\sqrt{3}(\sqrt{6} - \sqrt{x^2})$

20. Simplify: $\dfrac{\sqrt{320}}{\sqrt{5}}$

21. Simplify: $\dfrac{3}{2 - \sqrt{5}}$

22. Solve: $\sqrt{3x - 2} - 4 = 0$

23. The selling price for a book is $29.40. The markup rate used by the bookstore is 20%. Find the cost of the book. Use the formula $S = C + rC$, where S is the selling price, C is the cost, and r is the markup rate.

24. How many ounces of pure water must be added to 40 oz of a 12% salt solution to make a salt solution that is 5% salt?

25. The sum of two numbers is twenty-one. The product of the two numbers is one hundred four. Find the two numbers.

26. A small water pipe takes twice as long to fill a tank as does a larger water pipe. With both pipes open, it takes 16 h to fill the tank. Find the time it would take the small pipe working alone to fill the tank.

27. Solve by graphing: $3x - 2y = 8$
$\qquad\qquad\qquad\qquad 4x + 5y = 3$

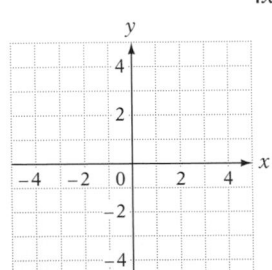

28. Graph the solution set of $3x + y \le 2$.

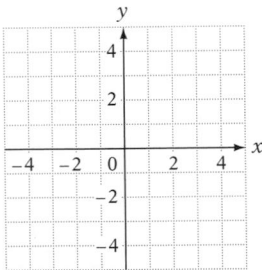

29. The square root of the sum of two consecutive integers is equal to 9. Find the smaller integer.

30. A stone is dropped from a building and hits the ground 5 s later. How high is the building? The equation for the distance an object falls in T seconds is $T = \sqrt{\dfrac{d}{16}}$, where d is the distance in feet.

CHAPTER

11

Quadratic Equations

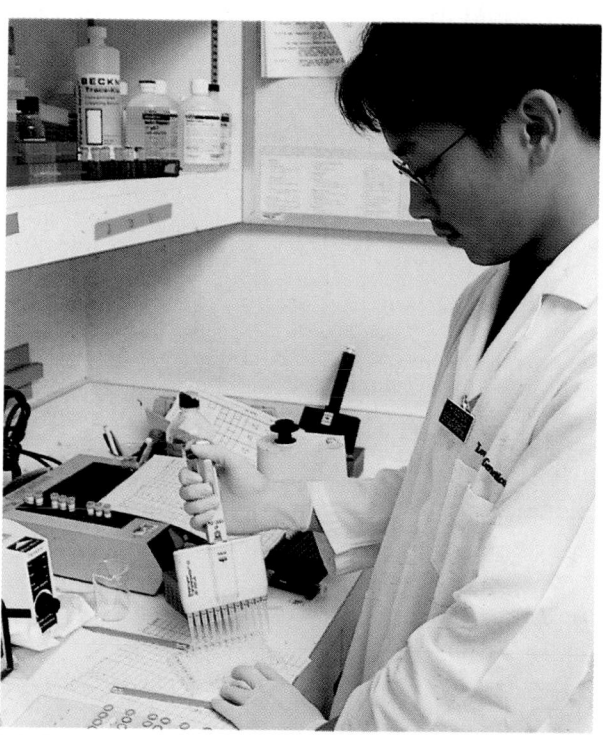

A forensic scientist assists police in the investigation of crimes. Chemistry, biology, and mathematics are critical tools for the forensic scientist when analyzing evidence such as matching the DNA of a suspect to the DNA found at a crime scene.

Objectives

Section 11.1
To solve a quadratic equation by factoring
To solve a quadratic equation by taking square roots

Section 11.2
To solve a quadratic equation by completing the square

Section 11.3
To solve a quadratic equation by using the quadratic formula

Section 11.4
To graph a quadratic equation of the form $y = ax^2 + bx + c$

Section 11.5
To solve application problems

$$(x - a)^2(x^2 + y^2) - bx^2 = 0$$

x

0

y

Algebraic Symbolism

The way in which an algebraic expression or equation is written has gone through several stages of development. First there was the *rhetoric*, which was in vogue until the late 13th century. In this method, expressions were written out in sentences. The word *res* was used to represent an unknown.

Rhetoric: From the additive *res* in the additive *res* results in a square *res*. From the three in an additive *res* comes three additive *res* and from the subtractive four in the additive *res* comes subtractive four *res*. From three in subtractive four comes subtractive twelve.

$$\text{Modern: } (x + 3)(x - 4) = x^2 - x - 12$$

The second stage was *syncoptic*, which was a shorthand in which abbreviations were used for words.

Syncoptic: *a* 6 in *b* quad − *c* plano 4 in *b* + *b* cub

Modern: $6ab^2 - 4cb + b^3$

The current modern stage, called the *symbolic* stage, began with the use of exponents rather than words to symbolize exponential expressions. This occurred near the beginning of the 17th century with the publication of the book *La Geometrie* by René Descartes. Modern notation is still evolving as mathematicians continue to search for convenient methods to symbolize concepts.

11.1 Solving Quadratic Equations by Factoring or by Taking Square Roots

Objective A   *To solve a quadratic equation by factoring* .... (35) CT

An equation of the form $ax^2 + bx + c = 0$, where a, b, and c are constants and $a \neq 0$, is a **quadratic equation.**

$4x^2 - 3x + 1 = 0$, $a = 4$, $b = -3$, $c = 1$
$3x^2 - 4 = 0$, $a = 3$, $b = 0$, $c = -4$
$\dfrac{x^2}{2} - 2x + 4 = 0$, $a = \dfrac{1}{2}$, $b = -2$, $c = 4$

A quadratic equation is also called a **second-degree equation.**

A quadratic equation is in **standard form** when the polynomial is in descending order and equal to zero.

Recall that the Principle of Zero Products states that if the product of two factors is zero, then at least one of the factors must be zero.

If $a \cdot b = 0$,
then $a = 0$ or $b = 0$.

The Principle of Zero Products can be used in solving quadratic equations.

➡ Solve by factoring: $2x^2 - x = 1$

$$2x^2 - x = 1$$
$$2x^2 - x - 1 = 0$$
$$(2x + 1)(x - 1) = 0$$
$$2x + 1 = 0 \qquad x - 1 = 0$$

$$2x = -1 \qquad x = 1$$

$$x = -\frac{1}{2}$$

- Write the equation in standard form.
- Factor.
- Use the Principle of Zero Products to set each factor equal to zero.
- Rewrite each equation in the form *variable = constant.*

TAKE NOTE

You should always check your solutions by substituting the proposed solutions back into the *original* equation.

Check:

$$\begin{array}{c|c} 2x^2 - x = 1 & \\ \hline 2\left(-\dfrac{1}{2}\right)^2 - \left(-\dfrac{1}{2}\right) & 1 \\ 2 \cdot \dfrac{1}{4} + \dfrac{1}{2} & 1 \\ \dfrac{1}{2} + \dfrac{1}{2} & 1 \\ 1 = 1 & \end{array}$$

$$\begin{array}{c|c} 2x^2 - x = 1 & \\ \hline 2(1)^2 - 1 & 1 \\ 2 \cdot 1 - 1 & 1 \\ 2 - 1 & 1 \\ 1 = 1 & \end{array}$$

The solutions are $-\dfrac{1}{2}$ and 1.

➡️ Solve by factoring: $3x^2 - 4x + 8 = (4x + 1)(x - 2)$

$3x^2 - 4x + 8 = (4x + 1)(x - 2)$

$3x^2 - 4x + 8 = 4x^2 - 7x - 2$

$0 = x^2 - 3x - 10$

$0 = (x - 5)(x + 2)$

$x - 5 = 0 \qquad x + 2 = 0$

$x = 5 \qquad\qquad x = -2$

- Multiply the factors on the right side of the equation.
- Write the equation in standard form.
- Factor.
- Use the Principle of Zero Products to set each factor equal to zero.
- Rewrite each equation in the form *variable = constant*.

Check:

$3x^2 - 4x + 8 = (4x + 1)(x - 2)$	
$3(5)^2 - 4(5) + 8$	$(4[5] + 1)(5 - 2)$
$3(25) - 20 + 8$	$(20 + 1)(3)$
$75 - 20 + 8$	$(21)(3)$
$63 = 63$	

$3x^2 - 4x + 8 = (4x + 1)(x - 2)$	
$3(-2)^2 - 4(-2) + 8$	$(4[-2] + 1)(-2 - 2)$
$3(4) + 8 + 8$	$(-8 + 1)(-4)$
$12 + 8 + 8$	$(-7)(-4)$
$28 = 28$	

The solutions are 5 and -2.

➡️ Solve by factoring: $x^2 - 10x + 25 = 0$

$x^2 - 10x + 25 = 0$

$(x - 5)(x - 5) = 0$

$x - 5 = 0 \qquad x - 5 = 0$

$x = 5 \qquad\qquad x = 5$

- Factor.
- Use the Principle of Zero Products.
- Solve each equation for *x*.

The solution is 5.

In this last example, 5 is called a **double root** of the quadratic equation.

Example 1

Solve by factoring: $\dfrac{z^2}{2} - \dfrac{z}{4} - \dfrac{1}{4} = 0$

Solution

$\dfrac{z^2}{2} - \dfrac{z}{4} - \dfrac{1}{4} = 0$

$4\left(\dfrac{z^2}{2} - \dfrac{z}{4} - \dfrac{1}{4}\right) = 4(0)$

- Multiply each side by 4.

$2z^2 - z - 1 = 0$

$(2z + 1)(z - 1) = 0$

$2z + 1 = 0 \qquad z - 1 = 0$

$2z = -1 \qquad\quad z = 1$

$z = -\dfrac{1}{2}$

The solutions are $-\dfrac{1}{2}$ and 1.

You Try It 1

Solve by factoring: $\dfrac{3y^2}{2} + y - \dfrac{1}{2} = 0$

Your solution

Solution on p. S25

Objective B   *To solve a quadratic equation by taking square roots* ....

Consider a quadratic equation of the form $x^2 = a$. This equation can be solved by factoring.

$$x^2 = 25$$
$$x^2 - 25 = 0$$
$$(x - 5)(x + 5) = 0$$
$$x = 5 \qquad x = -5$$

The solutions are 5 and -5. The solutions are plus or minus the same number, which is frequently written by using $\pm$; for example, "the solutions are ± 5." Because ± 5 can be written as $\pm\sqrt{25}$, an alternative method of solving this equation is suggested.

The Square Root Property of an Equality

If $x^2 = a$, then $x = \pm\sqrt{a}$.

➡ Solve by taking square roots: $x^2 = 25$

$$x^2 = 25$$
$$\sqrt{x^2} = \sqrt{25}$$
$$x = \pm\sqrt{25} = \pm 5$$

• Take the square root of each side of the equation. Then simplify.

The solutions are 5 and -5.

➡ Solve by taking square roots: $3x^2 = 36$

$$3x^2 = 36$$
$$x^2 = 12$$
$$\sqrt{x^2} = \sqrt{12}$$
$$x = \pm\sqrt{12} = \pm 2\sqrt{3}$$

• Solve for x^2.
• Take the square root of each side.
• Simplify.

The solutions are $2\sqrt{3}$ and $-2\sqrt{3}$.

➡ Solve by taking square roots: $49y^2 - 25 = 0$

$$49y^2 - 25 = 0$$
$$49y^2 = 25$$
$$y^2 = \frac{25}{49}$$
$$\sqrt{y^2} = \sqrt{\frac{25}{49}}$$
$$y = \pm\frac{5}{7}$$

• Solve for y^2.

• Take the square root of each side.

• Simplify.

The solutions are $\frac{5}{7}$ and $-\frac{5}{7}$.

An equation that contains the square of a binomial can be solved by taking square roots.

➡ Solve by taking square roots: $2(x - 1)^2 - 36 = 0$

$$2(x - 1)^2 - 36 = 0$$
$$2(x - 1)^2 = 36$$ • Solve for $(x - 1)^2$.
$$(x - 1)^2 = 18$$
$$\sqrt{(x - 1)^2} = \sqrt{18}$$ • Take the square root of each side of the equation.
$$x - 1 = \pm\sqrt{18}$$
$$x - 1 = \pm 3\sqrt{2}$$ • Simplify.

$$x - 1 = 3\sqrt{2} \qquad x - 1 = -3\sqrt{2}$$ • Solve for x.
$$x = 1 + 3\sqrt{2} \qquad x = 1 - 3\sqrt{2}$$

The solutions are $1 + 3\sqrt{2}$ and $1 - 3\sqrt{2}$.

Example 2
Solve by taking square roots:
$x^2 + 16 = 0$

Solution
$$x^2 + 16 = 0$$
$$x^2 = -16$$
$$\sqrt{x^2} = \sqrt{-16}$$

$\sqrt{-16}$ is not a real number.

The equation has no real number solution.

You Try It 2
Solve by taking square roots:
$x^2 + 81 = 0$

Your solution

Example 3
Solve by taking square roots:
$5(y - 4)^2 = 25$

Solution
$$5(y - 4)^2 = 25$$
$$(y - 4)^2 = 5$$
$$\sqrt{(y - 4)^2} = \sqrt{5}$$
$$y - 4 = \pm\sqrt{5}$$
$$y = 4 \pm\sqrt{5}$$

The solutions are $4 + \sqrt{5}$ and $4 - \sqrt{5}$.

You Try It 3
Solve by taking square roots:
$7(z + 2)^2 = 21$

Your solution

Solutions on p. S25

11.1 Exercises

· ·

Objective A

Solve by factoring.

1. $x^2 + 2x - 15 = 0$ **2.** $t^2 + 3t - 10 = 0$ **3.** $z^2 - 4z + 3 = 0$ **4.** $s^2 - 5s + 4 = 0$

5. $p^2 + 3p + 2 = 0$ **6.** $v^2 + 6v + 5 = 0$ **7.** $x^2 - 6x + 9 = 0$ **8.** $y^2 - 8y + 16 = 0$

9. $12y^2 + 8y = 0$ **10.** $6x^2 - 9x = 0$ **11.** $r^2 - 10 = 3r$ **12.** $t^2 - 12 = 4t$

13. $3v^2 - 5v + 2 = 0$ **14.** $2p^2 - 3p - 2 = 0$ **15.** $3s^2 + 8s = 3$

16. $3x^2 + 5x = 12$ **17.** $\dfrac{3}{4}z^2 - z = -\dfrac{1}{3}$ **18.** $\dfrac{r^2}{2} = 1 - \dfrac{r}{12}$

19. $4t^2 = 4t + 3$ **20.** $5y^2 + 11y = 12$ **21.** $4v^2 - 4v + 1 = 0$

22. $9s^2 - 6s + 1 = 0$ **23.** $x^2 - 9 = 0$ **24.** $t^2 - 16 = 0$

25. $4y^2 - 1 = 0$ **26.** $9z^2 - 4 = 0$ **27.** $x + 15 = x(x - 1)$

28. $p + 18 = p(p - 2)$ **29.** $r^2 - r - 2 = (2r - 1)(r - 3)$ **30.** $s^2 + 5s - 4 = (2s + 1)(s - 4)$

Objective B

Solve by taking square roots.

31. $x^2 = 36$ **32.** $y^2 = 49$ **33.** $v^2 - 1 = 0$

34. $z^2 - 64 = 0$ **35.** $4x^2 - 49 = 0$ **36.** $9w^2 - 64 = 0$

37. $9y^2 = 4$

38. $4z^2 = 25$

39. $16v^2 - 9 = 0$

40. $25x^2 - 64 = 0$

41. $y^2 + 81 = 0$

42. $z + 49 = 0$

43. $w^2 - 24 = 0$

44. $v^2 - 48 = 0$

45. $(x - 1)^2 = 36$

46. $(y + 2)^2 = 49$

47. $2(x + 5)^2 = 8$

48. $4(z - 3)^2 = 100$

49. $9(x - 1)^2 - 16 = 0$

50. $4(y + 3)^2 - 81 = 0$

51. $49(v + 1)^2 - 25 = 0$

52. $81(y - 2)^2 - 64 = 0$

53. $(x - 4)^2 - 20 = 0$

54. $(y + 5)^2 - 50 = 0$

55. $(x + 1)^2 + 36 = 0$

56. $2\left(z - \dfrac{1}{2}\right)^2 = 12$

57. $3\left(v + \dfrac{3}{4}\right)^2 = 36$

APPLYING THE CONCEPTS

Solve for x.

58. $(x^2 - 1)^2 = 9$

59. $(x^2 + 3)^2 = 25$

60. $(6x^2 - 5)^2 = 1$

61. $ax^2 - bx = 0, a > 0$ and $b > 0$

62. $ax^2 - b = 0, a > 0$ and $b > 0$

63. $x^2 = x$

64. The value P of an initial investment of A dollars after two years is given by $P = A(1 + r)^2$, where r is the annual percentage rate earned by the investment. If an initial investment of \$1500 grew to a value of \$1782.15 in two years, what was the annual percentage rate?

65. An initial investment of \$5000 grew to a value of \$5832 in two years. Use the formula in Exercise 64 to find the annual percentage rate.

66. The kinetic energy of a moving body is given by $E = \dfrac{1}{2}mv^2$, where E is the kinetic energy, m is the mass, and v is the velocity. What is the velocity of a moving body whose mass is 5 kg and whose kinetic energy is 250 newton-meters?

67. On a certain type of street surface, the equation $d = 0.0074v^2$ can be used to approximate the distance d a car traveling v miles per hour will slide when its brakes are applied. After applying the brakes, the owner of a car involved in an accident skidded 40 ft. Did the traffic officer investigating the accident issue the car owner a ticket for speeding if the speed limit is 65 mph?

11.2 Solving Quadratic Equations by Completing the Square

Objective A   *To solve a quadratic equation by completing the square* ....

Recall that a perfect-square trinomial is the square of a binomial.

Perfect-Square Trinomial		**Square of a Binomial**
$x^2 + 6x + 9$	=	$(x + 3)^2$
$x^2 - 10x + 25$	=	$(x - 5)^2$
$x^2 + 8x + 16$	=	$(x + 4)^2$

For each perfect-square trinomial, the square of $\frac{1}{2}$ of the coefficient of x equals the constant term.

$$x^2 + 6x + 9, \qquad \left(\frac{1}{2} \cdot 6\right)^2 = 9$$

$$x^2 - 10x + 25, \qquad \left[\frac{1}{2}(-10)\right]^2 = 25$$

$$x^2 + 8x + 16, \qquad \left(\frac{1}{2} \cdot 8\right)^2 = 16$$

Adding to a binomial the constant term that makes it a perfect-square trinomial is called **completing the square.**

➡ Complete the square of $x^2 - 8x$. Write the resulting perfect-square trinomial as the square of a binomial.

$$\left[\frac{1}{2}(-8)\right]^2 = 16$$ • Find the constant term.

$$x^2 - 8x + 16$$ • Complete the square of $x^2 - 8x$ by adding the constant term.

$$x^2 - 8x + 16 = (x - 4)^2$$ • Write the resulting perfect-square trinomial as the square of a binomial.

➡ Complete the square of $y^2 + 5y$. Write the resulting perfect-square trinomial as the square of a binomial.

$$\left(\frac{1}{2} \cdot 5\right)^2 = \left(\frac{5}{2}\right)^2 = \frac{25}{4}$$ • Find the constant term.

$$y^2 + 5y + \frac{25}{4}$$ • Complete the square of $y^2 + 5y$ by adding the constant term.

$$y^2 + 5y + \frac{25}{4} = \left(y + \frac{5}{2}\right)^2$$ • Write the resulting perfect-square trinomial as the square of a binomial.

A quadratic equation that cannot be solved by factoring can be solved by completing the square. Add to each side of the equation the term that completes the square. Rewrite the quadratic equation in the form $(x + a)^2 = b$. Take the square root of each side of the equation and then solve for x.

POINT OF INTEREST

Early mathematicians solved quadratic equations by literally *completing the square.* For these mathematicians, all equations had geometric interpretations. They found that a quadratic equation could be solved by making certain figures into squares. See the fourth "Projects and Group Activities" at the end of this chapter for an idea of how this was done.

➡ Solve by completing the square: $x^2 + 8x - 2 = 0$

$$x^2 + 8x - 2 = 0$$
$$x^2 + 8x = 2$$ • Add 2 to each side of the equation.

$$x^2 + 8x + \left(\frac{1}{2} \cdot 8\right)^2 = 2 + \left(\frac{1}{2} \cdot 8\right)^2$$ • Complete the square of $x^2 + 8x$. Add $\left(\frac{1}{2} \cdot 8\right)^2$ to each side of the equation.

$$x^2 + 8x + 16 = 2 + 16$$ • Simplify.

$$(x + 4)^2 = 18$$ • Factor the perfect-square trinomial.

$$\sqrt{(x + 4)^2} = \sqrt{18}$$ • Take the square root of each side of the equation.

$$x + 4 = \pm\sqrt{18} = \pm3\sqrt{2}$$ • Solve for x.

$$x + 4 = -3\sqrt{2} \qquad x + 4 = 3\sqrt{2}$$
$$x = -4 - 3\sqrt{2} \qquad x = -4 + 3\sqrt{2}$$

Check:

$x^2 + 8x - 2 = 0$	
$(-4 - 3\sqrt{2})^2 + 8(-4 - 3\sqrt{2}) - 2$	0
$16 + 24\sqrt{2} + 18 - 32 - 24\sqrt{2} - 2$	0
	$0 = 0$

$x^2 + 8x - 2 = 0$	
$(-4 + 3\sqrt{2})^2 + 8(-4 + 3\sqrt{2}) - 2$	0
$16 - 24\sqrt{2} + 18 - 32 + 24\sqrt{2} - 2$	0
	$0 = 0$

The solutions are $-4 - 3\sqrt{2}$ and $-4 + 3\sqrt{2}$.

If the coefficient of the second-degree term is not 1, a step in completing the square is to multiply each side of the equation by the reciprocal of that coefficient.

➡ Solve by completing the square: $2x^2 - 3x + 1 = 0$

$$2x^2 - 3x + 1 = 0$$
$$2x^2 - 3x = -1$$ • Subtract 1 from each side of the equation.

$$\frac{1}{2}(2x^2 - 3x) = \frac{1}{2} \cdot (-1)$$ • To complete the square, the coefficient of x^2 must be 1. Multiply each side of the equation by $\frac{1}{2}$.

$$x^2 - \frac{3}{2}x = -\frac{1}{2}$$

$$x^2 - \frac{3}{2}x + \left[\frac{1}{2}\left(-\frac{3}{2}\right)\right]^2 = -\frac{1}{2} + \left[\frac{1}{2}\left(-\frac{3}{2}\right)\right]^2$$ • Complete the square. Add $\left[\frac{1}{2}\left(-\frac{3}{2}\right)\right]^2$ to each side of the equation.

$$x^2 - \frac{3}{2}x + \frac{9}{16} = -\frac{1}{2} + \frac{9}{16}$$ • Simplify.

$$\left(x - \frac{3}{4}\right)^2 = \frac{1}{16}$$ • Factor the perfect-square trinomial.

$$\sqrt{\left(x - \frac{3}{4}\right)^2} = \sqrt{\frac{1}{16}}$$ • Take the square root of each side of the equation.

$$x - \frac{3}{4} = \pm\frac{1}{4}$$ • Solve for x.

$$x - \frac{3}{4} = -\frac{1}{4} \qquad x - \frac{3}{4} = \frac{1}{4}$$
$$x = \frac{1}{2} \qquad x = 1$$

The solutions are $\frac{1}{2}$ and 1.

Example 1

Solve by completing the square:
$2x^2 - 4x - 1 = 0$

Solution

$2x^2 - 4x - 1 = 0$

$2x^2 - 4x = 1$

$\frac{1}{2}(2x^2 - 4x) = \frac{1}{2} \cdot 1$

$x^2 - 2x = \frac{1}{2}$

Complete the square.

$x^2 - 2x + 1 = \frac{1}{2} + 1$

$(x - 1)^2 = \frac{3}{2}$

$\sqrt{(x - 1)^2} = \sqrt{\frac{3}{2}}$

$x - 1 = \pm \frac{\sqrt{6}}{2}$

$x - 1 = \frac{\sqrt{6}}{2} \qquad\qquad x - 1 = -\frac{\sqrt{6}}{2}$

$x = 1 + \frac{\sqrt{6}}{2} \qquad\qquad x = 1 - \frac{\sqrt{6}}{2}$

$= \frac{2 + \sqrt{6}}{2} \qquad\qquad = \frac{2 - \sqrt{6}}{2}$

Check:

$$
\begin{array}{c|c}
2x^2 - 4x - 1 = 0 & \\
\hline
2\left(\frac{2 + \sqrt{6}}{2}\right)^2 - 4\left(\frac{2 + \sqrt{6}}{2}\right) - 1 & 0 \\
2\left(\frac{4 + 4\sqrt{6} + 6}{4}\right) - 2(2 + \sqrt{6}) - 1 & 0 \\
2 + 2\sqrt{6} + 3 - 4 - 2\sqrt{6} - 1 & 0 \\
& 0 = 0
\end{array}
$$

$$
\begin{array}{c|c}
2x^2 - 4x - 1 = 0 & \\
\hline
2\left(\frac{2 - \sqrt{6}}{2}\right)^2 - 4\left(\frac{2 - \sqrt{6}}{2}\right) - 1 & 0 \\
2\left(\frac{4 - 4\sqrt{6} + 6}{4}\right) - 2(2 - \sqrt{6}) - 1 & 0 \\
2 - 2\sqrt{6} + 3 - 4 + 2\sqrt{6} - 1 & 0 \\
& 0 = 0
\end{array}
$$

The solutions are $\frac{2 + \sqrt{6}}{2}$ and $\frac{2 - \sqrt{6}}{2}$.

You Try It 1

Solve by completing the square:
$3x^2 - 6x - 2 = 0$

Your solution

Solution on p. S25

Example 2
Solve by completing the square:
$x^2 + 4x + 5 = 0$

Solution
$x^2 + 4x + 5 = 0$
$$x^2 + 4x = -5$$

Complete the square.

$$x^2 + 4x + 4 = -5 + 4$$
$$(x + 2)^2 = -1$$
$$\sqrt{(x + 2)^2} = \sqrt{-1}$$

$\sqrt{-1}$ is not a real number.

The quadratic equation has no real number solution.

You Try It 2
Solve by completing the square:
$x^2 + 6x + 12 = 0$

Your solution

Example 3
Solve $\dfrac{x^2}{4} + \dfrac{3x}{2} + 1 = 0$ by completing the square. Approximate the solutions to the nearest thousandth.

Solution
$$\frac{x^2}{4} + \frac{3x}{2} + 1 = 0$$
$$4\left(\frac{x^2}{4} + \frac{3x}{2} + 1\right) = 4(0)$$
$$x^2 + 6x + 4 = 0$$
$$x^2 + 6x = -4$$

Complete the square.

$$x^2 + 6x + 9 = -4 + 9$$
$$(x + 3)^2 = 5$$
$$\sqrt{(x + 3)^2} = \sqrt{5}$$
$$x + 3 = \pm\sqrt{5}$$

$x + 3 = \sqrt{5}$	$x + 3 = -\sqrt{5}$
$x = -3 + \sqrt{5}$	$x = -3 - \sqrt{5}$
$\approx -3 + 2.236$	$\approx -3 - 2.236$
≈ -0.764	≈ -5.236

The solutions are approximately -0.764 and -5.236.

You Try It 3
Solve $\dfrac{x^2}{8} + x + 1 = 0$ by completing the square. Approximate the solutions to the nearest thousandth.

Your solution

Solutions on p. S25

11.2 Exercises

Objective A

Solve by completing the square.

1. $x^2 + 2x - 3 = 0$ **2.** $y^2 + 4y - 5 = 0$ **3.** $z^2 - 6z - 16 = 0$ **4.** $w^2 + 8w - 9 = 0$

5. $x^2 = 4x - 4$ **6.** $z^2 = 8z - 16$ **7.** $v^2 - 6v + 13 = 0$ **8.** $x^2 + 4x + 13 = 0$

9. $y^2 + 5y + 4 = 0$ **10.** $v^2 - 5v - 6 = 0$ **11.** $w^2 + 7w = 8$ **12.** $y^2 + 5y = -4$

13. $v^2 + 4v + 1 = 0$ **14.** $y^2 - 2y - 5 = 0$ **15.** $x^2 + 6x = 5$

16. $w^2 - 8w = 3$ **17.** $\dfrac{z^2}{2} = z + \dfrac{1}{2}$ **18.** $\dfrac{y^2}{10} = y - 2$

19. $p^2 + 3p = 1$ **20.** $r^2 + 5r = 2$ **21.** $t^2 - 3t = -2$

22. $z^2 - 5z = -3$ **23.** $v^2 + v - 3 = 0$ **24.** $x^2 - x = 1$

25. $y^2 = 7 - 10y$ **26.** $v^2 = 14 + 16v$ **27.** $r^2 - 3r = 5$

28. $s^2 + 3s = -1$ **29.** $t^2 - t = 4$ **30.** $y^2 + y - 4 = 0$

31. $x^2 - 3x + 5 = 0$ **32.** $z^2 + 5z + 7 = 0$ **33.** $2t^2 - 3t + 1 = 0$

34. $2x^2 - 7x + 3 = 0$ **35.** $2r^2 + 5r = 3$ **36.** $2y^2 - 3y = 9$ **37.** $2s^2 = 7s - 6$

38. $2x^2 = 3x + 20$ **39.** $2v^2 = v + 1$ **40.** $2z^2 = z + 3$ **41.** $3r^2 + 5r = 2$

42. $3t^2 - 8t = 3$ **43.** $3y^2 + 8y + 4 = 0$ **44.** $3z^2 - 10z - 8 = 0$ **45.** $4x^2 + 4x - 3 = 0$

46. $4v^2 + 4v - 15 = 0$ **47.** $6s^2 + 7s = 3$ **48.** $6z^2 = z + 2$ **49.** $6p^2 = 5p + 4$

50. $6t^2 = t - 2$ **51.** $4v^2 - 4v - 1 = 0$ **52.** $2s^2 - 4s - 1 = 0$

Solve by completing the square. Approximate the solutions to the nearest thousandth.

53. $y^2 + 3y = 5$ **54.** $w^2 + 5w = 2$ **55.** $2z^2 - 3z = 7$

56. $2x^2 + 3x = 11$ **57.** $4x^2 + 6x - 1 = 0$ **58.** $4x^2 + 2x - 3 = 0$

APPLYING THE CONCEPTS

59. Explain why the equation $(x - 2)^2 = -4$ does not have a real-number solution.

Solve.

60. $\dfrac{x^2}{6} - \dfrac{x}{3} = 1$ **61.** $\sqrt{x + 2} = x - 4$ **62.** $\sqrt{3x + 4} - x = 2$

63. $\dfrac{x}{3} + \dfrac{3}{x} = \dfrac{8}{3}$ **64.** $\dfrac{x + 1}{2} + \dfrac{3}{x - 1} = 4$ **65.** $\dfrac{x - 2}{3} + \dfrac{2}{x + 2} = 4$

66. $4\sqrt{x + 1} - x = 4$ **67.** $\sqrt{2x^2 + 7} = x + 2$ **68.** $3\sqrt{x - 1} + 3 = x$

69. A basketball player shoots at a basket 25 ft away. The height of the ball above the ground at time t is given by $h = -16t^2 + 32t + 6.5$. How many seconds after the ball is released does it hit the basket? *Hint:* When it hits the basket, $h = 10$ ft.

70. A ball player hits a ball. The height of the ball above the ground can be approximated by the equation $h = -16t^2 + 76t + 5$. When will the ball hit the ground? *Hint:* The ball strikes the ground when $h = 0$ ft.

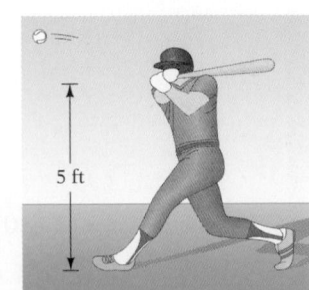

5 ft

11.3 Solving Quadratic Equations by Using the Quadratic Formula

Objective A *To solve a quadratic equation by using the quadratic formula* .... (36)

Any quadratic equation can be solved by completing the square. Applying this method to the standard form of a quadratic equation produces a formula that can be used to solve any quadratic equation.

Solve $ax^2 + bx + c = 0$ by completing the square.

$$ax^2 + bx + c = 0$$

Add the opposite of the constant term to each side of the equation.

$$ax^2 + bx + c + (-c) = 0 + (-c)$$
$$ax^2 + bx = -c$$

Multiply each side of the equation by the reciprocal of a, the coefficient of x^2.

$$\frac{1}{a}(ax^2 + bx) = \frac{1}{a}(-c)$$
$$x^2 + \frac{b}{a}x = -\frac{c}{a}$$

Complete the square by adding $\left(\frac{1}{2} \cdot \frac{b}{a}\right)^2$ to each side of the equation.

$$x^2 + \frac{b}{a}x + \left(\frac{1}{2} \cdot \frac{b}{a}\right)^2 = \left(\frac{1}{2} \cdot \frac{b}{a}\right)^2 - \frac{c}{a}$$
$$x^2 + \frac{b}{a}x + \frac{b^2}{4a^2} = \frac{b^2}{4a^2} - \frac{c}{a}$$

Simplify the right side of the equation.

$$x^2 + \frac{b}{a}x + \frac{b^2}{4a^2} = \frac{b^2}{4a^2} - \left(\frac{c}{a} \cdot \frac{4a}{4a}\right)$$
$$x^2 + \frac{b}{a}x + \frac{b^2}{4a^2} = \frac{b^2}{4a^2} - \frac{4ac}{4a^2}$$
$$x^2 + \frac{b}{a}x + \frac{b^2}{4a^2} = \frac{b^2 - 4ac}{4a^2}$$

Factor the perfect-square trinomial on the left side of the equation.

$$\left(x + \frac{b}{2a}\right)^2 = \frac{b^2 - 4ac}{4a^2}$$

Take the square root of each side of the equation.

$$\sqrt{\left(x + \frac{b}{2a}\right)^2} = \sqrt{\frac{b^2 - 4ac}{4a^2}}$$
$$x + \frac{b}{2a} = \pm\frac{\sqrt{b^2 - 4ac}}{2a}$$

Solve for x.

$$x + \frac{b}{2a} = \frac{\sqrt{b^2 - 4ac}}{2a} \qquad\qquad x + \frac{b}{2a} = -\frac{\sqrt{b^2 - 4ac}}{2a}$$
$$x = -\frac{b}{2a} + \frac{\sqrt{b^2 - 4ac}}{2a} \qquad\qquad x = -\frac{b}{2a} - \frac{\sqrt{b^2 - 4ac}}{2a}$$
$$= \frac{-b + \sqrt{b^2 - 4ac}}{2a} \qquad\qquad = \frac{-b - \sqrt{b^2 - 4ac}}{2a}$$

The Quadratic Formula

The solutions of $ax^2 + bx + c = 0$, $a \neq 0$, are

$$\frac{-b \pm \sqrt{b^2 - 4ac}}{2a}$$

➡ Solve by using the quadratic formula: $2x^2 = 4x - 1$.

First write the equation in standard form. Then use the quadratic formula.

$$2x^2 = 4x - 1$$
$$2x^2 - 4x + 1 = 0$$
$$x = \frac{-b \pm \sqrt{b^2 - 4ac}}{2a}$$
$$= \frac{-(-4) \pm \sqrt{(-4)^2 - (4 \cdot 2 \cdot 1)}}{2 \cdot 2}$$
$$= \frac{4 \pm \sqrt{16 - 8}}{4} = \frac{4 \pm \sqrt{8}}{4}$$
$$= \frac{4 \pm 2\sqrt{2}}{4} = \frac{2 \pm \sqrt{2}}{2}$$

- Subtract $4x$ and add 1 to each side of the equation.
- The quadratic formula.
- $a = 2$, $b = -4$, $c = 1$. Replace a, b, and c by their values.
- Simplify.

The solutions are $\frac{2 + \sqrt{2}}{2}$ and $\frac{2 - \sqrt{2}}{2}$.

Example 1
Solve by using the quadratic formula:
$2x^2 - 3x + 1 = 0$

Solution
$2x^2 - 3x + 1 = 0$ • $a = 2$, $b = -3$, $c = 1$
$$x = \frac{-(-3) \pm \sqrt{(-3)^2 - 4(2)(1)}}{2 \cdot 2}$$
$$= \frac{3 \pm \sqrt{9 - 8}}{4} = \frac{3 \pm \sqrt{1}}{4} = \frac{3 \pm 1}{4}$$
$$x = \frac{3 + 1}{4} \qquad x = \frac{3 - 1}{4}$$
$$= \frac{4}{4} = 1 \qquad = \frac{2}{4} = \frac{1}{2}$$

The solutions are 1 and $\frac{1}{2}$.

You Try It 1
Solve by using the quadratic formula:
$3x^2 + 4x - 4 = 0$

Your solution

Example 2
Solve by using the quadratic formula:
$\frac{x^2}{2} = 2x - \frac{5}{4}$

Solution $\frac{x^2}{2} = 2x - \frac{5}{4}$
$$4\left(\frac{x^2}{2}\right) = 4\left(2x - \frac{5}{4}\right)$$
$$2x^2 = 8x - 5$$
$2x^2 - 8x + 5 = 0$ • $a = 2$, $b = -8$, $c = 5$
$$x = \frac{-(-8) \pm \sqrt{(-8)^2 - 4(2)(5)}}{2 \cdot 2}$$
$$= \frac{8 \pm \sqrt{64 - 40}}{4} = \frac{8 \pm \sqrt{24}}{4}$$
$$= \frac{8 \pm 2\sqrt{6}}{4} = \frac{4 \pm \sqrt{6}}{2}$$

The solutions are $\frac{4 + \sqrt{6}}{2}$ and $\frac{4 - \sqrt{6}}{2}$.

You Try It 2
Solve by using the quadratic formula:
$\frac{x^2}{4} + \frac{x}{2} = \frac{1}{4}$

Your solution

Solutions on p. S26

11.3 Exercises

Objective A

Solve by using the quadratic formula.

1. $x^2 - 4x - 5 = 0$

2. $y^2 + 3y + 2 = 0$

3. $z^2 - 2z - 15 = 0$

4. $v^2 + 5v + 4 = 0$

5. $y^2 = 2y + 3$

6. $w^2 = 3w + 18$

7. $r^2 = 5 - 4r$

8. $z^2 = 3 - 2z$

9. $2y^2 - y - 1 = 0$

10. $2t^2 - 5t + 3 = 0$

11. $w^2 + 3w + 5 = 0$

12. $x^2 - 2x + 6 = 0$

13. $p^2 - p = 0$

14. $2v^2 + v = 0$

15. $4t^2 - 9 = 0$

16. $4s^2 - 25 = 0$

17. $4y^2 + 4y = 15$

18. $6y^2 + 5y - 4 = 0$

19. $2x^2 + x + 1 = 0$

20. $3r^2 - r + 2 = 0$

21. $\dfrac{1}{2}t^2 - t = \dfrac{5}{2}$

22. $y^2 - 4y = 6$

23. $\dfrac{1}{3}t^2 + 2t - \dfrac{1}{3} = 0$

24. $z^2 + 4z + 1 = 0$

25. $w^2 = 4w + 9$

26. $y^2 = 8y + 3$

27. $9y^2 + 6y - 1 = 0$

28. $9s^2 - 6s - 2 = 0$

29. $4p^2 + 4p + 1 = 0$

30. $9z^2 + 12z + 4 = 0$

31. $\dfrac{x^2}{2} = x - \dfrac{5}{4}$

32. $r^2 = \dfrac{5}{3}r - 2$

33. $4p^2 + 16p = -11$

34. $4y^2 - 12y = -1$

35. $4x^2 = 4x + 11$

36. $4s^2 + 12s = 3$ **37.** $9v^2 = -30v - 23$ **38.** $9t^2 = 30t + 17$

Solve by using the quadratic formula. Approximate the solutions to the nearest thousandth.

39. $x^2 - 2x - 21 = 0$ **40.** $y^2 + 4y - 11 = 0$ **41.** $s^2 - 6s - 13 = 0$

42. $w^2 + 8w - 15 = 0$ **43.** $2p^2 - 7p - 10 = 0$ **44.** $3t^2 - 8t - 1 = 0$

45. $4z^2 + 8z - 1 = 0$ **46.** $4x^2 + 7x + 1 = 0$ **47.** $5v^2 - v - 5 = 0$

APPLYING THE CONCEPTS

48. Factoring, completing the square, and using the quadratic formula are three methods of solving quadratic equations. Describe each method, and cite the advantages and disadvantages of using each.

49. Explain why the equation $0x^2 + 3x + 4 = 0$ cannot be solved by the quadratic formula.

50. Solve $x^2 + ax + b = 0$ for x.

51. True or False?
a. The equations $x = \sqrt{12 - x}$ and $x^2 = 12 - x$ have the same solutions.
b. If $\sqrt{a} + \sqrt{b} = c$, then $a + b = c^2$.
c. $\sqrt{9} = \pm 3$
d. $\sqrt{x^2} = |x|$

Solve.

52. $\sqrt{x + 3} = x - 3$ **53.** $\sqrt{x + 4} = x + 4$ **54.** $\sqrt{x + 1} = x - 1$

55. $\sqrt{x^2 + 2x + 1} = x - 1$ **56.** $\dfrac{x}{4} + \dfrac{3}{x} = \dfrac{5}{2}$ **57.** $\dfrac{x + 1}{5} - \dfrac{4}{x - 1} = 2$

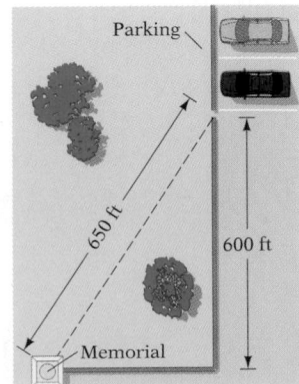

58. An L-shaped sidewalk from the parking lot to a memorial is shown in the figure at the right. The distance directly across the grass to the memorial is 650 ft. The distance to the corner is 600 ft. Find the distance from the corner to the memorial.

59. A commuter plane leaves an airport traveling due south at 400 mph. Another plane leaving at the same time travels due east at 300 mph. Find the distance between the two planes after 2 h.

11.4 Graphing Quadratic Equations in Two Variables

Objective A   **To graph a quadratic equation of the form $y = ax^2 + bx + c$** ....

An equation of the form $y = ax^2 + bx + c$, $a \neq 0$, is a **quadratic equation in two variables.** Examples of quadratic equations in two variables are shown at the right.

$$y = 3x^2 - x + 1$$
$$y = -x^2 - 3$$
$$y = 2x^2 - 5x$$

For these equations, y is a function of x, and we can write $f(x) = ax^2 + bx + c$. This represents a **quadratic function.**

The graph of a quadratic equation in two variables is a **parabola.** The graph is cup shaped and opens either up or down. The graphs of two parabolas are shown below.

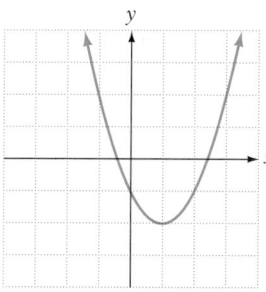

Parabola that opens up

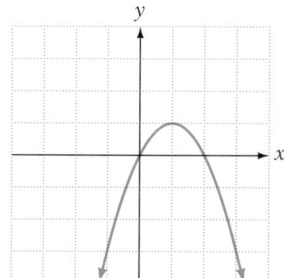

Parabola that opens down

➡ Graph $y = x^2 - 2x - 3$.

x	y
0	-3
1	-4
-1	0
2	-3
3	0

• Find several solutions of the equation. Because the graph is not a straight line, several solutions must be found in order to determine the cup shape. Display the ordered-pair solutions in a table.

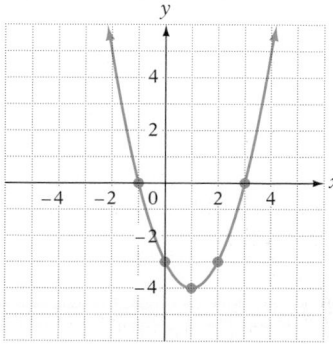

• Graph the ordered-pair solutions on a rectangular coordinate system. Draw a parabola through the points.

➡ Graph $y = -2x^2 + 1$.

x	y
0	1
1	-1
-1	-1
2	-7
-2	-7

• Find enough solutions of the equation to determine the cup shape. Display the ordered-pair solutions in a table.

• Graph the ordered-pair solutions on a rectangular coordinate system. Draw a parabola through the points.

Note in the example on page 493 that the coefficient of x^2 is **positive** and the graph **opens up.** In the example above, the coefficient of x^2 is **negative** and the graph **opens down.**

Example 1 Graph $y = x^2 - 2x$.

Solution

x	y
0	0
1	-1
-1	3
2	0
3	3

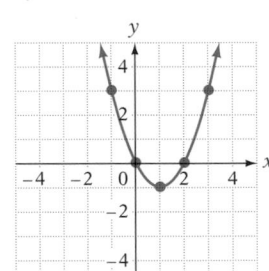

You Try It 1 Graph $y = x^2 + 2$.

Your solution

Example 2 Graph $y = -x^2 + 4x - 4$.

Solution

x	y
0	-4
1	-1
2	0
3	-1
4	-4

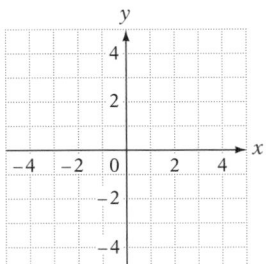

You Try It 2 Graph $y = -x^2 - 2x - 1$.

Your solution

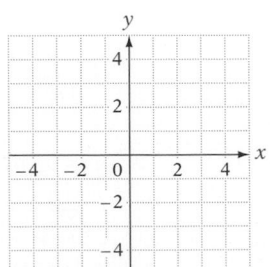

Solutions on p. S26

11.4 Exercises

Objective A

Graph.

1. $y = x^2$

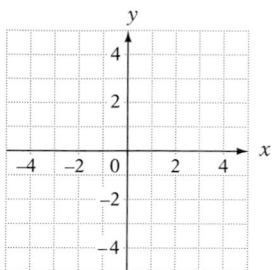

2. $y = -x^2$

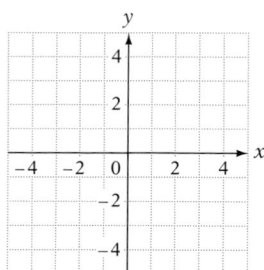

3. $y = -x^2 + 1$

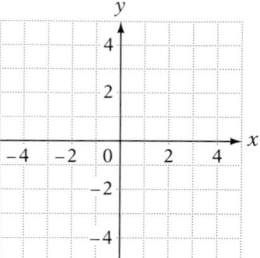

4. $y = x^2 - 1$

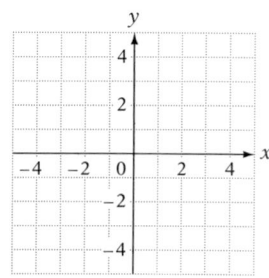

5. $y = 2x^2$

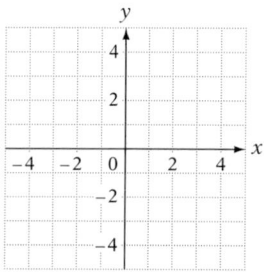

6. $y = \dfrac{1}{2}x^2$

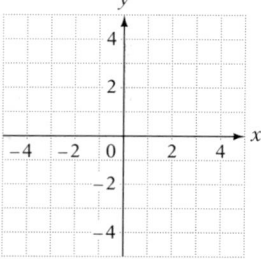

7. $y = -\dfrac{1}{2}x^2 + 1$

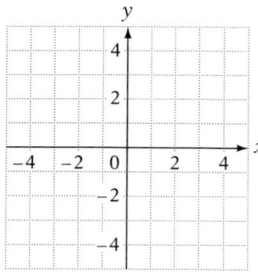

8. $y = 2x^2 - 1$

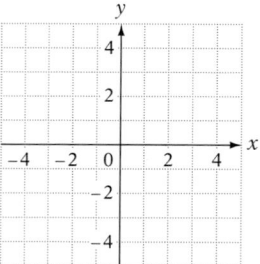

9. $y = x^2 - 4x$

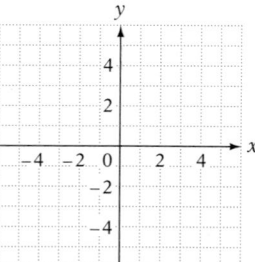

10. $y = x^2 + 4x$

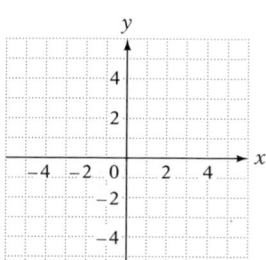

11. $y = x^2 - 2x + 3$

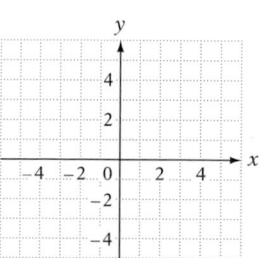

12. $y = x^2 - 4x + 2$

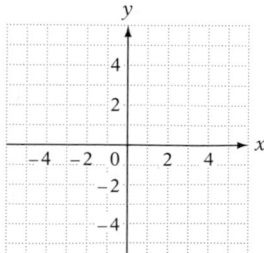

13. $y = -x^2 + 2x + 3$

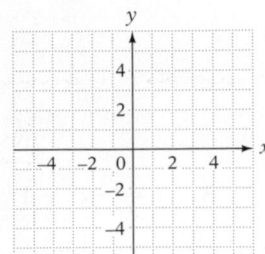

14. $y = -x^2 - 2x + 3$

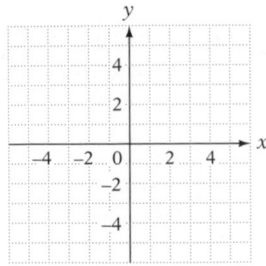

15. $y = -x^2 + 4x - 4$

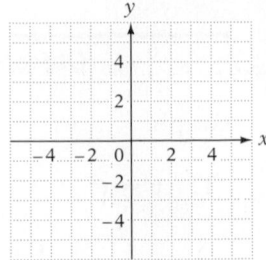

16. $y = -x^2 + 6x - 9$

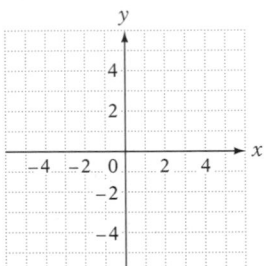

17. $y = (x - 2)^2$

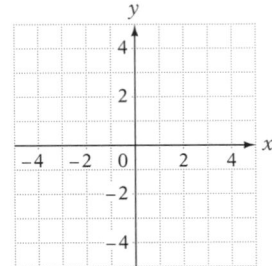

18. $y = -(x + 1)^2$

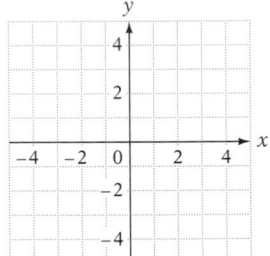

APPLYING THE CONCEPTS

Determine whether the graph of the equation opens up or down.

19. $y = -\dfrac{1}{3}x^2 + 5$

20. $y = x^2 - 2x + 3$

21. $y = -x^2 + 4x - 1$

Show that the equation is a quadratic equation in two variables by writing it in the form $y = ax^2 + bx + c$.

22. $y + 1 = (x - 4)^2$

23. $y - 2 = 3(x + 1)^2$

24. $y - 4 = 2(x - 3)^2$

The x-intercepts of the graph of $y = ax^2 + bx + c$ occur when $y = 0$. Therefore, the x-coordinate of an x-intercept is a solution of $ax^2 + bx + c = 0$. Determine the x-intercepts of the graphs of the following equations.

25. $y = x^2 - 9$

26. $y = x^2 - 4x$

27. $y = 2x^2 - x - 1$

Evaluate the function.

28. Find $f(3)$ when $f(x) = x^2 + 3$.

29. Find $g(2)$ when $g(x) = x^2 - 2x - 3$.

30. Find $S(-2)$ when $S(t) = 2t^2 - 3t - 1$.

31. Find $P(-3)$ when $P(x) = 3x^2 - 6x - 7$.

11.5 Application Problems

Objective A   *To solve application problems* ....

The application problems in this section are varieties of those problems solved earlier in the text. Each of the strategies for the problems in this section will result in a quadratic equation.

➡ In 5 h, two campers rowed 12 mi down a stream and then rowed back to their campsite. The rate of the stream's current was 1 mph. Find the rate at which the campers rowed.

> **Strategy for Solving an Application Problem**
>
> 1. Determine the type of problem. For example, is it a distance-rate problem, a geometry problem, or a work problem?

The problem is a distance-rate problem.

> 2. Choose a variable to represent the unknown quantity. Write numerical or variable expressions for all the remaining quantities. These results can be recorded in a table.

The unknown rate of the campers: r

	Distance	÷	Rate	=	Time
Downstream	12	÷	$r + 1$	=	$\dfrac{12}{r + 1}$
Upstream	12	÷	$r - 1$	=	$\dfrac{12}{r - 1}$

> 3. Determine how the quantities are related.

TAKE NOTE

The time going downstream plus the time going upstream is equal to the time of the entire trip.

TAKE NOTE

The solution $r = -\dfrac{1}{5}$ is not possible, because the rate cannot be a negative number.

The total time of the trip was 5 h.

$$\frac{12}{r + 1} + \frac{12}{r - 1} = 5$$

$$(r + 1)(r - 1)\left(\frac{12}{r + 1} + \frac{12}{r - 1}\right) = (r + 1)(r - 1)5$$

$$(r - 1)12 + (r + 1)12 = (r^2 - 1)5$$

$$12r - 12 + 12r + 12 = 5r^2 - 5$$

$$24r = 5r^2 - 5$$

$$0 = 5r^2 - 24r - 5$$

$$0 = (5r + 1)(r - 5)$$

$$5r + 1 = 0 \qquad\qquad r - 5 = 0$$

$$5r = -1 \qquad\qquad\quad r = 5$$

$$r = -\frac{1}{5}$$

The rowing rate was 5 mph.

Example 1

A painter and the painter's apprentice working together can paint a room in 2 h. The apprentice working alone requires 3 more hours to paint the room than the painter requires working alone. How long does it take the painter working alone to paint the room?

You Try It 1

The length of a rectangle is 2 m more than the width. The area is 15 m². Find the width.

Strategy

- This is a work problem.

- Time for the painter to paint the room: t
  Time for the apprentice to paint the room: $t + 3$

	Rate	Time	Part
Painter	$\dfrac{1}{t}$	2	$\dfrac{2}{t}$
Apprentice	$\dfrac{1}{t+3}$	2	$\dfrac{2}{t+3}$

- The sum of the parts of the task completed must equal 1.

Your strategy

Solution

$$\frac{2}{t} + \frac{2}{t+3} = 1$$

$$t(t+3)\left(\frac{2}{t} + \frac{2}{t+3}\right) = t(t+3) \cdot 1$$

$$(t+3)2 + t(2) = t(t+3)$$

$$2t + 6 + 2t = t^2 + 3t$$

$$0 = t^2 - t - 6$$

$$0 = (t-3)(t+2)$$

$$t - 3 = 0 \qquad t + 2 = 0$$

$$t = 3 \qquad\quad t = -2$$

The solution $t = -2$ is not possible.

The time is 3 h.

Your solution

Solution on p. S26

11.5 Exercises

· ·

Objective A   *Application Problems*

1. The height of a triangle is 2 m more than twice the length of the base. The area of the triangle is 20 m². Find the height of the triangle and the length of the base.

2. The length of a rectangle is 4 ft more than twice the width. The area of the rectangle is 160 ft². Find the length and width of the rectangle.

3. The area of the batter's box on a major league baseball field is 24 ft². The length of the batter's box is 2 ft more than the width. Find the length and width of the batter's box. (Area = *LW*)

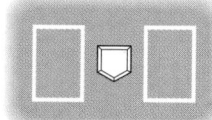

4. The length of the batter's box on a softball field is 1 ft less than twice the width. The area of the batter's box is 15 ft². Find the length and width of the batter's box.

5. The length of a swimming pool is twice the width. The area of the pool is 5000 ft². Find the length and width of the pool. (Area = *LW*)

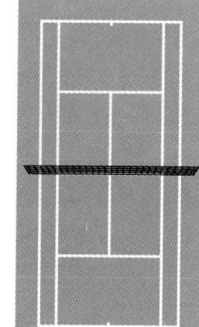

6. The length of the singles tennis court is 24 ft more than twice the width. The area of the tennis court is 2106 ft². Find the length and width of the court. (Area = *LW*)

7. One computer takes 21 min longer to calculate the value of a complex equation than a second computer. Working together, these computers complete the calculation in 10 min. How long would it take each computer, working separately, to calculate the value?

8. A tank has two drains. One drain takes 16 min longer to empty the tank than does a second drain. With both drains open, the tank is emptied in 6 min. How long would it take each drain, working alone, to empty the tank?

9. Using one engine of a ferryboat, it takes 6 h longer to cross a channel than it does using a second engine alone. Using both engines, the ferryboat can make the crossing in 4 h. How long would it take each engine, working alone, to power the ferryboat across the channel?

10. An apprentice mason takes 8 h longer to build a small fireplace than an experienced mason. Working together, they can build the fireplace in 3 h. How long would it take each mason, working alone, to complete the fireplace?

11. It took a small plane 2 h more to fly 375 mi against the wind than to fly the same distance with the wind. The rate of the wind was 25 mph. Find the rate of the plane in calm air.

12. It took a motorboat 1 h more to travel 36 mi against the current than to go 36 mi with the current. The rate of the current was 3 mph. Find the rate of the boat in calm water.

APPLYING THE CONCEPTS

13. The sum of the squares of four consecutive integers is 86. Find the four integers.

14. The hypotenuse of a right triangle is $\sqrt{13}$ cm. One leg is 1 cm shorter than twice the length of the other leg. Find the lengths of the legs of the right triangle.

15. The radius of a large pizza is 1 in. less than twice the radius of a small pizza. The difference between the areas of the two pizzas is 33π in^2. Find the radius of the large pizza.

16. The perimeter of a rectangular garden is 54 ft. The area of the garden is 180 ft^2. Find the length and width of the garden.

17. The distance, s, a car needs to come to a stop on a certain surface depends on the velocity, in feet per second, v, of the car when the brakes are applied. The equation is given by $s = 0.0344v^2 - 0.758v$. What is the maximum velocity a car can have when the brakes are applied and stop within 150 ft?

18. A square piece of cardboard is to be formed into a box to transport pizzas. The box is formed by cutting 2-inch square corners from the cardboard and folding them up as shown in the figure at the right. If the volume of the box is 512 in^3, what are the dimensions of the cardboard?

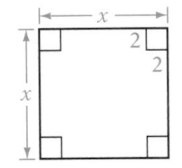 

19. The hang time of a football that is kicked on the opening kickoff is given by $s = -16t^2 + 88t + 1$, where s is the height of the football t seconds after leaving the kicker's foot. What is the hang time of a kickoff that hits the ground without being caught?

20. A wire 8 ft long is cut into two pieces. A circle is formed from one piece and a square is formed from the other. The total area of both figures is given by $A = \frac{1}{16}(8 - x)^2 + \frac{x^2}{4\pi}$. What is the length of each piece of wire if the total area is 4.5 ft^2?

Focus on Problem Solving

Algebraic Manipulation and Graphing Techniques

Problem solving is often easier when we have both algebraic manipulation and graphing techniques at our disposal. Solving quadratic equations and graphing quadratic equations in two variables are used here to solve problems involving profit.

A company's revenue, R, is the total amount of money the company earned by selling its products. The cost, C, is the total amount of money the company spent to manufacture and sell its products. A company's profit, P, is the difference between the revenue and cost: $P = R - C$. A company's revenue and cost may be represented by equations.

A company manufactures and sells woodstoves. The total monthly cost, in dollars, to produce n woodstoves is $C = 30n + 2000$. Write a variable expression for the company's monthly profit if the revenue, in dollars, obtained from selling all n woodstoves is $R = 150n - 0.4n^2$.

$P = R - C$
$P = 150n - 0.4n^2 - (30n + 2000)$ • Replace R by $150n - 0.4n^2$ and C
$P = -0.4n^2 + 120n - 2000$ by $30n + 2000$. Then simplify.

How many woodstoves must the company manufacture and sell in order to make a profit of $6000 a month?

$P = -0.4n^2 + 120n - 2000$
$6000 = -0.4n^2 + 120n - 2000$ • Substitute 6000 for P.
$0 = -0.4n^2 + 120n - 8000$ • Write the equation in
                                     standard form.
$0 = n^2 - 300n + 20{,}000$ • Divide each side of the
                                     equation by -0.4.
$0 = (n - 100)(n - 200)$ • Factor.
$n - 100 = 0$ $n - 200 = 0$ • Solve for n.
    $n = 100$ $n = 200$

The company will make a monthly profit of $6000 if either 100 or 200 woodstoves are manufactured and sold.

The graph of $P = -0.4n^2 + 120n - 2000$ is shown at the right. Note that when $P = 6000$, the values of n are 100 and 200.

Also note that the coordinates of the highest point on the graph are (150, 7000). This means that the company makes a *maximum* profit of $7000 per month when 150 woodstoves are manufactured and sold.

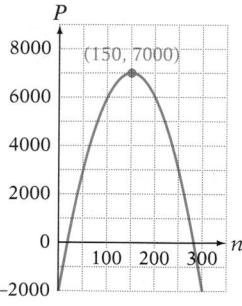

1. The total cost, in dollars, for a company to produce and sell n guitars per month is $C = 240n + 1200$. The company's revenue, in dollars, from selling all n guitars is $R = 400n - 2n^2$.

   a. How many guitars must the company produce and sell each month in order to make a monthly profit of $1200?

   b. Graph the profit equation. What is the maximum monthly profit the company can make?

Projects and Group Activities

Graphical Solutions of Quadratic Equations

The *real* number solutions of quadratic equations can be approximated by graphing. Recall that to find an *x*-intercept for a graph, replace *y* by 0 and solve for *x*. For instance, to find the *x*-intercepts of $y = x^2 - 3x - 5$, first replace *y* by zero. That produces the quadratic equation $0 = x^2 - 3x - 5$. The solutions of this equation can be found by using the quadratic formula or by graphing $y = x^2 - 3x - 5$ and approximating the *x*-intercepts.

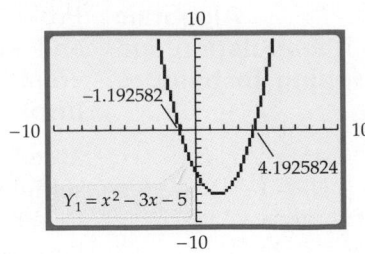

The approximate solutions are -1.192582 and 4.1925824.

1. Graphically approximate the solutions of $2x^2 - 3x - 7 = 0$.

2. Graphically approximate the solutions of $x^2 + 5x = 1$. *Suggestion:* First write the equation in standard form.

3. Graphically approximate the solution of $\pi x^2 - \sqrt{17}x - \dfrac{1}{\sqrt{3}} = 0$.

4. The solution of $0.5x^2 - 2x + 2 = 0$ is a double root. Graphically approximate the solution and explain how the graph of $y = 0.5x^2 - 2x + 2$ confirms that statement.

5. There are no real number solutions of $x^2 + 4x + 5 = 0$. Explain how the graph of $y = x^2 + 4x + 5$ confirms that statement.

Properties of Polynomials

The graph of a fifth-degree polynomial with 4 *turning points* is shown at the right. In this project you will graph various polynomials and try to make a conjecture as to the relationship between the degree of a polynomial and the number of turning points in its graph. For each of the following, graph the equation. Record the degree of the equation and the number of turning points.

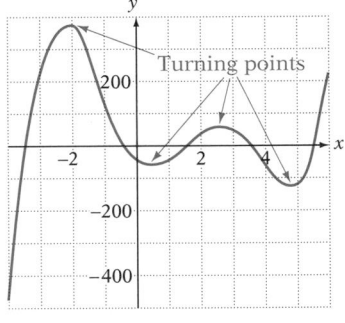

Turning points

1. Graph: $y = x^3 + 1$

2. Graph: $y = x^3 + 2x^2 - 5x - 6$

3. Graph: $y = x^4 - x^3 - 11x^2 - x - 12$

4. Graph: $y = x^4 - 2x^3 - 13x^2 + 14x + 24$

5. Graph: $y = x^5 - 2$

6. Graph: $y = x^5 - 3x^4 - 11x^3 + 27x^2 + 10x - 24$

7. Graph: $y = x^5 - 2x^4 - 10x^3 + 10x^2 - 11x + 12$

Make a conjecture as to a relationship between the degree of a polynomial and the number of turning points in its graph. Graph a few more polynomials of your choosing and see whether your conjecture is valid for those graphs. If not, refine your conjecture and test it again.

Iterative Calculations

Consider the three expressions

$$p + 3p(1 - p) \qquad p(4 - 3p) \qquad 4p - 3p^2$$

When these expressions are written in simplest form, they each become $4p - 3p^2$. It would seem that if you used a graphing calculator to evaluate these expressions, each one should give the same result. However, that is not the case, as we show in this project.

We begin with $p = 0.5$. Evaluating each of the expressions gives the same result, 0.1925. Now replace p in each expression with the current value in the display, 0.1925 in this case. This is called *feedback* because we are feeding our outputs back into each expression as inputs. Each new evaluation is called an *iteration*. The table below shows the results of performing the calculations on a *TI-83* calculator.

Iteration	$p + 3p(1 - p)$	$p(4 - 3p)$	$4p - 3p^2$
1	0.1925	0.1925	0.1925
2	0.65883125	0.65883125	0.65883125
3	1.333149152	1.333149152	1.333149152
4	7.366232839E-4	7.366232839E-4	7.366232838E-4
5	0.0029448653	0.0029448653	0.0029448653
6	0.0117534445	0.0117534445	0.0117534445
7	0.0465993476	0.0465993476	0.0465993475
20	1.121356187	1.121356207	1.121356084
30	0.9471633048	0.9471899467	0.9470331284
40	0.5648166575	0.5352103994	0.7113151932

Note that for the 40th iteration the values are approximately 0.03 different between columns 2 and 3, and 0.15 different between columns 2 and 4.

1. Use a calculator to find the first 40 iterations for $p = 0.025$ for $4p - 3p^2$ and $p + 3p(1 - p)$.

2. Use a calculator to find the first 40 iterations for $p = 0.5$ for $4p - 3p^2$ and $p + 3p(1 - p)$.

3. Expressions of the form $p + rp(1 - p)$ [which is the form of $p + 3p(1 - p)$ with $r = 3$] are called Verhulst population models. Make up your own expression of this form, choosing some other value of r and a value of p.

4. Write a short paragraph on Verhulst population models.

Geometric Construction of Completing the Square

Completing the square as a method of solving a quadratic equation has been known for centuries. The Persian mathematician Al-Khwarismi used this method in a textbook written around 825 A.D. The method was very geometric. That is, Al-Khwarismi literally completed a square. To understand how this method works, consider the following geometric shapes: a square whose area is x^2, a rectangle whose area is x, and another square whose area is 1.

Now consider the expression $x^2 + 6x$. From our discussion in this chapter, to complete the square, we added $\left(\frac{1}{2} \cdot 6\right)^2 = 3^2 = 9$ to the expression. Here is the geometric construction that Al-Khwarismi used.

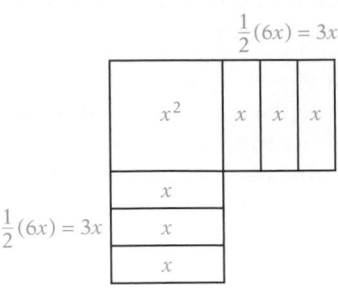

9 squares were added

Note that it is necessary to add 9 squares to the figure to "complete the square." One of the difficulties of using a geometric method such as this is that it cannot easily be extended to $x^2 - 6x$. There is no way to draw an area of $-6x$! That really did not bother Al-Khwarismi much. Negative numbers were not a significant part of mathematics until well into the 13th century.

1. Show how Al-Khwarismi would have completed the square for $x^2 + 4x$.
2. Show how Al-Khwarismi would have completed the square for $x^2 + 10x$.
3. Do the geometric constructions for Exercises 1 and 2 correspond to the algebraic method shown in this chapter?

Chapter Summary

Key Words A *quadratic equation* is an equation of the form $ax^2 + bx + c = 0$, where $a \neq 0$. A quadratic equation is also called a *second-degree equation*.

A quadratic equation is in *standard form* when the polynomial is in descending order and equal to zero.

A *quadratic equation in two variables* is given by $y = ax^2 + bx + c$, where $a \neq 0$.

A *quadratic function* is given by $f(x) = ax^2 + bx + c$, where $a \neq 0$. The graph of a quadratic function is a *parabola*.

Essential Rules *The Quadratic Formula*

$$x = \frac{-b \pm \sqrt{b^2 - 4ac}}{2a}$$

The Square Root Property

If $x^2 = a$, then $x = \pm\sqrt{a}$.

Chapter Review

1. Solve by factoring: $6x^2 + 13x - 28 = 0$

2. Solve by taking square roots:
$49x^2 = 25$

3. Solve by completing the square:
$x^2 + 2x - 24 = 0$

4. Solve by using the quadratic formula:
$x^2 + 5x - 6 = 0$

5. Solve by completing the square:
$2x^2 + 5x = 12$

6. Solve by factoring: $12x^2 + 10 = 29x$

7. Solve by taking square roots:
$(x + 2)^2 - 24 = 0$

8. Solve by using the quadratic formula:
$2x^2 + 3 = 5x$

9. Solve by factoring: $6x(x + 1) = x - 1$

10. Solve by taking square roots:
$4y^2 + 9 = 0$

11. Solve by completing the square:
$x^2 - 4x + 1 = 0$

12. Solve by using the quadratic formula:
$x^2 - 3x - 5 = 0$

13. Solve by completing the square:
$x^2 + 6x + 12 = 0$

14. Solve by factoring: $(x + 9)^2 = x + 11$

15. Solve by taking square roots:
$\left(x - \dfrac{1}{2}\right)^2 = \dfrac{9}{4}$

16. Solve by completing the square:
$4x^2 + 16x = 7$

17. Solve by using the quadratic formula:
$x^2 - 4x + 8 = 0$

18. Solve by using the quadratic formula:
$2x^2 + 5x + 2 = 0$

19. Graph $y = -3x^2$.

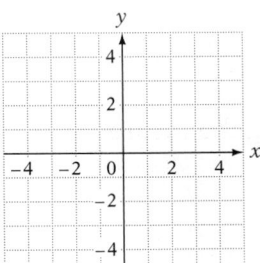

20. Graph $y = -\dfrac{1}{4}x^2$.

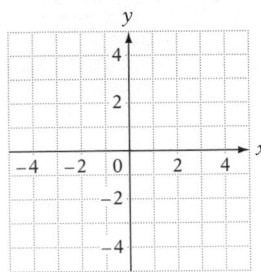

21. Graph $y = 2x^2 + 1$.

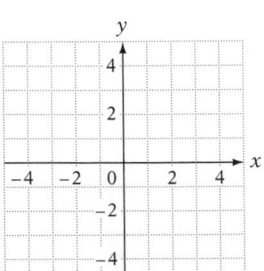

22. Graph $y = x^2 - 4x + 3$.

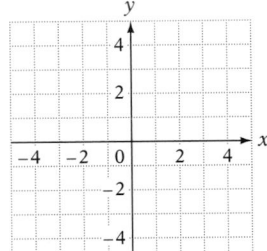

23. Graph $y = -x^2 + 4x - 5$.

24. It took a hawk half an hour more to fly 70 mi against the wind than to go 40 mi with the wind. The rate of the wind was 5 mph. Find the rate of the hawk in calm air.

Chapter Test

1. Solve by factoring: $x^2 - 5x - 6 = 0$

2. Solve by factoring: $3x^2 + 7x = 20$

3. Solve by taking square roots:
$2(x - 5)^2 - 50 = 0$

4. Solve by taking square roots:
$3(x + 4)^2 - 60 = 0$

5. Solve by completing the square:
$x^2 + 4x - 16 = 0$

6. Solve by completing the square:
$x^2 + 3x = 8$

7. Solve by completing the square:
$2x^2 - 6x + 1 = 0$

8. Solve by completing the square:
$2x^2 + 8x = 3$

9. Solve by using the quadratic formula:
$x^2 + 4x + 2 = 0$

10. Solve by using the quadratic formula:
$x^2 - 3x = 6$

11. Solve by using the quadratic formula:
$2x^2 - 5x - 3 = 0$

12. Solve by using the quadratic formula:
$3x^2 - x = 1$

13. Graph $y = x^2 + 2x - 4$.

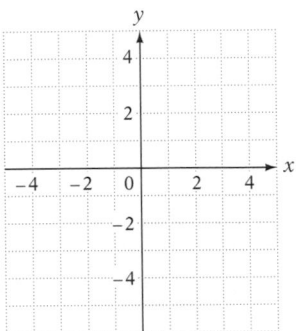

14. The length of a rectangle is 2 ft less than twice the width. The area of the rectangle is 40 ft². Find the length and width of the rectangle.

15. It took a motorboat 1 h more to travel 60 mi against a current than it took the boat to travel 60 mi with the current. The rate of the current was 1 mph. Find the rate of the boat in calm water.

Cumulative Review

1. Simplify: $2x - 3[2x - 4(3 - 2x) + 2] - 3$

2. Solve: $-\frac{3}{5}x = -\frac{9}{10}$

3. Solve: $2x - 3(4x - 5) = -3x - 6$

4. Simplify: $(2a^2b)^2(-3a^4b^2)$

5. Simplify: $(x^2 - 8) \div (x - 2)$

6. Factor: $3x^3 + 2x^2 - 8x$

7. Simplify: $\frac{3x^2 - 6x}{4x - 6} \div \frac{2x^2 + x - 6}{6x^3 - 24x}$

8. Simplify: $\frac{x}{2(x - 1)} - \frac{1}{(x - 1)(x + 1)}$

9. Simplify: $\dfrac{1 - \dfrac{7}{x} + \dfrac{12}{x^2}}{2 - \dfrac{1}{x} - \dfrac{15}{x^2}}$

10. Find the x- and y-intercepts for the graph of the line $4x - 3y = 12$.

11. Find the equation of the line that contains the point $(-3, 2)$ and has slope $-\frac{4}{3}$.

12. Solve by substitution:
$3x - y = 5$
$\quad y = 2x - 3$

13. Solve by the addition method:
$3x + 2y = 2$
$5x - 2y = 14$

14. Solve: $2x - 3(2 - 3x) > 2x - 5$

15. Simplify: $(\sqrt{a} - \sqrt{2})(\sqrt{a} + \sqrt{2})$

16. Simplify: $\dfrac{\sqrt{108a^7b^3}}{\sqrt{3a^4b}}$

17. Simplify: $\dfrac{\sqrt{3}}{5 + 2\sqrt{3}}$

18. Solve: $3 = 8 - \sqrt{5x}$

19. Solve by factoring: $6x^2 - 17x = -5$

20. Solve by taking square roots:
$2(x - 5)^2 = 36$

21. Solve by completing the square:
$3x^2 + 7x = -3$

22. Solve by using the quadratic formula:
$2x^2 - 3x - 2 = 0$

23. Find the cost per pound of a mixture made from 20 lb of cashews that cost $3.50 per pound and 50 lb of peanuts that cost $1.75 per pound.

24. A stock investment of 100 shares paid a dividend of $215. At this rate, how many additional shares are required for the investor to earn a dividend of $752.50?

25. A 720-mile trip from one city to another takes 3 h when a plane is flying with the wind. The return trip, against the wind, takes 4.5 h. Find the rate of the plane in still air and the rate of the wind.

26. A student received a 70, a 91, an 85, and a 77 on four tests in a mathematics class. What scores on the last test will enable the student to receive a minimum of 400 points?

27. The sum of the squares of three consecutive odd integers is 83. Find the middle odd integer.

28. A jogger ran 7 mi at a constant rate, and then reduced the rate by 3 mph and ran an additional 8 mi at the reduced rate. The total time spent jogging the 15 mi was 3 h. Find the jogger's rate for the last 8 mi.

29. Graph $2x - 3y > 6$.

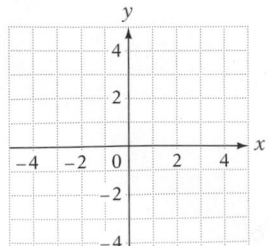

30. Graph $y = x^2 - 2x - 3$.

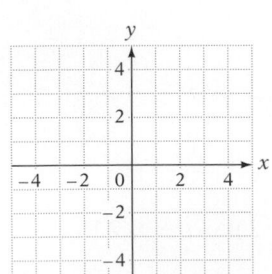

Final Exam

1. Evaluate $-|-3|$.

2. Subtract: $-15 - (-12) - 3$

3. Simplify: $-2^4 \cdot (-2)^4$

4. Simplify: $-7 - \dfrac{12 - 15}{2 - (-1)} \cdot (-4)$

5. Evaluate $\dfrac{a^2 - 3b}{2a - 2b^2}$ when $a = 3$ and $b = -2$.

6. Simplify: $6x - (-4y) - (-3x) + 2y$

7. Simplify: $(-15z)\left(-\dfrac{2}{5}\right)$

8. Simplify: $-2[5 - 3(2x - 7) - 2x]$

9. Solve: $20 = -\dfrac{2}{5}x$

10. Solve: $4 - 2(3x + 1) = 3(2 - x) + 5$

11. Write $\dfrac{1}{8}$ as a percent.

12. Find 19% of 80.

13. Simplify: $(2x^2 - 5x + 1) - (5x^2 - 2x - 7)$

14. Simplify: $(-3xy^3)^4$

15. Simplify: $(3x^2 - x - 2)(2x + 3)$

16. Simplify: $\dfrac{(-2x^2y^3)^3}{(-4xy^4)^2}$

17. Simplify: $\dfrac{12x^2y - 16x^3y^2 - 20y^2}{4xy^2}$

18. Simplify: $(5x^2 - 2x - 1) \div (x + 2)$

19. Simplify: $(4x^{-2}y)^2(2xy^{-2})^{-2}$

20. Given $f(t) = \dfrac{t}{t + 1}$, find $f(3)$.

21. Factor: $x^2 - 5x - 6$

22. Factor: $6x^2 - 5x - 6$

23. Factor: $8x^3 - 28x^2 + 12x$

24. Factor: $25x^2 - 16$

25. Factor: $2a(4 - x) - 6(x - 4)$

26. Factor: $75y - 12x^2y$

27. Solve: $2x^2 = 7x - 3$

28. Simplify: $\dfrac{2x^2 - 3x + 1}{4x^2 - 2x} \cdot \dfrac{4x^2 + 4x}{x^2 - 2x + 1}$

29. Simplify: $\dfrac{5}{x + 3} - \dfrac{3x}{2x - 5}$

30. Simplify: $x - \dfrac{1}{1 - \dfrac{1}{x}}$

31. Solve: $\dfrac{5x}{3x - 5} - 3 = \dfrac{7}{3x - 5}$

32. Solve $a = 3a - 2b$ for a.

33. Find the slope of the line that contains the points $(-1, -3)$ and $(2, -1)$.

34. Find the equation of the line that contains the point $(3, -4)$ and has slope $-\dfrac{2}{3}$.

35. Solve by substitution:
$y = 4x - 7$
$y = 2x + 5$

36. Solve by the addition method:
$4x - 3y = 11$
$2x + 5y = -1$

37. Solve: $4 - x \geq 7$

38. Solve: $2 - 2(y - 1) \leq 2y - 6$

39. Simplify: $\sqrt{49x^6}$

40. Simplify: $2\sqrt{27a} + 8\sqrt{48a}$

41. Simplify: $\dfrac{\sqrt{3}}{\sqrt{5} - 2}$

42. Solve: $\sqrt{2x - 3} + 4 = 5$

43. Solve by factoring:
$3x^2 - x = 4$

44. Solve by using the quadratic formula:
$4x^2 - 2x - 1 = 0$

45. Translate and simplify "the sum of twice a number and three times the difference between the number and two."

46. Because of depreciation, the value of an office machine is now $2400. This is 80% of its original value. Find the original value.

47. The manufacturer's cost for a laser printer is $900. The manufacturer then sells the printer for $1485. What is the markup rate?

48. An investment of $3000 is made at an annual simple interest rate of 8%. How much additional money must be invested at 11% so that the total interest earned is 10% of the total investment?

49. A grocer mixes 4 lb of peanuts that cost $2 per pound with 2 lb of walnuts that cost $5 per pound. What is the cost per pound of the resulting mixture?

50. A pharmacist mixes together 20 L of a solution that is 60% acid and 30 L of a solution that is 20% acid. What is the percent concentration of the acid in the mixture?

51. At 2 P.M. a small plane had been flying 1 h when a change of wind direction doubled its average ground speed. The pilot completed the 860-kilometer trip in 2.5 h. How far did the plane travel in the first hour?

52. The angles of a triangle are such that the second angle is 10° more than the first angle and the third angle is 10° more than the second angle. Find the measure of each of the three angles.

53. The sum of the squares of three consecutive integers is 50. Find the middle integer.

54. The length of a rectangle is 5 m more than the width. The area of the rectangle is 50 m². Find the dimensions of the rectangle.

55. A paint formula requires 2 oz of dye for every 15 oz of base paint. How many ounces of dye are required for 120 oz of base paint?

56. It takes a chef 1 h to prepare a dinner. The chef's apprentice can prepare the dinner in 1.5 h. How long would it take the chef and the apprentice, working together, to prepare the dinner?

57. With the current, a motorboat travels 50 mi in 2.5 h. Against the current, it takes twice as long to travel 50 mi. Find the rate of the boat in calm water and the rate of the current.

58. Flying against the wind, it took a pilot $\frac{1}{2}$ h longer to travel 500 mi than it took flying with the wind. The rate of the plane in calm air is 225 mph. Find the rate of the wind.

59. Graph the line that has slope $-\frac{1}{2}$ and y-intercept $(0, -3)$.

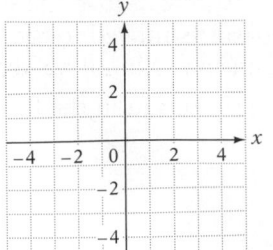

60. Graph $y = x^2 - 4x + 3$.

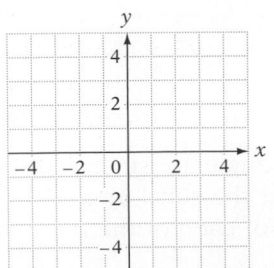

Appendix: Guidelines for Using Graphing Calculators

TEXAS INSTRUMENTS TI-83

To evaluate an expression

a. Press the $\boxed{Y=}$ key. A menu showing \Y₁ = through \Y₇ = will be displayed vertically with a blinking cursor to the right of \Y₁ =. Press $\boxed{\text{CLEAR}}$, if necessary, to delete an unwanted expression.

b. Input the expression to be evaluated. For example, to input the expression $-3a^2b - 4c$, use the following keystrokes:

$\boxed{(-)}$ 3 $\boxed{\text{ALPHA}}$ A $\boxed{\wedge}$ 2 $\boxed{\text{ALPHA}}$ B $\boxed{-}$ 4 $\boxed{\text{ALPHA}}$ C $\boxed{\text{2nd}}$ QUIT

Note the difference between the keys for a negative sign $\boxed{(-)}$ and a *minus* sign $\boxed{-}$.

c. Store the value of each variable that will be used in the expression. For example, to evaluate the expression above when $a = 3$, $b = -2$, and $c = -4$, use the following keystrokes:

3 $\boxed{\text{STO}\triangleright}$ $\boxed{\text{ALPHA}}$ A $\boxed{\text{ENTER}}$ $\boxed{(-)}$ 2 $\boxed{\text{STO}\triangleright}$ $\boxed{\text{ALPHA}}$ B $\boxed{\text{ENTER}}$ $\boxed{(-)}$ 4 $\boxed{\text{STO}\triangleright}$ $\boxed{\text{ALPHA}}$ C $\boxed{\text{ENTER}}$

These steps store the value of each variable.

d. Press $\boxed{\text{VARS}}$ $\boxed{\triangleright}$ $\boxed{1}$ $\boxed{1}$ $\boxed{\text{ENTER}}$. The value for the expression, Y₁, for the given values is displayed; in this case, Y₁ = 70.

To graph a function

a. Press the $\boxed{Y=}$ key. A menu showing \Y₁ = through \Y₇ = will be displayed vertically with a blinking cursor to the right of \Y₁ =. Press $\boxed{\text{CLEAR}}$, if necessary, to delete an unwanted expression.

b. Input the expression for each function that is to be graphed. Press $\boxed{\text{X,T,θ,}n}$ to input x. For example, to input $y = x^3 + 2x^2 - 5x - 6$, use the following keystrokes:

$\boxed{\text{X,T,θ,}n}$ $\boxed{\wedge}$ 3 $\boxed{+}$ 2 $\boxed{\text{X,T,θ,}n}$ $\boxed{\wedge}$ 2 $\boxed{-}$ 5 $\boxed{\text{X,T,θ,}n}$ $\boxed{-}$ 6

c. Set the domain and range by pressing $\boxed{\text{WINDOW}}$. Enter the values for the minimum x-value (Xmin), the maximum x-value (Xmax), the distance between tick marks on the x-axis (Xscl), the minimum y-value (Ymin), the maximum y-value (Ymax), and the distance between tick marks on the y-axis (Yscl). Now press $\boxed{\text{GRAPH}}$. For the graph shown at the left, Xmin = -10, Xmax = 10, Xscl = 1, Ymin = -10, Ymax = 10, and Yscl = 1. This is called the standard viewing rectangle. Pressing $\boxed{\text{ZOOM}}$ $\boxed{6}$ is a quick way to set the calculator to the standard viewing rectangle. *Note:* This will also immediately graph the function in that window.

d. Press the $\boxed{Y=}$ key. The equal sign has a black rectangle around it. This indicates that the function is active and will be graphed when the $\boxed{\text{GRAPH}}$ key is pressed. A function is deactivated by using the arrow keys. Move the cursor over the equal sign and press $\boxed{\text{ENTER}}$. When the cursor is moved to the right, the black rectangle will not be present and that equation will not be active.

e. Graphing some radical equations requires special care. To graph the function $y = \sqrt{2x + 3}$, enter the following keystrokes:

$\boxed{Y=}$ $\boxed{\text{2nd}}$ $\sqrt{}$ 2 $\boxed{\text{X,T,θ,}n}$ $\boxed{+}$ 3 $\boxed{)}$

The graph is shown below.

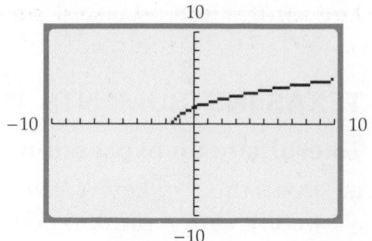

To display the *x*-coordinates of rectangular coordinates as integers

a. Set the viewing window as follows: Xmin = −47, Xmax = 47, Xscl = 10, Ymin = −31, Ymax = 31, Yscl = 10.

b. Graph the function and use the TRACE feature. Press $\boxed{\text{TRACE}}$ and then move the cursor with the $\boxed{\triangleleft}$ and $\boxed{\triangleright}$ keys. The values of *x* and *y* = *f*(*x*) displayed on the bottom of the screen are the coordinates of a point on the graph.

To display the *x*-coordinates of rectangular coordinates in tenths

a. Set the viewing window as follows: $\boxed{\text{ZOOM}}$ $\boxed{4}$

b. Graph the function and use the $\boxed{\text{TRACE}}$ feature. Press $\boxed{\text{TRACE}}$ and then move the cursor with the $\boxed{\triangleleft}$ and $\boxed{\triangleright}$ keys. The values of *x* and *y* = *f*(*x*) displayed on the bottom of the screen are the coordinates of a point on the graph.

To evaluate a function for a given value of *x*, or to produce ordered pairs of a function

a. Input the equation; for example, input $y_1 = 2x^3 - 3x + 2$.

b. Press $\boxed{\text{2nd}}$ QUIT.

c. Input a value for *x*; for example, to input 3 press 3 $\boxed{\text{STO}\triangleright}$ $\boxed{\text{X,T,}\theta\text{,}n}$ $\boxed{\text{ENTER}}$.

d. Press $\boxed{\text{VARS}}$ $\boxed{\triangleright}$ $\boxed{1}$ $\boxed{1}$ $\boxed{\text{ENTER}}$. The value for the expression, Y₁, for the given *x*-value is displayed, in this case, Y₁ = 47. An ordered pair of the function is (3, 47).

e. Repeat steps **c.** and **d.** to produce as many pairs as desired. The TABLE feature of the *TI-83* can also be used to determine pairs.

ZOOM FEATURES

To zoom in or out on a graph

a. Here are two methods of using ZOOM. The first method uses the built-in features of the calculator. Move the cursor to a point on the graph that is of interest. Press $\boxed{\text{ZOOM}}$. The ZOOM menu will appear. Press $\boxed{2}$ $\boxed{\text{ENTER}}$ to zoom in on the graph by the amount shown under the SET FACTORS menu. The center of the new graph is the location at which you placed the cursor. Press $\boxed{\text{ZOOM}}$ $\boxed{3}$ $\boxed{\text{ENTER}}$ to zoom out on the graph by the amount under the SET FACTORS menu. (The SET FACTORS menu is accessed by pressing $\boxed{\text{ZOOM}}$ $\boxed{\triangleright}$ $\boxed{4}$.)

b. The second method uses the ZBOX option under the ZOOM menu. To use this method, press $\boxed{\text{ZOOM}}$ $\boxed{1}$. A cursor will appear on the graph. Use the arrow keys to move the cursor to a portion of the graph that is of interest. Press $\boxed{\text{ENTER}}$. Now use the arrow keys to draw a box around the portion of the graph you wish to see. Press $\boxed{\text{ENTER}}$. The portion of the graph defined by the box will be drawn.

c. Pressing $\boxed{\text{ZOOM}}$ $\boxed{6}$ resets the window to the standard 10 × 10 viewing window.

SOLVING EQUATIONS

This discussion is based on the fact that the solution of an equation can be related to the x-intercepts of a graph. For instance, the real solutions of the equation $x^2 = x + 1$ are the x-intercepts of the graph of $f(x) = x^2 - x - 1$, which are the zeros of f.

To solve $x^2 = x + 1$, rewrite the equation with all terms on one side. The equation is now $x^2 - x - 1 = 0$. Think of this equation as $Y_1 = x^2 - x - 1$. The x-intercepts of the graph of Y_1 are the solutions of the equation $x^2 = x + 1$.

a. Enter $x^2 - x - 1$ into Y_1.

b. Graph the equation. You may need to adjust the viewing window so that the x-intercepts are visible.

c. Press $\boxed{\text{2nd}}$ CALC $\boxed{2}$.

d. Move the cursor to a point on the curve that is to the left of an x-intercept. Press $\boxed{\text{ENTER}}$.

e. Move the cursor to a point on the curve that is to the right of an x-intercept. Press $\boxed{\text{ENTER}}$.

f. Press $\boxed{\text{ENTER}}$.

g. The root is shown as the x-coordinate on the bottom of the screen; in this case, the root is approximately -0.618034. To find the next intercept, repeat steps **c.** through **f.** The SOLVER feature under the MATH menu can also be used to find solutions of equations.

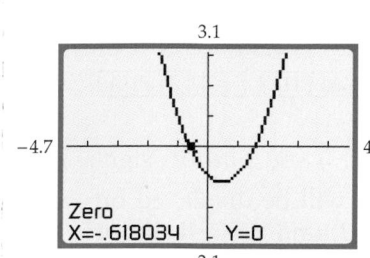

SOLVING SYSTEMS OF EQUATIONS IN TWO VARIABLES

To solve a system of equations

To solve $\quad \begin{aligned} y &= x^2 - 1 \\ \tfrac{1}{2}x + y &= 1 \end{aligned}$,

a. Solve each equation for y.

b. Enter the first equation as Y_1. For instance, $Y_1 = x^2 - 1$.

c. Enter the second equation as Y_2. For instance, $Y_2 = 1 - \tfrac{1}{2}x$.

d. Graph both equations. (*Note:* The point of intersection must appear on the screen. It may be necessary to adjust the viewing window so that the point(s) of intersection are displayed.)

e. Press $\boxed{\text{2nd}}$ CALC $\boxed{5}$.

f. Move the cursor to the left of the first point of intersection. Press $\boxed{\text{ENTER}}$.

g. Move the cursor to the right of the first point of intersection. Press $\boxed{\text{ENTER}}$.

h. Press $\boxed{\text{ENTER}}$.

i. The first point of intersection is $(-1.686141, 1.8430703)$.

j. Repeat steps **e.** through **h.** for each point of intersection.

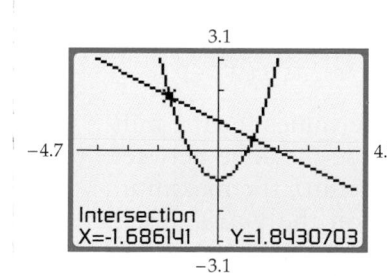

FINDING MINIMUM OR MAXIMUM VALUES OF A FUNCTION

a. Enter the function into Y_1. The equation $y = x^2 - x - 1$ is used here.

b. Graph the equation. You may need to adjust the viewing window so that the maximum or minimum points are visible.

c. Press $\boxed{\text{2nd}}$ CALC $\boxed{3}$ to determine a minimum value or press $\boxed{\text{2nd}}$ CALC $\boxed{4}$ to determine a maximum value.

d. Move the cursor to a point on the curve that is to the left of the minimum (maximum). Press $\boxed{\text{ENTER}}$.

e. Move the cursor to a point on the curve that is to the right of the minimum (maximum). Press ENTER.

f. Press ENTER.

g. The minimum (maximum) is shown as the y-coordinate on the bottom of the screen; in this case the minimum value is -1.25.

SHARP EL-9600

To evaluate an expression

a. The SOLVER mode of the calculator is used to evaluate expressions. To enter SOLVER mode, press 2ndF SOLVER CL. The expression $-3a^2b - 4c$ must be entered as the equation $-3a^2b - 4c = t$. The letter t can be any letter other than one used in the expression. Use the following keystrokes to input $-3a^2b - 4c = t$:

(−) 3 ALPHA A a^b 2 ▷ ALPHA B − 4 ALPHA C ALPHA = ALPHA T ENTER

Note the difference between the keys for a *negative* sign $(-)$ and a *minus* sign.

b. After you press ENTER, variables used in the equation will be displayed on the screen. To evaluate the expression for $a = 3$, $b = -2$, and $c = -4$, input each value, pressing ENTER after each number. When the cursor moves to T, press 2ndF EXE. T = 70 will appear on the screen. This is the value of the expression. To evaluate the expression again for different values of a, b, and c, press 2ndF QUIT and then 2ndF SOLVER.

c. Press ⊞⊟⊠⊘ to return to normal operation.

To graph a function

a. Press the Y= key. The screen will show Y1 through Y8.

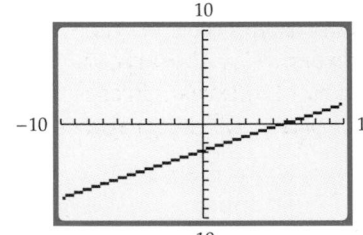

b. Input the expression for a function that is to be graphed. Press X/T/θ/n to enter an x. For example, to input $y = \frac{1}{2}x - 3$, use the following keystrokes:

Y= CL (1 ÷ 2) X/T/θ/n − 3 ENTER

c. Set the viewing window by pressing WINDOW. Enter the values for the minimum x-value (Xmin), the maximum x-value (Xmax), the distance between tick marks on the x-axis (Xscl), the minimum y-value (Ymin), the maximum y-value (Ymax), and the distance between tick marks on the y-axis (Yscl). Press ENTER after each entry. Press GRAPH. For the graph shown at the left, enter Xmin $= -10$, Xmax $= 10$, Ymin $= -10$, Ymax $= 10$. Press GRAPH.

d. Press Y= to return to the equation. The equal sign has a black rectangle around it. This indicates that the function is active and will be graphed when the GRAPH key is pressed. A function is deactivated by using the arrow keys. Move the cursor over the equal sign and press ENTER. When the cursor is moved to the right, the black rectangle will not be present and that equation will not be active.

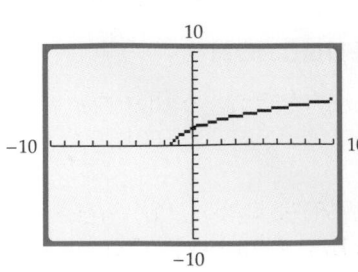

e. Graphing some radical equations requires special care. To graph the function $y = \sqrt{2x + 3}$, enter the following keystrokes:

Y= CL 2ndF √ 2 X/T/θ/n + 3 ▷ GRAPH

The graph is shown at the left.

To display the *xy*-coordinates as integers

a. Press ZOOM ▷ 8.

b. Graph the function. Press TRACE. Use the left and right arrow keys to trace along the graph of the function. The x- and y-coordinates of the function are shown on the bottom of the screen.

To display the *xy*-coordinates in tenths

a. Press ZOOM ▷ 7.

b. Graph the function. Press TRACE .Use the left and right arrow keys to trace along the graph of the function. The x- and y-coordinates of the function are shown on the bottom of the screen.

To evaluate a function for a given value of x, or to produce ordered pairs of the function

a. Press Y= . Input the expression. For instance, input
Y= CL 2 X/T/θ/n ∧ 3 − 3 X/T/θ/n + 2. Press ENTER .

b. Press $\boxed{\begin{smallmatrix} + & - \\ × & ÷ \end{smallmatrix}}$. Store the x-coordinate of the ordered pair you want in X/T/θ/n .
For instance, enter 3 STO X/T/θ/n ENTER .

c. Press VARS ENTER 1 ENTER . The value of y, 47, will be displayed on the screen. The ordered pair is (3, 47). The TABLE feature of the calculator can also be used to find many ordered pairs for a function.

ZOOM FEATURES OF THE SHARP EL-9600

To zoom in or out on a graph

a. Here are two methods of using ZOOM. The first method uses the built-in features of the calculator. Move the cursor to a point on the graph that is of interest. Press ZOOM . The ZOOM menu will appear. Press 3 to zoom in on the graph by the amount shown by FACTOR. The center of the new graph is the location at which you placed the cursor. Press ZOOM 4 to zoom out on the graph by the amount shown in FACTOR.

b. The second method uses the BOX option under the ZOOM menu. To use this method, press ZOOM 2. A cursor will appear on the screen. Use the arrow keys to move the cursor to a portion of the graph that is of interest. Press ENTER . Use the arrow keys to draw a box around the portion of the graph you wish to see. Press ENTER .

SOLVING EQUATIONS OR SYSTEMS OF EQUATIONS IN TWO VARIABLES

This discussion is based on the fact that the real solutions of an equation can be related to the x-intercepts of a graph. For instance, the real solutions of $x^2 = x + 1$ are the x-intercepts of the graph of $f(x) = x^2 - x - 1$, which are the zeros of f.

To solve $x^2 = x + 1$, rewrite the equation with all terms on one side of the equation. The equation is now $x^2 - x - 1 = 0$. Think of this equation as $Y_1 = x^2 - x - 1$. The x-intercepts of the graph of Y_1 are the solutions of the equation $x^2 = x + 1$.

a. Enter $x^2 - x - 1$ into Y_1.

b. Graph the equation. You may need to adjust the viewing window so that the x-intercepts are visible.

c. Press 2ndF CALC 5

d. A solution is shown as the x-coordinate at the bottom of the screen. To find the next intercept, move the cursor to the right of the first x-intercept. Then press 2ndF CALC 5.

SOLVING SYSTEMS OF EQUATIONS

To solve a system of equations

a. Solve each equation for y.

b. Press $\boxed{\text{Y=}}$ and then enter both equations.

c. Graph the equations. You may need to adjust the viewing window so that the point of intersection is visible.

d. Press $\boxed{\text{2ndF}}$ CALC 2 to find the point of intersection. Pressing $\boxed{\text{2ndF}}$ CALC 2 again will find the next point of intersection.

e. The x- and y-coordinates at the bottom of the screen are the coordinates for the point of intersection.

FINDING MAXIMUM AND MINIMUM VALUES OF A FUNCTION

a. Press $\boxed{\text{Y=}}$ and then enter the function.

b. Graph the equation. You may need to adjust the viewing window so that the maximum (minimum) are visible.

c. Press $\boxed{\text{2ndF}}$ CALC 3 for the minimum value of the function or $\boxed{\text{2ndF}}$ CALC 4 for the maximum value of the fuction.

d. The y-coordinate at the bottom of the screen is the maximum (minimum).

CASIO *CFX-9850G*

To evaluate an expression

a. Press $\boxed{\text{MENU}}$ $\boxed{5}$. Use the arrow keys to highlight Y_1.

b. Input the expression to be evaluated. For example, to input the expression $-3A^2B - 4C$, use the following keystrokes:

$\boxed{(-)}$ 3 $\boxed{\text{ALPHA}}$ A $\boxed{x^2}$ $\boxed{\text{ALPHA}}$ B $\boxed{-}$ 4 $\boxed{\text{ALPHA}}$ C $\boxed{\text{EXE}}$

Note the difference between the keys for a *negative* sign $\boxed{(-)}$ and a *minus* sign $\boxed{-}$.

c. Press $\boxed{\text{MENU}}$ 1. Store the value of each variable that will be used in the expression. For example, to evaluate the expression above when $A = 3$, $B = -2$, and $C = -4$, use the following keystrokes:

3 $\rightarrow$ $\boxed{\text{ALPHA}}$ A $\boxed{\text{EXE}}$ $\boxed{(-)}$ 2 $\rightarrow$ $\boxed{\text{ALPHA}}$ B $\boxed{\text{EXE}}$ $\boxed{(-)}$ 4 $\rightarrow$ $\boxed{\text{ALPHA}}$ C $\boxed{\text{EXE}}$

These steps store the value of each variable.

d. Press $\boxed{\text{VARS}}$ $\boxed{\text{F4}}$ $\boxed{\text{F1}}$ 1 $\boxed{\text{EXE}}$.

The value of the expression, Y_1, for the given values is displayed; in this case, $Y_1 = 70$.

To graph a function

a. Press Menu $\boxed{5}$ to obtain the GRAPH FUNCTION Menu.

b. Input the function that you desire to graph. Press $\boxed{\text{X,}\theta\text{,T}}$ to input the variable x. For example, to input $y = x^3 + 2x^2 - 5x - 6$, use the following keystrokes:

$\boxed{\text{X,}\theta\text{,T}}$ $\boxed{\wedge}$ 3 $\boxed{+}$ 2 $\boxed{\text{X,}\theta\text{,T}}$ $\boxed{x^2}$ $\boxed{-}$ 5 $\boxed{\text{X,}\theta\text{,T}}$ $\boxed{-}$ 6 $\boxed{\text{EXE}}$

c. Set the viewing window by pressing $\boxed{\text{SHIFT}}$ $\boxed{\text{F3}}$ and the Range Parameter Menu will appear. Enter the values for the minimum x-value (Xmin), maximum x-value (Xmax), units between tick marks on the x-axis (Xscl), minimum y-value (Ymin), maximum y-value (Ymax), and the units between tick marks on the y-axis (Yscl). Press $\boxed{\text{EXE}}$ after each of the 6 entries above. Press $\boxed{\text{EXIT}}$, or $\boxed{\text{SHIFT}}$ $\boxed{\text{QUIT}}$, to leave the Range Parameter Menu.

d. Press $\boxed{\text{F6}}$ to draw the graph. For the graph shown at the left, Xmin $= -10$, Xmax $= 10$, Xscl $= 1$, Ymin $= -10$, Ymax $= 10$, Yscl $= 1$.

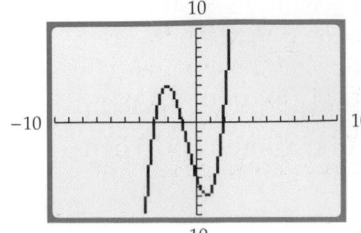

e. In the equation for Y_1, there is a rectangle around the equal sign. This indicates that this function is *active* and will be graphed when the ⬜F6⬜ key is pressed. A function is deactivated by using the ⬜F1⬜ key. After using this key once, the rectangle around the equal sign will not be present and that function will not be graphed.

To display the *x*-coordinates of rectangular coordinates as integers

a. Set the Range as follows: For example, set $Xmin = -63$, $Xmax = 63$, $Xscl = 10$, $Ymin = -32$, $Ymax = 32$, $Yscl = 10$.

b. Graph a function and use the Trace feature. Press ⬜F1⬜ and then move the cursor with the ⬜◁⬜ and the ⬜▷⬜ keys. The values of x and $y = f(x)$ displayed on the bottom of the screen are the coordinates of a point on the graph. Observe that the x-value is given as an integer.

To display the *x*-coordinates of rectangular coordinates in tenths

a. Set the Range as follows: For example, set $Xmin = -6.3$, $Xmax = 6.3$. A quick way to choose these range parameter settings is to press ⬜F1⬜ from the V-Window Menu.

b. Graph a function and use the Trace feature. Press ⬜F1⬜ and then move the cursor with the ⬜◁⬜ and the ⬜▷⬜ keys. The values of x and $y = f(x)$ displayed on the bottom of the screen are the coordinates of a point on the graph. Observe that the x-value is given as a decimal that terminates in the first decimal place (tenths).

To evaluate a function for a given value of *x*, or to produce ordered pairs of the function

a. Press ⬜MENU⬜ ⬜5⬜.

b. Input the function to be evaluated. For example, input $2x^3 - 3x + 2$ into Y_1.

c. Press ⬜MENU⬜ 1.

d. Input a value for x; for example, to input 3 press

$3 \rightarrow$ ⬜X,θ,T⬜ ⬜EXE⬜

e. Press ⬜VARS⬜ ⬜F4⬜ ⬜F1⬜ 1 ⬜EXE⬜.

The value of Y_1 for the given value $x = 3$ is displayed. In this case, $Y_1 = 47$.

ZOOM FEATURES

To zoom in or out on a graph

a. After drawing a graph, press ⬜SHIFT⬜ Zoom to display the Zoom/Auto Range menu. To zoom in on a graph by a factor of 2 on the x-axis and a factor of 1.5 on the y-axis:
Press ⬜F2⬜ to display the Factor Input Screen. Input the zoom factors for each axis: 2 ⬜EXE⬜ 1 ⬜·⬜ 5 ⬜EXE⬜ ⬜EXIT⬜. Press ⬜F3⬜ to redraw the graph according to the factors specified above. To specify the center point of the enlarged (reduced) display after pressing ⬜SHIFT⬜ Zoom use the arrow keys to move the pointer to the position you wish to become the center of the next display. You can repeat the zoom procedures as needed. If you wish to see the original graph, press ⬜F6⬜ ⬜F1⬜. This procedure resets the range parameters to their original values and redraws the graph.

b. A second method of zooming makes use of the Box Zoom Function. To use this method, first draw a graph. Then press ⬜SHIFT⬜ Zoom ⬜F1⬜. Now use the arrow (cursor) keys to move the pointer. Once the pointer is located at a portion of the graph that is of interest, press ⬜EXE⬜. Now use the arrow keys to draw a box around the portion of the graph you wish to see. Press ⬜EXE⬜. The portion of the graph defined by the box will be drawn.

SOLVING EQUATIONS

This discussion is based on the fact that the real solutions of an equation can be related to the x-intercepts of a graph. For instance, the real solutions of $x^2 = x + 1$ are the x-intercepts of the graph of $f(x) = x^2 - x - 1$, which are the zeros of f.

To solve $x^2 = x + 1$, rewrite the equation with all terms on one side. The equation is now $x^2 - x - 1 = 0$. Think of this equation as $Y_1 = x^2 - x - 1$. The x-intercepts of the graph of Y_1 are the solutions of the equation $x^2 = x + 1$.

a. Enter $x^2 - x - 1$ into Y_1.

b. Graph the equation. You may need to adjust the viewing window so that the x-intercept is visible.

c. Press $\boxed{\text{SHIFT}}$ G-SOLV $\boxed{\text{F1}}$.

d. The root is shown as the x-coordinate on the bottom of the screen; in this case, the root is approximately -0.618034. To find the next x-intercept, press the right arrow key.

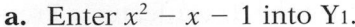

The EQUA Mode (Press $\boxed{\text{MENU}}$ $\boxed{\text{ALPHA}}$ A) can also be used to find solutions of linear, quadratic, and cubic equations.

SOLVING SYSTEMS OF TWO EQUATIONS IN TWO VARIABLES

The following discussion is based on the concept that the solutions of a system of two equations are represented by the point(s) of intersections of the graphs.

The system of equations $\begin{array}{l} y = x^2 - 1 \\ \frac{1}{2}x + y = 1 \end{array}$ will be solved.

a. Solve each equation for y.

b. Enter the first equation in the Graph Menu as Y_1. For instance, let $Y_1 = x^2 - 1$.

c. Enter the second equation as Y_2. For instance, let $Y_2 = 1 - \frac{1}{2}x$.

d. Graph both equations. (*Note:* The point of intersection must appear on the screen. It may be necessary to adjust the viewing window so that the point of intersection that is of interest is the only intersection point that is displayed.)

e. Press $\boxed{\text{SHIFT}}$ G-SOL $\boxed{\text{F5}}$ $\boxed{\text{EXE}}$.

f. The display will show that the graphs intersect at $(-1.686141, 1.8430703)$. To find the next intersect, repeat step **e**.

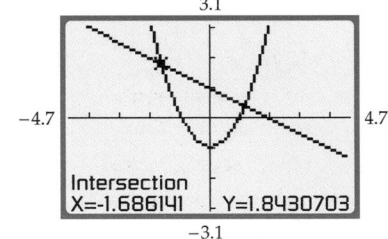

FINDING MINIMUM OR MAXIMUM VALUES OF A FUNCTION

a. Enter the function into the graphing menu. For this example we have used $y = x^2 - x - 1$.

b. Graph the function. Adjust the viewing window so that the maximum or minimum is visible.

c. Press $\boxed{\text{SHIFT}}$ G-SOL $\boxed{\text{F2}}$ $\boxed{\text{EXE}}$ for a maximum and $\boxed{\text{F3}}$ $\boxed{\text{EXE}}$ for a minimum.

d. The local maximum (minimum) is shown as the y-coordinate on the bottom of the screen; in this case, the minimum value is -1.25.

Table of Symbols

$+$	add	$<$	is less than
$-$	subtract	$\leq$	is less than or equal to
$\cdot, \times, (a)(b)$	multiply	$>$	is greater than
$\dfrac{a}{b}, \div, a\overline{)b}$	divide	$\geq$	is greater than or equal to
$(\ )$	parentheses, a grouping symbol	(a, b)	an ordered pair whose first component is a and whose second component is b
$[\ ]$	brackets, a grouping symbol	$^{\circ}$	degree (for angles)
π	pi, a number approximately equal to $\dfrac{22}{7}$ or 3.14	$\sqrt{a}$	the principal square root of a
$-a$	the opposite, or additive inverse, of a	$\varnothing, \{\ \}$	the empty set
$\dfrac{1}{a}$	the reciprocal, or multiplicative inverse, of a	$|a|$	the absolute value of a
$=$	is equal to	$\cup$	union of two sets
$\approx$	is approximately equal to	$\cap$	intersection of two sets
$\neq$	is not equal to	$\in$	is an element of (for sets)

Table of Measurement Abbreviations

U.S. Customary System

Length		**Capacity**		**Weight**		**Area**	
in.	inches	oz	fluid ounces	oz	ounces	in²	square inches
ft	feet	c	cups	lb	pounds	ft²	square feet
yd	yards	qt	quarts			yd²	square yards
mi	miles	gal	gallons			mi²	square miles

Metric System

Length		**Capacity**		**Weight/Mass**		**Area**	
mm	millimeter (0.001 m)	ml	milliliter (0.001 L)	mg	milligram (0.001 g)	cm²	square centimeters
cm	centimeter (0.01 m)	cl	centiliter (0.01 L)	cg	centigram (0.01 g)	m²	square meters
dm	decimeter (0.1 m)	dl	deciliter (0.1 L)	dg	decigram (0.1 g)		
m	meter	L	liter	g	gram		
dam	decameter (10 m)	dal	decaliter (10 L)	dag	decagram (10 g)		
hm	hectometer (100 m)	hl	hectoliter (100 L)	hg	hectogram (100 g)		
km	kilometer (1000 m)	kl	kiloliter (1000 L)	kg	kilogram (1000 g)		

Time

h	hours	min	minutes	s	seconds

Solutions to Chapter 1 "You Try It"

SECTION 1.1

You Try It 1 $A = \{1, 2, 3, 4, 5, 6\}$

You Try It 2 $-5 < -1$
$-1 = -1$
$5 > -1$

The element 5 is greater than -1.

You Try It 3 $|-5| = 5$
$-|-23| = -23$

You Try It 4 $-(-11) = 11$
$-0 = 0$
$-(8) = -8$

You Try It 5 $|-37| = 37$
$|0| = 0$
$|29| = 29$

SECTION 1.2

You Try It 1 $100 + (-43) = 57$

You Try It 2 $(-51) + 42 + 17 + (-102)$
$= -9 + 17 + (-102)$
$= 8 + (-102)$
$= -94$

You Try It 3 $19 - (-32) = 19 + 32$
$= 51$

You Try It 4 $-9 - (-12) - 17 - 4$
$= -9 + 12 + (-17) + (-4)$
$= 3 + (-17) + (-4)$
$= -14 + (-4)$
$= -18$

You Try It 5

Strategy   To find the difference between the two average temperatures, subtract the smaller number (-130) from the larger number (-17).

Solution $-17 - (-130) = -17 + 130 = 113$

The difference is $113°F$.

SECTION 1.3

You Try It 1 $8(-9)10 = -72(10)$
$= -720$

You Try It 2 $(-2)3(-8)7 = -6(-8)7$
$= 48(7)$
$= 336$

You Try It 3 $(-135) \div (-9) = 15$

You Try It 4 $\dfrac{-72}{4} = -18$

You Try It 5 $-\dfrac{36}{-12} = -(-3)$
$= 3$

You Try It 6

Strategy
To find the average low temperature:
• Add the seven temperature readings.
• Divide the sum by 7.

Solution
$-6 + (-7) + 0 + (-5) + (-8) + (-1) + (-1) = -28$
$-28 \div 7 = -4$

The average daily low temperature was $-4°C$.

SECTION 1.4

You Try It 1
$$\begin{array}{r} 0.444 \\ 9\overline{)4.000} \\ \underline{-3\ 6} \\ 40 \\ \underline{-36} \\ 40 \\ \underline{-36} \\ 4 \end{array}$$
$\dfrac{4}{9} = 0.\overline{4}$

You Try It 2 $125\% = 125\left(\dfrac{1}{100}\right) = \dfrac{125}{100} = 1\dfrac{1}{4}$
$125\% = 125(0.01) = 1.25$

You Try It 3 $16\dfrac{2}{3}\% = 16\dfrac{2}{3}\left(\dfrac{1}{100}\right) = \dfrac{50}{3}\left(\dfrac{1}{100}\right) = \dfrac{1}{6}$

You Try It 4 $\dfrac{9}{16} = \dfrac{9}{16}(100\%) = \dfrac{900}{16}\% = 56.25\%$
or $56\dfrac{1}{4}\%$

You Try It 5 $0.043 = 0.043(100\%) = 4.3\%$

You Try It 6 The LCM of 9 and 12 is 36.

$$\frac{5}{9} - \frac{11}{12} = \frac{20}{36} - \frac{33}{36} = \frac{20}{36} + \frac{-33}{36}$$

$$= \frac{20 + (-33)}{36} = \frac{-13}{36} = -\frac{13}{36}$$

You Try It 7 The LCM of 8, 6, and 4 is 24.

$$-\frac{7}{8} - \frac{5}{6} + \frac{3}{4} = -\frac{21}{24} - \frac{20}{24} + \frac{18}{24}$$

$$= \frac{-21}{24} + \frac{-20}{24} + \frac{18}{24}$$

$$= \frac{-21 + (-20) + 18}{24}$$

$$= \frac{-23}{24} = -\frac{23}{24}$$

You Try It 8 $16.127 - 67.91 = 16.127 + (-67.91)$
$$= -51.783$$

You Try It 9 The product is negative.

$$-\frac{7}{12} \times \frac{9}{14} = -\frac{7 \cdot 9}{12 \cdot 14}$$

$$= -\frac{\overset{1}{\cancel{7}} \cdot \overset{1}{\cancel{3}} \cdot 3}{2 \cdot 2 \cdot \underset{1}{\cancel{3}} \cdot 2 \cdot \underset{1}{\cancel{7}}}$$

$$= -\frac{3}{8}$$

You Try It 10 The quotient is positive.

$$-\frac{3}{8} \div \left(-\frac{5}{12}\right) = \frac{3}{8} \times \frac{12}{5}$$

$$= \frac{3 \cdot 12}{8 \cdot 5} = \frac{3 \cdot \overset{1}{\cancel{2}} \cdot \overset{1}{\cancel{2}} \cdot 3}{\underset{1}{\cancel{2}} \cdot \underset{1}{\cancel{2}} \cdot 2 \cdot 5} = \frac{9}{10}$$

You Try It 11 The product is negative.
Multiply the absolute values.
$-5.44 \times 3.8 = -20.672$

You Try It 12 The quotient is negative.
Divide the absolute values.

$$\begin{array}{r} 0.231 \\ 1.7\,\overline{)0.3\,940} \\ \underline{-3\,4} \\ 54 \\ \underline{-51} \\ 30 \\ \underline{-17} \\ 13 \end{array}$$

$-0.394 \div 1.7 \approx -0.23$

You Try It 13

Strategy To find the percent of the population that is in the baby-boomer generation:
• Find the total population by adding the numbers in all four generations.
• Divide the number of people in the baby-boomer generation (77.6 million) by the total population.

Solution $72.4 + 44.6 + 77.6 + 68.3 = 262.9$

The population of the United States is 262.9 million.

$$\frac{77.6}{262.9} \approx 0.295 \approx 30\%$$

The baby-boomers make up about 30% of the population of the United States.

SECTION 1.5

You Try It 1 $-6^3 = -(6 \cdot 6 \cdot 6) = -216$

You Try It 2 $(-3)^4 = (-3)(-3)(-3)(-3) = 81$

You Try It 3 $(3^3)(-2)^3 = (3)(3)(3) \cdot (-2)(-2)(-2)$
$$= 27(-8) = -216$$

You Try It 4 $\left(-\frac{2}{5}\right)^2 = \left(-\frac{2}{5}\right)\left(-\frac{2}{5}\right) = \frac{4}{25}$

You Try It 5 $-3(0.3)^3 = -3(0.3)(0.3)(0.3)$
$$= -0.9(0.3)(0.3)$$
$$= -0.27(0.3) = -0.081$$

You Try It 6 $(6.97 - 4.72)^2 \cdot 4.5 \div 0.05$
$$= (2.25)^2 \cdot 4.5 \div 0.05$$
$$= 5.0625 \cdot 4.5 \div 0.05$$
$$= 22.78125 \div 0.05$$
$$= 455.625$$

You Try It 7 $18 - 5[8 - 2(2 - 5)] \div 10$
$$= 18 - 5[8 - 2(-3)] \div 10$$
$$= 18 - 5[8 + 6] \div 10$$
$$= 18 - 5[14] \div 10$$
$$= 18 - 70 \div 10$$
$$= 18 - 7$$
$$= 11$$

You Try It 8 $36 \div (8 - 5)^2 - (-3)^2 \cdot 2$
$$= 36 \div (3)^2 - (-3)^2 \cdot 2$$
$$= 36 \div 9 - 9 \cdot 2$$
$$= 4 - 9 \cdot 2$$
$$= 4 - 18$$
$$= -14$$

You Try It 9 $\dfrac{5}{8} \div \left(\dfrac{1}{3} - \dfrac{3}{4} \right) + \dfrac{7}{12}$
$$= \dfrac{5}{8} \div \left(-\dfrac{5}{12} \right) + \dfrac{7}{12}$$
$$= \dfrac{5}{8} \cdot \left(-\dfrac{12}{5} \right) + \dfrac{7}{12}$$
$$= -\dfrac{3}{2} + \dfrac{7}{12}$$
$$= -\dfrac{18}{12} + \dfrac{7}{12}$$
$$= -\dfrac{11}{12}$$

Solutions to Chapter 2 "You Try It"

SECTION 2.1

You Try It 1 -4 is the constant term.

You Try It 2 $2xy + y^2$
$2(-4)(2) + (2)^2$
$$= 2(-4)(2) + 4$$
$$= (-8)(2) + 4$$
$$= (-16) + 4$$
$$= -12$$

You Try It 3 $\dfrac{a^2 + b^2}{a + b}$

$$\dfrac{5^2 + (-3)^2}{5 + (-3)} = \dfrac{25 + 9}{5 + (-3)}$$
$$= \dfrac{34}{2}$$
$$= 17$$

You Try It 4 $x^3 - 2(x + y) + z^2$
$(2)^3 - 2[2 + (-4)] + (-3)^2$
$$= 8 - 2(-2) + 9$$
$$= 8 + 4 + 9$$
$$= 12 + 9$$
$$= 21$$

SECTION 2.2

You Try It 1 $3a - 2b - 5a + 6b = -2a + 4b$

You Try It 2 $-3y^2 + 7 + 8y^2 - 14 = 5y^2 - 7$

You Try It 3 $-5(4y^2) = -20y^2$

You Try It 4 $-7(-2a) = 14a$

You Try It 5 $(-5x)(-2) = 10x$

You Try It 6 $5(3 + 7b) = 15 + 35b$

You Try It 7 $(3a - 1)5 = 15a - 5$

You Try It 8 $-8(-2a + 7b) = 16a - 56b$

You Try It 9 $3(12x^2 - x + 8) = 36x^2 - 3x + 24$

You Try It 10 $3(-a^2 - 6a + 7) = -3a^2 - 18a + 21$

You Try It 11 $3y - 2(y - 7x) = 3y - 2y + 14x$
$$= y + 14x$$

You Try It 12
$-2(x - 2y) - (-x + 3y) = -2x + 4y + x - 3y$
$$= -x + y$$

You Try It 13
$3y - 2[x - 4(2 - 3y)] = 3y - 2[x - 8 + 12y]$
$$= 3y - 2x + 16 - 24y$$
$$= -2x - 21y + 16$$

SECTION 2.3

You Try It 1   the <u>difference between</u> <u>twice</u> n and <u>one-third of</u> n

$2n - \dfrac{1}{3} n$

You Try It 2   the <u>quotient of</u> 7 <u>less than</u> b and 15

$\dfrac{b - 7}{15}$

You Try It 3 an unknown number: n
the cube of the number: n^3
the total of ten and the cube of the number: $10 + n^3$

$-4(10 + n^3)$

You Try It 4 the unknown number: x
the difference between the number and sixty: $x - 60$

$5(x - 60) = 5x - 300$

You Try It 5 the speed of the older model: s
the new jet operates at twice the speed of the older model: $2s$

You Try It 6 the length of the longer piece: y
the length of the shorter piece: $6 - y$

Solutions to Chapter 3 "You Try It"

SECTION 3.1

You Try It 1

$$\frac{5 - 4x = 8x + 2}{5 - 4\left(\frac{1}{4}\right) \mid 8\left(\frac{1}{4}\right) + 2}$$
$$5 - 1 \mid 2 + 2$$
$$4 = 4$$

Yes, $\frac{1}{4}$ is a solution.

You Try It 2

$$\frac{10x - x^2 = 3x - 10}{10(5) - (5)^2 \mid 3(5) - 10}$$
$$50 - 25 \mid 15 - 10$$
$$25 \neq 5$$

No, 5 is not a solution.

You Try It 3

$$\frac{5}{6} = y - \frac{3}{8}$$
$$\frac{5}{6} + \frac{3}{8} = y - \frac{3}{8} + \frac{3}{8}$$
$$\frac{29}{24} = y$$

The solution is $\frac{29}{24}$.

You Try It 4

$$-\frac{2}{5}x = 6$$
$$\left(-\frac{5}{2}\right)\left(-\frac{2}{5}x\right) = \left(-\frac{5}{2}\right)(6)$$
$$x = -15$$

The solution is -15.

You Try It 5

$$4x - 8x = 16$$
$$-4x = 16$$
$$\frac{-4x}{-4} = \frac{16}{-4}$$
$$x = -4$$

The solution is -4.

You Try It 6

$$P \cdot B = A$$
$$\frac{1}{6}B = 18 \qquad \bullet\ 16\frac{2}{3}\% = \frac{1}{6}$$
$$6 \cdot \frac{1}{6}B = 6 \cdot 18$$
$$B = 108$$

18 is $16\frac{2}{3}\%$ of 108.

You Try It 7

Strategy To find the percent, solve the basic percent equation using $B = 47.1$ and $A = 23.1$. The percent is unknown.

Solution
$$P \cdot B = A$$
$$P(47.1) = 23.1$$
$$\frac{P(47.1)}{47.1} = \frac{23.1}{47.1}$$
$$P \approx 49.0\%$$

The March 1997 deficit was 49.0% of the March 1996 deficit.

SECTION 3.2

You Try It 1

$$5x + 7 = 10$$
$$5x + 7 - 7 = 10 - 7$$
$$5x = 3$$
$$\frac{5x}{5} = \frac{3}{5}$$
$$x = \frac{3}{5}$$

The solution is $\frac{3}{5}$.

You Try It 2

$$2 = 11 + 3x$$
$$2 - 11 = 11 - 11 + 3x$$
$$-9 = 3x$$

$$\frac{-9}{3} = \frac{3x}{3}$$

$$-3 = x$$

The solution is -3.

You Try It 3 $x - 5 + 4x = 25$

$$5x - 5 = 25$$

$$5x - 5 + 5 = 25 + 5$$

$$5x = 30$$

$$\frac{5x}{5} = \frac{30}{5}$$

$$x = 6$$

The solution is 6.

You Try It 4

Strategy   Given: $S = 986$

$$r = 45\% = 0.45$$

Unknown: C

Solution $S = C + rC$

$$986 = C + 0.45C$$

$$986 = 1.45C$$

$$680 = C$$

The cost of the outboard motor is $680.

You Try It 5

Strategy   Given: $S = 159$

$$r = 25\% = 0.25$$

Unknown: R

Solution $S = R - rR$

$$159 = R - 0.25R$$

$$159 = 0.75R$$

$$212 = R$$

The regular price of the garage door opener is $212.

You Try It 6

Strategy   To find the depth, replace P with the given value and solve for D.

Solution

$$P = 15 + \frac{1}{2}D$$

$$45 = 15 + \frac{1}{2}D$$

$$45 - 15 = 15 - 15 + \frac{1}{2}D$$

$$30 = \frac{1}{2}D$$

$$2(30) = 2 \cdot \frac{1}{2}D$$

$$60 = D$$

The depth is 60 ft.

SECTION 3.3

You Try It 1 $5x + 4 = 6 + 10x$

$$5x - 10x + 4 = 6 + 10x - 10x$$

$$-5x + 4 = 6$$

$$-5x + 4 - 4 = 6 - 4$$

$$-5x = 2$$

$$\frac{-5x}{-5} = \frac{2}{-5}$$

$$x = -\frac{2}{5}$$

The solution is $-\frac{2}{5}$.

You Try It 2 $5x - 10 - 3x = 6 - 4x$

$$2x - 10 = 6 - 4x$$

$$2x + 4x - 10 = 6 - 4x + 4x$$

$$6x - 10 = 6$$

$$6x - 10 + 10 = 6 + 10$$

$$6x = 16$$

$$\frac{6x}{6} = \frac{16}{6}$$

$$x = \frac{8}{3}$$

The solution is $\frac{8}{3}$.

You Try It 3 $5x - 4(3 - 2x) = 2(3x - 2) + 6$

$$5x - 12 + 8x = 6x - 4 + 6$$

$$13x - 12 = 6x + 2$$

$$13x - 6x - 12 = 6x - 6x + 2$$

$$7x - 12 = 2$$

$$7x - 12 + 12 = 2 + 12$$

$$7x = 14$$

$$\frac{7x}{7} = \frac{14}{7}$$

$$x = 2$$

The solution is 2.

You Try It 4 $-2[3x - 5(2x - 3)] = 3x - 8$

$$-2[3x - 10x + 15] = 3x - 8$$

$$-2[-7x + 15] = 3x - 8$$

$$14x - 30 = 3x - 8$$

$$14x - 3x - 30 = 3x - 3x - 8$$

$$11x - 30 = -8$$

$$11x - 30 + 30 = -8 + 30$$

$$11x = 22$$

$$\frac{11x}{11} = \frac{22}{11}$$

$$x = 2$$

The solution is 2.

You Try It 5   Solve $2x = 5x + 6$ for x.

$$2x = 5x + 6$$
$$-3x = 6$$
$$x = -2$$

Evaluate $-2x + 7$ for $x = -2$.

$$-2x + 7$$
$$-2(-2) + 7 = 4 + 7$$
$$= 11$$

You Try It 6

Strategy   To find the location of the fulcrum when the system balances, replace the variables F_1, F_2, and d in the lever system equation by the given values and solve for x.

Solution

$$F_1 \cdot x = F_2 \cdot (d - x)$$
$$45x = 80(25 - x)$$
$$45x = 2000 - 80x$$
$$45x + 80x = 2000 - 80x + 80x$$
$$125x = 2000$$
$$\frac{125x}{125} = \frac{2000}{125}$$
$$x = 16$$

The fulcrum is 16 ft from the 45-pound force.

SECTION 3.4

You Try It 1

The smaller number: n
The larger number: $12 - n$

The total of three times the smaller number and six	amounts to	seven less than the product of four and the larger number

$$3n + 6 = 4(12 - n) - 7$$
$$3n + 6 = 48 - 4n - 7$$
$$3n + 6 = 41 - 4n$$
$$3n + 4n + 6 = 41 - 4n + 4n$$
$$7n + 6 = 41$$
$$7n + 6 - 6 = 41 - 6$$
$$7n = 35$$
$$\frac{7n}{7} = \frac{35}{7}$$
$$n = 5$$

$$12 - n = 12 - 5 = 7$$

The smaller number is 5.
The larger number is 7.

You Try It 2

Strategy   • First consecutive integer: n
Second consecutive integer: $n + 1$
Third consecutive integer: $n + 2$
• The sum of the three integers is -6.

Solution

$$n + (n + 1) + (n + 2) = -6$$
$$3n + 3 = -6$$
$$3n = -9$$
$$n = -3$$

$$n + 1 = -3 + 1 = -2$$
$$n + 2 = -3 + 2 = -1$$

The three consecutive integers are -3, -2, and -1.

You Try It 3

Strategy
To find the number of tickets that you are purchasing, write and solve an equation using x to represent the number of tickets purchased.

Solution

$3.50 plus $17.50 for each ticket	equals	$161

$$3.50 + 17.50x = 161$$
$$3.50 - 3.50 + 17.50x = 161 - 3.50$$
$$17.50x = 157.50$$
$$\frac{17.50x}{17.50} = \frac{157.50}{17.50}$$
$$x = 9$$

You purchased 9 tickets.

You Try It 4

Strategy
To find the length, write and solve an equation using x to represent the length of the shorter piece and $22 - x$ to represent the length of the longer piece.

Solution

The longer piece	is	4 in. more than twice the shorter piece

$$22 - x = 2x + 4$$
$$22 - x - 2x = 2x - 2x + 4$$
$$22 - 3x = 4$$
$$22 - 22 - 3x = 4 - 22$$
$$-3x = -18$$
$$\frac{-3x}{-3} = \frac{-18}{-3}$$
$$x = 6$$

$$22 - x = 22 - 6 = 16$$

The shorter piece is 6 in.
The longer piece is 16 in.

SECTION 3.5

You Try It 1

Strategy   To find the length of each side, use the formula for the perimeter of a square. Substitute 52 for P and solve for s.

Solution
$$P = 4s$$
$$52 = 4s$$
$$13 = s$$

The length of each side of the patio is 13 ft.

You Try It 2

Strategy   To find the supplement, let x represent the supplement of a $107°$ angle. Use the fact that supplementary angles are two angles whose sum is $180°$ to write an equation. Solve for x.

Solution
$$x + 107° = 180°$$
$$x = 73°$$

The supplement of a $107°$ angle is a $73°$ angle.

You Try It 3

Strategy   The angles labeled are adjacent angles of intersecting lines and are, therefore, supplementary angles. To find x, write an equation and solve for x.

Solution
$$x + (3x + 20°) = 180°$$
$$4x + 20° = 180°$$
$$4x = 160°$$
$$x = 40°$$

You Try It 4

Strategy $2x = y$ because alternate exterior angles have the same measure. $(x + 15°) + y = 180°$ because adjacent angles of intersecting lines are supplementary angles. Substitute $2x$ for y and solve for x.

Solution
$$(x + 15°) + 2x = 180°$$
$$3x + 15° = 180°$$
$$3x = 165°$$
$$x = 55°$$

You Try It 5

Strategy   • To find the measure of angle a, use the fact that $\angle a$ and $\angle y$ are vertical angles.

• To find the measure of angle b, use the fact that the sum of the measures of the interior angles of a triangle is $180°$.
• To find the measure of angle d, use the fact that the sum of an interior and an exterior angle is $180°$.

Solution $\angle a = \angle y = 55°$

$$\angle a + \angle b + 90° = 180°$$
$$55° + \angle b + 90° = 180°$$
$$\angle b + 145° = 180°$$
$$\angle b = 35°$$

$$\angle d + \angle b = 180°$$
$$\angle d + 35° = 180°$$
$$\angle d = 145°$$

You Try It 6

Strategy   To find the measure of the third angle, use the fact that the sum of the measures of the interior angles of a triangle is $180°$. Write an equation using x to represent the measure of the third angle. Solve the equation for x.

Solution
$$x + 90° + 27° = 180°$$
$$x + 117° = 180°$$
$$x = 63°$$

The measure of the third angle is $63°$.

SECTION 3.6

You Try It 1

Strategy   • Pounds of $.55 fertilizer: x

	Amount	Cost	Value
$.80 fertilizer	20	$.80	0.80(20)
$.55 fertilizer	x	$.55	0.55x
$.75 fertilizer	20 + x	$.75	0.75(20 + x)

• The sum of the values before mixing equals the value after mixing.

Solution
$$0.80(20) + 0.55x = 0.75(20 + x)$$
$$16 + 0.55x = 15 + 0.75x$$
$$16 - 0.20x = 15$$
$$-0.20x = -1$$
$$x = 5$$

5 lb of the $.55 fertilizer must be added.

You Try It 2

Strategy • Liters of 6% solution: x

	Amount	Percent	Quantity
6% solution	x	0.06	$0.06x$
12% solution	5	0.12	$5(0.12)$
8% solution	$x + 5$	0.08	$0.08(x + 5)$

• The sum of the quantities before mixing equals the quantity after mixing.

Solution
$$0.06x + 5(0.12) = 0.08(x + 5)$$
$$0.06x + 0.60 = 0.08x + 0.40$$
$$0.06x + 0.20 = 0.08x$$
$$0.20 = 0.02x$$
$$10 = x$$

The pharmacist adds 10 L of the 6% solution to the 12% solution to get an 8% solution.

You Try It 3

Strategy • Rate of the first train: r
Rate of the second train: $2r$

	Rate	Time	Distance
1st train	r	3	$3r$
2nd train	$2r$	3	$3(2r)$

• The sum of the distances traveled by each train equals 288 mi.

Solution
$$3r + 3(2r) = 288$$
$$3r + 6r = 288$$
$$9r = 288$$
$$r = 32$$

$$2r = 2(32) = 64$$

The first train is traveling at 32 mph. The second train is traveling at 64 mph.

You Try It 4

Strategy • Time spent flying out: t
Time spent flying back: $5 - t$

	Rate	Time	Distance
Out	150	t	$150t$
Back	100	$5 - t$	$100(5 - t)$

• The distance out equals the distance back.

Solution
$$150t = 100(5 - t)$$
$$150t = 500 - 100t$$
$$250t = 500$$
$$t = 2 \quad \text{(The time out was 2 h.)}$$

$$\text{The distance} = 150t = 150(2)$$
$$= 300 \text{ mi}$$

The parcel of land was 300 mi away.

Solutions to Chapter 4 "You Try It"

SECTION 4.1

You Try It 1
$$(-4x^3 + 2x^2 - 8) + (4x^3 + 6x^2 - 7x + 5)$$
$$= (-4x^3 + 4x^3) + (2x^2 + 6x^2) + (-7x) + (-8 + 5)$$
$$= 8x^2 - 7x - 3$$

You Try It 2
$$6x^3 \qquad + 2x + 8$$
$$-9x^3 + 2x^2 - 12x - 8$$
$$\overline{-3x^3 + 2x^2 - 10x}$$

You Try It 3
$$(-4w^3 + 8w - 8) - (3w^3 - 4w^2 - 2w - 1)$$
$$= (-4w^3 + 8w - 8)$$
$$\quad + (-3w^3 + 4w^2 + 2w + 1)$$
$$= -7w^3 + 4w^2 + 10w - 7$$

You Try It 4
$$13y^3 \qquad\quad - 6y - 7$$
$$\quad - 4y^2 + 6y + 9$$
$$\overline{13y^3 - 4y^2 \qquad + 2}$$

SECTION 4.2

You Try It 1
$$(8m^3n)(-3n^5) = [8(-3)](m^3)(n \cdot n^5)$$
$$= -24m^3n^6$$

You Try It 2
$$(12p^4q^3)(-3p^5q^2) = [12(-3)](p^4 \cdot p^5)(q^3 \cdot q^2)$$
$$= -36p^9q^5$$

You Try It 3
$$(-3a^4bc^2)^3 = (-3)^{1 \cdot 3}a^{4 \cdot 3}b^{1 \cdot 3}c^{2 \cdot 3}$$
$$= (-3)^3a^{12}b^3c^6$$
$$= -27a^{12}b^3c^6$$

You Try It 4

$$(-xy^4)(-2x^3y^2)^2 = (-xy^4)[(-2)^{1\cdot2}x^{3\cdot2}y^{2\cdot2}]$$
$$= (-xy^4)[(-2)^2x^6y^4]$$
$$= (-xy^4)(4x^6y^4)$$
$$= -4x^7y^8$$

SECTION 4.3

You Try It 1 $(-2y + 3)(-4y) = 8y^2 - 12y$

You Try It 2
$$-a^2(3a^2 + 2a - 7) = -3a^4 - 2a^3 + 7a^2$$

You Try It 3

$$
\begin{array}{r}
2y^3 + 2y^2 \qquad\quad - 3 \\
3y - 1 \\
\hline
-2y^3 - 2y^2 \qquad\quad + 3 \\
6y^4 + 6y^3 \qquad\quad - 9y \\
\hline
6y^4 + 4y^3 - 2y^2 - 9y + 3
\end{array}
$$

You Try It 4
$$(4y - 5)(2y - 3) = 8y^2 - 12y - 10y + 15$$
$$= 8y^2 - 22y + 15$$

You Try It 5
$$(3b + 2)(3b - 5) = 9b^2 - 15b + 6b - 10$$
$$= 9b^2 - 9b - 10$$

You Try It 6 $(2a + 5c)(2a - 5c) = 4a^2 - 25c^2$

You Try It 7 $(3x + 2y)^2 = 9x^2 + 12xy + 4y^2$

You Try It 8

Strategy   To find the area, replace the variable r in the equation $A = \pi r^2$ by $(x - 4)$ and solve for A.

Solution $A = \pi r^2$
$A = \pi(x - 4)^2$
$A = \pi(x^2 - 8x + 16)$
$A = \pi x^2 - 8\pi x + 16\pi$

The area of the circle is $(\pi x^2 - 8\pi x + 16\pi)$ ft^2.

SECTION 4.4

You Try It 1 $(-2x^2)(x^{-3}y^{-4})^{-2} = (-2x^2)(x^6y^8)$
$$= -2x^8y^8$$

You Try It 2 $\dfrac{(6a^{-2}b^3)^{-1}}{(4a^3b^{-2})^{-2}} = \dfrac{6^{-1}a^2b^{-3}}{4^{-2}a^{-6}b^4}$
$$= 4^2(6^{-1}a^8b^{-7})$$
$$= \dfrac{16a^8}{6b^7} = \dfrac{8a^8}{3b^7}$$

You Try It 3 $\left[\dfrac{6r^3s^{-3}}{9r^3s^{-1}}\right]^{-2} = \left[\dfrac{2r^0s^{-2}}{3}\right]^{-2}$
$$= \dfrac{2^{-2}s^4}{3^{-2}} = \dfrac{9s^4}{4}$$

You Try It 4 $0.000000961 = 9.61 \times 10^{-7}$

You Try It 5 $7.329 \times 10^6 = 7,329,000$

SECTION 4.5

You Try It 1
$$\dfrac{24x^2y^2 - 18xy + 6y}{6xy} = \dfrac{24x^2y^2}{6xy} - \dfrac{18xy}{6xy} + \dfrac{6y}{6xy}$$
$$= 4xy - 3 + \dfrac{1}{x}$$

You Try It 2

$$
\begin{array}{r}
x^2 + 2x - 1 \\
2x - 3\overline{)2x^3 + x^2 - 8x - 3} \\
\underline{2x^3 - 3x^2} \\
4x^2 - 8x \\
\underline{4x^2 - 6x} \\
-2x - 3 \\
\underline{-2x + 3} \\
-6
\end{array}
$$

$(2x^3 + x^2 - 8x - 3) \div (2x - 3)$
$$= x^2 + 2x - 1 - \dfrac{6}{2x - 3}$$

You Try It 3

$$
\begin{array}{r}
x^2 + x - 1 \\
x - 1\overline{)x^3 + 0x^2 - 2x + 1} \\
\underline{x^3 - x^2} \\
x^2 - 2x \\
\underline{x^2 - x} \\
-x + 1 \\
\underline{-x + 1} \\
0
\end{array}
$$

$(x^3 - 2x + 1) \div (x - 1) = x^2 + x - 1$

Solutions to Chapter 5 "You Try It"

SECTION 5.1

You Try It 1 The GCF is $7a^2$.

$$14a^2 - 21a^4b = 7a^2(2) + 7a^2(-3a^2b)$$
$$= 7a^2(2 - 3a^2b)$$

You Try It 2 The GCF is 9.

$$27b^2 + 18b + 9$$
$$= 9(3b^2) + 9(2b) + 9(1)$$
$$= 9(3b^2 + 2b + 1)$$

You Try It 3
The GCF is $3x^2y^2$.

$$6x^4y^2 - 9x^3y^2 + 12x^2y^4$$
$$= 3x^2y^2(2x^2) + 3x^2y^2(-3x) + 3x^2y^2(4y^2)$$
$$= 3x^2y^2(2x^2 - 3x + 4y^2)$$

You Try It 4 $2y(5x - 2) - 3(2 - 5x)$
$$= 2y(5x - 2) + 3(5x - 2)$$
$$= (5x - 2)(2y + 3)$$

You Try It 5 $a^2 - 3a + 2ab - 6b$
$$= (a^2 - 3a) + (2ab - 6b)$$
$$= a(a - 3) + 2b(a - 3)$$
$$= (a - 3)(a + 2b)$$

You Try It 6 $2mn^2 - n + 8mn - 4$
$$= (2mn^2 - n) + (8mn - 4)$$
$$= n(2mn - 1) + 4(2mn - 1)$$
$$= (2mn - 1)(n + 4)$$

You Try It 7 $2xy - 6y - 12 + 4x$
$$= (2xy - 6y) - (12 - 4x)$$
$$= 2y(x - 3) - 4(3 - x)$$
$$= 2y(x - 3) + 4(x - 3)$$
$$= (x - 3)(2y + 4)$$

SECTION 5.2

You Try It 1
Find the positive factors of 20 whose sum is 9.

Factors	Sum
1, 20	21
2, 10	12
4, 5	9

$$x^2 + 9x + 20 = (x + 4)(x + 5)$$

You Try It 2
Find the factors of -18 whose sum is 7.

Factors	Sum
+1, −18	−17
−1, +18	17
+2, −9	−7
−2, +9	7
+3, −6	−3
−3, +6	+3

$$x^2 + 7x - 18 = (x + 9)(x - 2)$$

You Try It 3
The GCF is $-2x$.

$$-2x^3 + 14x^2 - 12x = -2x(x^2 - 7x + 6)$$

Factor the trinomial $x^2 - 7x + 6$. Find two negative factors of 6 whose sum is -7.

Factors	Sum
−3, −2	−5
−6, −1	−7

$$-2x^3 + 14x^2 - 12x = -2x(x - 6)(x - 1)$$

You Try It 4
The GCF is 3.

$$3x^2 - 9xy - 12y^2 = 3(x^2 - 3xy - 4y^2)$$

Factor the trinomial.

Find the factors of -4 whose sum is -3.

Factors	Sum
+1, −4	−3
−1, +4	3
+2, −2	0

$$3x^2 - 9xy - 12y^2 = 3(x + y)(x - 4y)$$

SECTION 5.3

You Try It 1
Factor the trinomial $2x^2 - x - 3$.

Positive factors of 2: 1, 2

Factors of -3: $+1, -3$
$-1, +3$

Trial Factors	Middle Term
$(x + 1)(2x - 3)$	$-3x + 2x = -x$
$(x - 3)(2x + 1)$	$x - 6x = -5x$
$(x - 1)(2x + 3)$	$3x - 2x = x$
$(x + 3)(2x - 1)$	$-x + 6x = 5x$

$$2x^2 - x - 3 = (x + 1)(2x - 3)$$

You Try It 2
The GCF is $-3y$.

$$-45y^3 + 12y^2 + 12y = -3y(15y^2 - 4y - 4)$$

Factor the trinomial $15y^2 - 4y - 4$.

Positive   Factors of -4: -1, 4
factors of 15: 1, 15   1, -4
              3, 5 -2, 2

Trial Factors	Middle Term
$(y - 1)(15y + 4)$	$4y - 15y = -11y$
$(y + 4)(15y - 1)$	$-y + 60y = 59y$
$(y + 1)(15y - 4)$	$-4y + 15y = 11y$
$(y - 4)(15y + 1)$	$y - 60y = -59y$
$(y - 2)(15y + 2)$	$2y - 30y = -28y$
$(y + 2)(15y - 2)$	$-2y + 30y = 28y$
$(3y - 1)(5y + 4)$	$12y - 5y = 7y$
$(3y + 4)(5y - 1)$	$-3y + 20y = 17y$
$(3y + 1)(5y - 4)$	$-12y + 5y = -7y$
$(3y - 4)(5y + 1)$	$3y - 20y = -17y$
$(3y - 2)(5y + 2)$	$6y - 10y = -4y$
$(3y + 2)(5y - 2)$	$-6y + 10y = 4y$

$$-45y^3 + 12y^2 + 12y = -3y(3y - 2)(5y + 2)$$

You Try It 3

Factors of -14 [$2(-7)$]	Sum
$-1, +14$	13
$1, -14$	-13
$2, -7$	-5
$-2, 7$	5

$$
\begin{aligned}
2a^2 + 13a - 7 &= 2a^2 - a + 14a - 7 \\
&= (2a^2 - a) + (14a - 7) \\
&= a(2a - 1) + 7(2a - 1) \\
&= (2a - 1)(a + 7)
\end{aligned}
$$

$$2a^2 + 13a - 7 = (2a - 1)(a + 7)$$

You Try It 4
The GCF is $5x$.

$$15x^3 + 40x^2 - 80x = 5x(3x^2 + 8x - 16)$$

Factors of -48 [$3(-16)$]	Sum
$-1, +48$	47
$+1, -48$	-47
$-2, +24$	22
$+2, -24$	-22
$-3, +16$	13
$+3, -16$	-13
$-4, +12$	8

$$
\begin{aligned}
3x^2 + 8x - 16 &= 3x^2 - 4x + 12x - 16 \\
&= (3x^2 - 4x) + (12x - 16) \\
&= x(3x - 4) + 4(3x - 4) \\
&= (3x - 4)(x + 4)
\end{aligned}
$$

$$
\begin{aligned}
15x^3 + 40x^2 - 80x &= 5x(3x^2 + 8x - 16) \\
&= 5x(3x - 4)(x + 4)
\end{aligned}
$$

SECTION 5.4

You Try It 1
$$25a^2 - b^2 = (5a)^2 - b^2 = (5a + b)(5a - b)$$

You Try It 2
$$
\begin{aligned}
n^4 - 81 &= (n^2)^2 - 9^2 = (n^2 + 9)(n^2 - 9) \\
&= (n^2 + 9)(n + 3)(n - 3)
\end{aligned}
$$

You Try It 3   Because $16y^2 = (4y)^2$, $1 = 1^2$, and $8y = 2(4y)(1)$, the trinomial is a perfect-square trinomial.

$$16y^2 + 8y + 1 = (4y + 1)^2$$

You Try It 4   Because $x^2 = (x)^2$, $36 = 6^2$, and $15x \neq 2(x)(6)$, the trinomial is not a perfect-square trinomial. Try to factor the trinomial by another method.

$$x^2 + 15x + 36 = (x + 3)(x + 12)$$

You Try It 5 $$
\begin{aligned}
&(x^2 - 6x + 9) - y^2 \\
&= (x - 3)^2 - y^2 \\
&= (x - 3 - y)(x - 3 + y)
\end{aligned}
$$

You Try It 6   The GCF is $3x$.

$$
\begin{aligned}
12x^3 - 75x &= 3x(4x^2 - 25) \\
&= 3x(2x + 5)(2x - 5)
\end{aligned}
$$

You Try It 7
Factor by grouping.

$$
\begin{aligned}
a^2b - 7a^2 - b + 7 &= (a^2b - 7a^2) - (b - 7) \\
&= a^2(b - 7) - (b - 7) \\
&= (b - 7)(a^2 - 1) \\
&= (b - 7)(a + 1)(a - 1)
\end{aligned}
$$

You Try It 8
The GCF is $4x$.

$$
\begin{aligned}
4x^3 + 28x^2 - 120x &= 4x(x^2 + 7x - 30) \\
&= 4x(x + 10)(x - 3)
\end{aligned}
$$

SECTION 5.5

You Try It 1 $2x(x + 7) = 0$

$$
\begin{array}{ll}
2x = 0 & x + 7 = 0 \\
x = 0 & x = -7
\end{array}
$$

The solutions are 0 and -7.

You Try It 2
$$4x^2 - 9 = 0$$
$$(2x - 3)(2x + 3) = 0$$

$$2x - 3 = 0 \qquad 2x + 3 = 0$$
$$2x = 3 \qquad\quad 2x = -3$$
$$x = \frac{3}{2} \qquad\quad x = -\frac{3}{2}$$

The solutions are $\dfrac{3}{2}$ and $-\dfrac{3}{2}$.

You Try It 3
$$(x + 2)(x - 7) = 52$$
$$x^2 - 5x - 14 = 52$$
$$x^2 - 5x - 66 = 0$$
$$(x + 6)(x - 11) = 0$$

$$x + 6 = 0 \qquad x - 11 = 0$$
$$x = -6 \qquad\quad x = 11$$

The solutions are -6 and 11.

You Try It 4

Strategy First positive consecutive integer: n
Second positive consecutive integer: $n + 1$

The sum of the squares of two positive consecutive integers is 61.

Solution
$$n^2 + (n + 1)^2 = 61$$
$$n^2 + n^2 + 2n + 1 = 61$$
$$2n^2 + 2n + 1 = 61$$
$$2n^2 + 2n - 60 = 0$$
$$2(n^2 + n - 30) = 0$$
$$2(n - 5)(n + 6) = 0$$

$$n - 5 = 0 \qquad n + 6 = 0$$
$$n = 5 \qquad\quad n = -6$$

Since -6 is not a positive integer, it is not a solution.

$$n = 5$$
$$n + 1 = 5 + 1 = 6$$

The two integers are 5 and 6.

You Try It 5

Strategy Width $= x$
Length $= 2x + 4$

The area of a rectangle is 96 in². Use the equation $A = L \cdot W$.

Solution
$$A = L \cdot W$$
$$96 = (2x + 4)x$$
$$96 = 2x^2 + 4x$$
$$0 = 2x^2 + 4x - 96$$
$$0 = 2(x^2 + 2x - 48)$$
$$0 = 2(x + 8)(x - 6)$$

$$x + 8 = 0 \qquad x - 6 = 0$$
$$x = -8 \qquad\quad x = 6$$

Since the width cannot be a negative number, -8 is not a solution.

$$x = 6$$
$$2x + 4 = 2(6) + 4 = 12 + 4 = 16$$

The length is 16 in. The width is 6 in.

Solutions to Chapter 6 "You Try It"

SECTION 6.1

You Try It 1

$$\frac{6x^5y}{12x^2y^3} = \frac{\overset{1}{2} \cdot \overset{1}{3} \cdot x^5y}{2 \cdot 2 \cdot \underset{1}{3} \cdot \underset{1}{x^2y^3}} = \frac{x^3}{2y^2}$$

You Try It 2

$$\frac{x^2 + 2x - 24}{16 - x^2} = \frac{\overset{-1}{\cancel{(x - 4)}}(x + 6)}{\underset{1}{\cancel{(4 - x)}}(4 + x)} = -\frac{x + 6}{x + 4}$$

You Try It 3

$$\frac{x^2 + 4x - 12}{x^2 - 3x + 2} = \frac{\overset{1}{\cancel{(x - 2)}}(x + 6)}{(x - 1)\underset{1}{\cancel{(x - 2)}}} = \frac{x + 6}{x - 1}$$

You Try It 4

$$\frac{12x^2 + 3x}{10x - 15} \cdot \frac{8x - 12}{9x + 18} = \frac{3x(4x + 1)}{5(2x - 3)} \cdot \frac{4(2x - 3)}{9(x + 2)}$$

$$= \frac{\overset{1}{\cancel{3}}x(4x + 1) \cdot 2 \cdot 2\overset{1}{\cancel{(2x - 3)}}}{5\underset{1}{\cancel{(2x - 3)}} \cdot \underset{1}{\cancel{3}} \cdot 3(x + 2)}$$

$$= \frac{4x(4x + 1)}{15(x + 2)}$$

You Try It 5

$$\frac{x^2 + 2x - 15}{9 - x^2} \cdot \frac{x^2 - 3x - 18}{x^2 - 7x + 6}$$

$$= \frac{(x - 3)(x + 5)}{(3 - x)(3 + x)} \cdot \frac{(x + 3)(x - 6)}{(x - 1)(x - 6)}$$

$$= \frac{\overset{-1}{\cancel{(x - 3)}}(x + 5) \cdot \overset{1}{\cancel{(x + 3)}}\overset{1}{\cancel{(x - 6)}}}{\underset{1}{\cancel{(3 - x)}}\underset{1}{\cancel{(3 + x)}} \cdot (x - 1)\underset{1}{\cancel{(x - 6)}}} = -\frac{x + 5}{x - 1}$$

You Try It 6

$$\frac{a^2}{4bc^2 - 2b^2c} \div \frac{a}{6bc - 3b^2} = \frac{a^2}{4bc^2 - 2b^2c} \cdot \frac{6bc - 3b^2}{a}$$

$$= \frac{a^2 \cdot 3\cancel{b}(2\cancel{c} - \cancel{b})}{2\cancel{b}c(2\cancel{c} - \cancel{b}) \cdot a} = \frac{3a}{2c}$$

You Try It 7

$$\frac{3x^2 + 26x + 16}{3x^2 - 7x - 6} \div \frac{2x^2 + 9x - 5}{x^2 + 2x - 15}$$

$$= \frac{3x^2 + 26x + 16}{3x^2 - 7x - 6} \cdot \frac{x^2 + 2x - 15}{2x^2 + 9x - 5}$$

$$= \frac{(3\cancel{x + 2})(x + 8) \cdot (\cancel{x + 5})(\cancel{x - 3})}{(3\cancel{x + 2})(\cancel{x - 3}) \cdot (2x - 1)(\cancel{x + 5})} = \frac{x + 8}{2x - 1}$$

SECTION 6.2

You Try It 1

$8uv^2 = 2 \cdot 2 \cdot 2 \cdot u \cdot v \cdot v$

$12uw = 2 \cdot 2 \cdot 3 \cdot u \cdot w$

$\text{LCM} = 2 \cdot 2 \cdot 2 \cdot 3 \cdot u \cdot v \cdot v \cdot w = 24uv^2w$

You Try It 2 $m^2 - 6m + 9 = (m - 3)(m - 3)$

$m^2 - 2m - 3 = (m + 1)(m - 3)$

$\text{LCM} = (m - 3)(m - 3)(m + 1)$

You Try It 3   The LCM is $36xy^2z$.

$$\frac{x - 3}{4xy^2} = \frac{x - 3}{4xy^2} \cdot \frac{9z}{9z} = \frac{9xz - 27z}{36xy^2z}$$

$$\frac{2x + 1}{9y^2z} = \frac{2x + 1}{9y^2z} \cdot \frac{4x}{4x} = \frac{8x^2 + 4x}{36xy^2z}$$

You Try It 4

The LCM is $(x + 2)(x - 5)(x + 5)$.

$$\frac{x + 4}{x^2 - 3x - 10} = \frac{x + 4}{(x + 2)(x - 5)} \cdot \frac{x + 5}{x + 5}$$

$$= \frac{x^2 + 9x + 20}{(x + 2)(x - 5)(x + 5)}$$

$$\frac{2x}{25 - x^2} = \frac{2x}{-(x^2 - 25)} = -\frac{2x}{(x - 5)(x + 5)} \cdot \frac{x + 2}{x + 2}$$

$$= -\frac{2x^2 + 4x}{(x + 2)(x - 5)(x + 5)}$$

SECTION 6.3

You Try It 1

$$\frac{2x^2}{x^2 - x - 12} - \frac{7x + 4}{x^2 - x - 12}$$

$$= \frac{2x^2 - (7x + 4)}{x^2 - x - 12} = \frac{2x^2 - 7x - 4}{x^2 - x - 12}$$

$$= \frac{(2x + 1)(\cancel{x - 4})}{(x + 3)(\cancel{x - 4})} = \frac{2x + 1}{x + 3}$$

You Try It 2

$$\frac{x^2 - 1}{x^2 - 8x + 12} - \frac{2x + 1}{x^2 - 8x + 12} + \frac{x}{x^2 - 8x + 12}$$

$$= \frac{(x^2 - 1) - (2x + 1) + x}{x^2 - 8x + 12} = \frac{x^2 - 1 - 2x - 1 + x}{x^2 - 8x + 12}$$

$$= \frac{x^2 - x - 2}{x^2 - 8x + 12} = \frac{(x + 1)(\cancel{x - 2})}{(\cancel{x - 2})(x - 6)} = \frac{x + 1}{x - 6}$$

You Try It 3

The LCM of the denominators is $24y$.

$$\frac{z}{8y} - \frac{4z}{3y} + \frac{5z}{4y} = \frac{z}{8y} \cdot \frac{3}{3} - \frac{4z}{3y} \cdot \frac{8}{8} + \frac{5z}{4y} \cdot \frac{6}{6}$$

$$= \frac{3z}{24y} - \frac{32z}{24y} + \frac{30z}{24y}$$

$$= \frac{3z - 32z + 30z}{24y} = \frac{z}{24y}$$

You Try It 4 $2 - x = -(x - 2)$

Therefore, $\dfrac{3}{2 - x} = \dfrac{-3}{x - 2}$.

The LCM is $x - 2$.

$$\frac{5x}{x - 2} - \frac{3}{2 - x} = \frac{5x}{x - 2} - \frac{-3}{x - 2}$$

$$= \frac{5x - (-3)}{x - 2} = \frac{5x + 3}{x - 2}$$

You Try It 5

The LCM is $(3x - 1)(x + 4)$.

$$\frac{4x}{3x - 1} - \frac{9}{x + 4} = \frac{4x}{3x - 1} \cdot \frac{x + 4}{x + 4} - \frac{9}{x + 4} \cdot \frac{3x - 1}{3x - 1}$$

$$= \frac{4x^2 + 16x}{(3x - 1)(x + 4)} - \frac{27x - 9}{(3x - 1)(x + 4)}$$

$$= \frac{(4x^2 + 16x) - (27x - 9)}{(3x - 1)(x + 4)}$$

$$= \frac{4x^2 + 16x - 27x + 9}{(3x - 1)(x + 4)}$$

$$= \frac{4x^2 - 11x + 9}{(3x - 1)(x + 4)}$$

You Try It 6   The LCM is $x - 3$.

$$2 - \frac{1}{x - 3} = 2 \cdot \frac{x - 3}{x - 3} - \frac{1}{x - 3}$$

$$= \frac{2x - 6}{x - 3} - \frac{1}{x - 3}$$

$$= \frac{2x - 6 - 1}{x - 3}$$

$$= \frac{2x - 7}{x - 3}$$

You Try It 7

$$\frac{2}{5 - x} = \frac{-2}{x - 5}$$

The LCM is $(x + 5)(x - 5)$.

$$\frac{2x - 1}{x^2 - 25} + \frac{2}{5 - x} = \frac{2x - 1}{(x + 5)(x - 5)} + \frac{-2}{x - 5}$$

$$= \frac{2x - 1}{(x + 5)(x - 5)} + \frac{-2}{x - 5} \cdot \frac{x + 5}{x + 5}$$

$$= \frac{2x - 1}{(x + 5)(x - 5)} + \frac{-2(x + 5)}{(x + 5)(x - 5)}$$

$$= \frac{2x - 1 + (-2)(x + 5)}{(x + 5)(x - 5)}$$

$$= \frac{2x - 1 - 2x - 10}{(x + 5)(x - 5)}$$

$$= \frac{-11}{(x + 5)(x - 5)}$$

$$= -\frac{11}{(x + 5)(x - 5)}$$

You Try It 8
The LCM is $(3x + 2)(x - 1)$.

$$\frac{2x - 3}{3x^2 - x - 2} + \frac{5}{3x + 2} - \frac{1}{x - 1}$$

$$= \frac{2x - 3}{(3x + 2)(x - 1)} + \frac{5}{3x + 2} \cdot \frac{x - 1}{x - 1}$$

$$- \frac{1}{x - 1} \cdot \frac{3x + 2}{3x + 2}$$

$$= \frac{2x - 3}{(3x + 2)(x - 1)} + \frac{5x - 5}{(3x + 2)(x - 1)}$$

$$- \frac{3x + 2}{(3x + 2)(x - 1)}$$

$$= \frac{(2x - 3) + (5x - 5) - (3x + 2)}{(3x + 2)(x - 1)}$$

$$= \frac{2x - 3 + 5x - 5 - 3x - 2}{(3x + 2)(x - 1)}$$

$$= \frac{4x - 10}{(3x + 2)(x - 1)} = \frac{2(2x - 5)}{(3x + 2)(x - 1)}$$

SECTION 6.4

You Try It 1
The LCM of 3, x, 9, and x^2 is $9x^2$.

$$\frac{\dfrac{1}{3} - \dfrac{1}{x}}{\dfrac{1}{9} - \dfrac{1}{x^2}} = \frac{\dfrac{1}{3} - \dfrac{1}{x}}{\dfrac{1}{9} - \dfrac{1}{x^2}} \cdot \frac{9x^2}{9x^2} = \frac{\dfrac{1}{3} \cdot 9x^2 - \dfrac{1}{x} \cdot 9x^2}{\dfrac{1}{9} \cdot 9x^2 - \dfrac{1}{x^2} \cdot 9x^2}$$

$$= \frac{3x^2 - 9x}{x^2 - 9} = \frac{3x(\cancel{x - 3})}{(\cancel{x - 3})(x + 3)} = \frac{3x}{x + 3}$$

You Try It 2
The LCM of x and x^2 is x^2.

$$\frac{1 + \dfrac{4}{x} + \dfrac{3}{x^2}}{1 + \dfrac{10}{x} + \dfrac{21}{x^2}} = \frac{1 + \dfrac{4}{x} + \dfrac{3}{x^2}}{1 + \dfrac{10}{x} + \dfrac{21}{x^2}} \cdot \frac{x^2}{x^2}$$

$$= \frac{1 \cdot x^2 + \dfrac{4}{x} \cdot x^2 + \dfrac{3}{x^2} \cdot x^2}{1 \cdot x^2 + \dfrac{10}{x} \cdot x^2 + \dfrac{21}{x^2} \cdot x^2}$$

$$= \frac{x^2 + 4x + 3}{x^2 + 10x + 21} = \frac{(x + 1)(\cancel{x + 3})}{(\cancel{x + 3})(x + 7)}$$

$$= \frac{x + 1}{x + 7}$$

You Try It 3
The LCM is $x - 5$.

$$\frac{x + 3 - \dfrac{20}{x - 5}}{x + 8 + \dfrac{30}{x - 5}} = \frac{x + 3 - \dfrac{20}{x - 5}}{x + 8 + \dfrac{30}{x - 5}} \cdot \frac{x - 5}{x - 5}$$

$$= \frac{(x + 3)(x - 5) - \dfrac{20}{x - 5} \cdot (x - 5)}{(x + 8)(x - 5) + \dfrac{30}{x - 5} \cdot (x - 5)}$$

$$= \frac{x^2 - 2x - 15 - 20}{x^2 + 3x - 40 + 30} = \frac{x^2 - 2x - 35}{x^2 + 3x - 10}$$

$$= \frac{(\cancel{x + 5})(x - 7)}{(x - 2)(\cancel{x + 5})} = \frac{x - 7}{x - 2}$$

SECTION 6.5

You Try It 1

$$\frac{x}{x+6} = \frac{3}{x} \quad \text{The LCM is } x(x+6).$$

$$\frac{x(x+6)}{1} \cdot \frac{x}{x+6} = \frac{x(x+6)}{1} \cdot \frac{3}{x}$$

$$x^2 = (x+6)3$$
$$x^2 = 3x + 18$$
$$x^2 - 3x - 18 = 0$$
$$(x+3)(x-6) = 0$$

$$x + 3 = 0 \qquad x - 6 = 0$$
$$x = -3 \qquad x = 6$$

Both -3 and 6 check as solutions.
The solutions are -3 and 6.

You Try It 2

$$\frac{5x}{x+2} = 3 - \frac{10}{x+2} \quad \text{The LCM is } x+2.$$

$$\frac{(x+2)}{1} \cdot \frac{5x}{x+2} = \frac{(x+2)}{1}\left(3 - \frac{10}{x+2}\right)$$

$$\frac{x+2}{1} \cdot \frac{5x}{x+2} = \frac{x+2}{1} \cdot 3 - \frac{x+2}{1} \cdot \frac{10}{x+2}$$

$$5x = (x+2)3 - 10$$
$$5x = 3x + 6 - 10$$
$$5x = 3x - 4$$
$$2x = -4$$
$$x = -2$$

-2 does not check as a solution.
The equation has no solution.

SECTION 6.6

You Try It 1

$$\frac{2}{x+3} = \frac{6}{5x+5}$$

$$\frac{(x+3)(5x+5)}{1} \cdot \frac{2}{x+3} = \frac{(x+3)(5x+5)}{1} \cdot \frac{6}{5x+5}$$

$$\frac{(x+3)(5x+5)}{1} \cdot \frac{2}{x+3} = \frac{(x+3)(5x+5)}{1} \cdot \frac{6}{5x+5}$$

$$(5x+5)2 = (x+3)6$$
$$10x + 10 = 6x + 18$$
$$4x + 10 = 18$$
$$4x = 8$$
$$x = 2$$

The solution is 2.

You Try It 2

Strategy To find the total area that 256 ceramic tiles will cover, write and solve a proportion using x to represent the number of square feet that 256 tiles will cover.

Solution
$$\frac{9}{16} = \frac{x}{256}$$

$$256\left(\frac{9}{16}\right) = 256\left(\frac{x}{256}\right)$$

$$144 = x$$

A 144-square-foot area can be tiled using 256 ceramic tiles.

You Try It 3

Strategy To find the area of triangle AOB:
• Solve a proportion to find the length of AO (the height of triangle AOB).
• Use the formula for the area of a triangle. AB is the base and AO is the height.

Solution
$$\frac{CD}{AB} = \frac{DO}{AO}$$

$$\frac{4}{10} = \frac{3}{AO}$$

$$10 \cdot AO \cdot \frac{4}{10} = 10 \cdot AO \cdot \frac{3}{AO}$$

$$4(AO) = 30$$
$$AO = 7.5$$

$$A = \frac{1}{2}bh$$
$$= \frac{1}{2}(10)(7.5)$$
$$= 37.5$$

The area of triangle AOB is 37.5 cm².

SECTION 6.7

You Try It 1

$$5x - 2y = 10$$
$$5x - 5x - 2y = -5x + 10$$
$$-2y = -5x + 10$$
$$\frac{-2y}{-2} = \frac{-5x + 10}{-2}$$
$$y = \frac{5}{2}x - 5$$

You Try It 2

$$s = \frac{A + L}{2}$$

$$2 \cdot s = 2\left(\frac{A + L}{2}\right)$$

$$2s = A + L$$

$$2s - A = A - A + L$$

$$2s - A = L$$

You Try It 3

$$S = a + (n - 1)d$$

$$S = a + nd - d$$

$$S - a = a - a + nd - d$$

$$S - a = nd - d$$

$$S - a + d = nd - d + d$$

$$S - a + d = nd$$

$$\frac{S - a + d}{d} = \frac{nd}{d}$$

$$\frac{S - a + d}{d} = n$$

You Try It 4

$$S = C + rC$$

$$S = (1 + r)C$$

$$\frac{S}{1 + r} = \frac{(1 + r)C}{1 + r}$$

$$\frac{S}{1 + r} = C$$

SECTION 6.8

You Try It 1

Strategy • Time for one printer to complete the job: t

	Rate	Time	Part
1st printer	$\frac{1}{t}$	2	$\frac{2}{t}$
2nd printer	$\frac{1}{t}$	5	$\frac{5}{t}$

• The sum of the parts of the task completed must equal 1.

Solution

$$\frac{2}{t} + \frac{5}{t} = 1$$

$$t\left(\frac{2}{t} + \frac{5}{t}\right) = t \cdot 1$$

$$2 + 5 = t$$

$$7 = t$$

Working alone, one printer takes 7 h to print the payroll.

You Try It 2

Strategy • Rate sailing across the lake: r
Rate sailing back: $3r$

	Distance	Rate	Time
Across	6	r	$\frac{6}{r}$
Back	6	$3r$	$\frac{6}{3r}$

• The total time for the trip was 2 h.

Solution

$$\frac{6}{r} + \frac{6}{3r} = 2$$

$$3r\left(\frac{6}{r} + \frac{6}{3r}\right) = 3r(2)$$

$$3r \cdot \frac{6}{r} + 3r \cdot \frac{6}{3r} = 6r$$

$$18 + 6 = 6r$$

$$24 = 6r$$

$$4 = r$$

The rate across the lake was 4 km/h.

Solutions to Chapter 7 "You Try It"

SECTION 7.1

You Try It 1

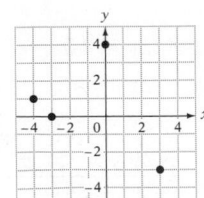

You Try It 2 $A(4, -2)$, $B(-2, 4)$.
The abscissa of D is 0.
The ordinate of C is 0.

You Try It 3

$$x - 3y = -14$$

$$\begin{array}{c|c} -2 - 3(4) & -14 \\ \hline -2 - 12 & -14 \\ -14 = -14 \end{array}$$

Yes, $(-2, 4)$ is a solution of $x - 3y = -14$.

You Try It 4

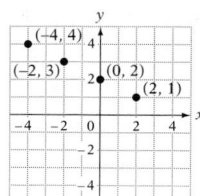

You Try It 4 $5x - 2y = 10$
$$-2y = -5x + 10$$
$$y = \frac{5}{2}x - 5$$

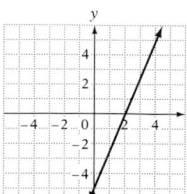

You Try It 5

$\{(145, 140), (140, 125), (150, 130), (165, 150), (140, 130), (165, 160)\}$

No, the relation is not a function. The two ordered pairs (140, 125) and (140, 130) have the same first coordinate but different second coordinates.

You Try It 6   Determine the ordered pairs defined by the equation. Replace x in $y = \frac{1}{2}x + 1$ by the given values and solve for y. $\{(-4, -1), (0, 1), (2, 2)\}$
Yes, y is a function of x.

You Try It 5 $x - 3y = 9$
$$-3y = -x + 9$$
$$y = \frac{1}{3}x - 3$$

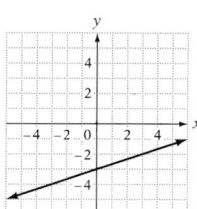

You Try It 7 $H(x) = \dfrac{x}{x - 4}$

$H(8) = \dfrac{8}{8 - 4}$

$H(8) = \dfrac{8}{4} = 2$

You Try It 6

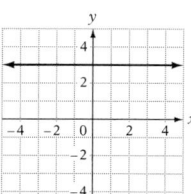

SECTION 7.2

You Try It 1

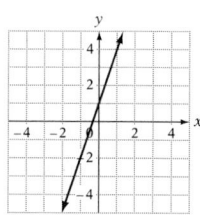

You Try It 7

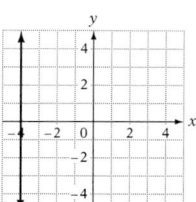

You Try It 2

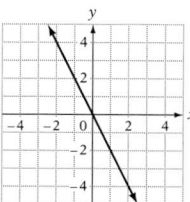

You Try It 8

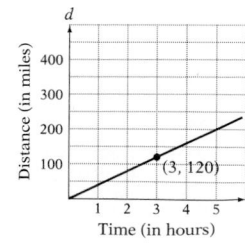

The ordered pair (3, 120) means that in 3 h the car will travel 120 mi.

You Try It 3

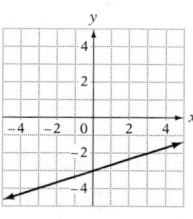

SECTION 7.3

You Try It 1   x-intercept: y-intercept:

$$y = 2x - 4 \qquad (0, b)$$
$$0 = 2x - 4 \qquad b = -4$$
$$-2x = -4 \qquad (0, -4)$$
$$x = 2$$
$$(2, 0)$$

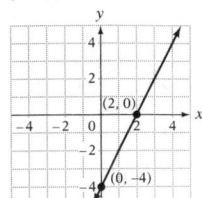

You Try It 2   Let $P_1 = (1, 4)$ and $P_2 = (-3, 8)$.

$$m = \frac{y_2 - y_1}{x_2 - x_1} = \frac{8 - 4}{-3 - 1} = \frac{4}{-4} = -1$$

The slope is -1.

You Try It 3   Let $P_1 = (-1, 2)$ and $P_2 = (4, 2)$.

$$m = \frac{y_2 - y_1}{x_2 - x_1} = \frac{2 - 2}{4 - (-1)} = \frac{0}{5} = 0$$

The slope is 0.

You Try It 4 $m = \dfrac{8650 - 6100}{1 - 4} = \dfrac{2550}{-3}$

$m = -850$

A slope of -850 means that the value of the car is decreasing at a rate of $850 per year.

You Try It 5   y-intercept $= (0, b) = (0, -1)$

$$m = -\frac{1}{4}$$

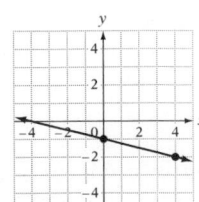

You Try It 6   Solve the equation for y.

$$x - 2y = 4$$
$$-2y = -x + 4$$
$$y = \frac{1}{2}x - 2$$

y-intercept $= (0, b) = (0, -2)$

$$m = \frac{1}{2}$$

SECTION 7.4

You Try It 1   Because the slope and y-intercept are known, use the slope-intercept formula, $y = mx + b$.

$$y = mx + b$$
$$y = \frac{5}{3}x + 2$$

You Try It 2 $m = \dfrac{3}{4}$ $(x_1, y_1) = (4, -2)$

$$y - y_1 = m(x - x_1)$$
$$y - (-2) = \frac{3}{4}(x - 4)$$
$$y + 2 = \frac{3}{4}x - 3$$
$$y = \frac{3}{4}x - 5$$

The equation of the line is $y = \dfrac{3}{4}x - 5$.

You Try It 3   Find the slope of the line between the two points.

$$m = \frac{y_2 - y_1}{x_2 - x_1} = \frac{1 - (-1)}{3 - (-6)} = \frac{2}{9}$$

Use the point-slope formula.

$$y - y_1 = m(x - x_1)$$
$$y - (-1) = \frac{2}{9}[x - (-6)]$$
$$y + 1 = \frac{2}{9}x + \frac{4}{3}$$
$$y = \frac{2}{9}x + \frac{1}{3}$$

You Try It 4

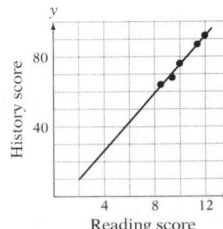

The slope of the line means that the grade on the history test increases 8.3 points for each 1-point increase in the grade on the reading test.

Solutions to Chapter 8 "You Try It"

SECTION 8.1

You Try It 1

$2x - 5y = 8$	
$2(-1) - 5(-2)$	8
$-2 + 10$	8
	$8 = 8$

$-x + 3y = -5$	
$-(-1) + 3(-2)$	-5
$1 + (-6)$	-5
	$-5 = -5$

Yes. $(-1, -2)$ is a solution of the system of equations.

You Try It 2

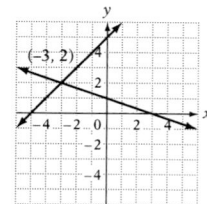

The solution is $(-3, 2)$.

You Try It 3

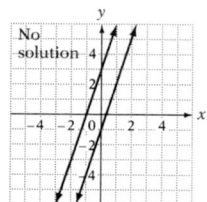

The lines are parallel. The system of equations is inconsistent and therefore does not have a solution.

SECTION 8.2

You Try It 1

(1) $7x - y = 4$
(2) $3x + 2y = 9$

Solve Equation (1) for y.

$$7x - y = 4$$
$$-y = -7x + 4$$
$$y = 7x - 4$$

Substitute in Equation (2).

$$3x + 2y = 9$$
$$3x + 2(7x - 4) = 9$$
$$3x + 14x - 8 = 9$$
$$17x - 8 = 9$$
$$17x = 17$$
$$x = 1$$

Substitute in Equation (1).

$$7x - y = 4$$
$$7(1) - y = 4$$
$$7 - y = 4$$
$$-y = -3$$
$$y = 3$$

The solution is $(1, 3)$.

You Try It 2

(1) $3x - y = 4$
(2) $y = 3x + 2$

$$3x - y = 4$$
$$3x - (3x + 2) = 4$$
$$3x - 3x - 2 = 4$$
$$-2 = 4$$

This is not a true equation. The system of equations is inconsistent and therefore does not have a solution.

You Try It 3

(1) $y = -2x + 1$
(2) $6x + 3y = 3$

$$6x + 3y = 3$$
$$6x + 3(-2x + 1) = 3$$
$$6x - 6x + 3 = 3$$
$$3 = 3$$

The system of equations is dependent. The solutions are the ordered pairs that satisfy the equation $y = -2x + 1$.

You Try It 4

Strategy   • Amount invested at 6.5%: x
Amount invested at 4.5%: y

	Principal	Rate	Interest
Amount at 6.5%	x	0.065	$0.065x$
Amount at 4.5%	y	0.045	$0.045y$

• The sum of the two investments is $330,000: $x + y = 330,000$. The interest earned at 6.5% equals the interest earned at 4.5%: $0.065x = 0.045y$

Solution
(1) $x + y = 330,000$
(2) $0.065x = 0.045y$

Solve Equation (2) for y.

$$(3) \qquad y = \frac{13}{9}x$$

Replace y by $\frac{13}{9}x$ in Equation (1) and solve for x.

$$x + y = 330{,}000$$
$$x + \frac{13}{9}x = 330{,}000$$
$$\frac{22}{9}x = 330{,}000$$
$$x = 135{,}000$$

Replace x by 135,000 in Equation (3) and solve for y.

$$y = \frac{13}{9}x$$
$$= \frac{13}{9}(135{,}000) = 195{,}000$$

$135,000 should be invested at 6.5% and $195,000 should be invested at 4.5%.

SECTION 8.3

You Try It 1   (1) $x - 2y = 1$
(2) $2x + 4y = 0$

Eliminate y.

$$2(x - 2y) = 2 \cdot 1$$
$$2x + 4y = 0$$

$$2x - 4y = 2$$
$$2x + 4y = 0$$

Add the equations.

$$4x = 2$$
$$x = \frac{2}{4} = \frac{1}{2}$$

Replace x in Equation (2).

$$2\left(\frac{1}{2}\right) + 4y = 0$$
$$1 + 4y = 0$$
$$4y = -1$$
$$y = -\frac{1}{4}$$

The solution is $\left(\frac{1}{2}, -\frac{1}{4}\right)$.

You Try It 2   (1) $2x - 3y = 4$
(2) $-4x + 6y = -8$

Eliminate y.

$$2(2x - 3y) = 2 \cdot 4$$
$$-4x + 6y = -8$$

$$4x - 6y = 8$$
$$-4x + 6y = -8$$

Add the equations.

$$0x + 0y = 0$$
$$0 = 0$$

The system of equations is dependent. The solutions are the ordered pairs that satisfy the equation $2x - 3y = 4$.

You Try It 3   (1) $4x + 5y = 11$
(2) $3y = x + 10$

Write equation (2) in the form $Ax + By = C$.

$$3y = x + 10$$
$$-x + 3y = 10$$

Eliminate x.

$$4x + 5y = 11$$
$$4(-x + 3y) = 4 \cdot 10$$

$$4x + 5y = 11$$
$$-4x + 12y = 40$$

Add the equations.

$$17y = 51$$
$$y = 3$$

Replace y in Equation (1).

$$4x + 5y = 11$$
$$4x + 5 \cdot 3 = 11$$
$$4x + 15 = 11$$
$$4x = -4$$
$$x = -1$$

The solution is $(-1, 3)$.

SECTION 8.4

You Try It 1

Strategy   • Rate of the current: c
Rate of the canoeist in calm water: r

	Rate	Time	Distance
With current	$r + c$	3	$3(r + c)$
Against current	$r - c$	5	$5(r - c)$

• The distance traveled with the current is 15 mi.
The distance traveled against the current is 15 mi.

Solution

$$3(r + c) = 15 \qquad \frac{1}{3} \cdot 3(r + c) = \frac{1}{3} \cdot 15$$

$$5(r - c) = 15 \qquad \frac{1}{5} \cdot 5(r - c) = \frac{1}{5} \cdot 15$$

$$r + c = 5$$

$$r - c = 3$$

$$2r = 8$$

$$r = 4$$

$$r + c = 5$$

$$4 + c = 5$$

$$c = 1$$

The rate of the current is 1 mph.
The rate of the canoeist in calm water is 4 mph.

You Try It 2

Strategy • Cost of an orange tree: x
Cost of a grapefruit tree: y
First purchase:

	Amount	Unit Cost	Value
Orange trees	25	x	$25x$
Grapefruit trees	20	y	$20y$

Second purchase:

	Amount	Unit Cost	Value
Orange trees	20	x	$20x$
Grapefruit trees	30	y	$30y$

• The total of the first purchase was $290.
The total of the second purchase was $330.

Solution

$$25x + 20y = 290 \qquad 4(25x + 20y) = 4 \cdot 290$$

$$20x + 30y = 330 \qquad -5(20x + 30y) = -5 \cdot 330$$

$$100x + 80y = 1160$$

$$-100x - 150y = -1650$$

$$-70y = -490$$

$$y = 7$$

$$25x + 20y = 290$$

$$25x + 20(7) = 290$$

$$25x + 140 = 290$$

$$25x = 150$$

$$x = 6$$

The cost of an orange tree is $6.
The cost of a grapefruit tree is $7.

Solutions to Chapter 9 "You Try It"

SECTION 9.1

You Try It 1 $A = \{-9, -7, -5, -3, -1\}$

You Try It 2 $A = \{1, 3, 5, \ldots\}$

You Try It 3 $A \cup B = \{-2, -1, 0, 1, 2, 3, 4\}$

You Try It 4 $C \cap D = \{10, 16\}$

You Try It 5 $A \cap B = \varnothing$

You Try It 6 $\{x \mid x < 59, x \in \text{positive even integers}\}$

You Try It 7 $\{x \mid x > -3, x \in \text{real numbers}\}$

You Try It 8   The solution set is the numbers greater than -2.

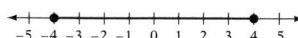

You Try It 9   The solution set is the numbers greater than -1 and the numbers less than -3.

You Try It 10   The solution set is the real numbers.

You Try It 11   The solution set is the numbers less than or equal to 4 and greater than or equal to -4.

SECTION 9.2

You Try It 1

$$x + 2 < -2$$

$$x + 2 - 2 < -2 - 2$$

$$x < -4$$

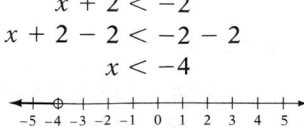

You Try It 2

$$5x + 3 > 4x + 5$$
$$5x - 4x + 3 > 4x - 4x + 5$$
$$x + 3 > 5$$
$$x + 3 - 3 > 5 - 3$$
$$x > 2$$

You Try It 3

$$-3x > -9$$
$$\frac{-3x}{-3} < \frac{-9}{-3}$$
$$x < 3$$

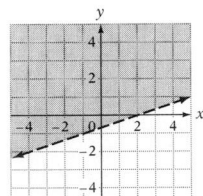

You Try It 4

$$-\frac{3}{4}x \geq 18$$
$$-\frac{4}{3}\left(-\frac{3}{4}x\right) \leq -\frac{4}{3}(18)$$
$$x \leq -24$$

You Try It 5

Strategy   To find the selling prices, write and solve an inequality using p to represent the possible selling prices.

Solution
$$0.70p > 314$$
$$p > 448.571$$

The dealer will make a profit if the selling price is greater than or equal to $448.58.

SECTION 9.3

You Try It 1

$$5 - 4x > 9 - 8x$$
$$5 - 4x + 8x > 9 - 8x + 8x$$
$$5 + 4x > 9$$
$$5 - 5 + 4x > 9 - 5$$
$$4x > 4$$
$$\frac{4x}{4} > \frac{4}{4}$$
$$x > 1$$

You Try It 2

$$8 - 4(3x + 5) \leq 6(x - 8)$$
$$8 - 12x - 20 \leq 6x - 48$$
$$-12 - 12x \leq 6x - 48$$
$$-12 - 12x - 6x \leq 6x - 6x - 48$$
$$-12 - 18x \leq -48$$
$$-12 + 12 - 18x \leq -48 + 12$$
$$-18x \leq -36$$
$$\frac{-18x}{-18} \geq \frac{-36}{-18}$$
$$x \geq 2$$

You Try It 3

Strategy   To find the maximum number of miles:
- Write an expression for the cost of each car, using x to represent the number of miles driven during the week.
- Write and solve an inequality.

Solution

Cost of a Company A car	is less than	cost of a Company B car

$$8(7) + 0.10x < 10(7) + 0.08x$$
$$56 + 0.10x < 70 + 0.08x$$
$$56 + 0.10x - 0.08x < 70 + 0.08x - 0.08x$$
$$56 + 0.02x < 70$$
$$56 - 56 + 0.02x < 70 - 56$$
$$0.02x < 14$$
$$\frac{0.02x}{0.02} < \frac{14}{0.02}$$
$$x < 700$$

The maximum number of miles is 699.

SECTION 9.4

You Try It 1

$$x - 3y < 2$$
$$x - x - 3y < -x + 2$$
$$-3y < -x + 2$$
$$\frac{-3y}{-3} > \frac{-x + 2}{-3}$$
$$y > \frac{1}{3}x - \frac{2}{3}$$

You Try It 2

$$2x - 4y \leq 8$$
$$2x - 2x - 4y \leq -2x + 8$$
$$-4y \leq -2x + 8$$
$$\frac{-4y}{-4} \geq \frac{-2x + 8}{-4}$$
$$y \geq \frac{1}{2}x - 2$$

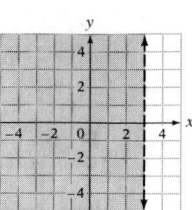

You Try It 3 $x < 3$

Solutions to Chapter 10 "You Try It"

SECTION 10.1

You Try It 1
$-5\sqrt{32} = -5\sqrt{2^5} = -5\sqrt{2^4 \cdot 2} = -5\sqrt{2^4}\sqrt{2}$
$\qquad = -5 \cdot 2^2\sqrt{2} = -20\sqrt{2}$

You Try It 2
$\sqrt{216} = \sqrt{2^3 \cdot 3^3} = \sqrt{2^2 \cdot 3^2(2 \cdot 3)}$
$\qquad = \sqrt{2^2 \cdot 3^2}\sqrt{2 \cdot 3} = 2 \cdot 3\sqrt{2 \cdot 3} = 6\sqrt{6}$

You Try It 3 $\sqrt{y^{19}} = \sqrt{y^{18} \cdot y} = \sqrt{y^{18}}\sqrt{y} = y^9\sqrt{y}$

You Try It 4 $\sqrt{45b^7} = \sqrt{3^2 \cdot 5 \cdot b^7} = \sqrt{3^2b^6(5 \cdot b)}$
$\qquad\qquad = \sqrt{3^2b^6}\sqrt{5b} = 3b^3\sqrt{5b}$

You Try It 5
$3a\sqrt{28a^9b^{18}} = 3a\sqrt{2^2 \cdot 7 \cdot a^9b^{18}}$
$\qquad\qquad = 3a\sqrt{2^2a^8b^{18}(7a)}$
$\qquad\qquad = 3a\sqrt{2^2a^8b^{18}}\sqrt{7a}$
$\qquad\qquad = 3a \cdot 2 \cdot a^4b^9\sqrt{7a} = 6a^5b^9\sqrt{7a}$

You Try It 6
$\sqrt{25(a + 3)^2} = \sqrt{5^2(a + 3)^2} = 5(a + 3)$
$\qquad\qquad = 5a + 15$

You Try It 7 $\sqrt{x^2 + 14x + 49} = \sqrt{(x + 7)^2} = x + 7$

SECTION 10.2

You Try It 1 $9\sqrt{3} + 3\sqrt{3} - 18\sqrt{3} = -6\sqrt{3}$

You Try It 2
$2\sqrt{50} - 5\sqrt{32} = 2\sqrt{2 \cdot 5^2} - 5\sqrt{2^5}$
$\qquad\qquad = 2\sqrt{5^2}\sqrt{2} - 5\sqrt{2^4}\sqrt{2}$
$\qquad\qquad = 2 \cdot 5\sqrt{2} - 5 \cdot 2^2\sqrt{2}$
$\qquad\qquad = 10\sqrt{2} - 20\sqrt{2}$
$\qquad\qquad = -10\sqrt{2}$

You Try It 3
$y\sqrt{28y} + 7\sqrt{63y^3}$
$\quad = y\sqrt{2^2 \cdot 7y} + 7\sqrt{3^2 \cdot 7 \cdot y^3}$
$\quad = y\sqrt{2^2}\sqrt{7y} + 7\sqrt{3^2 \cdot y^2}\sqrt{7y}$
$\quad = y \cdot 2\sqrt{7y} + 7 \cdot 3 \cdot y\sqrt{7y}$
$\quad = 2y\sqrt{7y} + 21y\sqrt{7y}$
$\quad = 23y\sqrt{7y}$

You Try It 4
$2\sqrt{27a^5} - 4a\sqrt{12a^3} + a^2\sqrt{75a}$
$\quad = 2\sqrt{3^3 \cdot a^5} - 4a\sqrt{2^2 \cdot 3 \cdot a^3} + a^2\sqrt{3 \cdot 5^2 \cdot a}$
$\quad = 2\sqrt{3^2 \cdot a^4}\sqrt{3a} - 4a\sqrt{2^2 \cdot a^2}\sqrt{3a}$
$\qquad + a^2\sqrt{5^2}\sqrt{3a}$
$\quad = 2 \cdot 3 \cdot a^2\sqrt{3a} - 4a \cdot 2 \cdot a\sqrt{3a} + a^2 \cdot 5\sqrt{3a}$
$\quad = 6a^2\sqrt{3a} - 8a^2\sqrt{3a} + 5a^2\sqrt{3a} = 3a^2\sqrt{3a}$

SECTION 10.3

You Try It 1 $\sqrt{5a}\sqrt{15a^3b^4}\sqrt{3b^5}$
$\qquad\qquad = \sqrt{225a^4b^9} = \sqrt{3^25^2a^4b^9}$
$\qquad\qquad = \sqrt{3^25^2a^4b^8}\sqrt{b} = 3 \cdot 5a^2b^4\sqrt{b}$
$\qquad\qquad = 15a^2b^4\sqrt{b}$

You Try It 2
$\sqrt{5x}(\sqrt{5x} - \sqrt{25y})$
$\quad = \sqrt{5^2x^2} - \sqrt{5^3xy}$
$\quad = \sqrt{5^2x^2} - \sqrt{5^2}\sqrt{5xy} = 5x - 5\sqrt{5xy}$

You Try It 3 $(2\sqrt{x} + 7)(2\sqrt{x} - 7) = 4(\sqrt{x})^2 - 7^2$
$\qquad\qquad\qquad\qquad\qquad\qquad = 4x - 49$

You Try It 4
$(3\sqrt{x} - \sqrt{y})(5\sqrt{x} - 2\sqrt{y})$
$\quad = 15(\sqrt{x})^2 - 6\sqrt{xy} - 5\sqrt{xy} + 2(\sqrt{y})^2$
$\quad = 15(\sqrt{x})^2 - 11\sqrt{xy} + 2(\sqrt{y})^2$
$\quad = 15x - 11\sqrt{xy} + 2y$

You Try It 5

$$\frac{\sqrt{15x^6y^7}}{\sqrt{3x^7y^9}} = \sqrt{\frac{15x^6y^7}{3x^7y^9}} = \sqrt{\frac{5}{xy^2}} = \frac{\sqrt{5}}{\sqrt{xy^2}}$$

$$= \frac{\sqrt{5}}{y\sqrt{x}} = \frac{\sqrt{5}}{y\sqrt{x}} \cdot \frac{\sqrt{x}}{\sqrt{x}} = \frac{\sqrt{5x}}{xy}$$

You Try It 6

$$\frac{\sqrt{3}}{\sqrt{3} - \sqrt{6}} = \frac{\sqrt{3}}{\sqrt{3} - \sqrt{6}} \cdot \frac{\sqrt{3} + \sqrt{6}}{\sqrt{3} + \sqrt{6}}$$

$$= \frac{3 + \sqrt{18}}{3 - 6} = \frac{3 + 3\sqrt{2}}{-3}$$

$$= \frac{3(1 + \sqrt{2})}{-3} = -1(1 + \sqrt{2})$$

$$= -1 - \sqrt{2}$$

You Try It 7

$$\frac{5 + \sqrt{y}}{1 - 2\sqrt{y}} = \frac{5 + \sqrt{y}}{1 - 2\sqrt{y}} \cdot \frac{1 + 2\sqrt{y}}{1 + 2\sqrt{y}}$$

$$= \frac{5 + 10\sqrt{y} + \sqrt{y} + 2(\sqrt{y})^2}{1 - 4y}$$

$$= \frac{5 + 11\sqrt{y} + 2y}{1 - 4y}$$

SECTION 10.4

You Try It 1 $\sqrt{4x} + 3 = 7$

$$\sqrt{4x} = 4$$

$$(\sqrt{4x})^2 = 4^2$$

$$4x = 16$$

$$x = 4$$

Check: $\dfrac{\sqrt{4x} + 3 = 7}{}$

$$\sqrt{4 \cdot 4} + 3 \;\big|\; 7$$

$$\sqrt{4^2} + 3 \;\big|\; 7$$

$$4 + 3 \;\big|\; 7$$

$$7 = 7$$

The solution is 4.

You Try It 2

$\sqrt{x} + \sqrt{x + 9} = 9$

$$\sqrt{x} = 9 - \sqrt{x + 9}$$

$$(\sqrt{x})^2 = (9 - \sqrt{x + 9})^2$$

$$x = 81 - 18\sqrt{x + 9} + (x + 9)$$

$$-90 = -18\sqrt{x + 9}$$

$$5 = \sqrt{x + 9}$$

$$5^2 = (\sqrt{x + 9})^2$$

$$25 = x + 9$$

$$16 = x$$

Check: $\dfrac{\sqrt{x} + \sqrt{x + 9} = 9}{}$

$$\sqrt{16} + \sqrt{16 + 9} \;\big|\; 9$$

$$4 + 5 \;\big|\; 9$$

$$9 = 9$$

The solution is 16.

You Try It 3

Strategy   To find the distance, use the Pythagorean Theorem. The hypotenuse is the length of the ladder. One leg is the distance from the bottom of the ladder to the base of the building. The distance along the building from the ground to the top of the ladder is the unknown leg.

Solution $a^2 = \sqrt{c^2 - b^2}$

$$= \sqrt{(8)^2 - (3)^2}$$

$$= \sqrt{64 - 9}$$

$$= \sqrt{55}$$

$$\approx 7.42$$

The distance is approximately 7.42 ft.

You Try It 4

Strategy   To find the length of the pendulum, replace T in the equation with the given value and solve for L.

Solution $T = 2\pi\sqrt{\dfrac{L}{32}}$

$$2.5 = 2(3.14)\sqrt{\frac{L}{32}}$$

$$2.5 = 6.28\sqrt{\frac{L}{32}}$$

$$\frac{2.5}{6.28} = \sqrt{\frac{L}{32}}$$

$$\left(\frac{2.5}{6.28}\right)^2 = \left(\sqrt{\frac{L}{32}}\right)^2$$

$$\frac{6.25}{39.4384} = \frac{L}{32}$$

$$(32)\left(\frac{6.25}{39.4384}\right) = (32)\left(\frac{L}{32}\right)$$

$$\frac{200}{39.4384} = L$$

$$5.07 \approx L$$

The length of the pendulum is 5.07 ft.

Solutions to Chapter 11 "You Try It"

SECTION 11.1

You Try It 1

$$\frac{3y^2}{2} + y - \frac{1}{2} = 0$$

$$2\left(\frac{3y^2}{2} + y - \frac{1}{2}\right) = 2(0)$$

$$3y^2 + 2y - 1 = 0$$

$$(3y - 1)(y + 1) = 0$$

$$3y - 1 = 0 \qquad y + 1 = 0$$
$$3y = 1 \qquad y = -1$$
$$y = \frac{1}{3}$$

The solutions are $\frac{1}{3}$ and -1.

You Try It 2

$$x^2 + 81 = 0$$
$$x^2 = -81$$
$$\sqrt{x^2} = \sqrt{-81}$$

$\sqrt{-81}$ is not a real number.

The equation has no real number solution.

You Try It 3

$$7(z + 2)^2 = 21$$
$$(z + 2)^2 = 3$$
$$\sqrt{(z + 2)^2} = \sqrt{3}$$
$$z + 2 = \pm\sqrt{3}$$
$$z = -2 \pm \sqrt{3}$$

The solutions are $-2 + \sqrt{3}$ and $-2 - \sqrt{3}$.

SECTION 11.2

You Try It 1

$$3x^2 - 6x - 2 = 0$$
$$3x^2 - 6x = 2$$

$$\frac{1}{3}(3x^2 - 6x) = \frac{1}{3} \cdot 2$$

$$x^2 - 2x = \frac{2}{3}$$

Complete the square.

$$x^2 - 2x + 1 = \frac{2}{3} + 1$$

$$(x - 1)^2 = \frac{5}{3}$$

$$\sqrt{(x - 1)^2} = \sqrt{\frac{5}{3}}$$

$$x - 1 = \pm\sqrt{\frac{5}{3}} = \pm\frac{\sqrt{15}}{3}$$

$$x - 1 = \frac{\sqrt{15}}{3} \qquad x - 1 = -\frac{\sqrt{15}}{3}$$

$$x = 1 + \frac{\sqrt{15}}{3} \qquad x = 1 - \frac{\sqrt{15}}{3}$$

$$= \frac{3 + \sqrt{15}}{3} \qquad = \frac{3 - \sqrt{15}}{3}$$

The solutions are $\frac{3 + \sqrt{15}}{3}$ and $\frac{3 - \sqrt{15}}{3}$.

You Try It 2

$$x^2 + 6x + 12 = 0$$
$$x^2 + 6x = -12$$
$$x^2 + 6x + 9 = -12 + 9$$
$$(x + 3)^2 = -3$$
$$\sqrt{(x + 3)^2} = \sqrt{-3}$$

$\sqrt{-3}$ is not a real number.

The quadratic equation has no real number solution.

You Try It 3

$$\frac{x^2}{8} + x + 1 = 0$$

$$8\left(\frac{x^2}{8} + x + 1\right) = 8(0)$$

$$x^2 + 8x + 8 = 0$$
$$x^2 + 8x = -8$$
$$x^2 + 8x + 16 = -8 + 16$$
$$(x + 4)^2 = 8$$
$$\sqrt{(x + 4)^2} = \sqrt{8}$$
$$x + 4 = \pm\sqrt{8} = \pm2\sqrt{2}$$
$$x + 4 = 2\sqrt{2} \qquad\qquad x + 4 = -2\sqrt{2}$$
$$x = -4 + 2\sqrt{2} \qquad\qquad x = -4 - 2\sqrt{2}$$
$$\approx -4 + 2(1.414) \qquad \approx -4 - 2(1.414)$$
$$\approx -4 + 2.828 \qquad\qquad \approx -4 - 2.828$$
$$\approx -1.172 \qquad\qquad\qquad \approx -6.828$$

The solutions are approximately -1.172 and -6.828.

SECTION 11.3

You Try It 1

$3x^2 + 4x - 4 = 0$

$a = 3, b = 4, c = -4$

$x = \dfrac{-(4) \pm \sqrt{(4)^2 - 4(3)(-4)}}{2 \cdot 3}$

$= \dfrac{-4 \pm \sqrt{16 + 48}}{6}$

$= \dfrac{-4 \pm \sqrt{64}}{6} = \dfrac{-4 \pm 8}{6}$

$x = \dfrac{-4 + 8}{6}$ $x = \dfrac{-4 - 8}{6}$

$= \dfrac{4}{6} = \dfrac{2}{3}$ $= \dfrac{-12}{6} = -2$

The solutions are $\dfrac{2}{3}$ and -2.

You Try It 2

$\dfrac{x^2}{4} + \dfrac{x}{2} = \dfrac{1}{4}$

$4\left(\dfrac{x^2}{4} + \dfrac{x}{2}\right) = 4\left(\dfrac{1}{4}\right)$

$x^2 + 2x = 1$

$x^2 + 2x - 1 = 0$

$a = 1, b = 2, c = -1$

$x = \dfrac{-(2) \pm \sqrt{(2)^2 - 4(1)(-1)}}{2 \cdot 1}$

$= \dfrac{-2 \pm \sqrt{4 + 4}}{2} = \dfrac{-2 \pm \sqrt{8}}{2}$

$= \dfrac{-2 \pm 2\sqrt{2}}{2} = -1 \pm \sqrt{2}$

The solutions are $-1 + \sqrt{2}$ and $-1 - \sqrt{2}$.

SECTION 11.4

You Try It 1

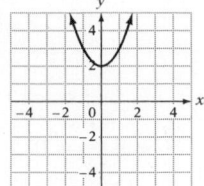

You Try It 2

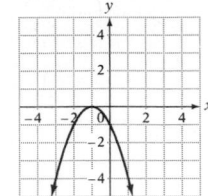

SECTION 11.5

You Try It 1

Strategy
- This is a geometry problem.
- Width of the rectangle: W
  Length of the rectangle: $W + 2$
- Use the equation $A = L \cdot W$.

Solution

$A = L \cdot W$

$15 = (W + 2)W$

$15 = W^2 + 2W$

$0 = W^2 + 2W - 15$

$0 = (W + 5)(W - 3)$

$W + 5 = 0$ $W - 3 = 0$

$W = -5$ $W = 3$

The solution -5 is not possible.
The width is 3 m.

Answers to Chapter 1 Odd-Numbered Exercises

SECTION 1.1

1. $8 > -6$ **3.** $-12 < 1$ **5.** $42 > 19$ **7.** $0 > -31$ **9.** $53 > -46$ **11.** false   **13.** true   **15.** false
17. true   **19.** true   **21.** $\{1, 2, 3, 4, 5, 6, 7, 8\}$ **23.** $\{1, 2, 3, 4, 5, 6, 7, 8\}$ **25.** $\{-6, -5, -4, -3, -2, -1\}$ **27.** 5
29. $-23, -18$ **31.** $21, 37$ **33.** $-52, -46, 0$ **35.** $-17, 0, 4, 29$ **37.** $5, 6, 7, 8, 9$ **39.** $-10, -9, -8, -7, -6, -5$
41. -4 **43.** 9   **45.** 36   **47.** 40   **49.** -39 **51.** 74   **53.** -82 **55.** -81 **57.** $|22| > |-19|$
59. $|-71| < |-92|$ **61.** $|12| < |-31|$ **63.** $|-28| < |43|$ **65a.** $11, 7, 3, -1, -5$ **b.** $11, 7, 3, 1, 5$ **67.** never true

SECTION 1.2

1. -11 **3.** -5 **5.** -83 **7.** -46 **9.** 0   **11.** -5 **13.** 9   **15.** 1   **17.** -10 **19.** -18 **21.** -41
23. -12 **25.** 0   **27.** -34 **29.** 0   **31.** -61 **33.** 27   **35.** 8   **37.** -7 **39.** -9 **41.** 9   **43.** -3
45. 18   **47.** -9 **49.** 11   **51.** -18 **53.** 0   **55.** 2   **57.** -138 **59.** -8 **61.** -12 **63.** -20
65. The difference is 399°C.   **67.** The difference is 7046 m.   **69.** The difference between the highest and lowest elevations is greatest in Asia.   **71.** The difference is 5182°C.   **73.** The total net loss was -303 million dollars.
75. The difference between the net losses in 1994 and in 1992 was 544 million dollars.   **77.** The difference is 16°F.
79. No. For example, $10 - (-8) = 18$.

SECTION 1.3

1. 42   **3.** -28 **5.** 60   **7.** -253 **9.** -238 **11.** -114 **13.** -105 **15.** 252   **17.** -240 **19.** 96
21. -216 **23.** -315 **25.** 420   **27.** 2880   **29.** -2772 **31.** 0   **33.** -2 **35.** 8   **37.** -7 **39.** -12
41. -6 **43.** -7 **45.** 11   **47.** -14 **49.** 15   **51.** -16 **53.** 0   **55.** -29 **57.** undefined   **59.** -11
61. undefined   **63.** The average daily high temperature was -26°F.   **65.** The five-day moving average was $10, -10, -5, -15, 15, 15$.   **67.** The score for the exam was 74.   **69.** -6 **71.** x is negative. Explanations will vary.

SECTION 1.4

1. $\frac{1}{3}$ **3.** $\frac{4}{11}$ **5.** $\frac{2}{3}$ **7.** $\frac{3}{2}$ **9.** 0   **11.** $\frac{3}{5}$ **13.** $\frac{11}{15}$ **15.** $\frac{1}{2}$ **17.** $0.1\overline{6}$ **19.** 0.125   **21.** $0.\overline{2}$ **23.** $0.\overline{45}$
25. $0.91\overline{6}$ **27.** 0.9375   **29.** $0.9\overline{4}$ **31.** $\frac{3}{4}$; 0.75   **33.** $\frac{16}{25}$; 0.64   **35.** $\frac{5}{4}$; 1.25   **37.** $\frac{19}{100}$; 0.19   **39.** $\frac{1}{20}$; 0.05
41. $\frac{1}{9}$ **43.** $\frac{1}{8}$ **45.** $\frac{2}{3}$ **47.** $\frac{1}{200}$ **49.** $\frac{5}{6}$ **51.** 0.073   **53.** 0.158   **55.** 0.003   **57.** 0.099   **59.** 1.212
61. 15%   **63.** 5%   **65.** 17.5%   **67.** 115%   **69.** 0.8%   **71.** 54%   **73.** $33\frac{1}{3}$%   **75.** $45\frac{5}{11}$%   **77.** 87.5%
79. $166\frac{2}{3}$%   **81.** $\frac{13}{12}$ **83.** $-\frac{5}{24}$ **85.** $-\frac{19}{24}$ **87.** $\frac{5}{26}$ **89.** $\frac{11}{8}$ **91.** $\frac{1}{12}$ **93.** $\frac{7}{24}$ **95.** 0   **97.** $-\frac{7}{16}$
99. $\frac{11}{24}$ **101.** 1   **103.** $\frac{11}{8}$ **105.** 8.022   **107.** -38.8 **109.** -6.192 **111.** 13.355   **113.** 4.676
115. -10.03 **117.** -60.03 **119.** 11.56   **121.** -0.88 **123.** -4.73 **125.** $-\frac{3}{8}$ **127.** $\frac{1}{10}$ **129.** $-\frac{4}{9}$
131. $-\frac{7}{30}$ **133.** $\frac{15}{64}$ **135.** $-\frac{10}{9}$ **137.** $-\frac{147}{32}$ **139.** $\frac{25}{8}$ **141.** $\frac{2}{3}$ **143.** 4.164   **145.** 4.347   **147.** -4.028
149. -2.22 **151.** -1.104 **153.** 0.506   **155.** -0.2376 **157.** $-274.\overline{4}$ **159.** -2.59 **161.** -5.11
163. -2060.55 **165.** 5% of the total is contributed by corporations.   **167a.** 47% of *Waterworld*'s total gross was from foreign countries.

b. 44% of *Judge Dredd's* total gross was its U.S. box-office gross.

c. *Judge Dredd* and *Spy Hard* grossed more than half their box-office incomes in foreign countries.

169.

$\frac{2}{3}$	$-\frac{1}{6}$	0
$-\frac{1}{2}$	$\frac{1}{6}$	$\frac{5}{6}$
$\frac{1}{3}$	$\frac{1}{2}$	$-\frac{1}{3}$

171. Answers will vary.   **173.** $a = 2, b = 3, c = 6$

SECTION 1.5

1. 36   **3.** -49 **5.** 9   **7.** 81   **9.** $\frac{1}{4}$ **11.** 0.09   **13.** 12   **15.** 0.216   **17.** -12 **19.** 16   **21.** -864

23. -1008 **25.** 3   **27.** $-77,760$ **29.** 9   **31.** 12   **33.** 1   **35.** 8   **37.** -16 **39.** 12   **41.** 13

43. -36 **45.** 13   **47.** 4   **49.** 15   **51.** -1 **53.** 4   **55.** 0.51   **57.** 1.7   **59.** $-\frac{1}{16}$

61. No. $6 + 2(4 - 9) = 6 + 2(-5) = 6 + (-10) = -4$. Do multiplication before addition.

CHAPTER REVIEW

1. -6 [1.2A]   **2.** 0.28 [1.4A]   **3.** -25 [1.5A]   **4.** 10 [1.5B]   **5.** $-4 < 2$ [1.1A]   **6.** 0.062 [1.4B]

7. -42 [1.3A]   **8.** $\frac{7}{12}$ [1.4C]   **9.** 60 [1.5B]   **10.** -4 [1.1A]   **11.** -1.068 [1.4C]   **12.** 62.5% [1.4B]

13. $0.1\overline{3}$ [1.4A]   **14.** -4 [1.2B]   **15.** 4 [1.1B]   **16.** 8 [1.3B]   **17.** -20 [1.3B]   **18.** $\frac{159}{200}$ [1.4B]

19. 31 [1.5B]   **20.** -13 [1.2A]   **21.** $54\frac{2}{7}\%$ [1.4B]   **22.** $\frac{16}{81}$ [1.5A]   **23.** -4.6224 [1.4D]   **24.** -5 [1.1B]

25. 1 [1.2B]   **26.** $-\frac{8}{15}$ [1.4D]   **27.** 7, 0, 9 [1.1B]   **28.** 81 [1.3A]   **29.** $-|6| < |-10|$ [1.1B]

30. 1 [1.5B]   **31.** The score for the exam was 98. [1.3C]   **32.** 17.8% of the messages is E-mail. [1.4E]
33. The difference is 396°C. [1.2C]

CHAPTER TEST

1. 17 [1.3B]   **2.** $83\frac{1}{3}\%$ [1.4B]   **3.** 12 [1.5A]   **4.** -5.3578 [1.4D]   **5.** -14 [1.2B]   **6.** $\frac{3}{8}$ [1.4B]

7. $\frac{1}{15}$ [1.4C]   **8.** 8 [1.5B]   **9.** 90 [1.3A]   **10.** 4 [1.1B]   **11.** -108 [1.5A]   **12.** 4 [1.1A]

13. $-2 > -40$ [1.1A]   **14.** -4 [1.1B]   **15.** $\frac{9}{20}$; 0.45 [1.4B]   **16.** -16 [1.2A]   **17.** -48 [1.3A]

18. 17 [1.5B]   **19.** 4 [1.2B]   **20.** $-\frac{1}{2}$ [1.4D]   **21.** 102.5% [1.4B]   **22.** 9 [1.5B]   **23.** $0.\overline{7}$ [1.4A]

24a. The annual losses would be $-\$12,560,000$.   **b.** The average monthly loss was $-\$5,070,000$. [1.3C]
25. The price of one share was $\$62\frac{5}{8}$. [1.4E]

Answers to Chapter 2 Odd-Numbered Exercises

SECTION 2.1

1. $2x^2, 5x, \underline{-8}$ **3.** $-a^4, \underline{6}$ **5.** $7\underline{x^2y}, 6xy^2$ **7.** $1, -9$ **9.** $1, -4, -1$ **11.** 10   **13.** 32   **15.** 21   **17.** 16
19. -9 **21.** 41   **23.** -7 **25.** 13   **27.** -15 **29.** 41   **31.** 1   **33.** 5   **35.** 1   **37.** 57   **39.** 5
41. 8   **43.** -3 **45.** -2 **47.** -4 **49.** 10   **51.** -25 **53.** 1   **55.** -23 **57a.** 2   **b.** 5   **c.** 6
d. 7

SECTION 2.2

1. $14x$ **3.** $5a$ **5.** $-6y$ **7.** $-3b - 7$ **9.** $5a$ **11.** $-2ab$ **13.** $5xy$ **15.** 0   **17.** $-\dfrac{5}{6}x$ **19.** $-\dfrac{1}{24}x^2$

21. $11x$ **23.** $7a$ **25.** $-14x^2$ **27.** $-x + 3y$ **29.** $17x - 3y$ **31.** $-2a - 6b$ **33.** $-3x - 8y$ **35.** $-4x^2 - 2x$
37. $12x$ **39.** $-21a$ **41.** $6y$ **43.** $8x$ **45.** $-6a$ **47.** $12b$ **49.** $-15x^2$ **51.** x^2 **53.** a **55.** x **57.** n
59. x **61.** y **63.** $3x$ **65.** $-2x$ **67.** $-8a^2$ **69.** $8y$ **71.** $4y$ **73.** $-2x$ **75.** $6a$ **77.** $-x - 2$
79. $8x - 6$ **81.** $-2a - 14$ **83.** $-6y + 24$ **85.** $35 - 21b$ **87.** $2 - 5y$ **89.** $15x^2 + 6x$ **91.** $2y - 18$
93. $-15x - 30$ **95.** $-6x^2 - 28$ **97.** $-6y^2 + 21$ **99.** $3x^2 - 3y^2$ **101.** $-4x + 12y$ **103.** $-6a^2 + 7b^2$
105. $4x^2 - 12x + 20$ **107.** $x - 3y + 4$ **109.** $-12a^2 - 20a + 28$ **111.** $12x^2 - 9x + 12$ **113.** $10x^2 - 20xy - 5y^2$
115. $-8b^2 + 6b - 9$ **117.** $a - 7$ **119.** $-11x + 13$ **121.** $-4y - 4$ **123.** $-2x - 16$ **125.** $14y - 45$
127. $a + 7b$ **129.** $6x + 28$ **131.** $5x - 75$ **133.** $4x - 4$ **135.** $2x - 9$ **137a.** False. $8 \div 4 \neq 4 \div 8$
b. False. $(8 \div 4) \div 2 \neq 8 \div (4 \div 2)$ **c.** False. $(7 - 5) - 1 \neq 7 - (5 - 1)$ **d.** False. $6 - 3 \neq 3 - 6$
139. No. 0 does not have a multiplicative inverse.   **141.** Answers will vary.

SECTION 2.3

1. $8 + y$ **3.** $t + 10$ **5.** $z + 14$ **7.** $x^2 - 20$ **9.** $\dfrac{3}{4}n + 12$ **11.** $8 + \dfrac{n}{4}$ **13.** $3(y + 7)$ **15.** $t(t + 16)$

17. $\dfrac{1}{2}x^2 + 15$ **19.** $5n^3 + n^2$ **21.** $r - \dfrac{r}{3}$ **23.** $x^2 - (x + 17)$ **25.** $9(z + 4)$ **27.** $12 - x$ **29.** $\dfrac{2}{3}x$ **31.** $\dfrac{2x}{9}$

33. $11x - 8$ **35.** $(x + 2) - 9; x - 7$ **37.** $\dfrac{7}{5 + x}$ **39.** $5 + \dfrac{1}{2}(x + 3); \dfrac{1}{2}x + \dfrac{13}{2}$ **41.** $(2x - 4) + x; 3x - 4$

43. $(x - 5)7; 7x - 35$ **45.** $\dfrac{2x + 5}{x}$ **47.** $x - (3x - 8); -2x + 8$ **49.** $3x + x; 4x$ **51.** $(x + 6) + 5; x + 11$

53. $x - (x + 10); -10$ **55.** $\dfrac{1}{6}x + \dfrac{4}{9}x; \dfrac{11}{18}x$ **57.** $\dfrac{x}{3} + x; \dfrac{4}{3}x$ **59.** average sale price of a home in Carmel: P; average sale price of a home in Vail: $P + 143{,}600$ **61.** $S, 12 - S$ **63.** distance traveled by the faster car: x; distance traveled by the slower car: $200 - x$ **65.** time to prepare Form 1040: t; time to prepare Schedule A: $\dfrac{1}{4}t$ **67.** world population in 1990: p; world population in 2050: $2p$ **69.** number of oxygen atoms: x; number of hydrogen atoms: $2x$
71. Answers will vary.

CHAPTER REVIEW

1. $3x^2 - 24x - 21$ [2.2C]   **2.** $11x$ [2.2A]   **3.** $8a - 4b$ [2.2A]   **4.** $-5n$ [2.2B]   **5.** 79 [2.1A]
6. $10x - 35$ [2.2C]   **7.** $12y^2 + 8y - 10$ [2.2C]   **8.** $-6a$ [2.2B]   **9.** $-42x^2$ [2.2B]   **10.** $-63 - 36x$ [2.2C]
11. $-5y$ [2.2A]   **12.** -4 [2.1A]   **13.** $24y + 30$ [2.2D]   **14.** $9c - 5d$ [2.2A]   **15.** $20x$ [2.2B]
16. $7x + 46$ [2.2D]   **17.** 29 [2.1A]   **18.** $-9r + 8s$ [2.2A]   **19.** $-4x^2 + 6x$ [2.2A]   **20.** $-90x + 25$ [2.2D]

21. $28a^2 - 8a + 12$ [2.2C]   **22.** $-4x + 20$ [2.2D]   **23.** -7 [2.1A]   **24.** $36y$ [2.2B]   **25.** $\frac{2}{3}(x + 10)$ [2.3A]

26. number of calories in an apple: a; number of calories in a candy bar: $2a + 8$ [2.3C]

27. $3x + 5(x - 1)$; $8x - 5$ [2.3B]   **28.** $4x$ [2.3A]   **29.** number of ten-dollar bills: T; number of five-dollar bills:

$35 - T$ [2.3C]   **30.** $2x - \frac{1}{2}x$; $\frac{3}{2}x$ [2.3B]   **31.** number of American League cards: A; number of National

League cards: $5A$ [2.3C]   **32.** $x - 6$ [2.3A]   **33.** $x + 2x$; $3x$ [2.3B]

CHAPTER TEST

1. $5x$ [2.2A]   **2.** $-6x^2 + 21y^2$ [2.2C]   **3.** $-x + 6$ [2.2D]   **4.** $-7x + 33$ [2.2D]   **5.** $-9x - 7y$ [2.2A]
6. 22 [2.1A]   **7.** $2x$ [2.2B]   **8.** $7x + 38$ [2.2D]   **9.** $-10x^2 + 15x - 30$ [2.2C]   **10.** $-2x - 5y$ [2.2A]
11. 3 [2.1A]   **12.** $3x$ [2.2B]   **13.** y^2 [2.2A]   **14.** $-4x + 8$ [2.2C]   **15.** $-10a$ [2.2B]
16. $2x + y$ [2.2D]   **17.** $36y$ [2.2B]   **18.** $15 - 35b$ [2.2C]   **19.** $a^2 - b^2$ [2.3A]
20. $10(x - 3)$; $10x - 30$ [2.3B]   **21.** $x + 2x^2$ [2.3B]   **22.** speed of return: s; speed of fastball: $2s$ [2.3C]
23. $\frac{6}{x} - 3$ [2.3B]   **24.** $b - 7b$ [2.3A]   **25.** shorter piece: x; longer piece: $4x - 3$ [2.3C]

CUMULATIVE REVIEW

1. -7 [1.2A]   **2.** 5 [1.2B]   **3.** 24 [1.3A]   **4.** -5 [1.3B]   **5.** 1.25 [1.4A]   **6.** $\frac{11}{48}$ [1.4C]   **7.** $\frac{1}{6}$ [1.4D]

8. $\frac{1}{4}$ [1.4D]   **9.** 75% [1.4B]   **10.** -5 [1.5B]   **11.** $\frac{53}{48}$ [1.5B]   **12.** 16 [2.1A]   **13.** $5x^2$ [2.2A]

14. $-7a - 10b$ [2.2A]   **15.** $6a$ [2.2B]   **16.** $30b$ [2.2B]   **17.** $24 - 6x$ [2.2C]   **18.** $6y - 18$ [2.2C]

19. $\frac{3}{8}$ [1.4B]   **20.** 0.0105 [1.4B]   **21.** $-8x^2 + 12y^2$ [2.2C]   **22.** $-9y^2 + 9y + 21$ [2.2C]

23. $-7x + 14$ [2.2D]   **24.** $5x - 43$ [2.2D]   **25.** $17x - 24$ [2.2D]   **26.** $-3x + 21y$ [2.2D]

27. $\frac{1}{2}b + b$ [2.3A]   **28.** $\frac{10}{y - 2}$ [2.3A]   **29.** $8 - \frac{x}{12}$ [2.3B]   **30.** $x + (x + 2)$; $2x + 2$ [2.3B]

31. $(3 + x)5 + 12$; $27 + 5x$ [2.3B]   **32.** speed of normal drive: s; speed of triple-speed drive: $3s$ [2.3C]

Answers to Chapter 3 Odd-Numbered Exercises

SECTION 3.1

1. yes   **3.** no   **5.** no   **7.** yes   **9.** yes   **11.** yes   **13.** no   **15.** yes   **17.** yes   **19.** yes   **21.** no

23. 6 **25.** 16 **27.** 7 **29.** -2 **31.** 1 **33.** 0 **35.** 3 **37.** -10 **39.** -3 **41.** -14 **43.** 2

45. 11 **47.** -9 **49.** -1 **51.** -14 **53.** -5 **55.** -1 **57.** 1 **59.** $-\frac{1}{2}$ **61.** $-\frac{3}{4}$ **63.** $\frac{1}{12}$ **65.** $-\frac{7}{12}$

67. 0.6529 **69.** -0.283 **71.** 9.257 **73.** -3 **75.** 0 **77.** -2 **79.** 9 **81.** 80 **83.** -4 **85.** 0

87. 8 **89.** -7 **91.** 12 **93.** -18 **95.** 15 **97.** -20 **99.** 0 **101.** 15 **103.** 75 **105.** $\frac{8}{3}$ **107.** $\frac{1}{3}$

109. $-\frac{1}{2}$ **111.** $-\frac{3}{2}$ **113.** $\frac{15}{7}$ **115.** 4 **117.** 3 **119.** 4.745 **121.** 2.06 **123.** -2.13 **125.** 28

127. 0.72 **129.** 64 **131.** 24% **133.** 7.2 **135.** 400 **137.** 9 **139.** 25% **141.** 5 **143.** 200%

145. 400 **147.** 7.7 **149.** 200 **151.** 400 **153.** 20 **155.** 80.34% **157.** 19% of the students are in the fine arts college.   **159.** 65% of the amount spent by companies was spent on sports.   **161.** The total electricity used for home lighting is 96.1 billion kWh.   **163.** There were about 2,482 million shares.   **165a.** More money was spent on new cars in 1986.   **b.** $41 billion more was spent on new cars in 1986.   **167a.** Answers will vary.   **b.** Answers will vary.   **169.** Answers will vary.   **171.** It is two times its original value.

SECTION 3.2

1. 3   **3.** 6   **5.** -1 **7.** -3 **9.** 2   **11.** 2   **13.** 5   **15.** -3 **17.** 6   **19.** 3   **21.** 1   **23.** 6   **25.** -7

27. 0   **29.** $\frac{3}{4}$ **31.** $\frac{4}{9}$ **33.** $\frac{1}{3}$ **35.** $-\frac{1}{2}$ **37.** $-\frac{3}{4}$ **39.** $\frac{1}{3}$ **41.** $-\frac{1}{6}$ **43.** 1   **45.** 1   **47.** 0   **49.** $\frac{13}{10}$

51. $\frac{2}{5}$ **53.** $-\frac{4}{3}$ **55.** $-\frac{3}{2}$ **57.** 18   **59.** 8   **61.** -16 **63.** 25   **65.** 21   **67.** 15   **69.** -16 **71.** -21

73. $\frac{15}{2}$ **75.** $-\frac{18}{5}$ **77.** 2   **79.** 3   **81.** 1   **83.** -2 **85.** 19   **87.** -1 **89.** -11 **91.** The markup rate is 60%.   **93.** The cost is $59.   **95.** The markup rate is 44.4%.   **97.** The cost is $8.50.   **99.** The discount rate is 23.2%.   **101.** The regular price is $300.   **103.** The markdown rate is 38%.   **105.** The regular price is $275.   **107.** The initial velocity is 8 ft/s.   **109.** The depreciated value will be $38,000 in 2 years.   **111.** The length is approximately 31.8 in.   **113.** The distance is 168 ft.   **115.** The population is approximately 51,000 people.   **117.** The year is 1952.   **119.** The markup is $18.   **121.** The regular price is $317.65.   **123.** 385   **125.** Answers will vary.   **127.** The distance and the speed of travel are needed.

SECTION 3.3

1. 2   **3.** 3   **5.** -1 **7.** 2   **9.** -2 **11.** -3 **13.** 0   **15.** -1 **17.** -3 **19.** -1 **21.** 4   **23.** $\frac{2}{3}$

25. $\frac{5}{6}$ **27.** $\frac{3}{4}$ **29.** -17 **31.** 41   **33.** 8   **35.** 1   **37.** 4   **39.** -1 **41.** -1 **43.** $-\frac{2}{3}$ **45.** $\frac{4}{3}$ **47.** $\frac{1}{2}$

49. $-\frac{1}{3}$ **51.** $\frac{10}{3}$ **53.** $-\frac{1}{4}$ **55.** 0   **57.** -1 **59.** The force applied must be 25 lb.   **61.** The fulcrum must be 6 ft from the 180-pound person.   **63.** The fulcrum must be 10 ft from the 128-pound acrobat.   **65.** The minimum force is 34.6 lb.   **67.** The breakeven point is 260 units.   **69.** The breakeven point is 520 units.   **71.** 3000 bats must be sold to break even.   **73.** no solution   **75.** 0   **77.** Yes. Answers will vary.

SECTION 3.4

1. $x - 15 = 7$; 22   **3.** $7x = -21$; -3 **5.** $9 - x = 7$; 2   **7.** $5 - 2x = 1$; 2   **9.** $2x + 5 = 15$; 5   **11.** $4x - 6 = 22$; 7   **13.** $3(4x - 7) = 15$; 3   **15.** $2(x - 25) = 3x$; -50 **17.** $3x - 1 = 15 - x$; 4, 11   **19.** $3x + 2(18 - x) = 44$; 8, 10   **21.** The integers are -8, -6, and -4.   **23.** The integers are 11, 13, and 15.   **25.** The integers are 6 and 8.   **27.** The integers are 2, 4, and 6.   **29.** The storage capacity is 2 gigabytes.   **31.** The customer used the service for 11 min.   **33.** The executive used the phone for 162 min.   **35.** The family used 515 kWh of electricity.   **37.** The pieces measure 6 yd and 8 yd.   **39.** The value of the stock account is $6000. The value of the mutual fund account is $4000.

41. Answers will vary.   **43.** contradiction   **45.** $-\frac{5}{16}$ **47.** 0

SECTION 3.5

1. The sides measure 50 ft, 50 ft, and 25 ft.   **3.** The length is 13 m. The width is 8 m.   **5.** The length is 40 ft. The width is 20 ft.   **7.** The sides measure 40 cm, 20 cm, and 50 cm.   **9.** The length is 130 ft. The width is 39 ft.

11. The width is 12 ft.   **13.** Each side measures 12 in.   **15.** The complement of a 28° angle is 62°.
17. The supplement of a 73° angle is 107°.   **19.** 35°   **21.** 20°   **23.** 53°   **25.** 121°   **27.** 15°   **29.** 18°
31. 45°   **33.** 49°   **35.** 12°   **37.** $\angle a = 122°$; $\angle b = 58°$ **39.** $\angle a = 44°$; $\angle b = 136°$ **41.** 20°   **43.** 40°
45. 128°   **47.** $\angle x = 160°$, $\angle y = 145°$ **49.** $\angle a = 40°$, $\angle b = 140°$ **51.** $75° - x$ **53.** The measure of the third angle
is 45°.   **55.** The measure of the third angle is 73°.   **57.** The measure of the third angle is 43°.   **59.** The length is
9 cm. The width is 4 cm.   **61.** Answers will vary.

SECTION 3.6

1. 20 oz of herbs should be used.   **3.** The cost of the mixture is $1.84 per pound.   **5.** 3 lb of caramel is needed.
7. 2 c of olive oil and 8 c of vinegar are used.   **9.** The cost is $3.00 per ounce.   **11.** 16 oz of the $400 alloy
should be used.   **13.** 37 lb of almonds and 63 lb of walnuts were used.   **15.** 228 adult tickets were sold.
17. The cost is $.70 per pound.   **19.** The resulting gold alloy is 24% gold.   **21.** 20 gal of the 15% acid solution
are used.   **23.** 30 lb of the yarn that is 25% wool is used.   **25.** 6.25 gal of the plant food that is 9% nitrogen is used.
27. The resulting mixture is 19% sugar.   **29.** 20 lb of the coffee that is 40% java beans are used.   **31.** 100 ml of the
7% solution and 200 ml of the 4% solution are used.   **33.** 150 oz of pure chocolate must be added.   **35.** The resulting
alloy is 50% silver.   **37.** The rate of the first plane is 105 mph. The rate of the second plane is 130 mph.   **39.** They
will be 3000 km apart at 11 A.M.   **41.** The cabin cruiser will be alongside the motorboat 2 h after the cabin cruiser leaves.
43. The distance from the airport to the corporate offices is 120 mi.   **45.** The rate of the car is 68 mph.   **47.** The
distance between the two airports is 300 mi.   **49.** The planes will pass each other 2.5 h after the plane leaves Seattle.
51. They will meet 1.5 h after they begin.   **53.** The bus overtakes the car 180 mi from the starting point.   **55.** 75 g
of pure water must be added.   **57.** 3.75 gal must be drained from the radiator and replaced by pure antifreeze.
59. The cyclist's average speed for the trip was $13\frac{1}{3}$ mph.

CHAPTER REVIEW

1. 21 [3.1B]   **2.** 10 [3.3B]   **3.** 7 [3.2A]   **4.** No [3.1A]   **5.** 20 [3.1C]   **6.** −2 [3.3B]   **7.** 30 is
250% of 12. [3.1D]   **8.** 4 [3.3A]   **9.** −1 [3.3B]   **10.** 4 [3.3A]   **11.** The cost is $671.25. [3.2B]
12. 68° [3.5B]   **13.** A force of 24 lb must be applied to the other end. [3.3C]   **14.** The average speed was
32 mph. [3.6C]   **15.** The discount rate is $33\frac{1}{3}$%. [3.2B]   **16.** $\angle x = 22°$, $\angle y = 158°$ [3.5B]   **17.** 7 qt of
cranberry juice and 3 qt of apple juice were used. [3.6A]   **18.** The integers are −1, 0, and 1. [3.4A]   **19.** The
angles measure 75°, 60°, and 45°. [3.5C]   **20.** $5n - 4 = 16$; 4 [3.4A]   **21.** The height of the Eiffel Tower is
993 ft. [3.4B]   **22.** The length is 80 ft. The width is 20 ft. [3.5A]   **23.** The jet overtakes the propeller-driven plane
600 mi from the starting point. [3.6C]   **24.** The numbers are 8 and 13. [3.4A]   **25.** The resulting mixture is 14%
butterfat. [3.6B]

CHAPTER TEST

1. −5 [3.3A]   **2.** −5 [3.1B]   **3.** −3 [3.2A]   **4.** 2 [3.3B]   **5.** No [3.1A]   **6.** 5 [3.2A]   **7.** 0.5% of 8
is 0.04. [3.1D]   **8.** $-\frac{1}{3}$ [3.3B]   **9.** 2 [3.3A]   **10.** −12 [3.1C]   **11.** 10 lb of the $.70 rye flour and 5 lb of the
$.40 wheat flour should be used. [3.6A]   **12.** 19° [3.5B]   **13.** The discount rate is 20%. [3.2B]
14. 200 calculators were produced. [3.2B]   **15.** The measure of one of the equal angles is 70°. [3.5C]   **16.** The
integers are 10, 12, and 14. [3.4A]   **17.** 1.25 gal of water must be used. [3.6B]   **18.** $\angle a = 138°$, $\angle b = 42°$ [3.5B]
19. $3x - 15 = 27$; 14 [3.4A]   **20.** The rate of the snowmobile was 6 mph. [3.6C]   **21.** There are 110 color TVs

made each day. [3.4B]   **22.** The two numbers are 8 and 10. [3.4A]   **23.** The distance between the two airports is 360 mi. [3.6C]   **24.** The sides measure 5 ft, 8 ft, and 10 ft. [3.5A]   **25.** The temperature of the water after mixing is 60°C. [3.3C]

CUMULATIVE REVIEW

1. 6 [1.2B]   **2.** -48 [1.3A]   **3.** $-\dfrac{19}{48}$ [1.4C]   **4.** -2 [1.4D]   **5.** 54 [1.5A]   **6.** 24 [1.5B]

7. 6 [2.1A]   **8.** $-17x$ [2.2A]   **9.** $-5a - 2b$ [2.2A]   **10.** $2x$ [2.2B]   **11.** $36y$ [2.2B]

12. $2x^2 + 6x - 4$ [2.2C]   **13.** $-4x + 14$ [2.2D]   **14.** $6x - 34$ [2.2D]   **15.** Yes [3.1A]   **16.** No [3.1A]

17. 19.2 [3.1D]   **18.** -25 [3.1C]   **19.** -3 [3.2A]   **20.** 3 [3.2A]   **21.** 13 [3.3B]   **22.** 2 [3.3B]

23. -3 [3.3A]   **24.** $\dfrac{1}{2}$ [3.3A]   **25.** The final temperature of the water is 60°C. [3.3C]

26. $12 - 5x = -18; 6$ [3.4A]   **27.** The area of the garage is 600 ft². [3.4B]   **28.** 20 lb of oat flour must be used. [3.6A]   **29.** 25 g of pure gold must be added. [3.6B]   **30.** The length is 12 ft. The width is 10 ft. [3.5A]

31. 131° [3.5B]   **32.** The measure of one of the angles is 60°. [3.5C]   **33.** The length of the track is 120 m. [3.6C]

Answers to Chapter 4 Odd-Numbered Exercises

SECTION 4.1

1. yes   **3.** no   **5.** yes   **7.** yes   **9.** binomial   **11.** trinomial   **13.** none   **15.** binomial   **17.** $-2x^2 + 3x$

19. $y^2 - 8$ **21.** $5x^2 + 7x + 20$ **23.** $x^3 + 2x^2 - 6x - 6$ **25.** $2a^3 - 3a^2 - 11a + 2$ **27.** $5x^2 + 8x$

29. $7x^2 + xy - 4y^2$ **31.** $3a^2 - 3a + 17$ **33.** $5x^3 + 10x^2 - x - 4$ **35.** $3r^3 + 2r^2 - 11r + 7$ **37.** $4x$

39. $3y^2 - 4y - 2$ **41.** $-7x - 7$ **43.** $4x^3 + 3x^2 + 3x + 1$ **45.** $y^3 + 5y^2 - 2y - 4$ **47.** $-y^2 - 13xy$

49. $2x^2 - 3x - 1$ **51.** $-2x^3 + x^2 + 2$ **53.** $3a^3 - 2$ **55.** $4y^3 + 2y^2 + 2y - 4$ **57.** $x^2 + 9x - 11$ **59.** Answers will vary.   **61.** Yes. For example, $(2x^3 + 3x - 4) + (-2x^3 + 5x^2 - 6) = 5x^2 + 3x - 10$.

SECTION 4.2

1. $30x^3$ **3.** $-42c^6$ **5.** $9a^7$ **7.** x^3y^4 **9.** $-10x^9y$ **11.** $12x^7y^8$ **13.** $-6x^3y^5$ **15.** x^4y^5z **17.** $a^3b^5c^4$

19. $-30a^5b^8$ **21.** $6a^5b$ **23.** $40y^{10}z^6$ **25.** $x^3y^3z^2$ **27.** $-24a^3b^3c^3$ **29.** $8x^7yz^6$ **31.** $30x^6y^8$ **33.** $-36a^3b^2c^3$

35. x^{15} **37.** x^{14} **39.** x^8 **41.** y^{12} **43.** $-8x^6$ **45.** x^4y^6 **47.** $9x^4y^2$ **49.** $-243x^{15}y^{10}$ **51.** $-8x^7$

53. $24x^8y^7$ **55.** a^4b^6 **57.** $64x^{12}y^3$ **59.** $-18x^3y^4$ **61.** $-8a^7b^5$ **63.** $-54a^9b^3$ **65.** $12x^2$ **67.** $2x^6y^2 + 9x^4y^2$

69. 0   **71.** $17x^4y^8$ **73.** true   **75.** False. $(x^2)^5 = x^{2 \cdot 5} = x^{10}$ **77.** No. $2^{(3^2)}$ is larger.   **79.** Answers will vary.

SECTION 4.3

1. $x^2 - 2x$ **3.** $-x^2 - 7x$ **5.** $3a^3 - 6a^2$ **7.** $-5x^4 + 5x^3$ **9.** $-3x^5 + 7x^3$ **11.** $12x^3 - 6x^2$ **13.** $6x^2 - 12x$

15. $3x^2 + 4x$ **17.** $-x^3y + xy^3$ **19.** $2x^4 - 3x^2 + 2x$ **21.** $2a^3 + 3a^2 + 2a$ **23.** $3x^6 - 3x^4 - 2x^2$

25. $-6y^4 - 12y^3 + 14y^2$ **27.** $-2a^3 - 6a^2 + 8a$ **29.** $6y^4 - 3y^3 + 6y^2$ **31.** $x^3y - 3x^2y^2 + xy^3$ **33.** $x^3 + 4x^2 + 5x + 2$

35. $a^3 - 6a^2 + 13a - 12$ **37.** $-2b^3 + 7b^2 + 19b - 20$ **39.** $-6x^3 + 31x^2 - 41x + 10$ **41.** $x^3 - 3x^2 + 5x - 15$

43. $x^4 - 4x^3 - 3x^2 + 14x - 8$ **45.** $15y^3 - 16y^2 - 70y + 16$ **47.** $5a^4 - 20a^3 - 5a^2 + 22a - 8$

49. $y^4 + 4y^3 + y^2 - 5y + 2$ **51.** $x^2 + 4x + 3$ **53.** $a^2 + a - 12$ **55.** $y^2 - 5y - 24$ **57.** $y^2 - 10y + 21$

59. $2x^2 + 15x + 7$ **61.** $3x^2 + 11x - 4$ **63.** $4x^2 - 31x + 21$ **65.** $3y^2 - 2y - 16$ **67.** $9x^2 + 54x + 77$

69. $21a^2 - 83a + 80$ **71.** $6a^2 - 25ab + 14b^2$ **73.** $2a^2 - 11ab - 63b^2$ **75.** $100a^2 - 100ab + 21b^2$

77. $15x^2 + 56xy + 48y^2$ **79.** $14x^2 - 97xy - 60y^2$ **81.** $56x^2 - 61xy + 15y^2$ **83.** $y^2 - 25$ **85.** $4x^2 - 9$

87. $x^2 + 2x + 1$ **89.** $9a^2 - 30a + 25$ **91.** $9x^2 - 49$ **93.** $4a^2 + 4ab + b^2$ **95.** $x^2 - 4xy + 4y^2$ **97.** $16 - 9y^2$
99. $25x^2 + 20xy + 4y^2$ **101.** The area is $(10x^2 - 35x)$ ft². **103.** The area is $(4x^2 + 4x + 1)$ km².
105. The area is $(4x^2 + 10x)$ m². **107.** The total area is $(60w + 3000)$ yd². **109.** $x^4 + 2x^3 - 5x^2 - 6x + 9$
111. $12x^2 - x - 20$ **113.** $x^3 - 7x^2 - 7$ **115.** No. Answers will vary.

SECTION 4.4

1. $\dfrac{1}{25}$ **3.** 64 **5.** $\dfrac{1}{27}$ **7.** 2 **9.** $\dfrac{1}{x^2}$ **11.** a^6 **13.** $\dfrac{4}{x^7}$ **15.** $\dfrac{2}{3z^2}$ **17.** $5b^8$ **19.** $\dfrac{x^2}{3}$ **21.** 1 **23.** -1
25. y^4 **27.** a^3 **29.** p^4 **31.** $2x^3$ **33.** $2k$ **35.** m^5n^2 **37.** $\dfrac{3r^2}{2}$ **39.** $-\dfrac{2a}{3}$ **41.** $\dfrac{1}{y^5}$ **43.** $\dfrac{1}{a^6}$ **45.** $\dfrac{1}{3x^3}$
47. $\dfrac{2}{3x^5}$ **49.** $\dfrac{y^4}{x^2}$ **51.** $\dfrac{2}{5m^3n^8}$ **53.** $\dfrac{1}{p^3q}$ **55.** $\dfrac{1}{2y^3}$ **57.** $\dfrac{7xz}{8y^3}$ **59.** $\dfrac{p^2}{2m^3}$ **61.** $-\dfrac{8x^3}{y^6}$ **63.** $\dfrac{9}{x^2y^4}$ **65.** $\dfrac{2}{x^4}$
67. $-\dfrac{5}{a^8}$ **69.** $-\dfrac{a^5}{8b^4}$ **71.** $\dfrac{10y^3}{x^4}$ **73.** $\dfrac{1}{2x^3}$ **75.** $\dfrac{3}{x^3}$ **77.** $\dfrac{1}{2x^2y^6}$ **79.** $\dfrac{1}{x^6y}$ **81.** $\dfrac{a^4}{y^{10}}$ **83.** $-\dfrac{1}{6x^3}$ **85.** $-\dfrac{a^2b}{6c^2}$
87. $-\dfrac{7b^6}{a^2}$ **89.** $\dfrac{s^8t^4}{4r^{12}}$ **91.** $\dfrac{125p^3}{27m^{15}n^6}$ **93.** 3.24×10^{-9} **95.** 3×10^{-18} **97.** 3.2×10^{16} **99.** 1.22×10^{-19}
101. 5.47×10^8 **103.** 0.000167 **105.** 68,000,000 **107.** 0.0000305 **109.** 0.00000000102 **111.** 6.023×10^{23}
113. 3.7×10^{-6} **115.** 1×10^{-9} **117.** 1.6×10^{-19} **119.** $\dfrac{1}{4}, \dfrac{1}{2}, 1, 2, 4$ **121.** $4, 2, 1, \dfrac{1}{2}, \dfrac{1}{4}$
123. False. $(2a)^{-3} = \dfrac{1}{(2a)^3} = \dfrac{1}{8a^3}$ **125.** False. $(2 + 3)^{-1} = (5)^{-1} = \dfrac{1}{5}$ **127.** $x^{-2}, x \neq 0$, is always positive. $x^{-2} = \dfrac{1}{x^2}$; since
x^2 is positive, $\dfrac{1}{x^2}$ is positive.

SECTION 4.5

1. $2a - 5$ **3.** $6y + 4$ **5.** $x - 2$ **7.** $-x + 2$ **9.** $x^2 + 3x - 5$ **11.** $x^4 - 3x^2 - 1$ **13.** $xy + 2$ **15.** $-3y^3 + 5$
17. $3x - 2 + \dfrac{1}{x}$ **19.** $-3x + 7 - \dfrac{6}{x}$ **21.** $4a - 5 + 6b$ **23.** $9x + 6 - 3y$ **25.** $b - 7$ **27.** $y - 5$ **29.** $2y - 7$
31. $2y + 6 + \dfrac{25}{y - 3}$ **33.** $x - 2 + \dfrac{8}{x + 2}$ **35.** $3y - 5 + \dfrac{20}{2y + 4}$ **37.** $6x - 12 + \dfrac{19}{x + 2}$ **39.** $b - 5 - \dfrac{24}{b - 3}$
41. $3x + 17 + \dfrac{64}{x - 4}$ **43.** $5y + 3 + \dfrac{1}{2y + 3}$ **45.** $4a + 1$ **47.** $2a + 9 + \dfrac{33}{3a - 1}$ **49.** $x^2 - 5x + 2$ **51.** $x^2 + 5$
53. $3ab$

CHAPTER REVIEW

1. $8b^2 - 2b - 15$ [4.3C] **2.** $21y^2 + 4y - 1$ [4.1A] **3.** $b^2 + 5b + 2 + \dfrac{7}{b - 7}$ [4.5B] **4.** $x^4y^8z^4$ [4.2A]

5. $-8x^3 - 14x^2 + 18x$ [4.3A] **6.** b^2 [4.4A] **7.** 64 [4.2B] **8.** $2x^2 + 3x - 8$ [4.1B] **9.** $\dfrac{2x^3}{3}$ [4.4A]

10. $25y^2 - 70y + 49$ [4.3D] **11.** $100a^{15}b^{13}$ [4.2B] **12.** $4b^4 + 12b^2 - 1$ [4.5A] **13.** $13y^3 - 12y^2 - 5y - 1$ [4.1B]

14. $10a^2 + 12a - 22$ [4.1A] **15.** $6y^3 + 17y^2 - 2y - 21$ [4.3B] **16.** $-\dfrac{2a^3}{3b^3}$ [4.4A]

17. $8a^3b^3 - 4a^2b^4 + 6ab^5$ [4.3A] **18.** $-2y^2 + y - 5$ [4.1B] **19.** $9x^4y^6$ [4.2B]
20. $12b^5 - 4b^4 - 6b^3 - 8b^2 + 5$ [4.3B] **21.** $2x^3 + 9x^2 - 3x - 12$ [4.1A] **22.** $-4y + 8$ [4.5A]
23. $a^2 - 49$ [4.3D] **24.** $-54a^{13}b^5c^7$ [4.2A] **25.** $2y - 9$ [4.5B] **26.** $\dfrac{x^4y^6}{9}$ [4.4A] **27.** $-20x^3y^5$ [4.2A]
28. $10a^2 + 31a - 63$ [4.3C] **29.** 1.27×10^{-7} [4.4B] **30.** 0.0000000000032 [4.4B]
31. The area is $(2w^2 - w)$ ft². [4.3E] **32.** The area is $(9x^2 - 12x + 4)$ in². [4.3E]

CHAPTER TEST

1. $4x^3 - 6x^2$ [4.3A]   **2.** $4x - 1 + \dfrac{3}{x^2}$ [4.5A]   **3.** $-\dfrac{4}{x^6}$ [4.4A]   **4.** $-6x^3y^6$ [4.2A]   **5.** $x - 1 + \dfrac{2}{x + 1}$ [4.5B]

6. $x^3 - 7x^2 + 17x - 15$ [4.3B]   **7.** $-8a^6b^3$ [4.2B]   **8.** $\dfrac{9y^{10}}{x^{10}}$ [4.4A]   **9.** $a^2 + 3ab - 10b^2$ [4.3C]

10. $4x^4 - 2x^2 + 5$ [4.5A]   **11.** $x + 7$ [4.5B]   **12.** $6y^4 - 9y^3 + 18y^2$ [4.3A]

13. $-4x^4 + 8x^3 - 3x^2 - 14x + 21$ [4.3B]   **14.** $16y^2 - 9$ [4.3D]   **15.** a^4b^7 [4.2A]   **16.** $8ab^4$ [4.4A]

17. $4a - 7$ [4.5A]   **18.** $-5a^3 + 3a^2 - 4a + 3$ [4.1B]   **19.** $4x^2 - 20x + 25$ [4.3D]   **20.** $2x + 3 + \dfrac{2}{2x - 3}$ [4.5B]

21. $-2x^3$ [4.4A]   **22.** $10x^2 - 43xy + 28y^2$ [4.3C]   **23.** $3x^3 + 6x^2 - 8x + 3$ [4.1A]   **24.** 3.02×10^{-9} [4.4B]

25. The area is $(\pi x^2 - 10\pi x + 25\pi)$ m². [4.3E]

CUMULATIVE REVIEW

1. $\dfrac{5}{144}$ [1.4C]   **2.** $\dfrac{5}{3}$ [1.5A]   **3.** $\dfrac{25}{11}$ [1.5B]   **4.** $-\dfrac{22}{9}$ [2.1A]   **5.** $5x - 3xy$ [2.2A]   **6.** $-9x$ [2.2B]

7. $-18x + 12$ [2.2D]   **8.** -16 [3.1C]   **9.** -16 [3.3A]   **10.** 15 [3.3B]   **11.** 22% [3.1D]

12. $4b^3 - 4b^2 - 8b - 4$ [4.1A]   **13.** $3y^3 + 2y^2 - 10y$ [4.1B]   **14.** a^9b^{15} [4.2A]   **15.** $-8x^3y^6$ [4.2A]

16. $6y^4 + 8y^3 - 16y^2$ [4.3A]   **17.** $10a^3 - 39a^2 + 20a - 21$ [4.3B]   **18.** $15b^2 - 31b + 14$ [4.3C]   **19.** $\dfrac{1}{2b^2}$ [4.4A]

20. $a - 7$ [4.5B]   **21.** 0.0000609 [4.4B]   **22.** $8x - 2x = 18; 3$ [3.4B]   **23.** The resulting mixture is 28% orange juice. [3.6B]   **24.** The car overtakes the cyclist 25 mi from the starting point. [3.6C]   **25.** The length is 15 m. The width is 6 m. [3.5A]

Answers to Chapter 5 Odd-Numbered Exercises

SECTION 5.1

1. $5(a + 1)$ **3.** $8(2 - a^2)$ **5.** $4(2x + 3)$ **7.** $6(5a - 1)$ **9.** $x(7x - 3)$ **11.** $a^2(3 + 5a^3)$ **13.** $y(14y + 11)$

15. $2x(x^3 - 2)$ **17.** $2x^2(5x^2 - 6)$ **19.** $4a^5(2a^3 - 1)$ **21.** $xy(xy - 1)$ **23.** $3xy(xy^3 - 2)$ **25.** $xy(x - y^2)$

27. $5y(y^2 - 4y + 2)$ **29.** $3y^2(y^2 - 3y - 2)$ **31.** $3y(y^2 - 3y + 8)$ **33.** $a^2(6a^3 - 3a - 2)$ **35.** $ab(2a - 5ab + 7b)$

37. $2b(2b^4 + 3b^2 - 6)$ **39.** $x^2(8y^2 - 4y + 1)$ **41.** $(y + 7)(a + z)$ **43.** $(3r + s)(a - b)$ **45.** $(t - 7)(m - 7)$

47. $(2y + 1)(4a - b)$ **49.** $(x + 2)(x + 2y)$ **51.** $(p - 2)(p - 3r)$ **53.** $(b - 4)(a + 6)$ **55.** $(z + y)(2z - 1)$

57. $(4v + 7)(2v - 3y)$ **59.** $(2x - 5)(x - 3y)$ **61.** $(3y - a)(y - 2)$ **63.** $(y + 1)(3x - y)$ **65.** $(t - 2)(3s + t)$

67a. $(2x + 5)(x + 3)$ **b.** $(x + 3)(2x + 5)$ **69.** 28 is the one perfect number between 20 and 30.   **71.** In the equation for the perimeter of a rectangle, when $L + W$ doubles, the perimeter doubles.

SECTION 5.2

1. $(x + 1)(x + 2)$ **3.** $(x - 2)(x + 1)$ **5.** $(a + 4)(a - 3)$ **7.** $(a - 1)(a - 2)$ **9.** $(a + 2)(a - 1)$

11. $(b - 3)(b - 3)$ **13.** $(b + 8)(b - 1)$ **15.** $(y + 11)(y - 5)$ **17.** $(y - 3)(y - 2)$ **19.** $(z - 5)(z - 9)$

21. $(z - 20)(z + 8)$ **23.** $(p + 3)(p + 9)$ **25.** $(x + 10)(x + 10)$ **27.** $(b + 4)(b + 5)$ **29.** $(x + 3)(x - 14)$

31. $(b - 5)(b + 4)$ **33.** $(y - 17)(y + 3)$ **35.** $(p - 7)(p + 3)$ **37.** nonfactorable over the integers

39. $(x - 5)(x - 15)$ **41.** $(p + 3)(p + 21)$ **43.** $(x + 2)(x + 19)$ **45.** $(x + 9)(x - 4)$ **47.** $(a + 4)(a - 11)$

49. $(a - 3)(a - 18)$ **51.** $(z + 21)(z - 7)$ **53.** $(c + 12)(c - 15)$ **55.** $(p + 9)(p + 15)$ **57.** $(c + 2)(c + 9)$

59. $(x + 15)(x - 5)$ **61.** $(x + 25)(x - 4)$ **63.** $(b - 4)(b - 18)$ **65.** $(a + 45)(a - 3)$ **67.** $(b - 7)(b - 18)$

69. $(z + 12)(z + 12)$ **71.** $(x - 4)(x - 25)$ **73.** $(x + 16)(x - 7)$ **75.** $3(x + 2)(x + 3)$ **77.** $-(x + 6)(x - 2)$

79. $a(b + 8)(b - 1)$ **81.** $x(y + 3)(y + 5)$ **83.** $-2a(a + 2)(a + 1)$ **85.** $4y(y + 6)(y - 3)$ **87.** $2x(x^2 - x + 2)$

89. $6(z + 5)(z - 3)$ **91.** $3a(a + 3)(a - 6)$ **93.** $(x + 7y)(x - 3y)$ **95.** $(a - 5b)(a - 10b)$ **97.** $(s + 8t)(s - 6t)$
99. nonfactorable over the integers **101.** $z^2(z + 10)(z - 8)$ **103.** $b^2(b + 2)(b - 5)$ **105.** $3y^2(y + 3)(y + 15)$
107. $-x^2(x - 12)(x + 1)$ **109.** $3y(x + 3)(x - 5)$ **111.** $-3x(x - 3)(x - 9)$ **113.** $(x - 3y)(x - 5y)$
115. $(a - 6b)(a - 7b)$ **117.** $(y + z)(y + 7z)$ **119.** $3y(x + 21)(x - 1)$ **121.** $3x(x + 4)(x - 3)$
123. $4z(z + 11)(z - 3)$ **125.** $4x(x + 3)(x - 1)$ **127.** $5(p + 12)(p - 7)$ **129.** $p^2(p + 12)(p - 3)$
131. $(t - 5s)(t - 7s)$ **133.** $(a + 3b)(a - 11b)$ **135.** $y(x + 6)(x - 9)$ **137.** $-12, 12, -36, 36$
139. $-22, -10, 10, 22$ **141.** $6, 10, 12$ **143.** $6, 10, 12$ **145.** $4, 6$

SECTION 5.3

1. $(2x + 1)(x + 1)$ **3.** $(2y + 1)(y + 3)$ **5.** $(2a - 1)(a - 1)$ **7.** $(2b - 1)(b - 5)$ **9.** $(2x - 1)(x + 1)$
11. $(2x + 1)(x - 3)$ **13.** $(2t - 5)(t + 2)$ **15.** $(3p - 1)(p - 5)$ **17.** $(4y - 1)(3y - 1)$ **19.** nonfactorable over
the integers **21.** $(2t - 1)(3t - 4)$ **23.** $(8x + 1)(x + 4)$ **25.** nonfactorable over the integers
27. $(4y + 5)(3y + 1)$ **29.** $(7a - 2)(a + 7)$ **31.** $(3b - 4)(b - 4)$ **33.** $(2z + 1)(z - 14)$ **35.** $(3p - 2)(p + 8)$
37. $2(2x + 1)(x + 1)$ **39.** $5(3y - 7)(y - 1)$ **41.** $x(2x - 1)(x - 5)$ **43.** $b(3a - 4)(a - 4)$ **45.** nonfactorable
over the integers **47.** $-3x(x + 4)(x - 3)$ **49.** $4(4y - 1)(5y - 1)$ **51.** $z(4z + 1)(2z + 3)$ **53.** $y(3x + 2)(2x - 5)$
55. $5(2t - 5)(t + 2)$ **57.** $p(3p - 1)(p - 5)$ **59.** $2(13z - 3)(z + 4)$ **61.** $2y(5y - 2)(y - 4)$ **63.** $yz(4z - 3)(z + 2)$
65. $3a(2a + 3)(7a - 3)$ **67.** $y(3x - 5y)(3x - 5y)$ **69.** $xy(3x - 4y)(3x - 4y)$ **71.** $(3x - 4)(2x - 3)$
73. $(5b - 2)(b + 7)$ **75.** $(3a + 8)(2a - 3)$ **77.** $(4z + 3)(z + 2)$ **79.** $(2p + 5)(11p - 2)$ **81.** $(8y + 9)(y + 1)$
83. $(3t + 1)(6t - 5)$ **85.** $(6b - 1)(b + 12)$ **87.** $(3x + 2)(3x + 2)$ **89.** $(3b - 2)(2b - 3)$ **91.** $(11b - 7)(3b + 5)$
93. $(3y - 4)(6y - 5)$ **95.** $(3a + 7)(5a - 3)$ **97.** $(2y - 5)(4y - 3)$ **99.** $(4z - 5)(2z + 3)$ **101.** nonfactorable over
the integers **103.** $(2z - 5)(5z - 2)$ **105.** $(6z + 7)(6z + 5)$ **107.** $(3x - 2y)(x + y)$ **109.** $(3a - b)(a + 2b)$
111. $(4y - 3z)(y - 2z)$ **113.** $-(z - 7)(z + 4)$ **115.** $-(x - 1)(x + 8)$ **117.** $3(3x - 4)(x + 5)$
119. $4(2x - 3)(3x - 2)$ **121.** $a^2(7a - 1)(5a + 2)$ **123.** $5(3b - 2)(b - 7)$ **125.** $(3x - 5y)(x - 7y)$
127. $3(8y - 1)(9y + 1)$ **129.** $-(x - 1)(x + 21)$ **131.** Answers will vary. **133.** $x(x - 1)$ **135.** $(2y + 1)(y + 3)$
137. $(4y - 3)(y - 3)$ **139.** $-1, 1, -5, 5$ **141.** $-1, 1, -5, 5$ **143.** $-3, 3, -9, 9$

SECTION 5.4

1. $(x - 2)(x + 2)$ **3.** $(a - 9)(a + 9)$ **5.** $(y + 1)^2$ **7.** $(a - 1)^2$ **9.** $(2x + 1)(2x - 1)$ **11.** $(x^3 - 3)(x^3 + 3)$
13. nonfactorable over the integers **15.** $(x + y)^2$ **17.** $(2a + 1)^2$ **19.** $(3x - 1)(3x + 1)$ **21.** $(1 + 8x)(1 - 8x)$
23. nonfactorable over the integers **25.** $(3a + 1)^2$ **27.** $(b^2 - 4a)(b^2 + 4a)$ **29.** $(2a - 5)^2$ **31.** $(3a - 7)^2$
33. $(5z + y)(5z - y)$ **35.** $(ab - 5)(ab + 5)$ **37.** $(5x - 1)(5x + 1)$ **39.** $(2a - 3b)^2$ **41.** $(2y - 9z)^2$
43. $\left(\dfrac{1}{x} - 2\right)\left(\dfrac{1}{x} + 2\right)$ **45.** $(3ab - 1)^2$ **47.** $2(2y - 1)(2y + 1)$ **49.** $3a(a + 1)^2$ **51.** $(m^2 + 16)(m + 4)(m - 4)$
53. $(9x + 4)(x + 1)$ **55.** $4y^2(2y + 3)^2$ **57.** $(y^4 + 9)(y^2 - 3)(y^2 + 3)$ **59.** $(5 - 2p)^2$ **61.** $(4x - 3 - y)(4x - 3 + y)$
63. $(x - 2 - y)(x - 2 + y)$ **65.** $5(x + 1)(x - 1)$ **67.** $x(x + 2)^2$ **69.** $x^2(x + 7)(x - 5)$ **71.** $5(b + 3)(b + 12)$
73. nonfactorable over the integers **75.** $2y(x + 11)(x - 3)$ **77.** $x(x^2 - 6x - 5)$ **79.** $3(y^2 - 12)$
81. $(2a + 1)(10a + 1)$ **83.** $y^2(x - 8)(x + 1)$ **85.** $5(2a - 3b)(a + b)$ **87.** $-2(x - 5)(x + 5)$ **89.** $b^2(a - 5)^2$
91. $ab(4a + b)(3a - b)$ **93.** $3a(2a - 1)^2$ **95.** $3(81 + a^2)$ **97.** $2a(2a - 5)(3a - 4)$ **99.** $a(2a + 5)^2$
101. $3b(3a - 1)^2$ **103.** $-6(x + 4)(x - 2)$ **105.** $x^2(x + y)(x - y)$ **107.** $2a(3a + 2)^2$ **109.** $-b(3a - 2)(2a + 1)$
111. $2x^2(2x - 3)(x - 8)$ **113.** $x^2(x + 5)(x - 5)$ **115.** $(a^2 + 4)(a + 2)(a - 2)$ **117.** $-3y^2(2y + 5)(4y - 3)$
119. $2(x - 3)(2a - b)$ **121.** $(y + 1)(y - 1)(a - b)$ **123.** $(x - y)(a + b)(a - b)$ **125.** $-12, 12$ **127.** $-16, 16$
129. $-10, 10$ **131.** $(2n + 1)^2 - 1 = 4n(n + 1)$. Since n or $n + 1$ is an even number, $4n(n + 1)$ is divisible by 8.

SECTION 5.5

1. -3 and -2 **3.** 7 and 3 **5.** 0 and 5 **7.** 0 and 9 **9.** 0 and $-\dfrac{3}{2}$ **11.** 0 and $\dfrac{2}{3}$ **13.** -2 and 5

15. 9 and -9 **17.** $\frac{7}{2}$ and $-\frac{7}{2}$ **19.** $\frac{1}{3}$ and $-\frac{1}{3}$ **21.** -2 and -4 **23.** -7 and 2 **25.** $-\frac{1}{2}$ and 5

27. $-\frac{1}{3}$ and $-\frac{1}{2}$ **29.** 0 and 3 **31.** 0 and 7 **33.** -1 and -4 **35.** 2 and 3 **37.** $\frac{1}{2}$ and -4 **39.** $\frac{1}{3}$ and 4

41. 3 and 9 **43.** 9 and -2 **45.** -1 and -2 **47.** -9 and 5 **49.** -7 and 4 **51.** -2 and -3 **53.** -8 and 9

55. 1 and 4 **57.** -5 and 2 **59.** The number is 6. **61.** The numbers are 2 and 4. **63.** The numbers are 4 and 5.

65. The numbers are 3 and 7. **67.** There will be 12 consecutive natural numbers. **69.** There are 6 teams.

71. The object will hit the ground 3 s later. **73.** It will be 3.75 s later. **75.** The length is 15 in. and the width is 5 in.

77. The height of the triangle is 14 m. **79.** The dimensions of the type area are 4 in. by 7 in. **81.** The radius of the

original circle is 3.81 in. **83.** Answers will vary. **85.** 0 and 1 **87.** 2 and 32 **89.** -9 and -1 **91.** 1 and 18

CHAPTER REVIEW

1. $(b - 3)(b - 10)$ [5.2A] **2.** $(x - 3)(4x + 5)$ [5.1B] **3.** nonfactorable over the integers [5.3A]

4. $5x(x^2 + 2x + 7)$ [5.1A] **5.** $7y^3(2y^6 - 7y^3 + 1)$ [5.1A] **6.** $(y - 4)(y + 9)$ [5.2A] **7.** $(2x - 7)(3x - 4)$ [5.3A]

8. $3ab(4a + b)$ [5.1A] **9.** $(a^3 + 10)(a^3 - 10)$ [5.4A] **10.** $n^2(n + 1)(n - 3)$ [5.2B] **11.** $(6y - 1)(2y + 3)$ [5.3A]

12. $2b(3b - 4)(2b - 7)$ [5.4B] **13.** $(3y^2 + 5z)(3y^2 - 5z)$ [5.4A] **14.** $(c + 6)(c + 2)$ [5.2A]

15. $(6a - 5)(3a + 2)$ [5.3B] **16.** $\frac{1}{4}$ and -7 [5.5A] **17.** $4x(x - 6)(x + 1)$ [5.2B] **18.** $3(a + 2)(a - 7)$ [5.2B]

19. $(2a + 5)(a - 12)$ [5.3B] **20.** -3 and 7 [5.5A] **21.** $(3a - 5b)(7x + 2y)$ [5.1B] **22.** $(ab + 1)(ab - 1)$ [5.4A]

23. $(2x + 5)(5x + 2y)$ [5.1B] **24.** $5(x + 2)(x - 3)$ [5.2B] **25.** $3(x + 6)^2$ [5.4B] **26.** $(3x - 2)(x - 5)$ [5.3B]

27. The length is 100 yd. The width is 60 yd. [5.5B] **28.** The distance between the screen and the projector

is 20 ft. [5.5B] **29.** The width of the frame is 1.5 in. or $1\frac{1}{2}$ in. [5.5B] **30.** The length of a side is 20 ft. [5.5B]

CHAPTER TEST

1. $(b + 6)(a - 3)$ [5.1B] **2.** $2y^2(y + 1)(y - 8)$ [5.2B] **3.** $4(x + 4)(2x - 3)$ [5.3B] **4.** $(2x + 1)(3x + 8)$ [5.3A]

5. $(a - 3)(a - 16)$ [5.2A] **6.** $2x(3x^2 - 4x + 5)$ [5.1A] **7.** $(x + 5)(x - 3)$ [5.2A] **8.** $\frac{1}{2}$ and $-\frac{1}{2}$ [5.5A]

9. $5(x^2 - 9x - 3)$ [5.1A] **10.** $(p + 6)^2$ [5.4A] **11.** 3 and 5 [5.5A] **12.** $3(x + 2y)^2$ [5.4B]

13. $(b + 4)(b - 4)$ [5.4A] **14.** $3y^2(2x + 1)(x + 1)$ [5.3B] **15.** $(p + 2)(p + 3)$ [5.2A] **16.** $(x - 2)(a + b)$ [5.1B]

17. $(p + 1)(x - 1)$ [5.1B] **18.** $3(a + 5)(a - 5)$ [5.4B] **19.** nonfactorable over the integers [5.3A]

20. $(x + 3)(x - 12)$ [5.2A] **21.** $(2a - 3b)^2$ [5.4A] **22.** $(2x + 7y)(2x - 7y)$ [5.4A] **23.** $\frac{3}{2}$ and -7 [5.5A]

24. The two numbers are 3 and 7. [5.5B] **25.** The length is 15 cm. The width is 6 cm. [5.5B]

CUMULATIVE REVIEW

1. 7 [1.2B] **2.** 4 [1.5B] **3.** -7 [2.1A] **4.** $15x^2$ [2.2B] **5.** 12 [2.2D] **6.** $\frac{2}{3}$ [3.1C] **7.** $\frac{7}{4}$ [3.3A]

8. 3 [3.3B] **9.** 45 [3.1D] **10.** $9a^6b^4$ [4.2B] **11.** $x^3 - 3x^2 - 6x + 8$ [4.3B] **12.** $4x + 8 + \frac{21}{2x - 3}$ [4.5B]

13. $\frac{y^6}{x^8}$ [4.4A] **14.** $(a - b)(3 - x)$ [5.1B] **15.** $5xy^2(3 - 4y^2)$ [5.1A] **16.** $(x - 7y)(x + 2y)$ [5.2A]

17. $(p - 10)(p + 1)$ [5.2A] **18.** $3a(2a + 5)(3a + 2)$ [5.3B] **19.** $(6a - 7b)(6a + 7b)$ [5.4A]

20. $(2x + 7y)^2$ [5.4A] **21.** $(3x - 2)(3x + 7)$ [5.3A] **22.** $2(3x - 4y)^2$ [5.4B] **23.** $(x - 3)(3y - 2)$ [5.1B]

24. $\frac{2}{3}$ and -7 [5.5A] **25.** The pieces measure 4 ft and 6 ft. [3.4B] **26.** The discount rate is 40%. [3.2B]

27. The measure of angle a is 72° and the measure of angle b is 108°. [3.5B]   **28.** The distance to the resort was 168 mi. [3.6C]   **29.** The integers are 10, 12, and 14. [3.4A]   **30.** The length of the base is 12 in. [5.5B]

Answers to Chapter 6 Odd-Numbered Exercises

SECTION 6.1

1. $\dfrac{3}{4x}$ **3.** $\dfrac{1}{x+3}$ **5.** -1 **7.** $\dfrac{2}{3y}$ **9.** $-\dfrac{3}{4x}$ **11.** $\dfrac{a}{b}$ **13.** $-\dfrac{2}{x}$ **15.** $\dfrac{y-2}{y-3}$ **17.** $\dfrac{x+5}{x+4}$ **19.** $\dfrac{x+4}{x-3}$

21. $-\dfrac{x+2}{x+5}$ **23.** $\dfrac{2(x+2)}{x+3}$ **25.** $\dfrac{2x-1}{2x+3}$ **27.** $-\dfrac{x+7}{x+6}$ **29.** $\dfrac{35ab^2}{24x^2y}$ **31.** $\dfrac{4x^3y^3}{3a^2}$ **33.** $\dfrac{3}{4}$ **35.** ab^2

37. $\dfrac{x^2(x-1)}{y(x+3)}$ **39.** $\dfrac{y(x-1)}{x^2(x+10)}$ **41.** $-ab^2$ **43.** $\dfrac{x+5}{x+4}$ **45.** 1 **47.** $-\dfrac{n-10}{n-7}$ **49.** $\dfrac{x(x+2)}{2(x-1)}$ **51.** $-\dfrac{x+2}{x-6}$

53. $\dfrac{x+5}{x-12}$ **55.** $\dfrac{7a^3y^2}{40bx}$ **57.** $\dfrac{4}{3}$ **59.** $\dfrac{3a}{2}$ **61.** $\dfrac{x^2(x+4)}{y^2(x+2)}$ **63.** $\dfrac{x(x-2)}{y(x-6)}$ **65.** $-\dfrac{3by}{ax}$ **67.** $\dfrac{(x+6)(x-3)}{(x+7)(x-6)}$

69. 1 **71.** $-\dfrac{x+8}{x-4}$ **73.** $\dfrac{2n+1}{2n-3}$ **75.** Yes; for example 3.00000001. $3 + 10^{-8}$ **77.** $5, -5$ **79.** $\dfrac{4x}{3y}$ **81.** $-\dfrac{1}{y^3}$

83. $\dfrac{b+2}{b-5}$

SECTION 6.2

1. $24x^3y^2$ **3.** $30x^4y^2$ **5.** $8x^2(x+2)$ **7.** $6x^2y(x+4)$ **9.** $36x(x+2)^2$ **11.** $6(x+1)^2$
13. $(x-1)(x+2)(x+3)$ **15.** $(2x+3)^2(x-5)$ **17.** $(x-1)(x-2)$ **19.** $(x-3)(x+2)(x+4)$
21. $(x+4)(x+1)(x-7)$ **23.** $(x-6)(x+6)(x+4)$ **25.** $(x-10)(x-8)(x+3)$ **27.** $(3x-2)(x-3)(x+2)$
29. $(x+2)(x-3)$ **31.** $(x-5)(x+1)$ **33.** $(x-3)(x-2)(x-1)(x-6)$ **35.** $\dfrac{5}{ab^2}, \dfrac{6b}{ab^2}$ **37.** $\dfrac{15y^2}{18x^2y}, \dfrac{14x}{18x^2y}$

39. $\dfrac{ay+5a}{y^2(y+5)}, \dfrac{6y}{y^2(y+5)}$ **41.** $\dfrac{a^2y+7a^2}{y(y+7)^2}, \dfrac{ay}{y(y+7)^2}$ **43.** $\dfrac{b}{y(y-4)}, -\dfrac{b^2y}{y(y-4)}$ **45.** $-\dfrac{3y-21}{(y-7)^2}, \dfrac{2}{(y-7)^2}$

47. $\dfrac{2y^2}{y^2(y-3)}, \dfrac{3}{y^2(y-3)}$ **49.** $\dfrac{x^3+4x^2}{(2x-1)(x+4)}, \dfrac{2x^2+x-1}{(2x-1)(x+4)}$ **51.** $\dfrac{3x^2+15x}{(x-5)(x+5)}, \dfrac{4}{(x-5)(x+5)}$

53. $\dfrac{x^2-1}{(x+5)(x-3)(x+1)}, \dfrac{x^2-3x}{(x+5)(x-3)(x+1)}$ **55.** $\dfrac{800}{10^5}, \dfrac{9}{10^5}$ **57.** $\dfrac{x^3-x}{x^2-1}, \dfrac{x}{x^2-1}$

59. $\dfrac{3c^2-3cd}{3(6c+d)(c+d)(c-d)}, \dfrac{6cd+d^2}{3(6c+d)(c+d)(c-d)}$

SECTION 6.3

1. $\dfrac{11}{y^2}$ **3.** $-\dfrac{7}{x+4}$ **5.** $\dfrac{8x}{2x+3}$ **7.** $\dfrac{5x+7}{x-3}$ **9.** $\dfrac{2x-5}{x+9}$ **11.** $\dfrac{-3x-4}{2x+7}$ **13.** $\dfrac{1}{x+5}$ **15.** $\dfrac{1}{x-6}$ **17.** $\dfrac{3}{2y-1}$

19. $\dfrac{1}{x-5}$ **21.** $\dfrac{4y+5x}{xy}$ **23.** $\dfrac{19}{2x}$ **25.** $\dfrac{5}{12x}$ **27.** $\dfrac{19x-12}{6x^2}$ **29.** $\dfrac{52y-35x}{20xy}$ **31.** $\dfrac{13x+2}{15x}$ **33.** $\dfrac{7}{24}$

35. $\dfrac{x+90}{45x}$ **37.** $\dfrac{x^2+2x+2}{2x^2}$ **39.** $\dfrac{2x^2+3x-10}{4x^2}$ **41.** $\dfrac{-x^2-4x+4}{x+4}$ **43.** $\dfrac{4x+7}{x+1}$ **45.** $\dfrac{4x^2+9x+9}{24x^2}$

47. $\dfrac{3x-1-2xy-3y}{xy^2}$ **49.** $\dfrac{20x^2+28x-12xy+9y}{24x^2y^2}$ **51.** $\dfrac{9x^2-3x-2xy-10y}{18xy^2}$ **53.** $\dfrac{7x-23}{(x-3)(x-4)}$

55. $\dfrac{-y-33}{(y+6)(y-3)}$ **57.** $\dfrac{3x^2+20x-8}{(x-4)(x+6)}$ **59.** $\dfrac{3(4x^2+5x-5)}{(x+5)(2x+3)}$ **61.** $\dfrac{-4x+5}{x-6}$ **63.** $\dfrac{2(y+2)}{(y-4)(y+4)}$ **65.** $-\dfrac{4x}{(x+1)^2}$

67. $\dfrac{2x-1}{(1+x)(1-x)}$ **69.** $\dfrac{14}{(x-5)^2}$ **71.** $\dfrac{-2(x+7)}{(x-7)(x+6)}$ **73.** $\dfrac{x-4}{x-6}$ **75.** $\dfrac{2x+1}{x-1}$ **77.** $\dfrac{-3(x^2+8x+25)}{(x-3)(x+7)}$

79. $\dfrac{2}{3}, \dfrac{3}{4}, \dfrac{4}{5}, \dfrac{50}{51}, \dfrac{100}{101}, \dfrac{1000}{1001}$ **81.** 1

SECTION 6.4

1. $\dfrac{x}{x-3}$ **3.** $\dfrac{2}{3}$ **5.** $\dfrac{y+3}{y-4}$ **7.** $\dfrac{2(2x+13)}{5x+36}$ **9.** $\dfrac{x+2}{x+3}$ **11.** $\dfrac{x-6}{x+5}$ **13.** $\dfrac{-x+2}{x+1}$ **15.** $x-1$ **17.** $\dfrac{1}{2x-1}$

19. $\dfrac{x-3}{x+5}$ **21.** $\dfrac{x-7}{x-8}$ **23.** $\dfrac{2y-1}{2y+1}$ **25.** $\dfrac{x-2}{2x-5}$ **27.** $\dfrac{-x-1}{4x-3}$ **29.** $\dfrac{x+1}{2(5x-2)}$ **31.** $\dfrac{5}{3}$ **33.** $-\dfrac{1}{x-1}$

35. $\dfrac{y+4}{2(y-2)}$ **37.** $\dfrac{x+1}{x-1}$ **39.** $\dfrac{y^2+x^2}{xy}$

SECTION 6.5

1. 3 **3.** 1 **5.** 9 **7.** 1 **9.** $\dfrac{1}{4}$ **11.** 1 **13.** -3 **15.** $\dfrac{1}{2}$ **17.** 8 **19.** 5 **21.** -1 **23.** 5

25. no solution **27.** 2 and 4 **29.** 4 and $-\dfrac{3}{2}$ **31.** 3 **33.** 4 **35.** 0 **37.** $-\dfrac{2}{5}$ **39.** 0 and $-\dfrac{2}{3}$

SECTION 6.6

1. 9 **3.** 12 **5.** 7 **7.** 6 **9.** 1 **11.** -6 **13.** 4 **15.** $-\dfrac{2}{3}$ **17.** There will be 20,000 voters voting in favor.

19. The two cities are 175 mi apart. **21.** The sales tax will be $97.50 higher. **23.** The recommended area of the window is 40 ft^2. **25.** There are an estimated 75 elk in the preserve. **27.** The length of side AC is 6.7 cm. **29.** The height of triangle ABC is 2.9 m. **31.** The perimeter of triangle DEF is 22.5 ft. **33.** The area of triangle ABC is 48 m^2. **35.** The length of BC is 6.25 cm. **37.** The length of DA is 6 in. **39.** The length of OP is 13 cm. **41.** The width of the river is 35 m. **43.** The first person's share of the winnings is $1.25 million. **45.** The basketball player made 210 shots.

SECTION 6.7

1. $y=-3x+10$ **3.** $y=4x-3$ **5.** $y=-\dfrac{3}{2}x+3$ **7.** $y=\dfrac{2}{5}x-2$ **9.** $y=-\dfrac{2}{7}x+2$ **11.** $y=-\dfrac{1}{3}x+2$

13. $y=\dfrac{2}{9}x-2$ **15.** $y=2x+5$ **17.** $x=-6y+10$ **19.** $x=\dfrac{1}{2}y+3$ **21.** $x=-\dfrac{3}{4}y+3$ **23.** $x=4y+3$

25. $t=\dfrac{d}{r}$ **27.** $T=\dfrac{PV}{nR}$ **29.** $l=\dfrac{P-2w}{2}$ **31.** $b_1=\dfrac{2A-hb_2}{h}$ **33.** $h=\dfrac{3V}{A}$ **35.** $S=C-Rt$ **37.** $P=\dfrac{A}{1+rt}$

39. $w=\dfrac{A}{S+1}$ **41a.** $S=\dfrac{F+BV}{B}$ **b.** The selling price per unit to break even is $180. **c.** The selling price per unit to break even is $75.

SECTION 6.8

1. It would take 2 h with both sprinklers working. **3.** It would take both skiploaders 3 h working together. **5.** It would take 30 h with both computers working. **7.** It would take 30 min with both air conditioners working. **9.** It would take the second pipeline 90 min to fill the tank. **11.** It would take the apprentice 15 h to construct the wall. **13.** It would take the second technician 3 h to complete the wiring. **15.** It would have taken one welder 40 h to complete the welds. **17.** It would take one machine 28 h working alone. **19.** The rate through the congested traffic is 20 mph. **21.** The rate of the jogger is 8 mph, and the rate of the cyclist is 20 mph. **23.** The rate of the jet is 360 mph. **25.** The rate of the motorcycle is 48 mph. **27.** The rate of the car is 48 mph. **29.** The rate of the wind is 20 mph. **31.** The rate of the gulf current is 6 mph. **33.** The rate of the trucker for the first 330 mi is 55 mph. **35.** The less-experienced helper can complete the job in 30 h. **37.** The bus usually travels 60 mph.

CHAPTER REVIEW

1. $\dfrac{b^3y}{10ax}$ [6.1C]   **2.** $\dfrac{7x + 22}{60x}$ [6.3B]   **3.** $\dfrac{x - 2}{3x - 10}$ [6.4A]   **4.** $-\dfrac{x + 6}{x + 3}$ [6.1A]   **5.** $\dfrac{2x^4}{3y^7}$ [6.1A]

6. 62 [6.6A]   **7.** $\dfrac{(3y - 2)^2}{(y - 1)(y - 2)}$ [6.1C]   **8.** $\dfrac{by^3}{6ax^2}$ [6.1B]   **9.** $\dfrac{x}{x - 7}$ [6.4A]

10. $\dfrac{3x^2 - x}{(2x + 3)(6x - 1)(3x - 1)}, \dfrac{24x^3 - 4x^2}{(2x + 3)(6x - 1)(3x - 1)}$ [6.2B]   **11.** $a = \dfrac{T - 2bc}{2b + 2c}$ [6.7A]   **12.** 2 [6.5A]

13. $c = \dfrac{100m}{i}$ [6.7A]   **14.** The equation has no solution. [6.5A]   **15.** $\dfrac{1}{x^2}$ [6.1C]   **16.** $\dfrac{2y - 3}{5y - 7}$ [6.3B]

17. $\dfrac{1}{x + 3}$ [6.3A]   **18.** $(5x - 3)(2x - 1)(4x - 1)$ [6.2A]   **19.** $y = -\dfrac{4}{9}x + 2$ [6.7A]   **20.** $\dfrac{8x + 5}{3x - 4}$ [6.1B]

21. 5 [6.5A]   **22.** $\dfrac{3x - 1}{x - 5}$ [6.3B]   **23.** 10 [6.6A]   **24.** 12 [6.6A]   **25.** The length of QO is 15 cm. [6.6C]

26. It would take 6 h to fill the pool using both hoses. [6.8A]   **27.** The rate of the car is 45 mph. [6.8B]

28. The rate of the wind is 20 mph. [6.8B]   **29.** The pitcher's ERA is 1.35. [6.6B]

CHAPTER TEST

1. $\dfrac{x^2 - 4x + 5}{(x - 2)(x + 3)}$ [6.3B]   **2.** -1 [6.6A]   **3.** $\dfrac{(x - 5)(2x - 1)}{(x + 3)(2x + 5)}$ [6.1B]   **4.** $\dfrac{2x^3}{3y^3}$ [6.1A]   **5.** $t = \dfrac{d - s}{r}$ [6.7A]

6. 2 [6.5A]   **7.** $-\dfrac{x + 5}{x + 1}$ [6.1A]   **8.** $3(2x - 1)(x + 1)$ [6.2A]   **9.** $\dfrac{5}{(2x - 1)(3x + 1)}$ [6.3B]   **10.** $\dfrac{x + 5}{x + 4}$ [6.1C]

11. $\dfrac{x - 3}{x - 2}$ [6.4A]   **12.** $\dfrac{3x + 6}{x(x - 2)(x + 2)}, \dfrac{x^2}{x(x - 2)(x + 2)}$ [6.2B]   **13.** $\dfrac{2}{x + 5}$ [6.3A]   **14.** $y = \dfrac{3}{8}x - 2$ [6.7A]

15. The equation has no solution. [6.5A]   **16.** $\dfrac{x + 1}{x^3(x - 2)}$ [6.1B]   **17.** The length of CE is 12.8 ft. [6.6C]   **18.** Two

additional pounds of salt are required. [6.6B]   **19.** It would take 4 h to fill the pool with both pipes turned on. [6.8A]

20. The rate of the wind is 20 mph. [6.8B]   **21.** 54 sprinklers are required. [6.6B]

CUMULATIVE REVIEW

1. $\dfrac{31}{30}$ [1.5B]   **2.** 21 [2.1A]   **3.** $5x - 2y$ [2.2A]   **4.** $-8x + 26$ [2.2D]   **5.** $-\dfrac{9}{2}$ [3.2A]   **6.** -12 [3.3B]

7. 10 [3.1D]   **8.** a^3b^7 [4.2A]   **9.** $a^2 + ab - 12b^2$ [4.3C]   **10.** $3b^3 - b + 2$ [4.5A]   **11.** $x^2 + 2x + 4$ [4.5B]

12. $(4x + 1)(3x - 1)$ [5.3A]   **13.** $(y - 6)(y - 1)$ [5.2A]   **14.** $a(2a - 3)(a + 5)$ [5.3B]

15. $4(b - 5)(b + 5)$ [5.4B]   **16.** -3 and $\dfrac{5}{2}$ [5.5A]   **17.** $\dfrac{2x^3}{3y^5}$ [6.1A]   **18.** $-\dfrac{x - 2}{x + 5}$ [6.1A]   **19.** 1 [6.1C]

20. $\dfrac{3}{(2x - 1)(x + 1)}$ [6.3B]   **21.** $\dfrac{x + 3}{x + 5}$ [6.4A]   **22.** 4 [6.5A]   **23.** 3 [6.6A]   **24.** $t = \dfrac{f - v}{a}$ [6.7A]

25. $5x - 13 = -8; 1$ [3.4A]   **26.** The 120-gram alloy is 70% silver. [3.6B]   **27.** The height is 6 in. and the base is

10 in. [5.5B]   **28.** A policy of $5000 would cost $80. [6.6B]   **29.** Working together, it would take the pipes 6 min to

fill the tank. [6.8A]   **30.** The rate of the current is 2 mph. [6.8B]

Answers to Chapter 7 Odd-Numbered Exercises

SECTION 7.1

1. 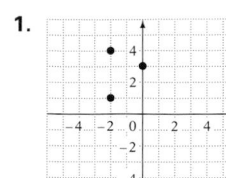   **3.** 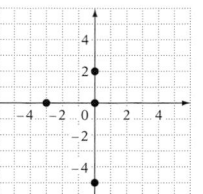   **5.**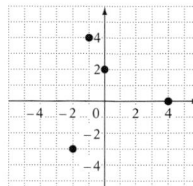

7. *A* is (2, 3), *B* is (4, 0), *C* is (−4, 1), and *D* is (−2, −2).   **9.** *A* is (−2, 5), *B* is (3, 4), *C* is (0, 0), and *D* is (−3, −2).

11a. The abscissa of point *A* is 2. The abscissa of point *C* is −4.   **b.** The ordinate of point *B* is 1. The ordinate of point

D is −3.   **13.** yes   **15.** no   **17.** no   **19.** no   **21.** 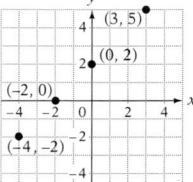   **23.**

25. 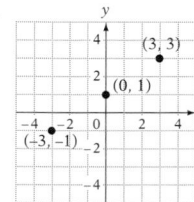   **27.** 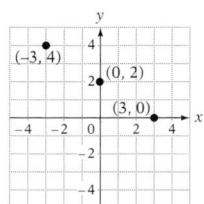   **29.** 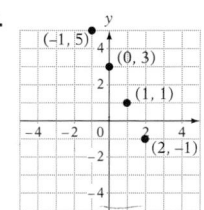   **31.**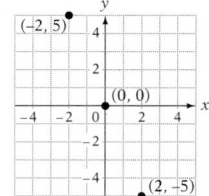

33. {(1, L), (0, L), (5, W), (8, W), (1, W), (3, W)}; no   **35.** {(197, 125), (205, 122), (257, 498), (226, 108), (205, 150)}; no

37. yes   **39.** no   **41.** yes   **43.** 8   **45.** 9   **47.** 2   **49.** −1   **51.** 22   **53.** $-\dfrac{3}{2}$ **55.** −7

57. The ordered pairs are being graphed in reverse order.   **59.** no

SECTION 7.2

1. 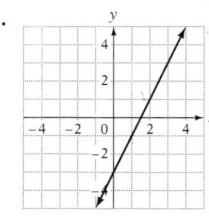   **3.** 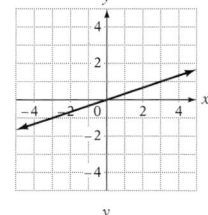   **5.** 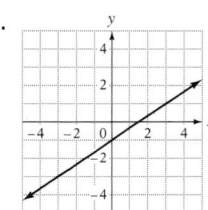   **7.**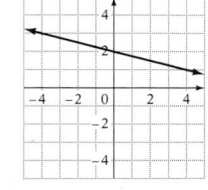

9. 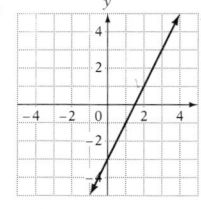   **11.** 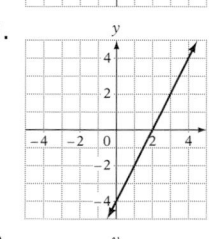   **13.** 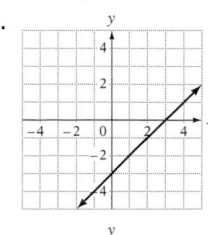   **15.**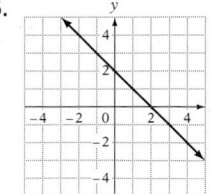

17. 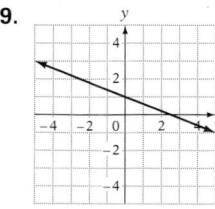   **19.** 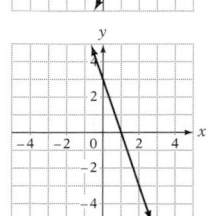   **21.** 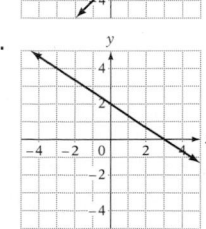   **23.**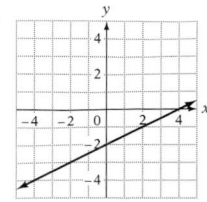

25.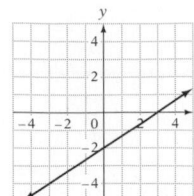

27.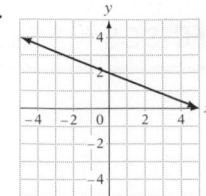

29.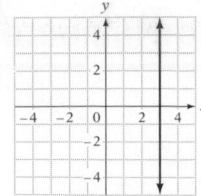

31.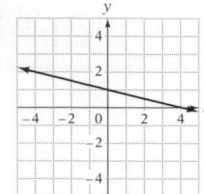

33.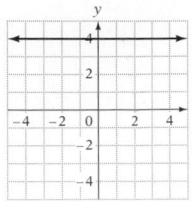

35.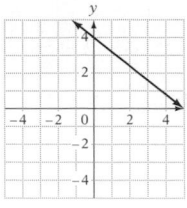

37. After flying for 3 min, the helicopter is 3.5 mi away from the victims.

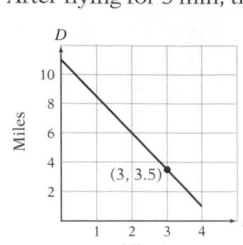

39. A dog 6 years old is equivalent in age to a human 40 years old.   **41.** increases; 3 units; 3 units

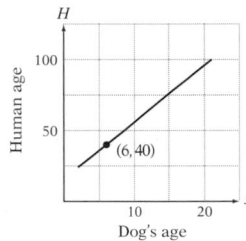

43. They are parallel lines.

SECTION 7.3

1. (3, 0), (0, −3)   **3.** (2, 0), (0, −6)   **5.** (10, 0), (0, −2)   **7.** (−4, 0), (0, 12)   **9.** (0, 0), (0, 0)   **11.** (6, 0), (0, 3)

13.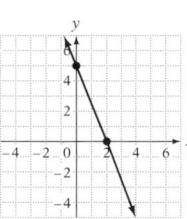

15.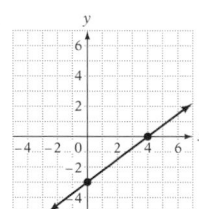

17.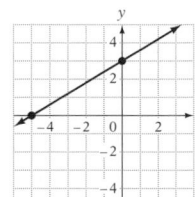

19. −2   **21.** $\frac{1}{3}$ **23.** $-\frac{5}{2}$ **25.** $-\frac{1}{2}$

27. −1   **29.** undefined   **31.** zero   **33.** $-\frac{1}{3}$ **35.** zero   **37.** $m = 0.8$ After being connected, each minute of a

transatlantic phone call costs $.80.   **39.** $m = -0.4$ The percent of the population that can afford a median-priced home
has decreased by 0.4% per year.

41.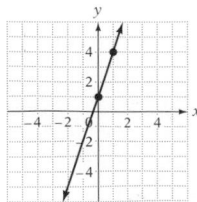

43.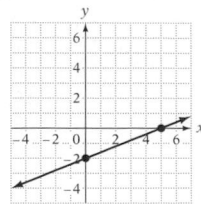

45.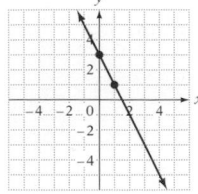

47.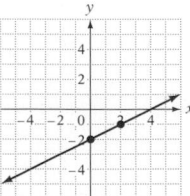

49.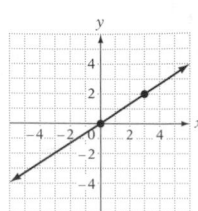

51.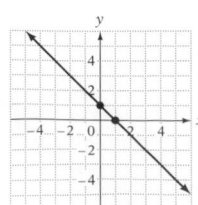

53.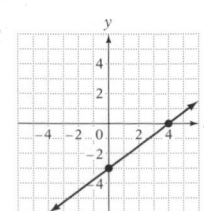

55.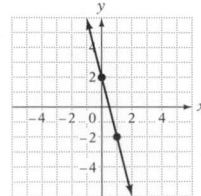

57. yes   **59.** $6\% = 0.06 = \dfrac{6}{100}$. A 6% grade means that the average slope of the road is $\dfrac{6}{100}$.

SECTION 7.4

1. $y = 2x + 2$ **3.** $y = -3x - 1$ **5.** $y = \dfrac{1}{3}x$ **7.** $y = \dfrac{3}{4}x - 5$ **9.** $y = -\dfrac{3}{5}x$ **11.** $y = \dfrac{1}{4}x + \dfrac{5}{2}$ **13.** $y = 2x - 3$

15. $y = -2x - 3$ **17.** $y = \dfrac{2}{3}x$ **19.** $y = \dfrac{1}{2}x + 2$ **21.** $y = -\dfrac{3}{4}x - 2$ **23.** $y = \dfrac{3}{4}x + \dfrac{5}{2}$

25. The number of hours of basic cable watched per person increases by 12.9 h per year.

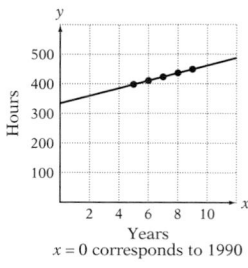

27. The number of visitors is decreasing by 2.1 million per year.

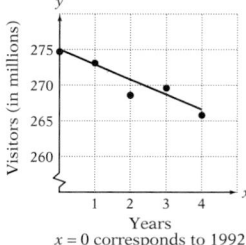

29. no   **31.** yes   **33.** $-\dfrac{3}{2}$ **35.** $n = -5$ **37.** $y = -\dfrac{2}{3}x + \dfrac{5}{3}$ **39.** The restriction is required to prevent division by 0.

CHAPTER REVIEW

1. a.

2.

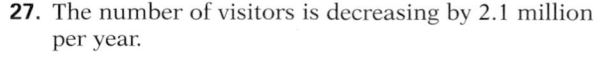   [7.1B]

3. $y = -\dfrac{8}{3}x + \dfrac{1}{3}$ [7.4B]

b. The abscissa of point A is -2.
c. The ordinate of point B is -4.   [7.1A]

4. $y = -\dfrac{5}{2}x + 16$ [7.4A]   **5.**

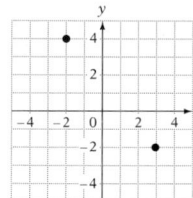   [7.2A]

6.

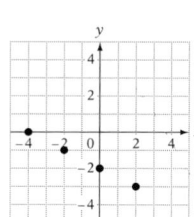   [7.2B]

7. $y = \dfrac{2}{3}x + 6$ [7.4A]

8. -1 [7.1D]   **9.** $y = -\dfrac{2}{3}x + \dfrac{11}{3}$ [7.4B]   **10.** yes   [7.1C]   **11.** $\dfrac{7}{11}$ [7.3B]   **12.** $(8, 0), (0, -12)$ [7.3A]

13. 0 [7.3B]   **14.**

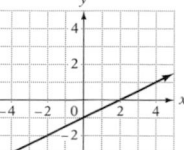   [7.3C]

15.

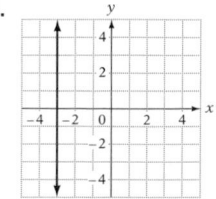   [7.2B]

16.

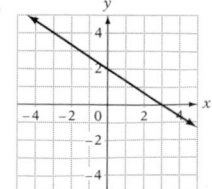   [7.3C]

17. 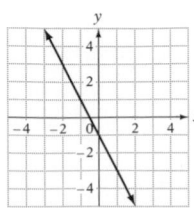 [7.2A]

18. 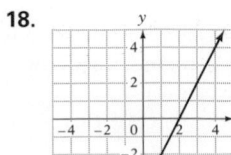 [7.3C]

19. 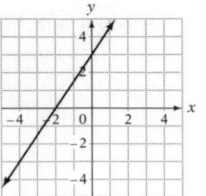 [7.2B]

20. {(55, 95), (57,101), (53, 94), (57, 98), (60, 100), (61, 105), (58, 97), (54, 95)}; no [7.1C]

21. The cost of 50 min of access time for one month is $97.50.

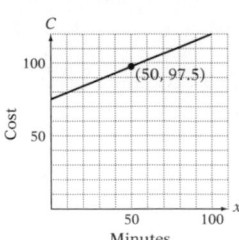 [7.2C]

22. The amount spent on health care is increasing $3.85 billion per year.

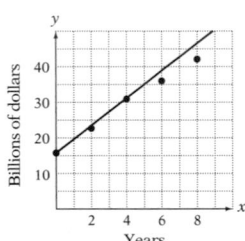 [7.4C]

CHAPTER TEST

1. (3, −3) [7.1B]　　**2.** 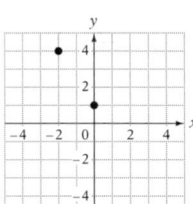　　**3.** yes [7.1C]　　**4.** $f(2) = 6$ [7.1D]　　**5.** $f(−1) = 3$ [7.1D]

[7.1B]

6. {(3.5, 25), (4.0, 30), (5.2, 45), (5.0, 38), (4.0, 42), (6.3, 12), (5.4, 34)}; no [7.1C]

7. 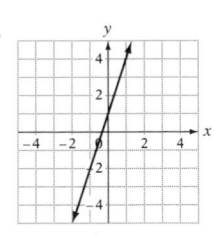 [7.2A]

8. 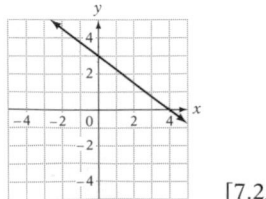 [7.2A]

9. 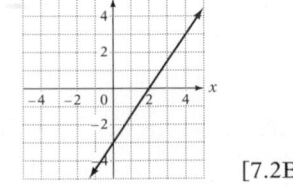 [7.2B]

10. 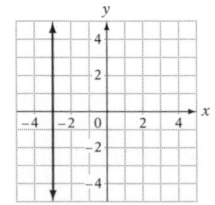 [7.2B]

11. 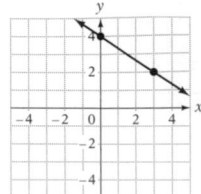 [7.3C]

12. 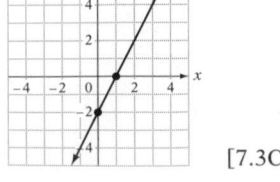 [7.3C]

13. After 1 s, the speed of the ball is 96 ft/s. [7.2C]

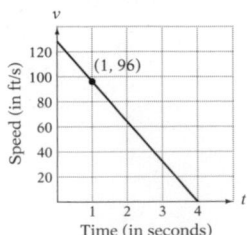

14. The slope of the line is 1.5 thousand. The tuition is increasing by $1500 per year. [7.3B]

15. 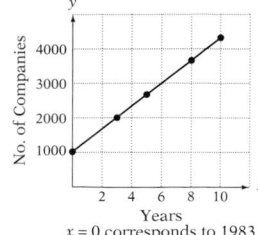 The number of mutual fund companies is increasing by 330 each year. [7.4C]

16. $(2, 0), (0, -3)$ [7.3A]   **17.** $(-2, 0), (0, 1)$ [7.3A]   **18.** 2 [7.3B]   **19.** zero [7.3B]   **20.** undefined [7.3B]

21. $-\dfrac{2}{3}$ [7.3B]   **22.** $y = 3x - 1$ [7.4A]   **23.** $y = \dfrac{2}{3}x + 3$ [7.4A]   **24.** $y = -\dfrac{5}{8}x - \dfrac{7}{8}$ [7.4B]

25. $y = -\dfrac{2}{7}x - \dfrac{4}{7}$ [7.4B]

CUMULATIVE REVIEW

1. -12 [1.5B]   **2.** $-\dfrac{5}{8}$ [2.1A]   **3.** $f(-2) = -\dfrac{2}{3}$ [7.1D]   **4.** $\dfrac{3}{2}$ [3.2A]   **5.** $\dfrac{19}{18}$ [3.3B]   **6.** $\dfrac{1}{15}$ [1.4B]

7. $-32x^8y^7$ [4.2B]   **8.** $-3x^2$ [4.4A]   **9.** $x + 3$ [4.5B]   **10.** $5(x + 2)(x + 1)$ [5.2B]   **11.** $(a + 2)(x + y)$ [5.1A]

12. 4 and -2 [5.5A]   **13.** $\dfrac{x^3(x + 3)}{y(x + 2)}$ [6.1B]   **14.** $\dfrac{3}{x + 8}$ [6.3A]   **15.** 2 [6.5A]   **16.** $y = \dfrac{4}{5}x - 3$ [6.7A]

17. $(-2, -5)$ [7.1B]   **18.** zero [7.3B]   **19.** $y = \dfrac{1}{2}x - 2$ [6.7A]   **20.** $y = -3x + 2$ [7.4A]

21. $y = 2x + 2$ [7.4A]   **22.** $y = \dfrac{2}{3}x - 3$ [7.4A]   **23.** The sale price is $62.30. [3.2B]   **24.** The measure of the first angle is 46°, the measure of the second angle is 43°, and the measure of the third angle is 91°. [3.5C]   **25.** The value of the home is $110,000. [6.6B]   **26.** It would take $3\dfrac{3}{4}$ h with both the electrician and the apprentice working. [6.8A]

27. 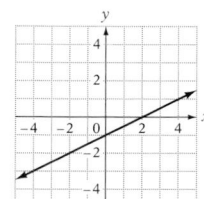 [7.2A]   **28.** 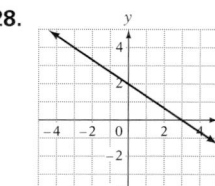 [7.3C]

Answers to Chapter 8 Odd-Numbered Exercises

SECTION 8.1

1. yes   **3.** yes   **5.** no   **7.** no   **9.** no   **11.** yes   **13.** yes   **15.** yes   **17.** no

19. 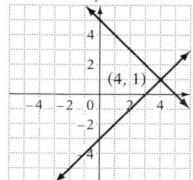   **21.** 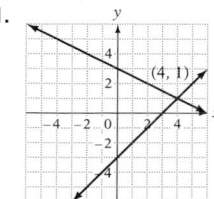   **23.** 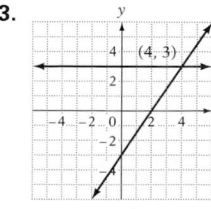   **25.**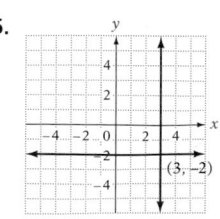

27. 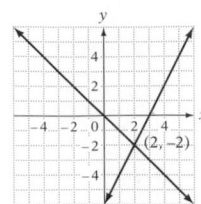 **29.** 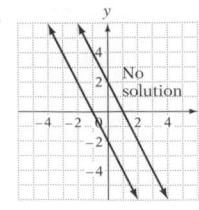 **31.** 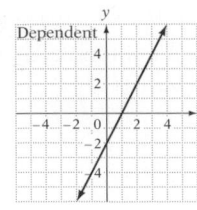 **33.**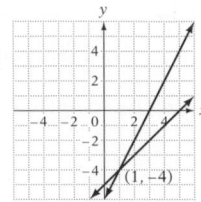

35. 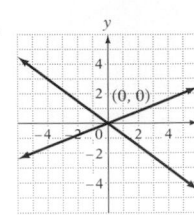 **37.** 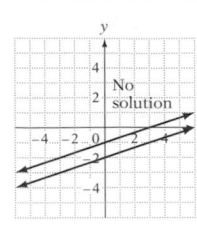 **39a.** sometimes true **b.** always true **c.** never true **d.** always true

41. The graphs are parallel if the system of equations are inconsistent.   **43.** Answers will vary.

SECTION 8.2

1. $(2, 1)$ **3.** $(4, 1)$ **5.** $(-1, 1)$ **7.** The system of equations is inconsistent and has no solution.   **9.** The system of equations is inconsistent and has no solution.   **11.** $\left(-\dfrac{3}{4}, -\dfrac{3}{4}\right)$ **13.** $(1, 1)$ **15.** $(2, 0)$ **17.** $(1, -2)$ **19.** $(0, 0)$

21. The system of equations is dependent. The solutions are the ordered pairs that satisfy the equation $2x - y = 2$.
23. $(-4, -2)$ **25.** $(10, 31)$ **27.** $(3, -10)$ **29.** $(-22, -5)$ **31.** \$1900 should be invested at 5% and \$1600 should be invested at 7.5%.   **33.** \$3600 must be invested at 6% and \$2400 must be invested at 9%.   **35.** \$4400 should be invested at 8% and \$1600 should be invested at 11%.   **37.** There was \$21,000 invested at 6.5%.   **39.** There was \$12,000 invested at 8% and \$8000 invested at 7%.   **41.** There was \$3750 invested in the second trust deed.   **43.** 1
45. Answers will vary.   **47.** The assertion is not correct. The solution is $(0, 2)$.   **49.** The research consultant invested \$45,000.   **51.** The simple interest earned was \$400. The compounded monthly interest earned was \$415. The compounded daily interest earned was \$416.39.

SECTION 8.3

1. $(5, -1)$ **3.** $(1, 3)$ **5.** $(1, 1)$ **7.** $(3, -2)$ **9.** The system is dependent. The solutions are the ordered pairs that satisfy the equation $2x - y = 1$.   **11.** $(3, 1)$ **13.** The system is dependent. The solutions are the ordered pairs that satisfy the equation $2x - 3y = 1$.   **15.** $\left(-\dfrac{13}{17}, -\dfrac{24}{17}\right)$ **17.** $(2, 0)$ **19.** $(0, 0)$ **21.** $(5, -2)$ **23.** $\left(\dfrac{32}{19}, -\dfrac{9}{19}\right)$
25. $(3, 4)$ **27.** $(1, -1)$ **29.** The system is dependent. The solutions are the ordered pairs that satisfy the equation $5x + 15y = 20$.   **31.** $(3, 1)$ **33.** $(-1, 2)$ **35.** $(1, 1)$ **37.** Answers will vary.   **39.** $A = 3; B = -1$

41a. All real numbers, $k \neq 1$ **b.** All real numbers, $k \neq \dfrac{3}{2}$ **c.** All real numbers, $k \neq 4$

SECTION 8.4

1. The rate of the whale in calm water is 35 mph. The rate of the current is 5 mph.   **3.** The rate of the rowing in calm water is 14 km/h. The rate of the current is 6 km/h.   **5.** The rate of the jet in calm air is 525 mph. The rate of the wind is 35 mph.   **7.** The rate of the helicopter in calm air is 225 mph. The rate of the wind is 45 mph.   **9.** The rate of the canoeist in calm water is 6 mph. The rate of the current is 1 mph.   **11.** The wheat flour cost \$.65 per pound, and the rye flour cost \$.70 per pound.   **13.** The prime time was \$.22 per minute, and the nonprime time was \$.15 per minute.
15. A submarine sandwich costs \$4.25, and an order of french fries costs \$.90.   **17.** There are 1 nickel and 2 dimes or 3 nickels and 1 dime.   **19.** There were 12.5 acres of good land and 87.5 acres of bad land.

CHAPTER REVIEW

1. yes [8.1A]   **2.** no [8.1A]   **3.** 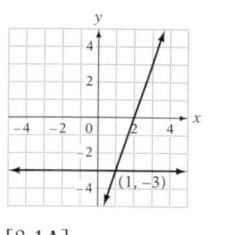   **4.** 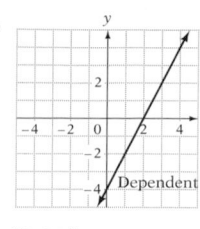   **5.**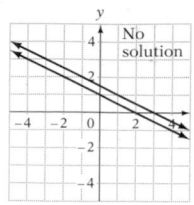

[8.1A]   [8.1A]   [8.1A]

6. $(-1, 1)$ [8.2A]   **7.** $(1, 6)$ [8.2A]   **8.** $(-3, 1)$ [8.3A]   **9.** $\left(-\dfrac{5}{6}, \dfrac{1}{2}\right)$ [8.3A]   **10.** no solution [8.2A]

11. $(1, 6)$ [8.2A]   **12.** $(1, -5)$ [8.3A]   **13.** no solution [8.3A]   **14.** The system is dependent. The solutions are the ordered pairs that satisfy the equation $y = -\dfrac{4}{3}x + 4$. [8.2A]   **15.** $(-1, -3)$ [8.2A]   **16.** The system is dependent. The solutions are the ordered pairs that satisfy the equation $3x + y = -2$. [8.3A]   **17.** $\left(\dfrac{2}{3}, -\dfrac{1}{6}\right)$ [8.3A]   **18.** The rate of the sculling team in calm water was 9 mph; the rate of the current was 3 mph. [8.4A]   **19.** There were 1300 shares at $6 per share and 200 shares at $25 per share. [8.4B]   **20.** The rate of the flight crew in calm air was 125 km/h; the rate of the wind was 15 km/h. [8.4A]   **21.** The rate of the plane in calm air was 105 mph; the rate of the wind was 15 mph. [8.4A]   **22.** The number of ads requiring $.25 was 130; the number of ads requiring $.45 was 60. [8.4B]   **23.** There was $7000 invested at 7% and $5000 invested at 8.5%. [8.2B]   **24.** There were 350 bushels of lentils and 200 bushels of corn. [8.4B]   **25.** There was $165,000 invested at 5.4% and $135,000 invested at 6.6%. [8.2B]

CHAPTER TEST

1. yes [8.1A]   **2.** yes [8.1A]   **3.**   **4.** $(3, 1)$ [8.2A]   **5.** $(1, -1)$ [8.2A]

[8.1A]

6. $(2, -1)$ [8.2A]   **7.** $\left(\dfrac{22}{7}, -\dfrac{5}{7}\right)$ [8.2A]   **8.** The system is inconsistent and has no solution. [8.2A]

9. $(2, 1)$ [8.3A]   **10.** $\left(\dfrac{1}{2}, -1\right)$ [8.3A]   **11.** The system of equations is dependent. The solutions are the ordered pairs that satisfy the equation $x + 2y = 8$. [8.3A]   **12.** $(2, -1)$ [8.3A]   **13.** $(1, -2)$ [8.3A]   **14.** The rate of the plane in calm air is 100 mph. The rate of the wind is 20 mph. [8.4A]   **15.** The price of a reserved-seat ticket is $10. The price of a general-admission ticket is $6. [8.4B]   **16.** There was $15,200 invested at 6.4% and $12,800 invested at 7.6%. [8.2B]

CUMULATIVE REVIEW

1. $\dfrac{3}{2}$ [2.1A]   **2.** $-\dfrac{3}{2}$ [3.1C]   **3.** $f(2) = 7$ [7.1D]   **4.** $-6a^3 + 13a^2 - 9a + 2$ [4.3B]   **5.** $-2x^5y^2$ [4.4A]

6. $2b - 1 + \dfrac{1}{2b - 3}$ [4.5B]   **7.** $-\dfrac{4y}{x^3}$ [4.4A]   **8.** $4y^2(xy - 4)(xy + 4)$ [5.4B]   **9.** 4 and -1 [5.5A]

10. $x - 2$ [6.1C]   **11.** $\dfrac{x^2 + 2}{(x - 1)(x + 2)}$ [6.3B]   **12.** $\dfrac{x - 3}{x + 1}$ [6.4A]   **13.** $-\dfrac{1}{5}$ [6.5A]   **14.** $r = \dfrac{A - P}{Pt}$ [6.7A]

15. The x-intercept is $(6, 0)$, and the y-intercept is $(0, -4)$. [7.3A]   **16.** $-\dfrac{7}{5}$ [7.3B]   **17.** $y = -\dfrac{3}{2}x$ [7.4A]

18. yes [8.1A]   **19.** $(-6, 1)$ [8.2A]   **20.** $(4, -3)$ [8.3A]   **21.** The amount invested at 9.6% is $3750. The amount invested at 7.2% is $5000.   [8.2B]   **22.** The rate of the freight train is 48 mph. The rate of the passenger train is 56 mph.   [3.6C]   **23.** A side of the original square measures 8 in.   [5.5B]   **24.** The rate of the wind is 30 mph.   [8.4A]

25.

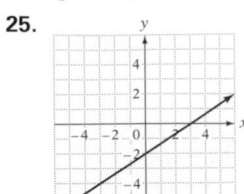

26.

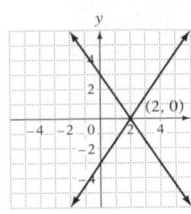

[7.2B]   [8.1A]

27. The rate of the boat in calm water is 14 mph.   [8.4A]   **28.** 35.3% of the mixture is sugar.   [3.6A]

Answers to Chapter 9 Odd-Numbered Exercises

SECTION 9.1

1. $A = \{16, 17, 18, 19, 20, 21\}$ **3.** $A = \{9, 11, 13, 15, 17\}$ **5.** $A = \{b, c\}$ **7.** $A \cup B = \{3, 4, 5, 6\}$
9. $A \cup B = \{-10, -9, -8, 8, 9, 10\}$ **11.** $A \cup B = \{a, b, c, d, e, f\}$ **13.** $A \cup B = \{1, 3, 7, 9, 11, 13\}$ **15.** $A \cap B = \{4, 5\}$
17. $A \cap B = \varnothing$ **19.** $A \cap B = \{c, d, e\}$ **21.** $\{x \mid x > -5, x \in \text{negative integers}\}$ **23.** $\{x \mid x > 30, x \in \text{integers}\}$
25. $\{x \mid x > 5, x \in \text{even integers}\}$ **27.** $\{x \mid x > 8, x \in \text{real numbers}\}$ **29.** ⊢+++++++⊕+++⊢ $-5\ -4\ -3\ -2\ -1\ 0\ 1\ 2\ 3\ 4\ 5$
31. $-5\ -4\ -3\ -2\ -1\ 0\ 1\ 2\ 3\ 4\ 5$ **33.** $-5\ -4\ -3\ -2\ -1\ 0\ 1\ 2\ 3\ 4\ 5$ **35.** $-5\ -4\ -3\ -2\ -1\ 0\ 1\ 2\ 3\ 4\ 5$
37. $-5\ -4\ -3\ -2\ -1\ 0\ 1\ 2\ 3\ 4\ 5$ **39.** Answers will vary.   **41a.** never true   **b.** always true   **c.** always true
43a. yes   **b.** yes

SECTION 9.2

1. $x < 2$ $-5\ -4\ -3\ -2\ -1\ 0\ 1\ 2\ 3\ 4\ 5$ **3.** $x > 3$ $-5\ -4\ -3\ -2\ -1\ 0\ 1\ 2\ 3\ 4\ 5$
5. $n \geq 3$ $-5\ -4\ -3\ -2\ -1\ 0\ 1\ 2\ 3\ 4\ 5$ **7.** $x \leq -4$ $-5\ -4\ -3\ -2\ -1\ 0\ 1\ 2\ 3\ 4\ 5$ **9.** $y \geq -9$ **11.** $x < 12$
13. $x \geq 5$ **15.** $x < -11$ **17.** $x \leq 10$ **19.** $x \geq -6$ **21.** $x > 2$ **23.** $d < -\frac{1}{6}$ **25.** $x \geq -\frac{31}{24}$ **27.** $x < \frac{5}{8}$
29. $x < \frac{5}{4}$ **31.** $x > \frac{5}{24}$ **33.** $x < -3.8$ **35.** $x \leq -1.2$ **37.** $x < 5.6$ **39.** $-5\ -4\ -3\ -2\ -1\ 0\ 1\ 2\ 3\ 4\ 5$ $x < 4$
41. $-5\ -4\ -3\ -2\ -1\ 0\ 1\ 2\ 3\ 4\ 5$ $y \geq 3$ **43.** $-5\ -4\ -3\ -2\ -1\ 0\ 1\ 2\ 3\ 4\ 5$ $x \leq 1$
45. $-5\ -4\ -3\ -2\ -1\ 0\ 1\ 2\ 3\ 4\ 5$ $x < -1$ **47.** $-5\ -4\ -3\ -2\ -1\ 0\ 1\ 2\ 3\ 4\ 5$ $b < -4$ **49.** $y \leq 0$ **51.** $x > \frac{2}{7}$
53. $x \leq -\frac{5}{2}$ **55.** $x < 16$ **57.** $x \geq 16$ **59.** $x \geq -14$ **61.** $x \leq 21$ **63.** $x > 0$ **65.** $x \leq -\frac{12}{7}$ **67.** $x > \frac{2}{3}$
69. $x \leq \frac{2}{3}$ **71.** $x \leq 2.3$ **73.** $x < -3.2$ **75.** $x \leq 5$ **77.** The team must win at least 11 more games to qualify for the tournament.   **79.** The organization must collect more than 440 lb of aluminum cans to collect the bonus.
81. The person needs at least 50 mg of vitamin C.   **83.** The student cannot earn an A grade for the course.
85. $\{c \mid c > 0, c \in \text{real numbers}\}$ **87.** $\{c \mid c \in \text{real numbers}\}$ **89.** $\{c \mid c > 0, c \in \text{real numbers}\}$ **91.** Answers will vary.

SECTION 9.3

1. $x < 4$ **3.** $x < -4$ **5.** $x \geq 1$ **7.** $x < 5$ **9.** $x < 0$ **11.** $x < 20$ **13.** $y \leq \frac{5}{2}$ **15.** $x < \frac{25}{11}$ **17.** $n \leq \frac{11}{18}$
19. $x \geq 6$ **21.** The agent expects to sell at most $20,000.   **23.** To exceed the $10 fee, a person must use the service more than 60 min.   **25.** The maximum amount that can be added is 8 oz.   **27.** The distance to the ski area is greater than 38 mi.   **29.** $\{1, 2\}$ **31.** $\{3, 4, 5\}$ **33.** $\{x \mid x \in \text{real numbers}\}$

SECTION 9.4

1. 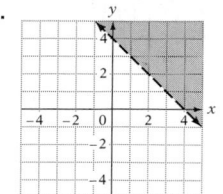   **3.** 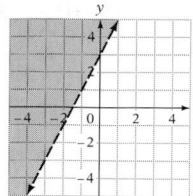   **5.** 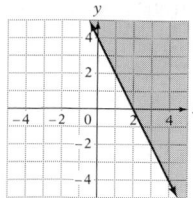   **7.**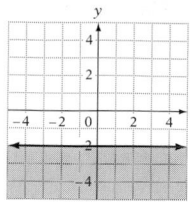

9. 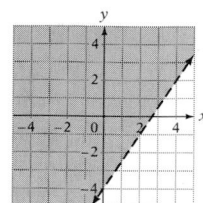   **11.** 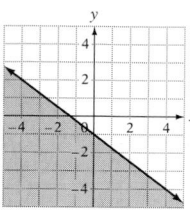   **13.** 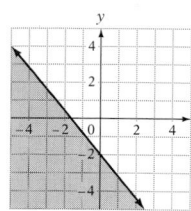   **15.**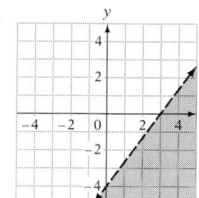

17. 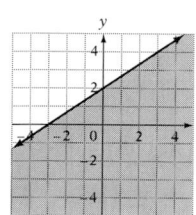   **19.** 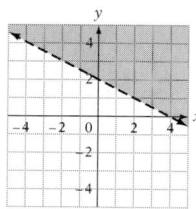   **21.** 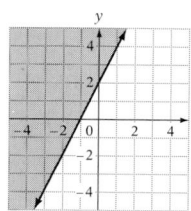   **23.** $x \le 3$

CHAPTER REVIEW

1. $x > 18$ [9.2A]   **2.** $A \cap B = \varnothing$ [9.1A]   **3.** $\{x \,|\, x > -8, x \in \text{odd integers}\}$ [9.1B]

4. $A \cup B = \{2, 4, 6, 8, 10\}$ [9.1A]   **5.** $A = \{1, 3, 5, 7\}$ [9.1A]   **6.** $x \ge 4$ [9.3A]

7. ⟨number line: -5 -4 -3 -2 -1 0 1 2 3 4 5⟩   [9.1C]   **8.** $x \ge -4$ [9.3A]   **9.** 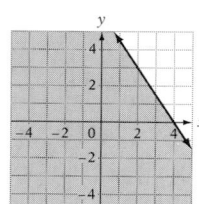   [9.4A]

10. 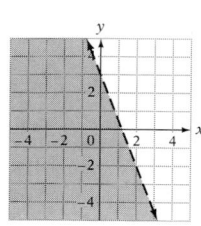   [9.4A]   **11.** $\{x \,|\, x > 3, x \in \text{real numbers}\}$ [9.1B]

12. $x > 2$ ⟨number line: -5 -4 -3 -2 -1 0 1 2 3 4 5⟩   [9.2A]   **13.** $A \cap B = \{1, 5, 9\}$ [9.1A]

14. ⟨number line: -5 -4 -3 -2 -1 0 1 2 3 4 5⟩   [9.1C]   **15.** ⟨number line: -5 -4 -3 -2 -1 0 1 2 3 4 5⟩   [9.1C]   **16.** $x \ge -3$ [9.2B]

17. $x > -18$ [9.3A]   **18.** $x < \dfrac{1}{2}$ [9.3A]   **19.** $x < -\dfrac{8}{9}$ [9.2B]   **20.** 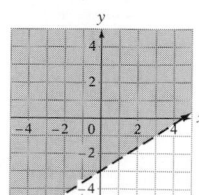   [9.4A]

21. $x \ge 4$ [9.3A]   **22.** Five or more residents make Florist B the more economical florists.   [9.3B]   **23.** The minimum length is 24 ft.   [9.3B]   **24.** The smallest integer that will satisfy the inequality is 32.   [9.2C]   **25.** The lowest score the student can receive is 72.   [9.2C]

CHAPTER TEST

1. 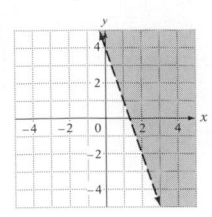 [9.1C]   **2.** $\{x \mid x < 50, x \in \text{positive integers}\}$ [9.1B]   **3.** $A = \{4, 6, 8\}$ [9.1A]

4. $x \le -3$ [9.3A]   **5.** $x > \dfrac{1}{8}$ [9.2A]   **6.** 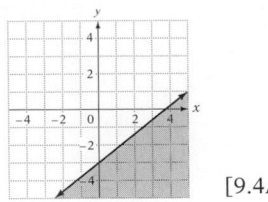 [9.1C]   **7.** $x < -1$ [9.3A]

8. $\{x \mid x > -23, x \in \text{real numbers}\}$ [9.1B]   **9.**

10.

[9.4A]   [9.4A]

11. $A \cap B = \{12\}$ [9.1A]   **12.** $x < -3$ [9.2A]   **13.** $x \ge -\dfrac{40}{3}$ [9.2B]

14. $x < -\dfrac{22}{7}$ [9.3A]   **15.** $x \ge 3$ [9.2B]   **16.** $x \ge -4$ [9.3A]   **17.** The child must grow at least 5 in. [9.2C]   **18.** The maximum width is 11 ft. [9.3B]   **19.** The allowable diameters are between 0.0389 in. and 0.0395 in. [9.2C]   **20.** The broker processed less than $75,000. [9.3B]

CUMULATIVE REVIEW

1. $40a - 28$ [2.2D]   **2.** $\dfrac{1}{8}$ [3.2A]   **3.** 4 [3.3B]   **4.** $-12a^7b^4$ [4.2B]   **5.** $-\dfrac{1}{b^4}$ [4.4A]

6. $4x - 2 - \dfrac{4}{4x - 1}$ [4.5B]   **7.** $f(-1) = 0$ [7.1D]   **8.** $3a^2(3x - 1)(3x + 1)$ [5.4B]   **9.** $\dfrac{1}{x + 2}$ [6.1C]

10. $\dfrac{18a}{(2a - 3)(a + 3)}$ [6.3B]   **11.** $-\dfrac{5}{9}$ [6.5A]   **12.** $C = S + Rt$ [6.7A]   **13.** $-\dfrac{7}{3}$ [7.3B]

14. $y = -\dfrac{3}{2}x - \dfrac{3}{2}$ [7.4A]   **15.** $(4, 1)$ [8.2A]   **16.** $(1, -4)$ [8.3A]   **17.** $A \cup B = \{-10, -2, 0, 1, 2\}$ [9.1A]

18. $\{x \mid x < 48, x \in \text{real numbers}\}$ [9.1B]   **19.** [9.1C]

20. $x > -2$ [9.2B]   **21.** $x < -15$ [9.2B]   **22.** $x > 2$ [9.3A]

23. $\{x \mid x \le -26, x \in \text{integers}\}$ [9.2C]   **24.** The maximum number of miles is 359. [9.3B]   **25.** There are 5000 fish in the lake. [6.6B]   **26.** The measure of the first angle is 65°, the measure of the second angle is 35°, and the measure of the third angle is 80°. [3.5C]   **27.**

28.

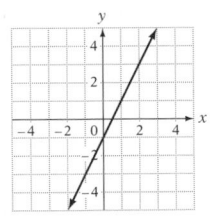   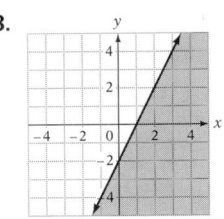

[7.2A]   [9.4A]

Answers to Chapter 10 Odd-Numbered Exercises

SECTION 10.1

1. 4   **3.** 7   **5.** $4\sqrt{2}$ **7.** $2\sqrt{2}$ **9.** $18\sqrt{2}$ **11.** $10\sqrt{10}$ **13.** $\sqrt{15}$ **15.** $\sqrt{29}$ **17.** $-54\sqrt{2}$ **19.** $3\sqrt{5}$

21. 0   **23.** $48\sqrt{2}$ **25.** 15.492   **27.** 16.971   **29.** 16   **31.** x^3 **33.** $y^7\sqrt{y}$ **35.** a^{10} **37.** x^2y^2 **39.** $2x^2$

41. $2x\sqrt{6}$ **43.** $2x^2\sqrt{15x}$ **45.** $7a^2b^4$ **47.** $3x^2y^3\sqrt{2xy}$ **49.** $2x^5y^3\sqrt{10xy}$ **51.** $4a^4b^5\sqrt{5a}$ **53.** $8ab\sqrt{b}$

55. x^3y **57.** $8a^2b^3\sqrt{5b}$ **59.** $6x^2y^3\sqrt{3y}$ **61.** $4x^3y\sqrt{2y}$ **63.** $5(a + 4)$ or $5a + 20$ **65.** $2(x + 2)^2$ or $2x^2 + 8x + 8$ **67.** $x + 2$ **69.** $y + 1$ **71.** No. For example, $\sqrt{4 + 9} \ne \sqrt{4} + \sqrt{9}$.   **73.** Answers will vary.

75. $\{3, 4, 5, 6, 7, 8, 9\}$ **77.** No. $\sqrt{18}$ still contains a perfect-square factor. $6\sqrt{2}$ **79a.** 2.9623   **b.** 2.0305

SECTION 10.2

1. $3\sqrt{2}$ **3.** $-\sqrt{7}$ **5.** $-11\sqrt{11}$ **7.** $10\sqrt{x}$ **9.** $-2\sqrt{y}$ **11.** $-11\sqrt{3b}$ **13.** $2x\sqrt{2}$ **15.** $-3a\sqrt{3a}$
17. $-5\sqrt{xy}$ **19.** $8\sqrt{5}$ **21.** $8\sqrt{2}$ **23.** $15\sqrt{2} - 10\sqrt{3}$ **25.** $\sqrt{x}$ **27.** $-12x\sqrt{3}$ **29.** $2xy\sqrt{x} - 3xy\sqrt{y}$
31. $-9x\sqrt{3x}$ **33.** $-13y^2\sqrt{2y}$ **35.** $4a^2b^2\sqrt{ab}$ **37.** $7\sqrt{2}$ **39.** $6\sqrt{x}$ **41.** $-3\sqrt{y}$ **43.** $-45\sqrt{2}$
45. $13\sqrt{3} - 12\sqrt{5}$ **47.** $32\sqrt{3} - 3\sqrt{11}$ **49.** $6\sqrt{x}$ **51.** $-34\sqrt{3x}$ **53.** $10a\sqrt{3b} + 10a\sqrt{5b}$ **55.** $-2xy\sqrt{3}$
57. $5\sqrt{2}$ **59.** Answers will vary. **61.** $-11\sqrt{2x + y}$ **63.** $13a\sqrt{a + 1}$

SECTION 10.3

1. 5 **3.** 6 **5.** x **7.** x^3y^2 **9.** $3ab^6\sqrt{2a}$ **11.** $12a^4b\sqrt{b}$ **13.** $2 - \sqrt{6}$ **15.** $x - \sqrt{xy}$ **17.** $5\sqrt{2} - \sqrt{5x}$
19. $4 - 2\sqrt{10}$ **21.** $x - 6\sqrt{x} + 9$ **23.** $3a - 3\sqrt{ab}$ **25.** $10abc$ **27.** $-2 + 2\sqrt{5}$ **29.** $16 + 10\sqrt{2}$
31. $6x + 10\sqrt{x} - 4$ **33.** $15x - 22y\sqrt{x} + 8y^2$ **35.** $x - y$ **37.** 3 **39.** 4 **41.** $6x^2$ **43.** $2x^2\sqrt{2y}$
45. $4x\sqrt{y}$ **47.** $\dfrac{2\sqrt{3x}}{3y}$ **49.** $\dfrac{-1 + \sqrt{2}}{2}$ **51.** $-\dfrac{5\sqrt{7} + 15}{2}$ **53.** $-\dfrac{5\sqrt{3} + 9}{2}$ **55.** $3 + \sqrt{6}$ **57.** $\dfrac{-12 + 3\sqrt{2}}{7}$
59. $\dfrac{14 - 9\sqrt{2}}{17}$ **61.** $\sqrt{15} + 2\sqrt{5}$ **63.** $\dfrac{x\sqrt{y} + y\sqrt{x}}{x - y}$ **65.** $4\sqrt{6} + 12$ **67.** The complete solution is available in the
Solutions Manual.

SECTION 10.4

1. 25 **3.** 144 **5.** 5 **7.** no solution **9.** -1 **11.** 1 **13.** 15 **15.** $\dfrac{7}{3}$ **17.** 45 **19.** no solution

21. The pitcher's mound is less than halfway between home plate and second base. **23.** The periscope would have to be
16.67 ft above the surface of the water. **25.** The height of the TV screen is 21.6 in. **27.** The child is 18.75 ft from the
center of the merry-go-round. **29.** The perimeter of the triangle is 30 units. **31.** Answers will vary. **33.** The area of
the fountain is 244.78 ft².

CHAPTER REVIEW

1. 3 [10.3A] **2.** $9a^2\sqrt{2ab}$ [10.1B] **3.** 12 [10.1A] **4.** $3a\sqrt{2} + 2a\sqrt{3}$ [10.3A] **5.** $-x\sqrt{3} - x\sqrt{5}$ [10.3B]
6. $-6\sqrt{30}$ [10.1A] **7.** 20 [10.4A] **8.** $20\sqrt{3}$ [10.1A] **9.** $7x^2y^4$ [10.3B] **10.** no solution [10.4A]
11. $18a\sqrt{5b} + 5a\sqrt{b}$ [10.2A] **12.** $20\sqrt{10}$ [10.1A] **13.** $7x^2y\sqrt{15xy}$ [10.2A] **14.** $8y + 10\sqrt{5y} - 15$ [10.3A]
15. $26\sqrt{3x}$ [10.2A] **16.** no solution [10.4A] **17.** $\dfrac{8\sqrt{x} + 24}{x - 9}$ [10.3B] **18.** $36x^8y^5\sqrt{3xy}$ [10.1B]
19. $2y^4\sqrt{6}$ [10.1B] **20.** $\dfrac{3}{5}$ [10.4A] **21.** $-6x^3y^2\sqrt{2y}$ [10.2A] **22.** $\dfrac{16\sqrt{a}}{a}$ [10.3B] **23.** The explorer would
weigh 144 lb on the surface of the earth. [10.4B] **24.** The depth of the water is 100 ft. [10.4B] **25.** The radius of
the sharpest corner is 25 ft. [10.4B]

CHAPTER TEST

1. $11x^4y$ [10.1B] **2.** $6x^2y\sqrt{y}$ [10.3A] **3.** $-5\sqrt{2}$ [10.2A] **4.** $3\sqrt{5}$ [10.1A] **5.** 9 [10.3B]
6. 25 [10.4A] **7.** $4a^2b^5\sqrt{2ab}$ [10.1B] **8.** $7ab\sqrt{a}$ [10.3B] **9.** $\sqrt{3} + 1$ [10.3B] **10.** $4x^2y^2\sqrt{5y}$ [10.3A]
11. no solution [10.4A] **12.** $21\sqrt{2y} - 12\sqrt{2x}$ [10.2A] **13.** $6x^3y\sqrt{2x}$ [10.1B] **14.** $y + 2\sqrt{y} - 15$ [10.3A]
15. $-2xy\sqrt{3xy} - 3xy\sqrt{xy}$ [10.2A] **16.** $\dfrac{17 - 8\sqrt{5}}{31}$ [10.3B] **17.** $a - \sqrt{ab}$ [10.3A] **18.** $5\sqrt{3}$ [10.1A]
19. The length of the pendulum is 7.30 ft. [10.4B] **20.** The larger integer is 51. [10.4B]

CUMULATIVE REVIEW

1. $-\dfrac{1}{12}$ [1.5B]   **2.** $2x + 18$ [2.2D]   **3.** $\dfrac{1}{13}$ [3.3B]   **4.** $6x^5y^5$ [4.2A]   **5.** $-2b^2 + 1 - \dfrac{1}{3b^2}$ [4.5A]

6. $f(-3) = 1$ [7.1D]   **7.** $2a(a - 5)(a - 3)$ [5.2B]   **8.** $\dfrac{1}{4(x + 1)}$ [6.1B]   **9.** $\dfrac{x + 3}{x - 3}$ [6.3B]   **10.** $\dfrac{5}{3}$ [6.5A]

11. $y = \dfrac{1}{2}x - 2$ [7.4A]   **12.** $(1, 1)$ [8.2A]   **13.** $(3, -2)$ [8.3A]   **14.** $x \le -\dfrac{9}{2}$ [9.3A]   **15.** $6\sqrt{3}$ [10.1A]

16. $-4\sqrt{2}$ [10.2A]   **17.** $4ab\sqrt{2ab} - 5ab\sqrt{ab}$ [10.2A]   **18.** $14a^5b^2\sqrt{2a}$ [10.3A]   **19.** $3\sqrt{2} - x\sqrt{3}$ [10.3A]

20. 8 [10.3B]   **21.** $-6 - 3\sqrt{5}$ [10.3B]   **22.** 6 [10.4A]   **23.** The book costs $24.50. [3.2B]   **24.** 56 oz of pure

water must be added. [3.6B]   **25.** The numbers are 13 and 8. [5.5B]   **26.** Working alone, it would take the small pipe

48 h to fill the tank. [6.8A]   **27.** $(2, -1)$ **28.**

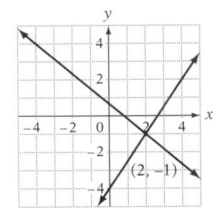

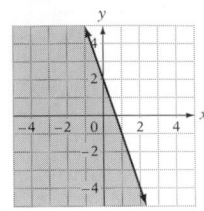

[8.1A]   [9.4A]

29. The smaller integer is 40. [10.4B]   **30.** The building is 400 ft high. [10.4B]

Answers to Chapter 11 Odd-Numbered Exercises

SECTION 11.1

1. -5 and 3   **3.** 1 and 3   **5.** -1 and -2 **7.** 3   **9.** 0 and $-\dfrac{2}{3}$ **11.** -2 and 5   **13.** $\dfrac{2}{3}$ and 1   **15.** -3 and $\dfrac{1}{3}$

17. $\dfrac{2}{3}$ **19.** $-\dfrac{1}{2}$ and $\dfrac{3}{2}$ **21.** $\dfrac{1}{2}$ **23.** -3 and 3   **25.** $-\dfrac{1}{2}$ and $\dfrac{1}{2}$ **27.** -3 and 5   **29.** 1 and 5   **31.** -6 and 6

33. -1 and 1   **35.** $-\dfrac{7}{2}$ and $\dfrac{7}{2}$ **37.** $-\dfrac{2}{3}$ and $\dfrac{2}{3}$ **39.** $-\dfrac{3}{4}$ and $\dfrac{3}{4}$ **41.** no real number solution   **43.** $-2\sqrt{6}$ and $2\sqrt{6}$

45. -5 and 7   **47.** -7 and -3 **49.** $-\dfrac{1}{3}$ and $\dfrac{7}{3}$ **51.** $-\dfrac{2}{7}$ and $-\dfrac{12}{7}$ **53.** $4 + 2\sqrt{5}$ and $4 - 2\sqrt{5}$

55. no real number solution   **57.** $-\dfrac{3}{4} + 2\sqrt{3}$ and $-\dfrac{3}{4} - 2\sqrt{3}$ **59.** $\sqrt{2}$ and $-\sqrt{2}$ **61.** 0 and $\dfrac{b}{a}$ **63.** 0 and 1

65. The annual percentage rate is 8%.   **67.** yes

SECTION 11.2

1. 1 and -3 **3.** 8 and -2 **5.** 2   **7.** no real number solution   **9.** -1 and -4 **11.** -8 and 1   **13.** $-2 + \sqrt{3}$

and $-2 - \sqrt{3}$ **15.** $-3 + \sqrt{14}$ and $-3 - \sqrt{14}$ **17.** $1 + \sqrt{2}$ and $1 - \sqrt{2}$ **19.** $\dfrac{-3 + \sqrt{13}}{2}$ and $\dfrac{-3 - \sqrt{13}}{2}$

21. 2 and 1   **23.** $\dfrac{-1 + \sqrt{13}}{2}$ and $\dfrac{-1 - \sqrt{13}}{2}$ **25.** $-5 + 4\sqrt{2}$ and $-5 - 4\sqrt{2}$ **27.** $\dfrac{3 + \sqrt{29}}{2}$ and $\dfrac{3 - \sqrt{29}}{2}$

29. $\dfrac{1 + \sqrt{17}}{2}$ and $\dfrac{1 - \sqrt{17}}{2}$ **31.** no real number solution   **33.** 1 and $\dfrac{1}{2}$ **35.** -3 and $\dfrac{1}{2}$ **37.** 2 and $\dfrac{3}{2}$

39. 1 and $-\dfrac{1}{2}$ **41.** -2 and $\dfrac{1}{3}$ **43.** -2 and $-\dfrac{2}{3}$ **45.** $\dfrac{1}{2}$ and $-\dfrac{3}{2}$ **47.** $\dfrac{1}{3}$ and $-\dfrac{3}{2}$ **49.** $-\dfrac{1}{2}$ and $\dfrac{4}{3}$

51. $\dfrac{1 + \sqrt{2}}{2}$ and $\dfrac{1 - \sqrt{2}}{2}$ **53.** -4.193 and 1.193 **55.** 2.766 and -1.266 **57.** -1.651 and 0.151 **59.** Answers will

vary.   **61.** 7   **63.** $4 + \sqrt{7}$ and $4 - \sqrt{7}$ **65.** $6 + \sqrt{58}$ and $6 - \sqrt{58}$ **67.** 1 and 3   **69.** The ball will hit the

basket 1.88 s after it is released.

SECTION 11.3

1. −1 and 5   **3.** −3 and 5   **5.** −1 and 3   **7.** −5 and 1   **9.** $-\dfrac{1}{2}$ and 1   **11.** no real number solution

13. 0 and 1   **15.** $-\dfrac{3}{2}$ and $\dfrac{3}{2}$ **17.** $-\dfrac{5}{2}$ and $\dfrac{3}{2}$ **19.** no real number solution   **21.** $1 + \sqrt{6}$ and $1 - \sqrt{6}$

23. $-3 + \sqrt{10}$ and $-3 - \sqrt{10}$ **25.** $2 + \sqrt{13}$ and $2 - \sqrt{13}$ **27.** $\dfrac{-1 + \sqrt{2}}{3}$ and $\dfrac{-1 - \sqrt{2}}{3}$ **29.** $-\dfrac{1}{2}$ **31.** no real

number solution   **33.** $\dfrac{-4 + \sqrt{5}}{2}$ and $\dfrac{-4 - \sqrt{5}}{2}$ **35.** $\dfrac{1 + 2\sqrt{3}}{2}$ and $\dfrac{1 - 2\sqrt{3}}{2}$ **37.** $\dfrac{-5 + \sqrt{2}}{3}$ and $\dfrac{-5 - \sqrt{2}}{3}$

39. 5.690 and −3.690   **41.** 7.690 and −1.690   **43.** 4.589 and −1.089   **45.** −2.118 and 0.118   **47.** 1.105 and
−0.905   **49.** Answers will vary.   **51a.** false   **b.** false   **c.** false   **d.** true   **53.** −3 and −4   **55.** The equation
has no solution.   **57.** −1 and 11   **59.** After 2 h the distance between the planes is 1000 mi.

SECTION 11.4

1. 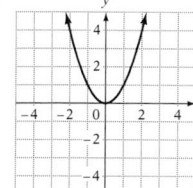   **3.** 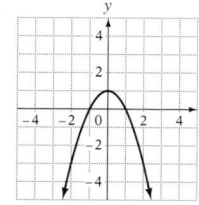   **5.** 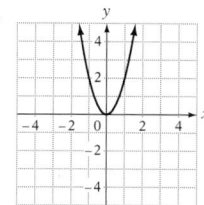   **7.**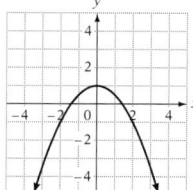

9. 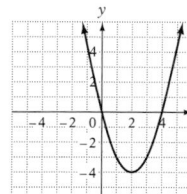   **11.** 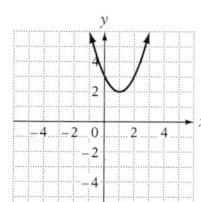   **13.** 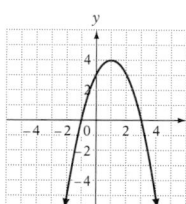   **15.**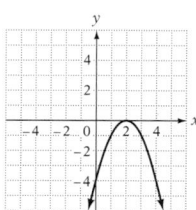

17. 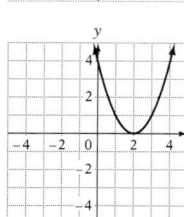   **19.** down   **21.** down   **23.** $y = 3x^2 + 6x + 5$ **25.** $(-3, 0)$ and $(3, 0)$

27. $\left(-\dfrac{1}{2}, 0\right)$ and $(1, 0)$ **29.** $g(2) = -3$ **31.** $P(-3) = 38$

SECTION 11.5

1. The length is 4 m; the height is 10 m.   **3.** The length of the batter's box is 6 ft; the width is 4 ft.   **5.** The length of
the pool is 100 ft; the width is 50 ft.   **7.** The first computer alone would take 35 min. The second computer alone would
take 14 min.   **9.** The first engine alone would take 12 h. The second engine alone would take 6 h.   **11.** The rate of the
plane is 100 mph.   **13.** The four consecutive integers are 3, 4, 5 and 6, or −6, −5, −4, and −3.   **15.** The radius of the
large pizza is 7 in.   **17.** The maximum velocity of the car is 78 ft/s.   **19.** The hang time is 5.5 s.

CHAPTER REVIEW

1. $\dfrac{4}{3}$ and $-\dfrac{7}{2}$ [11.1A]   **2.** $-\dfrac{5}{7}$ and $\dfrac{5}{7}$ [11.1B]   **3.** −6 and 4 [11.2A]   **4.** −6 and 1 [11.3A]

5. -4 and $\frac{3}{2}$ [11.2A]   **6.** 2 and $\frac{5}{12}$ [11.1A]   **7.** $-2 - 2\sqrt{6}$ and $-2 + 2\sqrt{6}$ [11.1B]   **8.** 1 and $\frac{3}{2}$ [11.3A]

9. $-\frac{1}{3}$ and $-\frac{1}{2}$ [11.1A]   **10.** no real number solution   [11.1B]   **11.** $2 - \sqrt{3}$ and $2 + \sqrt{3}$ [11.2A]

12. $\frac{3 - \sqrt{29}}{2}$ and $\frac{3 + \sqrt{29}}{2}$ [11.3A]   **13.** no real number solution   [11.2A]   **14.** -7 and -10 [11.1A]

15. -1 and 2 [11.1B]   **16.** $\frac{-4 - \sqrt{23}}{2}$ and $\frac{-4 + \sqrt{23}}{2}$ [11.2A]   **17.** no real number solution   [11.3A]

18. -2 and $-\frac{1}{2}$ [11.3A]   **19.** 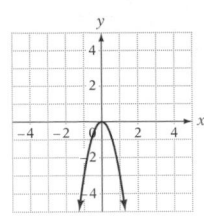 [11.4A]   **20.** 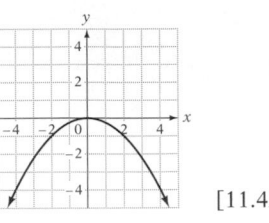 [11.4A]

21. 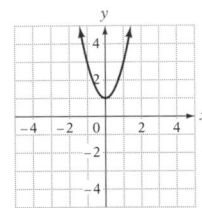 [11.4A]   **22.** 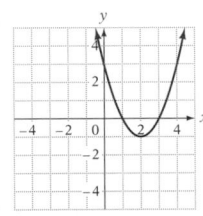 [11.4A]   **23.** 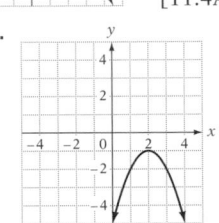 [11.4A]

24. The rate of the hawk in calm air is 75 mph.   [11.5A]

CHAPTER TEST

1. 6 and -1 [11.1A]   **2.** -4 and $\frac{5}{3}$ [11.1A]   **3.** 0 and 10 [11.1B]   **4.** $-4 + 2\sqrt{5}$ and $-4 - 2\sqrt{5}$ [11.1B]

5. $-2 + 2\sqrt{5}$ and $-2 - 2\sqrt{5}$ [11.2A]   **6.** $\frac{-3 + \sqrt{41}}{2}$ and $\frac{-3 - \sqrt{41}}{2}$ [11.2A]   **7.** $\frac{3 + \sqrt{7}}{2}$ and $\frac{3 - \sqrt{7}}{2}$ [11.2A]

8. $\frac{-4 + \sqrt{22}}{2}$ and $\frac{-4 - \sqrt{22}}{2}$ [11.2A]   **9.** $-2 + \sqrt{2}$ and $-2 - \sqrt{2}$ [11.3A]   **10.** $\frac{3 + \sqrt{33}}{2}$ and $\frac{3 - \sqrt{33}}{2}$ [11.3A]

11. $-\frac{1}{2}$ and 3 [11.3A]   **12.** $\frac{1 + \sqrt{13}}{6}$ and $\frac{1 - \sqrt{13}}{6}$ [11.3A]   **13.**

[11.4A]

14. The length is 8 ft. The width is 5 ft.   [11.5A]   **15.** The rate of the boat in calm water is 11 mph.   [11.5A]

CUMULATIVE REVIEW

1. $-28x + 27$ [2.2D]   **2.** $\frac{3}{2}$ [3.1C]   **3.** 3 [3.3B]   **4.** $-12a^8b^4$ [4.2B]   **5.** $x + 2 - \frac{4}{x - 2}$ [4.5B]

6. $x(3x - 4)(x + 2)$ [5.3B]   **7.** $\frac{9x^2(x - 2)^2}{(2x - 3)^2}$ [6.1C]   **8.** $\frac{x + 2}{2(x + 1)}$ [6.3B]   **9.** $\frac{x - 4}{2x + 5}$ [6.4A]   **10.** The x-intercept is

$(3, 0)$, and the y-intercept is $(0, -4)$.   [7.3A]   **11.** $y = -\frac{4}{3}x - 2$ [7.4A]   **12.** $(2, 1)$ [8.2A]   **13.** $(2, -2)$ [8.3A]

14. $x > \frac{1}{9}$ [9.3A]   **15.** $a - 2$ [10.3A]   **16.** $6ab\sqrt{a}$ [10.3B]   **17.** $\frac{-6 + 5\sqrt{3}}{13}$ [10.3B]   **18.** 5 [10.4A]

19. $\frac{5}{2}$ and $\frac{1}{3}$ [11.1A]   **20.** $5 + 3\sqrt{2}$ and $5 - 3\sqrt{2}$ [11.1B]   **21.** $\frac{-7 + \sqrt{13}}{6}$ and $\frac{-7 - \sqrt{13}}{6}$ [11.2A]

22. 2 and $-\dfrac{1}{2}$ [11.3A]   **23.** The cost of the mixture is \$2.25 per pound. [3.6A]   **24.** 250 additional shares are required. [6.6B]   **25.** The rate of the plane in still air is 200 mph. The rate of the wind is 40 mph. [8.4A]   **26.** The student must receive a score of 77 or above. [9.2C]   **27.** The integer is -5 or 5. [11.5A]   **28.** The rate for the last 8 mi was 4 mph. [11.5A]   **29.**

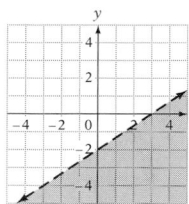

[9.4A]   **30.**

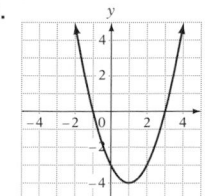

[11.4A]

FINAL EXAM

1. -3 [1.1B]   **2.** -6 [1.2B]   **3.** -256 [1.5A]   **4.** -11 [1.5B]   **5.** $-\dfrac{15}{2}$ [2.1A]   **6.** $9x + 6y$ [2.2A]

7. $6z$ [2.2B]   **8.** $16x - 52$ [2.2D]   **9.** -50 [3.1C]   **10.** -3 [3.3B]   **11.** 12.5% [1.4B]   **12.** 15.2 [3.1D]

13. $-3x^2 - 3x + 8$ [4.1B]   **14.** $81x^4y^{12}$ [4.2B]   **15.** $6x^3 + 7x^2 - 7x - 6$ [4.3B]   **16.** $-\dfrac{x^4y}{2}$ [4.4A]

17. $\dfrac{3x}{y} - 4x^2 - \dfrac{5}{x}$ [4.5A]   **18.** $5x - 12 + \dfrac{23}{x + 2}$ [4.5B]   **19.** $\dfrac{4y^6}{x^6}$ [4.4A]   **20.** $\dfrac{3}{4}$ [7.1D]

21. $(x - 6)(x + 1)$ [5.2A]   **22.** $(3x + 2)(2x - 3)$ [5.3A]   **23.** $4x(2x - 1)(x - 3)$ [5.3B]

24. $(5x - 4)(5x + 4)$ [5.4A]   **25.** $2(a + 3)(4 - x)$ [5.1B]   **26.** $3y(5 - 2x)(5 + 2x)$ [5.4B]   **27.** $\dfrac{1}{2}$ and 3 [5.5A]

28. $\dfrac{2(x + 1)}{x - 1}$ [6.1B]   **29.** $\dfrac{-3x^2 + x - 25}{(2x - 5)(x + 3)}$ [6.3B]   **30.** $\dfrac{x^2 - 2x}{x - 1}$ [6.4A]   **31.** 2 [6.5A]   **32.** $a = b$ [6.7A]

33. $\dfrac{2}{3}$ [7.3B]   **34.** $y = -\dfrac{2}{3}x - 2$ [7.4A]   **35.** $(6, 17)$ [8.2A]   **36.** $(2, -1)$ [8.3A]   **37.** $x \le -3$ [9.2A]

38. $y \ge \dfrac{5}{2}$ [9.3A]   **39.** $7x^3$ [10.1B]   **40.** $38\sqrt{3a}$ [10.2A]   **41.** $\sqrt{15} + 2\sqrt{3}$ [10.3B]   **42.** 2 [10.4A]

43. -1 and $\dfrac{4}{3}$ [11.1A]   **44.** $\dfrac{1 + \sqrt{5}}{4}$ and $\dfrac{1 - \sqrt{5}}{4}$ [11.3A]   **45.** $2x + 3(x - 2)$, $5x - 6$ [2.3B]   **46.** The original value is \$3000. [3.1D]   **47.** The markup rate is 65%. [3.2B]   **48.** An additional \$6000 must be invested. [8.2B]   **49.** The mixture costs \$3 per pound. [3.6A]   **50.** The percent concentration of the acid in the mixture is 36%. [3.6B]   **51.** In the first hour, the plane flew 215 km. [3.6C]   **52.** The measures of the angles are 50°, 60°, and 70°. [3.5C]   **53.** The integer is 4 or -4. [11.5A]   **54.** The length is 10 m. The width is 5 m. [5.5B]   **55.** Sixteen ounces of dye are required for 120 oz of base paint. [6.6B]   **56.** Working together, it would take 0.6 h to prepare the dinner. [6.8A]   **57.** The rate of the boat in calm water is 15 mph. The rate of the current is 5 mph. [8.4A]   **58.** The rate of the wind is 25 mph. [11.5A]   **59.**

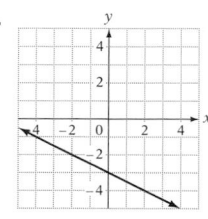

[7.3C]   **60.**

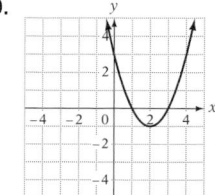

[11.4A]

Glossary

abscissa The first number in an ordered pair. It measures a horizontal distance and is also called the first coordinate. (Sec. 7.1)

absolute value of a number The distance of the number from zero on the number line. (Sec. 1.1)

acute angle An angle whose measure is between 0° and 90°. (Sec. 3.5)

addend In addition, a number being added. (Sec. 1.2)

addition The process of finding the total of two numbers. (Sec. 1.2)

addition method An algebraic method of finding an exact solution of a system of linear equations. (Sec. 8.3)

additive inverses Numbers that are the same distance from zero on the number line, but on opposite sides; also called opposites. (Sec. 1.1, 2.2)

adjacent angles Two angles that share a common side. (Sec. 3.5)

alternate exterior angles Two angles that are on opposite sides of the transversal and outside the parallel lines. (Sec. 3.5)

alternate interior angles Two angles that are on opposite sides of the transversal and between the parallel lines. (Sec. 3.5)

analytic geometry Geometry in which a coordinate system is used to study the relationships between variables. (Sec. 7.1)

arithmetic mean of values Average determined by calculating the sum of the values and then dividing that result by the number of values. (Sec. 1.3)

axes The two number lines that form a rectangular coordinate system; also called coordinate axes. (Sec. 7.1)

base In exponential notation, the factor that is multiplied the number of times shown by the exponent. (Sec. 1.5)

basic percent equation Percent times base equals amount. (Sec. 3.1)

binomial A polynomial of two terms. (Sec. 4.1)

clearing denominators Removing denominators from an equation that contains fractions by multiplying each side of the equation by the LCM of the denominators. (Sec. 6.5)

coefficient The number part of a variable term. (Sec. 2.1)

combining like terms Using the Distributive Property to add the coefficients of like variable terms; adding like terms of a variable expression. (Sec. 2.2)

complementary angles Two angles whose sum is 90°. (Sec. 3.5)

completing the square Adding to a binomial the constant term that makes it a perfect-square trinomial. (Sec. 11.2)

complex fraction A fraction whose numerator or denominator contains one or more fractions. (Sec. 6.4)

conjugates Binomial expressions that differ only in the sign of a term. The expressions $a + b$ and $a - b$ are conjugates. (Sec. 10.3)

consecutive even integers Even integers that follow one another in order. (Sec. 3.4)

consecutive integers Integers that follow one another in order. (Sec. 3.4)

consecutive odd integers Odd integers that follow one another in order. (Sec. 3.4)

constant term A term that includes no variable part; also called a constant. (Sec. 2.1)

coordinate axes The two number lines that form a rectangular coordinate system; also simply called axes. (Sec. 7.1)

coordinates of a point The numbers in an ordered pair that is associated with a point. (Sec. 7.1)

corresponding angles Two angles that are on the same side of the transversal and are both acute angles or are both obtuse angles. (Sec. 3.5)

cost The price that a business pays for a product. (Sec. 3.2)

decimal notation Notation in which a number consists of a whole-number part, a decimal point, and a decimal part. (Sec. 1.4)

degree A unit used to measure angles. (Sec. 3.5)

degree of a polynomial in one variable The largest exponent that appears on the variable. (Sec. 4.1)

dependent system of equations A system of equations that has an infinite number of solutions. (Sec. 8.1)

dependent variable In a function, the variable whose value depends on the value of another variable known as the independent variable. (Sec. 7.1)

descending order The terms of a polynomial in one variable arranged so that the exponents on the variable decrease from left to right. The polynomial $9x^5 - 2x^4 + 7x^3 + x^2 - 8x + 1$ is in descending order. (Sec. 4.1)

discount The amount by which a retailer reduces the regular price of a product for a promotional sale. (Sec. 3.2)

discount rate The percent of the regular price that the discount represents. (Sec. 3.2)

domain The set of first coordinates of the ordered pairs in a relation. (Sec. 7.1)

element of a set One of the objects in a set. (Sec. 1.1, 9.1)

empty set The set that contains no elements; also called the null set. (Sec. 9.1)

equation A statement of the equality of two mathematical expressions. (Sec. 3.1)

equilateral triangle A triangle in which all three sides are of equal length. (Sec. 3.5)

equivalent equations Equations that have the same solution. (Sec. 3.1)

evaluating a function Replacing x in $f(x)$ with some value and then simplifying the numerical expression that results. (Sec. 7.1)

evaluating a variable expression Replacing each variable by its value and then simplifying the resulting numerical expression. (Sec. 2.1)

even integer An integer that is divisible by 2. (Sec. 3.4)

exponent In exponential notation, the elevated number that indicates how many times the base occurs in the multiplication. (Sec. 1.5)

exponential form The expression 2^5 is in exponential form. Compare *factored form*. (Sec. 1.5)

factor In multiplication, a number being multiplied. (Sec. 1.3)

factor a polynomial To write the polynomial as a product of other polynomials. (Sec. 5.1)

factor a trinomial of the form $x^2 + bx + c$ To express the trinomial as the product of two binomials. (Sec. 5.1)

factored form The expression $2 \cdot 2 \cdot 2 \cdot 2 \cdot 2$ is in factored form. Compare *exponential form*. (Sec. 1.5)

first coordinate The first number in an ordered pair. It measures a horizontal distance and is also called the abscissa. (Sec. 7.1)

FOIL A method of finding the product of two binomials; the letters stand for First, Outer, Inner, and Last. (Sec. 4.3)

formula A literal equation that states rules about measurements. (Sec. 6.7)

function A relation in which no two ordered pairs that have the same first coordinate have different second coordinates. (Sec. 7.1)

functional notation A function designated by $f(x)$, which is the value of the function at x. (Sec. 7.1)

graph of a relation The graph of the ordered pairs that belong to the relation. (Sec. 7.1)

graph of an equation in two variables A graph of the ordered-pair solutions of the equation. (Sec. 7.2)

graph of an integer A heavy dot directly above that number on the number line. (Sec. 1.1)

graph of an ordered pair The dot drawn at the coordinates of the point in the plane. (Sec. 7.1)

graphing a point in the plane Placing a dot at the location given by the ordered pair; also called plotting a point in the plane. (Sec. 7.1)

greater than A number a is greater than another number b, written $a > b$, if a is to the right of b on the number line. (Sec. 1.1)

greater than or equal to The symbol $\geq$ means "is greater than or equal to." (Sec. 1.1)

greatest common factor The greatest common factor (GCF) of two or more integers is the greatest integer that is a factor of all the integers. The greatest common factor of two or more monomials is the product of the GCF of the coefficients and the common variable factors. (Sec. 5.1)

half-plane The solution set of an inequality in two variables. (Sec. 9.4)

hypotenuse In a right triangle, the side opposite the 90° angle. (Sec. 10.4)

inconsistent system of equations A system of equations that has no solution. (Sec. 8.1)

independent system of equations A system of equations that has one solution. (Sec. 8.1)

independent variable In a function, the variable that varies independently and whose value determines the value of the dependent variable. (Sec. 7.1)

inequality An expression that contains the symbol $>$, $<$, $\geq$ (is greater than or equal to), or $\leq$ (is less than or equal to). (Sec. 9.1)

integers The numbers $\dots, -3, -2, -1, 0, 1, 2, 3, \dots$. (Sec 1.1)

intersection of sets A and B The set that contains the elements that are common to both A and B. (Sec. 9.1)

irrational number The decimal representation of an irrational number never repeats or terminates and can only be approximated. (Sec. 1.4, 10.1)

isosceles triangle A triangle that has two equal angles and two equal sides. (Sec. 3.5)

least common denominator The smallest number that is a multiple of each denominator in question. (Sec. 1.4)

least common multiple (LCM) The LCM of two or more numbers is the smallest number that contains the prime factorization of each number. The LCM of two or more polynomials is the polynomial of least degree that contains the factors of each polynomial. (Sec. 1.4, 6.2)

less than A number a is less than another number b, written $a < b$, if a is to the left of b on the number line. (Sec. 1.1)

less than or equal to The symbol $\leq$ means "is less than or equal to". (Sec. 1.1)

like terms Terms of a variable expression that have the same variable part. (Sec. 2.2)

line of best fit A line drawn to approximate data that are graphed as points in a coordinate system. (Sec. 7.4)

linear equation in two variables An equation of the form $y = mx + b$, where m and b are constants; also called a linear function. (Sec. 7.2)

linear function An equation of the form $y = mx + b$, where m and b are constants; also called a linear equation in two variables. (Sec. 7.2)

linear model A first-degree equation that is used to describe a relationship between quantities. (Sec. 7.4)

literal equation An equation that contains more than one variable. (Sec. 6.7)

markdown The amount by which a retailer reduces the regular price of a product for a promotional sale. (Sec. 3.2)

markup The difference between selling price and cost. (Sec. 3.2)

markup rate The percent of retailer's cost that the markup represents. (Sec. 3.2)

monomial A number, a variable, or a product of numbers and variables; a polynomial of one term. (Sec. 4.1)

multiplicative inverse of a number The reciprocal of a number. (Sec. 2.2)

natural numbers The numbers 1, 2, 3, ... (Sec. 1.1)

negative integers The numbers ..., -4, -3, -2, -1. (Sec. 1.1)

negative slope A property of a line that slants downward to the right. (Sec. 7.3)

nonfactorable over the integers A polynomial that does not factor using only integers. (Sec. 5.2)

null set The set that contains no elements; also called the empty set. (Sec. 9.1)

numerical coefficient The number part of a variable term. When the numerical coefficient is 1 or -1, the 1 is usually not written. (Sec. 2.1)

obtuse angle An angle whose measure is between $90°$ and $180°$. (Sec. 3.5)

odd integer An integer that is not divisible by 2. (Sec. 3.4)

opposite of a polynomial The polynomial created when the sign of each term of the original polynomial is changed. (Sec. 4.1)

opposites Numbers that are the same distance from zero on the number line, but on opposite sides; also called additive inverses. (Sec. 1.1)

ordered pair Pair of numbers, such as (a, b) that can be used to identify a point in the plane determined by the axes of a rectangular coordinate system. (Sec. 7.1)

Order of Operations Agreement A set of rules that tell us in what order to perform the operations that occur in a numerical expression. (Sec. 1.6)

ordinate The second number in an ordered pair. It measures a vertical distance and is also called the second coordinate. (Sec. 7.1)

origin The point of intersection of the two coordinate axes that form a rectangular coordinate system. (Sec. 7.1)

parabola The graph of a quadratic equation in two variables. (Sec. 11.4)

parallel lines Lines that never meet; the distance between them is always the same. (Sec. 3.5)

percent Parts of 100. (Sec. 1.4)

perfect square The square of an integer (Sec. 10.1)

perfect-square trinomial A trinomial that is a product of a binomial and itself. (Sec. 5.4)

perimeter The distance around a plane geometric figure. (Sec. 3.5)

perpendicular lines Intersecting lines that form right angles. (Sec. 3.5)

plane Flat surface determined by the intersection of two lines. (Sec. 7.1)

plotting a point in the plane Placing a dot at the location given by the ordered pair; also called graphing a point in the plane. (Sec. 7.1)

point-slope formula If (x_1, y_1) is a point on a line with slope m, then $y - y_1 = m(x - x_1)$. (Sec. 7.4)

polynomial A variable expression in which the terms are monomials. (Sec. 4.1)

positive integers The integers, 1, 2, 3, 4, ... (Sec. 1.1)

positive slope A property of a line that slants upward to the right. (Sec. 7.3)

prime polynomial A polynomial that is nonfactorable over the integers. (Sec. 5.2)

principal square root The positive square root of a number. (Sec. 10.1)

product In multiplication, the result of multiplying two numbers. (Sec. 1.3)

proportion An equation that states the equality of two ratios or rates. (Sec. 6.6)

Pythagorean Theorem The square of the hypotenuse of a right triangle is equal to the sum of the squares of the two legs. (Sec. 10.4)

quadrant One of the four regions into which the two axes of a rectangular coordinate system divide the plane. (Sec. 7.1)

quadratic equation An equation of the form $ax^2 + bx + c = 0$, where a, b, and c are constants and a is not equal to zero; also called a second-degree equation. (Sec. 5.5, 11.1)

quadratic equation in two variables An equation of the form $y = ax^2 + bx + c$, where a is not equal to zero. (Sec. 11.4)

quadratic function A quadratic function is given by $f(x) = ax^2 + bx + c$, where a is not equal to zero. (Sec. 11.4)

radical The symbol $\sqrt{}$, which is used to indicate the positive, or principal, square root of a number. (Sec. 10.1)

radical equation An equation that contains a variable expression in a radicand. (Sec. 10.4)

radicand In a radical expression, the expression under the radical sign. (Sec. 10.1)

range The set of second coordinates of the ordered pairs in a relation. (Sec. 7.1)

rate The quotient of two quantities that have different units. (Sec. 6.6)

rate of work That part of a task that is completed in one unit of time. (Sec. 6.8)

ratio The quotient of two quantities that have the same unit. (Sec. 6.6)

rational expression A fraction in which the numerator or denominator is a polynomial. (Sec. 6.1)

rational number A number that can be written in the form a/b where a and b are integers and b is not equal to zero. (Sec. 1.4)

rationalizing the denominator The procedure used to remove a radical from the denominator of a fraction. (Sec. 10.3)

real numbers The rational numbers and the irrational numbers. (Sec. 1.4)

reciprocal Interchanging the numerator and denominator of a rational number yields that number's reciprocal. (Sec. 2.2, 6.1)

rectangular coordinate system System formed by two number lines, one horizontal and one vertical, that intersect at the zero point of each line. (Sec. 7.1)

relation Any set of ordered pairs. (Sec. 7.1)

repeating decimal Decimal that is formed when dividing the numerator of its fractional counterpart by the denominator results in a decimal part wherein a block of digits repeats infinitely. (Sec. 1.4)

right angle An angle whose measure is 90 degrees. (Sec. 3.5)

roster method Method of writing a set by enclosing a list of the elements in braces. (Sec. 1.1, 9.1)

scatter diagram A graph of collected data as points in a coordinate system. (Sec. 7.4)

scientific notation Notation in which each number is expressed as the product of two factors, one a number between 1 and 10 and the other a power of ten. (Sec. 4.4)

second coordinate The second number in an ordered pair. It measures a vertical distance and is also called the ordinate. (Sec. 7.1)

second-degree equation An equation of the form $ax^2 + bx + c = 0$, where a, b, and c are constants and a is not equal to zero; also called a quadratic equation. (Sec. 11.1)

selling price The price for which a business sells a product to a customer. (Sec. 3.2)

set A collection of objects. (Sec. 1.1, 9.1)

set-builder notation A method of designating a set that makes use of a variable and a certain property that only elements of that set possess. (Sec. 9.1)

similar objects Similar objects have the same shape but not necessarily the same size. (Sec. 6.6)

simplest form of a fraction A fraction is in simplest form when there are no common factors in the numerator and the denominator. (Sec. 1.4)

simplest form of a rational expression A rational expression is in simplest form when the numerator and denominator have no common factors. (Sec. 6.1)

slope The measure of the slant of a line. The symbol for slope is m. (Sec. 7.3)

slope-intercept form The slope-intercept form of an equation of a straight line is $y = mx + b$. (Sec. 7.3)

solution of a system of equations in two variables An ordered pair that is a solution of each equation of the system. (Sec. 8.1)

solution of an equation A number that, when substituted for the variable, results in a true equation. (Sec. 3.1)

solution of an equation in two variables An ordered pair whose coordinates make the equation a true statement. (Sec. 7.1)

solution set of an inequality A set of numbers, each element of which, when substituted for the variable, results in a true inequality. (Sec. 9.2)

solving an equation Finding a solution of the equation. (Sec. 3.1)

square root A square root of a positive number x is a number a for which $a^2 = x$. (Sec. 10.1)

standard form A quadratic equation is in standard form when the polynomial is in descending order and equal to zero. $ax^2 + bx + c = 0$ is in standard form. (Sec. 5.5, 11.1)

straight angle An angle whose measure is 180 degrees. (Sec. 3.5)

substitution method An algebraic method of finding an exact solution of a system of equations. (Sec. 8.2)

sum In addition, the total of two or more numbers. (Sec. 1.2)

supplementary angles Two angles whose sum is 180°. (Sec. 3.5)

system of equations Equations that are considered together. (Sec. 8.1)

terminating decimal Decimal that is formed when dividing the numerator of its fractional counterpart by the denominator results in a remainder of zero. (Sec. 1.4)

terms of a variable expression The addends of the expression. (Sec. 2.1)

transversal A line intersecting two other lines at two different points. (Sec. 3.5)

triangle A three-sided closed figure. (Sec. 3.5)

trinomial A polynomial of three terms. (Sec. 4.1)

undefined slope A property of a vertical line. (Sec. 7.3)

uniform motion The motion of a moving object whose speed and direction do not change. (Sec. 3.6, 6.8)

union of sets A and B The set that contains all the elements of A and all the elements of B. (Sec. 9.1)

value of the variable The number assigned to the variable. (Sec. 2.1)

variable A letter of the alphabet used to stand for a number that is unknown or that can change. (Sec. 1.1)

variable expression An expression that contains one or more variables. (Sec. 2.1)

variable part In a variable term, the variable or variables and their exponents. (Sec. 2.1)

variable term A term composed of a numerical coefficient and a variable part. (Sec. 2.1)

vertical angles Two angles that are on opposite sides of the intersection of two lines. (Sec. 3.5)

x-coordinate The abscissa in an xy-coordinate system. (Sec. 7.1)

x-intercept The point at which a graph crosses the x-axis. (Sec. 7.3)

xy-coordinate system A rectangular coordinate system in which the horizontal axis is labeled x and the vertical axis is labeled y. (Sec. 7.1)

y-coordinate The ordinate in an xy-coordinate system. (Sec. 7.1)

y-intercept The point at which a graph crosses the y-axis. (Sec. 7.3)

zero slope A property of a horizontal line. (Sec. 7.3)

Index